The Flowering of Man

A Tzotzil Botany of Zinacantán

ABRIDGED EDITION

DENNIS E. BREEDLOVE
AND ROBERT M. LAUGHLIN

SMITHSONIAN INSTITUTION PRESS

WASHINGTON AND LONDON

The original two-volume edition of *The Flowering of Man: A Tzotzil Botany of Zinacantán* was published as Smithsonian Contributions to Anthropology, no. 35 (Washington, D.C.: Smithsonian Institution Press, 1993).

Library of Congress Cataloging-in-Publication Data
Breedlove, Dennis Eugene.
  The flowering of man : a Tzotzil botany of Zinacantán / Dennis E. Breedlove and Robert M. Laughlin.—Abridged ed.
     p. cm.
  Originally published: 1993, in series: Smithsonian contributions to anthropology ; no. 35.
  Includes bibliographical references and index.
  ISBN 1-56098-897-5 (alk. paper)
   1. Tzotzil Indians—Ethnobotany. 2. Names, Tzotzil. 3. Tzotzil Indians—Social life and customs.
  4. Ethnobotany—Mexico—Zinacantán. 5. Zinacantán (Mexico)—Social life and customs. I. Laughlin, Robert M. II. Title.

  F1221.T9 B73   2000
  581.6′3′097275221   99-059833

British Library Cataloguing-in-Publication Data available

Manufactured in the United States of America
07 06 05 04 03 02 01 00 5 4 3 2 1

∞ The paper used in this publication meets the minimum requirements of the American National Standard for Information Sciences—Permanence of Paper for Printed Library Materials ANSI Z39.48-1984.

For permission to reproduce illustrations appearing in this book, please correspond directly with Robert M. Laughlin, Department of Anthropology, Room 302, National Museum of Natural History, Washington, D.C. 20560-0112. The Smithsonian Institution Press does not retain reproduction rights for these illustrations individually, or maintain a file of addresses for photo sources.

Contents

FIGURES

MAPS

EPIGRAPHS

What is ethnobotany? Is it the study of the flowering of man?
Thomas Newby White III

In order to amuse (Dr. Johnson) till dinner should be ready, he was taken out to walk in the garden. The master of the house, thinking it proper to introduce something scientifick into the conversation, addressed him thus: "Are you a botanist, Dr. Johnson?" "No, Sir (answered Johnson), I am not a botanist; and (alluding, no doubt, to his near-sightedness), should I wish to become a botanist, I must turn myself into a reptile."

James Boswell

One April day I had a talk with a native about the blue flowers which were abundant and in great variety at the side of the path. This was on the slope of a hill looking to the sea, about a mile from Mousehole. I saw a girl crossing a grass field, and as she was making for a gate opening on to the path, I waited for her and when she came out we went on together for some distance.

But when I talked to her about the flowers growing in profusion by the hedge-side and along the borders of the path she assured me that she never looked at them and knew nothing about them. Well, yes, she did know three or four wild flowers by their names.

"But surely," I said, "You must know these that are so common—these little blue flowers, for instance, what do you call them?" and I plucked a spray of speedwell. She said they were violets, and when I picked a violet and pointed out the difference in shape and size and colour she agreed that they were a little unlike when you looked at them, "but," she said, "we never look at them and we call all these little blue ones violets." "But," I persisted, "flowers are the most beautiful things on the earth and we all love and admire them and are glad to see them again in spring—surely you must know something more than you say about them—you must have been accustomed to gather them in your childhood." But she would not have it. "We never take notice of wild flowers," she said; "they are no use and we call them all violets—all these blue ones." And she pointed to the hedge-side, where there were violet, forget-me-not, bird's eye and ground-ivy all growing together.

W.H. Hudson

May I pass before Thy flowery face,
    May I pass before Thy flowery eyes,
Holy torches,
    Holy candles.
For one moment,
    For two moments,
I arrive kneeling,
    I arrive bending low,
At the thresholds,
    At the altars,
Of the holy fathers,
    The holy mothers,
My flowery Father,
    My flowery Lord.

Romin Teratol

—Como estan las flores?

M.W. Laughlin

—Ya estamos floriendo!

Xun Lopis Mentes (smiling broadly)

v

Foreword

From the chronicles of Herodotus, with their detailed notes on the food habits observed by him and other travelers, to the records of medicinal uses of plants compiled by Otto Brunfels and other pre-Linnaean medieval herbalists, and the token chapter or paragraphs on "subsistence behavior" in the most recent ethnographic report, beliefs and practices regarding plants have been a subject of long-standing interest in the wider study of human thought and behavior. The cumulative result is a vast body of information regarding people's relationships with the plant world, although for any given people our knowledge of their folk botany tends to be partial. With this book, the Tzotzil Maya join a handful of peoples for whom a comprehensive (if never complete) ethnobotany seems attainable.

In North America, plant uses were the subject of many specialized studies in the early decades of the twentieth century, resulting largely from the "salvage ethnography" attempts by researchers from the Bureau of American Ethnology and by students in the Boas-Kroeber-Lowie tradition. These monographs typically consisted of two parts: an introductory section, describing the general ecological features of the area, with an ethnographic sketch of its aboriginal inhabitants; and the main section of the report, including a list of the economically useful plants found in the region, the "native name" for each of the plants, and a description of the plant lore and ways in which each was used in secular and ceremonial life. Such information was generally obtained by seeking out native speakers of the language concerned who also remembered the relevant details of social life, which often was no longer a living reality. The search frequently entailed the use of only one or a few informants (usually aged) who provided all that we will ever know, except for what archaeology might tell us, regarding the thoughts, beliefs, and behavior of populations sometimes numbering in the thousands.

This utilization of few informants and reliance on "memory culture," both of which were unavoidable conditions of research in societies that had undergone radical changes, and sometimes near-extinction, in the nineteenth century, doubtless had significant effects on the quality as well as the quantity of the information obtained. Two further limitations, moreover, constrained ethnobotanical research of this kind by the very definitions of the problems it set for itself. The first of these restrictions derived from the selection of the focus of investigation, viz., plants that were utilized in "important" ways. Instead of investigating relationships with the plant world in a broad sense, "Classical Ethnobotany" had a much narrower, although legitimate, concern, and resembled what has come to be known as "Economic Botany." The second major internal restriction of these studies was rooted in their relegation of the investigation of linguistic and semantic aspects of plant knowledge to a minor place in the endeavor. Although "native names" for plants were collected and reported whenever possible, there was seldom shown any intensive concern with the conceptual systems of nomenclature and classification that underlay informants' labeling of plant specimens. The emphasis was nearly always on what people *did with* plants, rather than what they *thought about* them.

A major turning point in ethnobotany was marked by Harold Conklin's doctoral dissertation at Yale University in 1954, "The Relation of Hanunóo Culture to the Plant World." There, and in subsequent published work, Conklin suggested a new program for the study of people's relationships with their botanical environments. The objective was to produce comprehensive and systematic descriptions of local floras as both biological and cultural phenomena, with ethnobotany inextricably embedded in ethnography. "Native names" for plants would no longer be mere appendages to information on plant uses, but would assume critical importance as both clues and tools for eliciting statements that, combined with first-hand observation of everyday life, would allow the ethnographer to construct models of how the natural world is conceptualized by those who live in it and draw sustenance (and not only of the physical kind) from it. With its emphasis on semantic analysis of terminological systems, and the modeling of culture as a system of concepts, categories, and rules or standards—including but not limited to those pertaining to plants—the "New Ethnobotany" emerged in the late 1950s and 1960s as one specialized focus within what would be called "Ethnoscience," "Ethnographic Semantics," and "the New Ethnography."

One of the major arenas in which these new approaches were tested and refined was the state of Chiapas in the central highlands of Mexico, where Evon Z. Vogt's "Harvard Chiapas Project" was initiated in 1957, a "project" that would involve well over 100 fieldworkers over the next two decades and include collaborators from the University of Chicago, Stanford University, and the University of California at Berkeley and Irvine. Vogt's Harvard students and colleagues concentrated on the Tzotzil-speaking Maya communities near the *ladino* town of San Cristóbal de Las Casas, while the collaborators focused on their Tzeltal-speaking neighbors. Among the earliest of Vogt's fieldworkers was Robert M. Laughlin, who began his research in Zinacantán in 1959 and has been returning regularly ever since; indeed, as I write these remarks he is headed there on another field trip.

As Laughlin relates in this book (p. 1), in 1963 he "resolved to compile a monumental dictionary of the Tzotzil language," to which his botanist colleague, Dennis E. Breedlove, responded: "How can you write a dictionary and leave out the plants?" Well, here are "the plants," but also much more. With his intimate knowledge of Zinacantec culture and everyday life, Laughlin realized that there was literally no end to "relevant material" in the pursuit of Tzotzil ethnobotany, conceived as "not merely the systematic study of the plant lore of a people, but rather a study of the flowering of man" (p. 5). And so more fieldwork was required—more plants to collect, more questions to ask, more texts to record, more activities to observe—and the stacks of cards and notebooks grew throughout the 1960s, 1970s, and 1980s.

During this time Breedlove also collaborated with another botanist, Peter H. Raven, and Brent Berlin, one of the Stanford ethnographers who was focusing on the ethnobotany of the Tenejapa Tzeltal neighbors of the Zinacantecs. That research resulted in the most influential series of early publications in "the New Ethnobotany," epitomized by the now-classic *Principles of Tzeltal Plant Classification* (Berlin, Breedlove, and Raven, 1974). Following the appearance of that book, Laughlin tells us (p. 9), he had in mind "a companion Tzotzil volume," but "soon this subject took on a life of its own."

Although Berlin's work has always been characterized by the deep immersion in Tzeltal culture implied by the phrase "a botanical ethnography" in the subtitle of his book, one of his major concerns was with elucidating the folk classification and nomenclature system employed by the Tzeltal. For Laughlin, "native taxonomy was not our goal, but rather our vehicle for reaching a better understanding of native thought" (p. 9). Thus, "The Flora" that makes up the bulk of the present book is not organized simply as "a native taxonomy explained in ultimate detail," but as "an encyclopedia of botanical information, demonstrating simultaneously the flowers and the flowering of man in Zinacantán" (p. 9).

But *The Flowering of Man* is even more than an encyclopedia. The best features of "Classical Ethnobotany" are incorporated as we are given remarkably detailed information on the complete flora of the region, including plant morphology, range, cultivation techniques (if applicable), and the "significance" of each plant for Zinacantecs, in both the secular and cosmological senses of the term. Sadly, we learn that much of the traditional folk knowledge of plants is disappearing rapidly, as is much of the vegetation itself and the Zinacantecs' direct utilization of their plant world. The past 25 years have been a period witnessing a "whirlwind of change" as the population has more than doubled, the economy has changed from its subsistence base to one oriented toward markets and money, and the society and culture have been radically transformed. Although the future of the Tzotzil may be uncertain, their past is reasonably well-known and it is documented herein, through

Laughlin's historical scholarship and his and Breedlove's research in the community over a thirty-year period. Thus we have an invaluable record, not of a "memory culture" but of one that was lived, observed, and recorded.

Throughout their decades of fieldwork, like Berlin and most practitioners of "ethnoscience," Laughlin and Breedlove have been appreciative of the heuristic value of formal elicitation and analytical methods, but also have been aware that these approaches must always be adjuncts to, rather than substitutes for, traditional ethnographic procedures, i.e., immersion in the language as it is spoken (and not merely elicited onto a tape recorder) and in everyday life as it is lived. The result is a richly contextualized systematic presentation of Tzotzil plant folk taxa and their interrelationships. The authors employ the analytic schema developed by Berlin and others, thereby adding another much-needed case to those now available from South America, New Guinea, Indonesia, and elsewhere, which have advanced our understanding of "universal" principles of folk biological classification and nomenclature and, in turn, general features of human cognition. Moreover, with such a comprehensive portrayal of Tzotzil folk botany, the prospects for controlled comparisons with that of the neighboring Tzeltal are obvious and exciting.

Finally, there is the poetry of it all, both literally, in Laughlin's treatment of descriptive phrases and analogies showing the "poetic association between the flora and man, between the flora and the cosmos" (p. 95), and emergent in his sensitive renderings of Tzotzil texts, shamans' prayers, and the ethnographic portraits of "Lordly Sunbeams" and the like, which suffuse the narrative portions of the book. Given the now-sizeable ethnographic literature on Zinacantán produced by other members of the Chiapas Project, Laughlin seizes this opportunity to give us humanistically drawn capsules, inviting us ever deeper into the Tzotzil "experience" of their plant world.

The Flowering of Man is, then, not only in part but in whole, a "cultural omnibus," combining Tzotzil economic botany, ethnoscience, and culture in the broadest sense: a mélange whose hybrid vigor augurs the flowering of a "Newer Ethnobotany."

Terence E. Hays
Department of Anthropology and Geography
Rhode Island College
Providence, Rhode Island, 1991

Acknowledgments

Through the years many members of the clerical staff of the Department of Anthropology at the Smithsonian Institution have fed seemingly endless revisions of multilingual text into their typewriters and word processors while, at the same time, keeping an itinerant curator in contact with his home base. For this we wish to give special thanks, in chronological order, to Paula Cardwell, Karen Willson, Laurice Stewart, Darla Hawkins, Maria Catala, Helen Morrill, Denise Hughes, and Lawan Tyson.

Johanna Humphrey, also of the Department of Anthropology, has been most helpful in transferring this material to computer diskettes.

Early documents included in this study were consulted in the Latin American Library, Tulane University, and the Archivo Histórico Diocesano de San Cristóbal.

We are indebted to Barbara Keller, who for over 12 years has been indispensable to us in keeping all the plant identification records and transferring them to the manuscript. Without her there could not be a *Flowering of Man*.

In our search for Mayan plant name cognates, we are indebted to the anthropologists and linguists who kindly made their word lists available to us. Terrence Kaufman's huge store of vocabularies collected by himself and by colleagues in the Proyecto Lingüístico Francisco Marroquín added cognates from many Mayan languages. Brent Berlin, Victoria Bricker, Nicholas Hopkins, and Kathryn Josserand generously responded to our pleas for more names.

Over the years a great number of professional botanists have helped with identification of plants in their respective areas of interest. These annotated specimens have been valuable sources of reference in the preparation of the treatment. In particular we thank F. Almeda, California Academy of Sciences (Melastomataceae, Symplocaceae); W.R. Anderson, (Malpighiaceae, Rubiaceae); R. Barneby, New York Botanical Garden (*Astragalus, Cassia, Chamaecrista, Dalea, Marina, Senna*); B. Bartholomew, California Academy of Sciences (Theaceae); D. Bates, Cornell University (Malvales); J. Beaman, Michigan State University (Caryophyllaceae); M. Bourell, California Academy of Sciences (Bryophyta); H. Bravo, Instituto de Biología, UNAM (Cactaceae); C.R. Broome, University of Maryland (*Centaurium*); W. Burger, Chicago Natural History Museum (Piperaceae); K. Burt-Utley, University of New Orleans (Begoniaceae); L. Constance, University of California, Berkeley (Hydrophyllaceae, Apiaceae); Thomas Croat, Missouri Botanical Garden (Araceae, Sapindaceae); T.F. Daniel, California Academy of Sciences (Acanthaceae); G. Davidse, Missouri Botanical Garden (Poaceae); A. Day, California Academy of Sciences (Polemoniaceae); A. Delgado S., Instituto de Biología, UNAM (*Phaseolus, Vigna*); D. Denham, Boulder, Colorado (Gesneriaceae); M. Denton, University of Washington (*Oxalis*); T. Duncan, University of California, Berkeley (*Ranunculus*); J.A. Dwyer, St. Louis University (Rubiaceae); F. Ehrendorfer, Botanisches Institut der Universität, Wien (*Galium*); C. Epling, deceased (Labiatae); C. Etienne, Santa Rosa (Polygalaceae); R.C. Foster, Harvard University (*Sisyrinchium*); P.A. Fryxell, Texas A & M University (Malvales); A. Gentry, Missouri Botanical Garden (Bignoniaceae); H.S. Gentry, Desert Botanical Garden (*Agave, Phaseolus*); T. Germán, Instituto de Biología, UNAM (*Galactia*); F.W. Gould, deceased (Poaceae); S. Graham, Kent State University (*Cuphea*); R. Grether G., UAMIZ (*Mimosa*); W.L. Handlos, Bailey Hortorium (*Tripogandra*); F.J. Hermann, U.S. Forest Service Herbarium (*Carex,* Juncaceae); H. Hernández M., Instituto de Biología, UNAM (*Calliandra*); M. Huft, Missouri Botanical Garden (Euphorbiaceae and Eriocaulaceae, *Smilax*); P.C. Hutchinson, Escondido, California (Cactaceae); H. Iltis, University of Wisconsin (Capparidaceae); H.S. Irwin, New

York Botanical Garden (*Cassia*); C. Jeffrey, Royal Botanic Gardens, Kew (Cucurbitaceae); M. Johnston, University of Texas, Austin (Rhamnaceae); B.T. Keller, California Academy of Sciences (Actinidiaceae and Dilleniaceae); H. Kennedy, Harold L. Lyon Arboretum (Marantaceae); M. Kimnach, Huntington Botanical Garden (Cactaceae, Crassulaceae); T. Koyama, New York Botanical Garden (Cyperaceae except *Carex*); B.A. Krukoff, deceased (*Erythrina,* Menispermaceae); J. Kuijt, University of Lethbridge (Loranthaceae); L.R. Landrum, Arizona State University (Myrtaceae); M. Lavin, University of Texas (*Cracca*); D. Lorence, Pacific Tropical Garden (Monimiaceae and Rubiaceae); C.L. Lundell, University of Texas, Dallas (Myrsinaceae, Myrtaceae, many other miscellaneous families); B. Maguire, New York Botanical Garden (*Cusia*); D. Mally, California Academy of Sciences (Orchidaceae); P.C. Mangelsdorf, Harvard University (races of maize); E. McClintock, University of California, Berkeley (ornamentals, Saxifragaceae); R. McVaugh, University of Michigan (Asteraceae, Lobeliaceae, Burseraceae, Rosaceae, Euphorbiaceae); F. Meyer, U.S. National Arboretum (*Valeriana, Magnolia*); H.N. Moldenke, Oregon (Eriocaulaceae, Verbenaceae); E. Molseed, deceased (Iradaceae, except *Sisyrinchium*); H.E. Moore, deceased (Geraniaceae, Arecaceae); Reid Moran, San Diego Natural History Museum (Crassulaceae); R.A. Moreno, Instituto de Biologia, (*Crotalaria*); C.V. Morton, deceased (ferns, *Smilax, Solanum*); C.H. Muller, University of California, Santa Barbara (*Quercus*); D. Neill, Missoui Botanical Garden (*Erythrina*); L.I. Nevling, Chicago Natural History Museum (Thymelaeaceae); R. Ornduff, University of California, Berkeley (*Nymphoides*); Timothy Plowman, deceased (Erythroxylaceae, *Brunfelsia*); T.P. Ramamoorthy, Instituto de Biologia, UNAM (Lamiaceae, *Ludwigia*); P.H. Raven, Missouri Botanical Garden (Onagraceae); K.H. Rechinger, Naturhistorisches Museum, Wien (*Rumex*); C. Reeder, University of Arizona (*Muhlenbergia, Sporobolus*); L. Rico A., Instituto de Biología, UNAM (*Acacia, Pithecellobium*); C.M. Rogers, Wayne State University (*Linum*); R.C. Rollins, Harvard University (Cruciferae); V. Rudd, California State University, Northridge (Fabaceae); J. Rzedowski, Instituto Politécnico Nacional, Mexico, D.F. (miscellaneous monocotyledons); J. Sauer, University of California, Los Angeles (Phytolaccaceae, Amaranthus); B. Schubert, Arnold Arboretum (*Desmodium, Dioscorea*); E.E. Sherff, deceased (Asteraceae, Coreopsidinae); L. Shinners, deceased (Convolvulaceae); C. Soto E., Instituto de Biología, UNAM (*Crotalaria*); M. Sousa S., Instituto de Biología, UNAM (Fabaceae); A.R. Smith, University of California, Berkeley (pteridophytes); L.B. Smith, National Museum of Natural History (Bromeliaceae, *Begonia*); H.C.M. Snelders, Utrecht (Burmanniaceae); T. Soderstrom, deceased (Poaceae, bamboos); J.A. Steyermark, Instituto Botánico, Caracas (Rubiaceae); J.L. Strother, University of California, Berkeley (Asteraceae); O. Téllez V., Instituto de Biologia, UNAM (*Tephrosia, Dioscorea*); R. Torres C., Instituto de Biologia, UNAM (*Bauhinia*); G. Tucker, Duke University (Cyperaceae); B.L. Turner, University of Texas, Austin (Asteraceae); J.F. Utley, University of New Orleans (Bromeliaceae); H.A. Wahl, Pennsylvania State University (*Chenopodium*); G. Wallace, Los Angeles State and County Arboretum (Monotropaceae); D. Wasshaussen, National Museum of Natural History (Acanthaceae); U.T. Waterfall, deceased (*Physalis*); R.E. Weaver, Arnold Arboretum (*Lisianthius*); G. Webster, University of Calfornia, Davis (Euphorbiaceae); T. Wendt, Herbario-Horatio, Escuela Nacional de Agricultura, Chapingo, Mexico (Polygalaceae); L.O. Williams, Chicago Natural History Museum (Orchidaceae and many families done in conjunction with the *Flora of Guatemala*); D.R. Windler, Towson State University (*Crotalaria, Neptunia*); R.P. Wunderlin, University of South Florida (*Bauhinia*); J. Wurdack, National Museum of Natural History (Melastomataceae); S. Zarate P., Instituto de Biología, UNAM (*Leucaena*).

J.F. Copp of La Jolla, California, has consistantly helped with transport of specimens and material to and from the field.

To provide the botanical sets with visual evidence, Terry Bell labored for a decade with infinite patience and artistry, transposing dried leaves and flowers and fleshy fruits to our plates.

Antun Teratol kindly lent us his tunic to be photographed by Douglas Bryant for the frontispiece.

Thor Anderson's illustrations faithfully dramatize the human setting of the flora of Zinacantán.

For their insights on culture change we are indebted to Frank Cancian, George Collier, and Daniel Mountjoy.

John Haviland has put this human setting into motion.

The authors' absences and presences, unpredictable as well as predictable, were suffered by their wives, Nancy Breedlove and Mimi Laughlin, with amazing grace. Their encouragement in this quixotic search for truth, for many truths, spurred us on and brought us home.

Financial support for this study was provided by the California Academy of Sciences and by the Smithsonian Institution through Fluid Research Fund awards, the Research Opportunities Fund, the Scholarly Studies Program, the Spencer Fullerton Baird Fund, and the Walcott Research Fund. Additional funding was provided by the National Geographic Society. A special thanks to Thomas, Marian, and Sarah Tilton for their help and support throughout the project.

Whatever truths are reported in this book were provided knowingly and unknowingly by our Zinacantec participants, particularly by Maryan Martinis who always knew he had the last word.

Robert M. Laughlin
1990

Key to Tzotzil Pronunciation

There are five Tzotzil vowels, a, e, i, o, u, pronounced as in Spanish. When they occur initially in a word they are pre-glottalized; that is, they begin abruptly, as in German. The following consonants are pronounced as in English: ch, (d, f, g, Spanish loans), k, l, m, n, p, s, t, and y. J is pronounced as h in English, tz as ts, x as sh, and r as in Spanish r, "pero." V is pronounced as in English, except when occurring in Spanish loan words that in Tzotzil form consonant clusters, such as kv (*kventa*), jv (*jveves*), when it is pronounced as a w. W occurs in only one loan word of unknown origin, *wapo*. ' is a glottal stop, pronounced as a "catch" in the voice, such as in uh-oh, or Hawai'i. The glottal catch combines with other consonants to form the glottalized consonants ch', k', p', t', and tz'. B is also a glottalized consonant. When b occurs before another consonant, or finally, it is pronounced as a pre-glottalized m. Stress is marked on three-syllable Spanish loans, otherwise it falls on the root syllable. The alphabetical order for Tzotzil is given as follows: a, ', b, ch, ch', d, e, f, g, i, j, k, k', l, m, n, o, p, p', r, s, t, t', tz, tz', u, v, x, and y.

Participants

The participants in this encyclopedic venture number many hundreds: men, women, and children. the majority of these were unwitting contributors who, by a chance remark, added another bit of information. Seventy-five individuals, representing 26 communities, were paid for their efforts. Because of the aura of suspicion aroused by taking a woman "into the woods" we hired only two women, on one occasion, as plant collectors. Consequently the source of our information is heavily weighted on the male side. Initial training in plant collecting was provided by j'Alux Mentes Ton of Tenejapa, who had been the principal consultant of Berlin and Breedlove. Xun Lopis Mentes of Chamula provided many leads for further investigation.

The persons named below served either as plant collectors or, being religious officials, had special knowledge of the plants used for church and chapel decoration. Many of the former spent hours in the preparation of plants and the supplying of knowledge about them. Fifty were from highland communities, 24 from temperate communities, and three from the lowlands (two of whom also provided information from the highlands). They varied in age from 18 years to their mid-sixties, but most were in their thirties or forties. Of these, four began working with us in the first stage of plant identification (1966) and resumed work in the second stage (1978–1980s). It is noteworthy, perhaps, that of the eight contributors who were shamans, five became so after engaging in extensive plant collecting.

Throughout the years of our research, Maryan Martinis, native of the upper end of Zinacantán Center, has been number one (as identified in Laughlin 1975). At the age of 35, when we initiated our project, he already possessed a remarkable storage of knowledge concerning the flora: plant habitats, morphology, growth, cultivation, and use. He was a fearless explorer who loved the challenge of penetrating every corner of the township, no matter how forbidding. He was undaunted by the steepest slopes and the most hostile residents. As team leader he would let no "new" plant go uncollected. With careful attention to detail and great economy he could describe and define hundreds of plants. This same keenness was ever present in his efforts to iron out our bewilderment and untangle our misperceptions. His fierce appearance was belied by a shrewd, canny sense of humor.

It is no wonder that this man became an unofficial lawyer for the town, and later rose rapidly through the religious hierarchy, reaching the pinnacle of grand alcalde before his mid-fifties. The ascent of Maryan Martinis was financed not only by us, but also by sensible, large-scale corn farming, by flower cultivation, and by the sale of flowers and fruits in Tuxtla Gutiérrez. During our last plant collecting expedition he slyly confessed his entrance into shamanhood.

Note: In the list below, (1) = 1966; (2) = 1978–1980; (1,2) = both 1966 and 1978–1980).

Community	*Personnel*
Apas	(1) Antun Tanjol, Maryan Ernantis, Telex Xulub Te'; (2) Manvel Perez Sanchez
Atz'am (Vo'-bitz)	(1) Chep Boch, Markux Xantis; (2) Lol Sanches Ernandes, Romin Sanches Ernandes
Bik'it Joyijel	(2) Maryan Vaskes Ernandes, Xun Ernandes Vaskes
Chak Toj	(2) Martin Vaskes Lopes
Chaynatik	(1,2) Xun Konte
Chikinibal Vo'	(2) Maryan Lopes Peres
Elan Vo'	(1) Xun Lopis; (2) Maryan Chiku'
Jech Toch'	(2) Maryan Jimenes Lopes
Jok' Ch'enom	(1) Mikel Konte; (2) Maryan Ernantis, Xun Montejo Ernandes

Jtek Lum	(1) Maryan Peres Mochilum, Romin Teratol; (1,2) Antzelmo Peres Peres, Chep Ernantis; (2) Loxa Krus, Maryan Teratol, Matal Lopis Tanchak, Rafael Peres Ramires, Xun Teratol Lopis
Kelem Ton	(2) Antun(?)
Masan	(2) Xun Tanchak
Muk'ta Jok'	(1) Manvel Ximenes; (2) Markux Ernandes Peres
Na Chij	(1) Chep Peres, Maryan Vaskis; (2) Manvel Peres Peres
Naben Chauk	(1) Mikel Vaskis; (2) Antun Vaskes, Manvel Vaskes Peres, Maryan Peres Buluch, Mikel Peres Peres, Petul Uch, Petul Vaskes
Paste'	(1) Maryan Xulub Te'; (2) Manvel Ernandes Peres, Martin Lopes Lopes, Romin Lopes Vaskes
Pat Osil	(1) Palas Xut; (2) Maryan de la Krus Peres, Petul de la Krus Ernandes
Petz Toj	(2) Xun Ernandes Konsares
P'ij	(2) Antun Vaskes
Sak Lum	(2) Antun Giyen Peres, Antun Giyen Peres, Manvel Giyen Peres, Xun Sanches Peres
San Mikulax	(2) Antun Xilon Ernandes, Lol Xilon Peres, Manvel Gomes Selestino, Xap Gomes Peres
Santa Rosa	(2) Petul Uch, Xun Teratol Lopes
Sek'emtik	(1) Antun Vaskis; (2) Lol Peres Asyenta, Lukax Montejo Sanches, Romin Peres, Telex Vaskes Peres
Selva	(2) Marselino Gomes Ernandes, Palas Gomes, Ernandes
Stzellejtik	
(in Vo'-ch'oj Vo' Alto)	(2) Matyo Tanchak, Palas Muchik
(in Vo'-ch'oj Vo' Bajo)	(1) Maryan Chiku', Maryan Sarate; (1,2) Maryan Martinis; (2) Petul Gonsales Peres, Xun Peres Peres, Xun Vaskes

Preface to the Abridged Edition

This new abridged edition of *The Flowering of Man* is designed for a broader audience, in the belief that we have much to learn from the Tzotzil people of Chiapas, Mexico.

Rather than sitting for hours gazing at a television screen or trapped in the Internet, the Tzotzil are constantly on the move, observing the natural world around them. Although traveling now more by car than by foot, and with their knowledge of the plant world greatly reduced, they still, young and old, can identify scores of plants. The spiraling cost of drugstore medicine has generated a surge of interest in herbal cures. The new globalized economy that has rendered corn farming unprofitable has meant that flower cultivation and sale is practically the only way for the Tzotzil to make a living. In fact the corn farmer has seen his worries about the approach of the millennium confirmed by the invasion of a giant weed-killer–resistant grass, growing over his head.

Despite the persistent use of herbicides, pesticides, and fertilizers—whose negative effects have become apparent—the Tzotzil believe strongly that humankind was created by the gods to work in harmony with nature. In the following pages you will see that the people of Zinacantán do not imagine themselves to be masters of the universe. Each walks for a few days, dreams for a few nights, never knowing which tomorrow will be his last. He and she work to thank the gods in the hope that they will be rewarded by another tomorrow.

Those wishing to explore the thousands of Tzotzil terms describing plants, plant growth, agricultural practices, and plant use, including recipes, may consult appendices 6 and 7 in volume II of the original 1993 edition of this work.

Robert M. Laughlin
2000

The Flowering of Man

A Tzotzil Botany of Zinacantán

Dennis E. Breedlove
and Robert M. Laughlin

From Beginning to End

A Personal Reminiscence by Robert M. Laughlin

The Old Look

It could not have been more inauspicious—the beginning of all this. Day after day I sat in Zinacantán in the dark of my host's thatched roof house dumbly trying to grasp the torrent of Tzotzil sounds. My desperation to stretch my legs, to escape the compound, inspired a new tactic: Learn plant names!

A dusty box of mostly sterile specimens sits in my Washington office, testament to my first botanical failure. Although the Zinacantecs accorded each of these bits of leaves and twigs a confusing multitude of names, the Smithsonian scholars claimed they could not be named at all!

Hoping to give focus to my fieldwork in Chiapas, my project director, Evon Vogt, suggested I study the economic basis of Zinacantán—corn cultivation. But I fled into the world of myths and dreams.

Four years later, in 1963, I resolved to compile a monumental dictionary of the Tzotzil language. Systematic compilation continued for three years, producing thousands of words. With a sigh of relief I decided the end was near. At this very time Dennis Breedlove was deeply involved with Brent Berlin and Peter Raven in their equally monumental ethnobotanic study of the neighboring Tzeltal Indians of Tenejapa. Perhaps I was celebrating my conclusion. "How can you write a dictionary and leave out the plants?" Dennis asked me accusingly. My feeble remonstrations prompted an immediate offer to provide equipment, training for myself and my plant collectors, followed by shipment and identification of my specimens. How could I refuse?

Because a description of my ethnobotanical efforts was provided in the introduction to my dictionary (Laughlin, 1975) I will draw freely from that source.

As a first step to arouse the interest of my Indian colleagues in botanical collecting and to give me some idea of the scope of the Tzotzil botanical lexicon, I asked four men from Zinacantán Center to write separate lists of all the plant names they could recall. Combining the results of their one day's endeavor produced a master list of over 650 names! The multiplicity was surprising, for Zinacantecs are far less dependent on uncultivated plants than the neighboring Tenejapanecs or even Chamulas.

The first collections were made on 14 February 1966. In an effort to assure some control over the naming procedure, the original team of from two to four collectors was comprised of residents of the ceremonial center only. Whenever possible, they collected an original and three copies of all plants in fruit and flower from each of the major habitats. The specimens were named separately by the collectors, numbered, and dried. A file of plant lore was developed with the aid of the following questionnaire, which I asked my collectors to apply to every plant soon after an example of it was secured.

1. What is it called? If it has another name, where do they use that name?

2. Have you heard stories about why it was named that?

3. If you don't know its name, what is it like?

4. Is it a tree, a plant, a vine, or not any of these?

5. Is there a form **-tik** or **-altik**? (expanse or large expanse of).

6. Where does it grow: in the highlands, temperate zone, or lowlands?

Dennis E. Breedlove, P.O. Box 564, Bolinas, California 94924. Robert M. Laughlin, Department of Anthropology, Smithsonian Institution, Washington, D.C. 20560.

7. Where does it grow: in the yard, in the woods, in fields, etc.?

8. Is it cultivated? When? How? Who does it?

9. What part of it is used?

10. Who uses it?

11. What is it used for?

12. Is it "cold" or "hot"?

13. What effect does it have?

14. How is it gathered? Who brings it? When? Is it bought or gathered?

15. How many are used?

16. How is it prepared?

17. Is it used alone or is there another ingredient? If so, what is it?

18. How is it taken?

19. How much is drunk? After meals or not?

20. When is it used? If it is medicine, how often is it taken?

21. Is it the preferred kind? If not, what is?

22. If it is poisonous, what remedy is there?

At the end of five months, overweening pride goaded me to try to determine whether my team's essential agreement on plant names and uses was shared by members of the outlying hamlets. Together, we chose individuals whom we thought would be knowledgeable. Several were shamans. Obvious ignoramuses were speedily replaced. Before collecting, each initiate was asked to name all of the plants that he could. His knowledge was tested against the master list from Zinacantán Center to fill out his own list and to spot variant pronunciations. On a rotating basis the additional collectors, ideally one from each of the major hamlets, accompanied by one or two from the original team, collected through January 1967. They, too, were asked to identify the plants and to respond to the items in the questionnaire. Over 3000 numbered specimens were obtained, of which several were species new to science; 1170 species were represented, as well as another 100 identifications at the generic level. Examples for nearly every one of the plant names on the master list were secured, and so the collection was comprehensive both from the botanical and lexical point of view.

This dry account gives no hint of the pleasures of plant collecting: the mornings spent in crisp pine forests and along torrid lowland stream beds, the nights beneath giant fig trees, the dizzying verbal duels as we sorted and prepared the plants for drying. Nor does it hint at the problems: the collectors sunk deep in hangovers, the collectors who, rather than wrinkling their pants, would rely on me to bother climbing a tree to wrench down a spectacular orchid. Imagine a collecting party: myself, three veteran teammates from the Center, and three hamlet beginners. Everyone has been instructed that I only want genuine names, and that unfamiliarity with the plant should cause no concern. First, the beginners would be asked to name each plant. If they answered, "I don't know," four or five times, the veterans would begin exchanging superior winks.

After the first 15 minutes of collecting, no plant was ever left unnamed. An enormous lexicon of several thousand names was created with extreme variations from one individual to the next. Some control was provided by having the members of the original team all from Zinacantán Center and by collecting in the same localities many times throughout the year. The variations seldom could be explained by noting the origins of the collectors, nor was it a simple question of the ignorance or wisdom of the collector, though this was a critical, but elusive factor. The impact of group dynamics upon the choice of plant names was terrible to behold. Of paramount importance was the social criteria of the collector within the team, such as his age or bonds of friendship. Social position and temperament often determined who would align with whom in assigning which names. Efforts to prevent collectors from influencing their colleagues' decisions frequently were unsuccessful. Even so, there was substantial agreement on culturally significant plants.

Having completed a year of collecting in January 1967, I returned to the "States" (USA). The botanical information, written in three languages, by various collaborators, formed a small mountain of lined paper pads, graph sheets, and typed lists, which had to be thoroughly threshed, sifted, and weighed. I had to decide which plant names were genuine and which spurious. Phone calls to Dennis in California were frequent. As the botanical identifications came trickling in, the Latin names and the common English names had to be matched with all their Tzotzil equivalents. An endless shuffling of cards filled every day from dawn to dark. As we slowly began to impose some order on the material, I became obsessed with doubts about the value of my collection. I was well aware that a project that had brought together 3000 specimens, 22 informants not always sober, and countless thousands of names would demonstrate inconsistencies.

I was haunted by an experiment I had tried just before I left Chiapas. No plant is more central to Zinacantec culture than corn. Everyone grows corn, everyone talks about corn, everyone depends upon corn for survival. My collaborators from Zinacantán Center collected 20 ears of corn that they claimed were different from each other and which they called by different names. I strung the ears up across the room and brought in five men, each from a different hamlet. I asked them to name the corn. They were free to handle the ears, chip off kernels, and so forth. If each informant had assigned a different name to each ear there would be 100 names. For these 20 ears that Paul Mangelsdorf assigned to 16 races the team provided 47 different Tzotzil names. Forty-one descriptive terms of such features as shape, color, habitat, season, and size were used to produce a majority of the distinctive names. Despite this extraordinary diversity, which might lead one to believe that these men were thoroughly confused by the array of corn—and they confessed bewilderment at the time—not a single one mistook an ear of highland corn for an ear of lowland corn, whereas the mistakes in identifying temperate corn that grows in the foothills only confirmed its intermediate quality.

FIGURE 1.—The valley of Zinacantán Center, 1977. (Photo by John Swope.)

Subsequent tests I performed in the "States" on professors and students only confirmed my fears that we lead our lives quite acceptably, undaunted by our prodigious ignorance about much that surrounds us. American testees coped no better identifying cars than bugs, cereals than vegetables. In compari-

son, the Zinacantec farmers had excelled. Why should I worry?

But I did! During the plant collecting enterprise I had watched with fascination, but also with horror, the development of a complex Tzotzil botanical taxonomy. My fellow collectors, confronted with hundreds of weeds that they had never paid the least attention to, became expert taxonomists, adept at distinguishing fine-grained differences in form and habitat, and applying names accordingly. The Tzotzil life forms ("vine," "tree," "plant") and generics were unaffected, but the specific and varietal names were a tribute to the perceptivity and inventiveness of teams of Tzotzil botanists.

Simultaneously, my anthropology colleagues (including Brent Berlin in Tenejapa) were engaged in discovering native taxonomies by means of "contrast level" studies and the elaboration of semantic dimension keys. The mapping of native words in hierarchies of different levels of generality—life form, genus, species, and variety—seemed entirely reasonable and incumbent upon me as I entered the plant names in the dictionary. I balked, however, at using keys, and called on natural scientists to back me up (Bulmer and Tyler, 1968:353):

In so far as Karam informants are prepared to construct artificial keys at the behest of the anthropologist, or even, possibly, instructing their children (we have no evidence on this point), the characters which they consciously draw attention to may, in fact, only constitute a very small part of the total configuration which is the basis for the informant's actual recognition of examples of particular specimens. As Simpson puts it, such, "non-technical recogniton—identification—is normally not by…separate characters but by a mental image of the whole animal."

Another technique that achieved its best results here in the highlands of Chiapas was "programmed specification," where native phrases and statements were carefully manipulated in a question and answer form "to elicit further statements about a given topic in a way that preserves as much of the native thought pattern as possible" (Colby, 1966:17). Although I appreciated the sophistication and precision of this method, which often illuminated the structure of segments of native thought, I was constrained by temperament from subduing either myself or my fellow lexicographers to such inexorable rigors. Even the very simple questionnaire that we used to derive plant lore soon proved frustrating. Some of the questions (2, 7, 10, 13, 21) evoked automatic answers or no answer at all. Others (15, 19) demanded a specificity that I didn't believe was real. For most herbal cures there is no traditionally accepted formula for the prescriptions nor for the quantity nor schedule of application.

As the dictionary went to press I was dogged by two major concerns regarding the botanical material: (1) the reliability of the entries, and (2) the cultural relevance of taxonomy. Addressing the first concern, I commented (Laughlin, 1975:16):

An informant's consistency can only be tested by multiple collections. The five botanists from Zinacantán Center collected an average of 1400 plants. Ten of the hamlet botanists collected an average of 380 plants, but even with this high number, multiple collections of a single plant cluster around the commonest plants. Not only must many collections be made, but there must be many collectors.

This is of utmost consequence in ethnoscientific studies. Nearly three years passed before 80% of my specimens were identified and this was achieved under inconceivably favorable circumstances. Unless the investigator combines a comprehensive knowledge of plants in general, with a specific knowledge of the flora of the particular area, he must wait for the specimens to be identified by a host of specialists in various herbaria. Few botanists wield such control, and certainly no anthropologist. Without the Latin referent, it is difficult to know which questions to ask. Knowing now that Zinacantecs use five different names for one species of mallow I could ask more pointed questions, but even then I would have to collect new specimens as vouchers, because my original dried specimens would be too greatly altered in form to be recognized by informants. And then I would have to wait for the new specimens to be identified to be sure that we had collected the same species. Only because of the uniquely comprehensive study by Berlin, Breedlove, and Raven of ethnobotany in the closely allied language, Tzeltal, is my data susceptible to some verification.

And I closed my remarks with (Laughlin, 1975:16–17):

As a last remonstrance, I would like to add the observations of two students of Navajo linguistic behavior. They point out that any domain can be classified in a multiplicity of ways, that a "people's perception of their culture is not always shown by taxonomy." They "suggest that ethnoscience should focus its attention on the total system of lexical semantic relationships in the cultural universe—not merely on the taxonomic one" (Perchonock and Werner, 1969:237).

How that should be done is not suggested by them nor will it be by me!

Mulberry Street

After relinquishing my ethnobotanical responsibilities so jauntily, it seems scarcely possible that just two years later, in 1975, Dennis and I were at it again: We reasoned that it would make good sense, for the benefit of botanists, to simply extract the plant entries from the dictionary and publish them separately, fortified with an introduction by Breedlove.

The next notion was far more treacherous. It involved the addition of considerable botanical material that I had excluded deliberately from the dictionary: yit'ix names. When the attributive, yit'ix, literally, "jealous," is placed before a plant name it denotes that the plant in question is similar to the named plant. The English attributives, "bastard," and "false," are comparable except that they specify a single species as, "bastard evening primrose," whereas yit'ix can be freely tacked onto the name of any plant with similar features. Although these are not true names, they obviously are of critical value in establishing relationships between plants. And so, all these names had to be added to the Tzotzil-Latin, Latin-Tzotzil card files that had been created for the production of the dictionary.

There existed still another set of information relative to an ethnobotany. Years before, at Dennis' suggestion, when we made the plant collections, I had recorded what name had been assigned to every plant by each member of the team. From the field notes I extracted now the number of times each named plant had been collected and how many people had identified it. The total of plant identifications was roughly 10,000!

This led us inexorably to the conclusion that we had amassed for ourselves an enormous responsibility that obliged us to return to "the field" to set our record straight, generating a Tzotzil ethnobotany that would rival in understanding and rigorous elegance the monumental *Principles of Tzeltal Plant Classification* (Berlin et al., 1974).

Now it became our task to convince our home institutions, and eventually the National Geographic Society, that our forays to Zinacantán merited their dollars! And so was spawned a series of modest proposals. In 1978, after a previous month-long joint endeavor, I opined that "a short field session" would do the trick—"fill in the gaps and provide solutions to taxonomic problems." Four years later I proposed "a final three-month field session." And now, in January 1987, I find myself still ensconced in "the field."

My procession of proposals, modest financially, glowed with vainglorious descriptions of our past achievements: "Never before have two related systems of native taxonomy been examined and compared with the depth and breadth of knowledge that can be marshalled by the principal investigators of this project." For the future flowering of our study I promised everything:

Introductory chapters will describe the geographic, botanical, and human setting, the economic, aesthetic, and ritual use of the flora, the methods of collection and interviewing, and the classificatory principles of the native taxonomic system. Because the research methods of the Tzeltal study have been outlined in print so meticulously, they will not require lengthy discussion in this study. Greater emphasis will be placed on the medicinal, symbolic, and ritual aspects of plants in Tzotzil culture. And as previous work among both the Tzeltal and Tzotzil have concentrated exclusively on men's plant knowledge, an attempt will be made to interview female weavers and midwives. It will be the purpose of the introductory chapters to demonstrate that ethnobotany is not merely the systematic study of the plant lore of a people, but rather a study of the flowering of man. In presenting the human habitat of the flora it will become abundantly clear that "the worlds in which different societies live are distinct worlds—not merely the same world with different labels attached" (Sapir, 1929:209).

This from the 1978 draft.

Two years later:

We will investigate the functional aspect of the taxonomy, going beyond the "whats" to the "whys." This project aims, then, to provide not only a detailed description of native plant taxonomy and use, but an exploration in depth of native world view.

Then from the 1981 draft:

…we may consider investigating the economic aspects of Zinacantec cultivation and marketing.

And to think that I saw it on Mulberry Street![1] So much for the visions. What were the attainments? Or, first, what intentions did we disregard?

We abandoned our plan to compare the Tzotzil and Tzeltal taxonomic systems, deciding to leave that for some other ethnoscientist. Nor did we compare the cultural significance of plants in Tenejapa and Zinacantán as Brent Berlin's and my focus of attention had not been identical, and Tenejapa shamans had been reluctant to reveal their medical knowledge.

I failed to interview female midwives and weavers, partly from shyness or laziness, and partly because of my inability to identify immediately the plants that would be involved. The proscription against taking women "into the woods" caused our title to be more literally true than we had intended or desired!

We carefully sidestepped an in-depth study of the functional aspect of the taxonomy, preferring to treat it simply as a convenient way for the Zinacantecs and ourselves to discuss the flora. Unprincipled perhaps?

Considerable investigation has already been made of traditional Zinacantec cultivation and marketing (Bunnin, 1966; Cancian, 1965, 1972; Collier, 1975). Enormously complex changes have occurred under government stimulus, and so a thorough update would have required a major study, requiring sophisticated economic expertise not available to us. Consequently, we chose to narrow our concentration and asked John Haviland to provide a description of the dynamics of the flower industry.

In my pleas for financial support I was quick to point out the urgency of our research:

It has become abundantly clear that the younger generation, because of truck transportation, does not know a quarter of what is known by the elders or by even the middle-aged people. This makes it all the more important to gather botanical information which may be returned to the people (1981).

In the past five years the environment, both natural and cultural, has changed at an ever more accelerating rate. Population pressure and industrial greed have brought the decimation of the forests and the reduction of arable land available to Indians. This, together with inflation and bilingualism, is propelling the younger generation out of their cornfields and into the oil fields. Traditional knowledge of the natural world, preserved only orally, is receding rapidly as modern civilization, with its factory-made materials for clothing, shelter, transport, agriculture, health,

---

[1]This refers to the outlandish vision of Theodor Seuss Geisel ("Dr. Seuss") in his *And to Think That I Saw It on Mulberry Street* (New York: The Vanguard Press).

education, and even ritual decoration, advances apace, changing forever the relationship between man and nature (1982).

Fortunately our pleas reached sympathetic ears!

The New Look

Confident that the native taxonomy of the Tzotzil flora would resemble closely the Tzeltal model, our first task on returning to Chiapas in 1976 was to try to discover some order in our mass of plant names. Although we eschewed folk keys and triad tests, we did use a modified paired comparison technique. Two of the most reliable members of the original collecting team (Antzelmo Peres and Chep Atz'am) were presented with stacks of cards. Each card contained a single plant name. I asked my colleagues to sort the cards into groups. After a morning's labor, working separately, they presented me with their results. The great majority of the cards were grouped together on the basis of morphology, a few because of their use. Many plants were set aside as belonging to no group. Of course Antzelmo's and Chep's taxonomies were not identical! The afternoon was spent arguing over the "truth." Some of the differences were resolved and some remained to be examined at a later date with other consultants.

Re-enlisting our major veteran plant collector, Maryan Martinis, as well as Antzelmo and Chep, we spent a month, Dennis and I together, taking one-day field trips to try to establish a bit of order on our material.

The following year a new dimension was added to our project by my discovery of a Spanish-Tzotzil dictionary compiled in Zinacantán (Laughlin and Haviland, 1988) almost surely at the end of the 16th century. It contained a significant number of plant names and revealed the degree of introduction of European plants at the time. It verified the persistence of Zinacantec plant names over a span of four hundred years. This dictionary, in addition, had a wealth of terms referring to agricultural practices.

In 1978, with nearly all the new collections identified, we established a work pattern that was to persist until the project's end. Joint sessions in California alternated with series of field trips. For 10 days (all that we could stand) we would pore over our original data and our new field notes, checking specimens painstakingly in the herbarium, sipping our tea. Then we would hurtle over the hill, with our Bohemias, to wrestle with our problems the next day under the Bolinas sun. We weeded out native misidentifications, and pruned away the excess native descriptive terminology. That is, the bewildering array of plant names that distinguished size, habitat, color, etc., often proved to be redundant, overlapping, or overloaded terms that were produced by the native collectors to prove that they were just as discriminating as the foreign collectors. From out of what seemed a veritable chaos of names in 1976 emerged a comprehensible and comprehensive native taxonomic structure. The first draft of "The Flora" was executed.

What We Did on the Road

Our collecting trips in Chiapas now had a new look. Gone were the days of five-man teams of Zinacantec collectors, drunk or sober, alone or chaufferred by an ignorant gringo anthropologist or by an even more ignorant *ladino* student, as they repeated or invented plant names by the score. No, now we managed some control! The team was composed always of botanist, anthropologist, and one or two (occasionally three), generally sober native collectors. Collectors from the hamlets were always accompanied by a collector from the center. In this way we could distinguish better between differences of opinion or the addition of merely synonymous names.

On many of our initial collecting ventures we would leave San Cristóbal around 8 or 9 A.M., drive slowly down a road, making frequent stops. Dennis would point to every different plant, tree, or vine and ask for its name, while I would inquire about its use. If Dennis wanted a collection, that would be made in quadruplicate when possible. We kept separate notebooks, noting the collection number in both. I included the Tzotzil names and the Latin name, if known. I would also jot down the life form and any cultural information for further questioning. We would eat a picnic lunch and return around dusk.

In the course of a single day 20 or 30 plants would have been collected and 200–300 species of plants would have been identified. If there were two native collectors, that meant 400–600 sight identifications! To our regret, now, we kept no tally of the number of plants that our consultants were unable to identify. Our trips were usually jovial affairs, sometimes raucous, as when Antzelmo cut a 15-foot white-flowered yucca inflorescence and marched with it at the head of our procession to the truck, intoning a mock prayer.

Increasingly the trips were targeted on a particular habitat or were designed to fill a known gap, solve a taxonomic problem, or to revise and expand my omnibus of Tzotzil botanical vocabulary. On the last matter, after I had shown five sagittate leaves to the same Zinacantec colleague in one day, to make sure of his consistency in applying descriptive terms, and in which endeavor he had offered me four synonyms, my daughter, who had accompanied us, commented to me, much to my surprise, "Dad, he must think you're awfully dumb!"

During the decade of 1976–1986 we made repeated visits to all the natural habitats known by Zinacantecs, in all seasons, and also, in all seasons, to the highland and lowland markets. During this same period our Zinacantec consultants made an additional 30,000 identifications.

After each collecting trip I would interview the consultants, from 9 A.M. to 2 P.M., in my office, notebook at hand, to glean any further information on the plants we had seen.

There were long periods in Chiapas when I was alone or Dennis was occupied with other projects, but always I had the consolation, the assurance, that he, by himself, or with the aid of a large company of botany colleagues, would provide us with reliable identifications—no mean feat!

FIGURE 2.—The triumvirate and their safari, 1981. (Photo by Nancy Breedlove.)

Two resources, drawn originally from the dictionary, and seeming to have added up to no more than a cultural midden, proved to be of extreme utility: the "Cultural Omnibus" and a digest of plant use. Both served as questionnaires for expanding and deepening my knowledge of the interaction between man and plants. Almost magically their volume was doubled, revealing many beliefs and practices that had entirely escaped my notice.

In addition I recorded, transcribed and translated a significant body of plant origin myths, agricultural prayers, and autobiographical accounts. For each plant of cultural significance I routinely inquired, **"Mi oy smelol?"** "Is there traditional knowledge about it?" This would often disclose what we would call "superstitious" beliefs about plant care or human interaction with plants. It might bring forth a sentence or two about the plant's origin, or a whole myth. Occasionally I

learned these traditional stories after a day of collecting in the lowlands, sitting around the fire, seldom equipped with a tape recorder. From the many folktales I had transcribed in the 1960s, told by both men and women, I selected sections relevant to this study. And so the mythic information included in "The Flora" varies greatly from mere snippets to whole transcribed narratives. This is the traditional knowledge that is passed on and shared by family members or fellow workers around the hearth, in the fields, or during any appropriate informal activity. I also made an effort to observe and sometimes participate in domestic, agricultural, or religious affairs for which my knowledge was decidedly limited. But, indeed, on almost every occasion that I was in contact with Zinacantecs, for whatever reason, planned or spontaneous, I came home with a new bit of botanical information.

Returning to California to prepare the second draft of "The

Flora," we were reminded continually of the necessity for extensive fieldwork by botanist-anthropologist-native consultant teams working throughout the year, for although our framework of investigation remained relatively intact, considerable revisions and additions were made.

Close examination of synonymous names and of **yit'ix** names provided independent evidence of the scope of each native generic and specific denominator. Often the collector, though he did not know, or could not recall the name of a plant, realized its similarity to known plants; e.g., he might call **k'isis**, the bald cypress, **yit'ix toj,** "false pine." Or his assertion that plant "a" was a "false b" demonstrated that while "a" was not "b," they were sufficiently similar to be included in the same set. Often a collector, incorrectly, would call plant "a" plant "b," which we had already concluded was a member of the same set. So, even consultants' errors were valuable in establishing the range of a set.

Returning once again to "the field" we checked every set, plant by plant, to add to or define more precisely the relationships, synonymy and use.

It became apparent that it was vain to search for *the* Zinacantec botanic taxonomy as every individual carries his own taxonomy, which itself may vary from one moment to the next. Instead, the taxonomy that emerged proved to be a pragmatic means to enter quickly into the Zinacantec realm of botany, following a map as accurate, as genuine, as that possessed by any native individual. Although no Zinacantec is familiar with every region or would agree to every detail, all Zinacantecs would be in substantial accord, for this was the product of the canvassing of many minds.

Variation is not limited to taxonomic structure, nor to the names for plants, but even extends to the adjectives that may be used to describe leaf shape, fruit shape, or the rustling sounds of windblown seeds.

On the Road Again

In 1982–1983 we narrowed our focus to those plants that were of critical importance to the culture for economic or religious reasons. Already we had amassed a bewildering profusion of varietal names for the major cultivated plants: corn, beans, squashes, chilies, fruits, and flowers.

In addition to joint market visits and journeys to the cultivated fields, I embarked on a survey designed to produce a complete inventory of the plants grown by Zinacantecs in the center, in each and every hamlet and colony as well as in several temperate localities, and in the lowlands generally. I visited nearly every community, discovering an extraordinary number of crops, particularly in the temperate zone, many recently introduced, whose presence had not been suspected by me, nor even by many Zinacantecs with whom I spoke. Highlanders denied their existence. Our chief consultant, Maryan Martinis, could not be persuaded that an elephant ear was cultivated, despite our visit to a planting!

The number of varieties, each of which had to be collected and analyzed, rife with synonymous names, reached astronomical proportions.

Equipped with a long list of the varieties of corn that had eluded us, I made an expedition to the lowlands with two Zinacantecs, to be greeted in sun-dried field after field by great white mounds of threshed corncobs. One week too late! After a breakdown, we drove for miles past empty fields, with occasional stops to make furtive dashes into fields to filch a few ratty ears. After futile searches for open restaurants or adequate camping sites we slept fitfully in my VW Safari, battered by a frigid wind, returning home the next day with our prizes. Persistence had prevailed, nearly every missing ear was in the bag!

No less challenging was my determination to make an inventory of all the plants, trees, and vines used to decorate each church or chapel, noting at what fiesta, how many plants were present, and by whom supplied. The suspicions of each clique of sacristans, stewards, and wardens had to be allayed even if it meant dancing with them the night through!

So much for Chiapas. I made pilgrimages to the John Wesley Powell Library of Anthropology (National Museum of Natural History), the Library of Congress, and the Cathedral of Learning (University of Pittsburgh) to examine dictionaries and word lists of every Mayan language to reveal related plant names.

Again in California, we confronted the problem that Linnaean taxonomy seldom stoops to consider the varieties of cultivated plants. How were we to cope with the endless varieties of bean, each exhibiting the finest distinctions, when nearly all these beans were subsumed by Linnaeus and his disciples under a single term, *Phaseolus vulgaris*? What we had characterized earlier as a "nomenclatural mess" of corn varieties finally surrendered to a sensible ordering by race. An exhaustive search of horticultural tomes uncovered a variety of pear now rarely cultivated in Zinacantán that is known to have been in cultivation in Europe since 1628!

The Finishing Touch

At this last stage we have fed "The Flora" and many of the introductory chapters into word processors, permitting us to revise the text continually: from shifting whole blocks of material, to revising cultural and botanical descriptions, updating fluctuating Latin names, and correcting typographical errors. This system also facilitates the creation of the necessary indices. If this is the end, what have we wrought?

Inspired at the outset by *Principles of Tzeltal Plant Classification* (Berlin et al., 1974), we strove to present a companion Tzotzil volume. But soon this subject took on a life of its own. Although we followed the neighboring work in broad outline, using "The Flora" as the base, with introductory discussions of research methods, native taxonomic principles, and the cultural utility of plants, we became convinced that the

Zinacantecs maintained a greater latitutude of choice, a greater variety and flexibility in their principles! "The truth" was overrun by many truths. Native taxonomy was not our goal, but rather our vehicle for reaching a better understanding of native thought, and for delivering a disparate collection of knowledge. Consequently, our presentation has been branded as "uneven." We take that as a compliment, a recognition of the very nature of a people's knowledge.

Instead of a native taxonomy explained in ultimate detail, this "Flora" is an encyclopedia of botanical information, demonstrating simultaneously the flowers and the flowering of man in Zinacantán. Or, if you wish, it may be seen as a flower cart of botanical knowledge.

It is clear that these "isolated peasants" share with millions of other Mayan peasants throughout southern Mexico and Guatemala a world view that is radically different from Western perceptions.

We hope, as you see this ungainly, overloaded vehicle pass by you will realize that it bears "a distinct world, not merely the same world with different labels attached!"

Phytogeography of Zinacantán

Dennis E. Breedlove

The township of Zinacantán is located along the dry western slope of the Central Plateau, which adjoins the Central Depression. Zinacantán is spread over 117 square kilometers with an additional 3249 hectares in the lowland colony of Santa Rosa. The vegetational types are dry in nature with pockets of wet vegetation occuring along steep canyons and near tops of the ridges of Pij (P'ij) and Cerro Huitepec (Muk'ta Vitz). The substrate rocks throughout most of the township are marine limestone of Cretaceous to Miocene age. There is a broad band of a sandy conglomerate near Ixtapa. The higher peaks have extrusions of volcanic rocks. The limestone slopes are dissected by steep-walled ravines and are punctuated by sink holes and caves. These limestones are 1000–2000 m thick and are capped with a red lateritic clay soil. The soil derived in the region of conglomerates is poor and sandy and supports a depauparate pine savanna. There is very little cultivation on this soil. A dark rich sandy clay loam is common on valley floors and alluvial fans and is the most prized for cultivation.

Originally, the dry exposed slopes supported a succession of dry forest types with Tropical Deciduous Forest, Thorn Woodland, and Short Tree Savanna at the lower elevations and Pine Oak Forest on the slopes above 1200 m. Wet forest associations were widespread at elevations above 1800 m especially on steep north slopes and slopes along major watercourses. Evergreen Cloud Forest was most common at the highest elevations and Pine Oak Liquidambar Forest or Montane Rain Forest probably at elevations between 1800 and 2300 m on the slopes surrounding the valleys of Navenchauc (Naben Chauk), Nachig (Na Chij) and Zinacantán Center (Jtek Lum). Temperate Riparian Forest is a major component along streams from 1400 to 2700 m. Seasonal Evergreen Forest is a common element along waterways and steep ravines at lower elevations (below 1400 m).

At the present time these primary forest types have a much reduced distribution in the township of Zinacantán. They exist only in areas that are inaccessable or infertile because of soil or elevation. Most of the present vegetation is composed of second growth shrub and forest associations that have considerably fewer species and are much less complex in their makeup. Fallow ground and cultivated land also account for a considerable portion of the township in any given year.

Climate

Most of Zinacantán has a mild, even climate. Annual rainfall varies from 90 mm to 250 mm, depending on the location. Although rain may fall in any month, most precipitation falls between May an October. There are three distinct seasons. The rains begin in mid-May with afternoon thundershowers, which continue until early October. There is often a 2–3 week hiatus (canicules or dog days) in late July and early August. From November into February the region is beset with a sequence of driving mist storms (nortes), which although they do not leave significant amounts of precipitation do make dirt roads and trails difficult to travel. At the lower elevations all but the very strongest of these storms are felt as high overcast. From February until the onset of rains in May is the dry season proper with only occasional local thunderstorms. This is the season to burn the fields. The sky is filled with a smoky haze, the sun often visible as a red disk. The hottest days of the year occur here.

As mentioned before, temperature and rainfall vary greatly throughout the township. At the lowest elevations (hot country, 500 to 1000 m) in the Central Depression and the lower edge of the Central Plateau, the mean monthly temperature varies from 22°C to 28°C, and the annual rainfall fluctuates from 95 to 125 mm. At intermediate elevations (temperate country or hamlets 1000 to 1800 m), the mean monthly temperatures vary from 17°C to 23°C while the annual rainfall ranges from 120 to 160 mm. At the highest elevations (cold country, 1800 to 2900 m), mean monthly temperatures vary from 10°C to 17°C, and the annual rainfall ranges from 125 to 220 mm. Throughout the region the coldest months are November through February. Frosts are common during these months in exposed areas at the highest elevations and occur occasionally on flats in the path of cold air drainage as low as 1500 m (E. Garcia, 1965, 1973).

Vegetation

Throughout the body of the text, reference is made to vegetational associations followed by a temperature-elevation statement (e.g., Tropical Deciduous Forest of temperate and lowland areas). The same associations may occur in more than one zone and have a different species composition or physiognomic aspect in the different areas. For this reason the vegetational associations are here given separate characterizations for each temperature-elevation zone in which they occur. For a complete treatment of the vegetational associations of Chiapas, reference should be made to Breedlove (1981).

HOT COUNTRY VEGETATION (500–1000 M)

Although most of the township of Zinacantán is not within

11

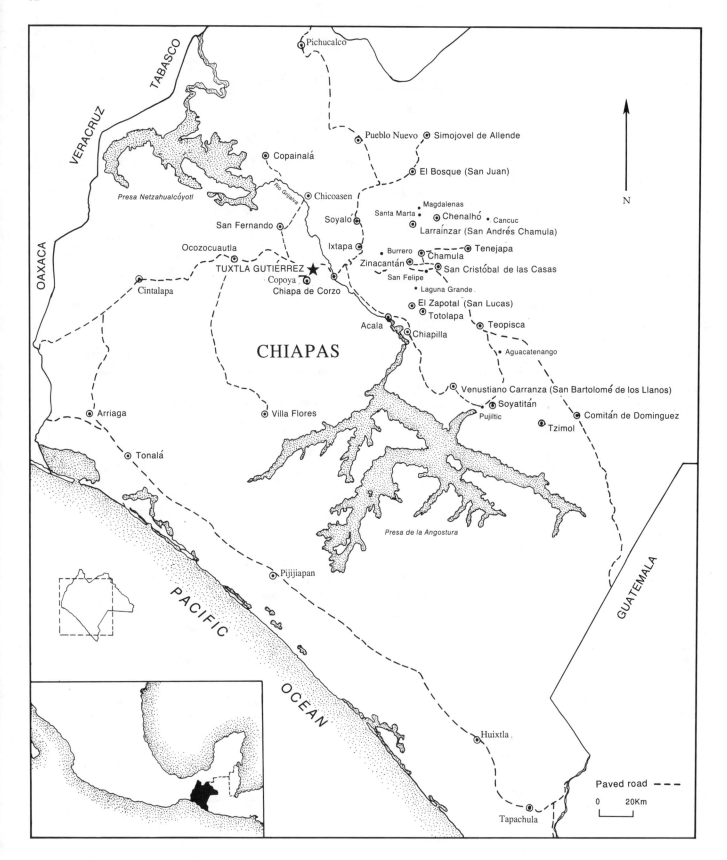

MAP 1.—Chiapas.

the limits of hot country, per se, much of the land the Zinacantecs rent for milpa is in the Central Depression and as such has typical hot country vegetation. The area has two overriding climatic factors that directly affect the type of vegetation present there. Very high monthly mean temperatures (22°C to 28°C) account for the large diversity of tropical genera, and a prolonged dry season (up to 7 months) is responsible for the deciduous nature of most of the vegetation.

TROPICAL DECIDUOUS FOREST.—This is a diverse and wide-ranging association, which occurs from Sinaloa to Panama. In the Central Depression of Chiapas, it is the most prominent and common vegetational association. Characteristically it has a tremendous number of species of trees that are co-dominant. These are deciduous or semi-deciduous and are usually 10 to 20 m tall with straight, slightly buttressed trunks and spreading crowns. The canopy consists of a single layer and can be continuous or discontinuous. With a few exceptions the forest is completely deciduous by March-April and many of the dominants flower at this time. The understory is sparse and made up mostly of annual growth during the rainy season. Lianas and epiphytes are not a conspicuous element except along ravines and ridges where they become locally abundant. This association grades into Seasonal Evergreen Forest along streams, into Short Tree Savanna in areas of poor soils, into Thorn Woodland in extreme dry locations, and finally grades into Pine Oak Forest with a rise in altitude. In the Central Depression the most common dominant trees are *Albizzia caribaea* (Urban) Britton & Rose, *Bucida buceras* L., *B.*

macrostachya Standley, *Bursera simaruba* (L.) Sargent, *Cecropia peltata* L., *Cedrela oaxacensis* C. de Candolle & Rose, *Ceiba aesculifolia* (Kunth) Britton & Baker, *Cochlospermum vitifolium* Willdenow ex Sprengel, *Cordia alliodora* (Ruiz & Pavon) Oken, *Elaeodendron trichotomum* (Turczaninow) Lundell, *Enterolobium cyclocarpum* (Jacquin) Grisebach, *Eysenhardtia adenostylis* Baillon, *Gliricidia sepium* (Jacquin) Steudel, *Godmania aesculifolia* (Kunth) Standley, *Heliocarpus terebinthinaceus* (de Candolle) Hochreutiner, *Hura polyandra* Baillon, *Hymenaea courabaril* L., *Leucaena* spp., *Luehea candida* (de Candolle) Martius, *Lysiloma acapulcense* (Kunth) Bentham, *L. auritum* (Schlechtendal) Bentham, *Pithecellobium dulce* (Roxburgh) Bentham, *Plumeria rubra* L., *Poeppigia procera* Presl, *Pseudobombax ellipticum* (Kunth) Dugand, *Spondias mombin* L., *Stemmadenia obovata* (Hooker & Arnott) Schumacher, *Swietenia humilis* Zuccarini, *Tabebuia chrysantha* (Jacquin) Nichols, *T. rosea* (Bertoloni) de Candolle.

THORN WOODLAND.—In especially dry locations such as the western slopes of low rocky ridges, there occurs an assemblage of shrubs and thin-trunked low trees. Many of the woody species are variously spiny or divaricately branched. A mature stand often presents an inpenetrable thicket 1 to 4 m tall. This association is found in areas that experience the severest dry seasons and most of the woody species are deciduous. During wet periods the understory is made up of a thin cover of grasses and herbs. Although this is a very common and widespread association in Mexico to the north of Chiapas, in the Central Depression it has a scattered and local occurrence. Legumes

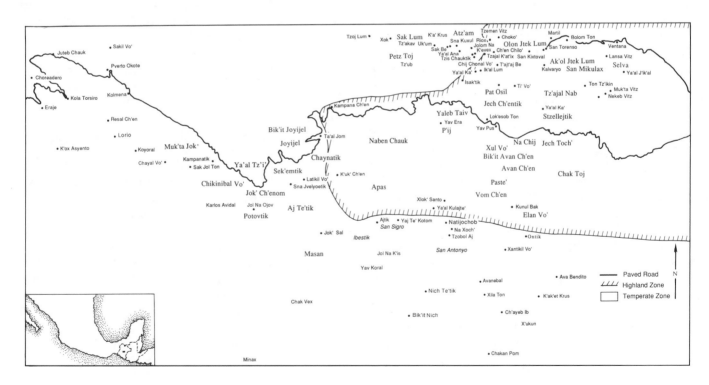

MAP 2.—Zinacantán.

and cacti are the most prominent members of this association. Some of the common species found here are *Acacia cochliacantha* Humboldt & Bonpland, *A. cornigera* (L.) Willdenow, *A. farnesiana* (L.) Willdenow, *A. pringlei* Rose, *Bauhinia pauletia* Persoon, *Bursera diversifolia* Rose, *Cordia dodecandra* de Candolle, *C. spinescens* L., *Dalea versicolor* Zuccarini, *Diphysa floribunda* Peyritsch, *Erythroxylon havanense* Jacquin, *Haematoxylon brasiletto* Karsten, *Jacquinia macrocarpa* Cavanilles, *Nopalea cochenillifera* (L.) Salm-Dyck, *N. lutea* Rose, *Opuntia* spp., *Piptadenia flava* Bentham, *Pisonia macranthocarpa* J. Donnell-Smith, *Pithecellobium lanceolatum* (Kunth) Bentham, *Prosopis juliflora* (Swartz) de Candolle, *Sageretia elegans* (Kunth) Brongniart, *Stenocereus eichlamii* (Britton & Rose) Buxbaum, *Zizyphus amole* (Sesse & Mocino) M.C Johnston.

SHORT TREE SAVANNA.—This vegetational formation occurs at scattered locations throughout the Central Depression. It is characterized by low-crowned trees spaced on a grassland. The soils are poorly drained and contain very litle nutrient material and are usually made up of compacted sandy deposits. Four species of trees, *Byrsonima crassifolia* (L.) de Candolle, *Crescentia alata* Kunth, *C. cujete* L., and *Curatella americana* L., essentially define this association. The grassland contains many species of herbs and grasses with *Trachypogon* spp. often dominant. The trees are usually 4 to 10 m tall; however, some individuals may attain a height of 20 m. *Acacia pennatula* (Schlechtendal & Chamisso) Bentham, *Pinus oocarpa* Schiede, *Psidium guineense* Swartz, or *Quercus oleoides* Schlechtendal & Chamisso often form savanna-like vegetation usually not in association with the four trees mentioned above.

EVERGREEN SEASONAL FOREST.—In areas where watercourses cut through hills or are otherwise protected, the forest that occurs along them reflects this protection with a much wetter tropical aspect. Most of the species of trees and also shrubs of the understory are evergreen. The canopy is continuous and often is formed in two layers. Many of the trees are buttressed and attain a height of 25 to 35 m. Lianas and large epiphytes (aroids and bromeliads) are common. The understory contains a diverse woody element. This forest experiences the same severe dry season as the surrounding deciduous vegetation. In the Central Depression it is restricted to a gallery-like aspect but elsewhere in Chiapas in areas with slightly more precipitation, it has a wider distribution and intergrades with Tropical and Montane Rain Forest associations. Some of the more common trees encountered in this formation are *Bernoullia flammea* Oliver, *Brosimum alicastrum* Swartz, *Bumelia pleistochasia* J. Donnell-Smith, *Calycophyllum candidissimum* (Vahl) de Candolle, *Ceiba pentandra* (L.) Gaertner, *Chrysophyllum mexicanum* Brandegee ex Standley, *Coccoloba barbadensis* Jacquin, *Cupania dentata* de Candolle, *Exothea paniculata* (Jussieu) Radlkofer, *Ficus glabrata* Kunth, *F. glaucescens* (Liebmann) Miquel, *Guettarda combsii* Urban, *Hyperbaena mexicana* Miers, *Licania arborea* Seemann, *Machaerium biovulatum* Michelli, *Rheedia edulis*

Triana & Planchon, *Sapindus saponaria* L., *Sterculia mexicana* R. Brown, *Styrax argentum* Presl. In the understory the following species are common: *Amyris chiapensis* Lundell, *Ardisia escallonioides* Schlechtendas & Chamisso, *Bourreria huanita* (LaLlave & Lexara) Hemsley, *Calyptranthes chiapensis* Lundell, *Chiococca sessilifolia* Miranda, *Clusia flava* Jacquin, *Dalbergia glabra* (Miller) Standley, *Eugenia acapulcensis* Steudel, *E. yunckeri* Standley, *Exostema caribaeum* (Jacquin) Roemer & Schultes, *Gentlea venosissima* (Ruiz & Pavon) Lundell, *Karwinskia calderonii* Standley, *Machaerium riparium* Brandegee, *Psychotria erythrocarpa* Schlechtendal.

TEMPERATE COUNTRY VEGETATION (1000–1800 M)

This is a zone of transition from the tropical vegetation types of the Central Depression to the cool north-temperate types of vegetation on the mountain peaks. The lower portion of this zone is mostly Tropical Deciduous Forest and Evergreen Seasonal Forest as described above. This part of temperate country is still under the effect of the rain shadow produced by the mass of the Central Plateau. There are many narrowly endemic species that occur here and are not found in the same vegetational associations at lower elevations in the Central Depression. Some of these are *Ateleia tomentosa* Rudd, *Catoferia chiapensis* A. Gray, *Erythrina goldmanii* Standley, *Eugenia carranzae* Lundell, *E. laughlinii* Lundell, *Euphorbia pseudofulva* Miranda, *Lopezia langmanniae* Miranda, *Micropholia sericea* L.O. Williams, *Phyllanthus mcvaughii* Webster, *Pitcairnia breedlovei* L.B. Smith. Pine Oak Forest interfingers with these associations and becomes the prevalent type of vegetation in the upper part of this zone. In the canyon that runs from Salinas (Atz'am) towards Ixtapa and in the upper reaches of the canyons that drain towards El Zapotal (San Lukax), Evergreen Seasonal Forest grades into Montane Rain Forest especially on the north slopes of the tributaries.

PINE OAK FOREST.—This association occurs on dry ridges and slopes from 1200 to 2600 m. Oaks are found singly or in small groups as low as 900 m and pines first appear about 1000 m. The trees are usually 15 to 40 m tall and openly spaced with a discontinuous canopy. The understory is composed of a low cover of herbs and shrubs or in some situations a grassland. This grassy cover may be artificially maintained by a combination of burning and grazing. Epiphytes are abundant especially on the horizontal branches of the oaks and are at times so numerous as to obscure those branches. Pine Oak Forest intergrades into Evergreen Cloud Forest on the ridges approaching the high peaks. Streams that run through zones of Pine Oak usually are lined with Temperate Riparian Forest or Evergreen Seasonal Forest at the lower edge of the temperate area. The most common trees found in this association are *Arbutus xalapensis* Kunth, *Buddleia skutchii* Morton, *Crataegus pubescens* (Kunth) Steudel, *Ehretia latifolia* de Candolle, *Erythrina chiapasana* Krukoff, *Juniperus gamboana* Martinez, *Pinus michoacana* Martinez, *P. montezumae* Lamb,

P. oaxacana Mirov, *P. oocarpa* Schiede, *P. patula* ssp. *tecunumanii* (Equilez & Perry) Styles, *P. pseudostrobus* Lindley, *P. teocote* Schlechtendal & Camisso, *Quercus acutifolia* Nee, *Q. candicans* Nee, *Q. castanea* Nee, *Q. crassifolia* Humboldt & Bonpland, *Q. crispipilis* Trelease, *Q. elliptica* Nee, *Q. laurina* Humboldt & Bonpland, *Q. peduncularis* Nee, *Q. polymorpha* Schlechtendal & Camisso, *Q. rugosa* Nee, *Q. segoviensis* Liebmann. The common woody plants of the understory are *Amelanchier nervosa* (Decaisne) Standley, *Buddleia crotonoides* A. Gray, *Calliandra grandiflora* (L'Heritier) Bentham, *Ceanothus coeruleus* Lagasca, *Chiococca phaenostemon* Schlechtendal, *Desmodium nicaraguense* Oersted ex Bentham & Oersted, *Garrya laurifolia* Hartweg, *Holodiscus argenteus* (L.f.) Maximowicz, *Ilex vomitoria* Aiton, *Indigofera thibaudiana* de Candolle, *Lippia chiapasensis* Moldenke, *Litsea neesiana* (Schaur) Hemsley, *Mahonia volcania* Standley & Steyermark, *Monnina xalapensis* Kunth, *Myrica cerifera* L., *Rhamnus mucronata* Schlechtendal, *R. serrata* Humboldt & Bonpland ex Schultes, *Rhus schiedeana* Schlechtendal, *R. terebinthifolia* Schlechtendal & Camisso, *Solanum chrysotrichum* Dunal, *S. lanceolatum* Cavanilles, *S. nigricans* Martens & Galeotti, *S. pubigerum* Dunal, *Ternstroemia oocarpa* Rose, *Viburnum hartwegii* Bentham.

Second-growth Shrub Associations: When Pine Oak Forest is cut over, the residue burned, planted to maize, and after a few years allowed to grow back, the regeneration begins with a scrub association that can last for as long as 10 years. This vegetation is extremely diverse and variable because the plants that are involved are from a variety of sources. Some are remnants of the forest that is being replaced; others are woody weeds that only occur after disturbances. Physically it is a dense cover of shrubs, vines, and rank herbs up to three meters tall. The most common species encountered are *Acacia angustissima* (Miller) Kuntze, *Acalypha unibracteata* Mueller de Aargau, *Ageratina pringlei* (Robinson & Greenman) King & H. Robinson, *Ambrosia cumanensis* Kunth, *Archibaccaris androgyna* (Brandegee) Blake, *Baccharis serraefolia* de Candolle, *B. trinervis* (Lamarck) Persoon, *B. vaccinioides* Kunth, *Bidens squarrosa* Kunth, *Bouvardia longiflora* (Cavanilles) Kunth, *Calea trichotoma* J, Donnell-Smith, *C. urticifolia* (Miller) de Candolle, *Calliandra grandiflora* (L'Heritier) Bentham, *C. houstoniana* (Miller) Kuntze, *Ceanothus coeruleus* Lagasca, *Chromolaena collina* (de Candolle) King & H. Robinson, *Comarostaphylos discolor* (Hooker) Diggs, *Coreopsis mutica* de Candolle, *Coriaria ruscifolia* L., *Desmanthodium perfoliatum* Bentham, *Galphimia glauca* Cavanilles, *Gaultheria odorata* Willdenow, *Lantana hirta* Graham, *L. hispida* Kunth, *Lippia graveolens* Kunth, *L. myriocephala* Schlechtendal & Camisso, *L. substrigosa* Turczaninow, *Malvaviscus arboreus* Cavanilles, *Montanoa hexagona* Robinson & Greenman, *Perymenium ghiesbreghtii* Robinson & Greenman, *Peteravenia phoenicolepis* (Robinson) King & H. Robinson, *Phyllanthus grandifolius* L., *Pluchea odorata* (L.) Cassini, *Rubus adenotrichus* Schlechtendal, *R. humistratus* Steudel, *R.*

trilobus Seringe, *Salvia cinnabarina* Martens & Galeotti, *S. holwayi* Blake, *S. lasiantha* Bentham, *S. myriantha* Epling, *S. polystachya* Ortega, *S. purpurea* Cavanilles, *S. rubiginosa* Bentham, *S. tiliifolia* Vahl, *Senna guatemalensis* var. *chiapensis* (Standley) Irwin & Barneby, *S. incarnata* (Bentham) Irwin & Barneby, *S. septentrionalis* (Viviani) Irwin & Barneby, *Smallanthus maculatus* (Cavanilles) H. Robinson, *Tithonia diversifolia* (Hemsley) A. Gray, *T. rotundifolia* (Miller) Blake, *T. tubaeformis* (Jacquin) Cassini, *Verbesina perymenioides* Schultz-Bipontinus ex Klatt, *V. turbascensis* Kunth, *Vernonia deppeana* Lessing, *V. leiocarpa* de Candolle, *Viguiera cordata* (Hooker & Arnott) D'Arcy.

MONTANE RAIN FOREST.—Throughout Chiapas this is a common formation on steep slopes between 1000 to 2000 m that experience some rain in all months of the year and have well-draining soils. In Zinacantán these conditions are very limited in distribution to a few remote locations. This association was much more widespread before the advent of intensive cultivation. There are two layers of canopy and a dense understory of woody plants. The canopy trees are usually 25 to 35 m tall. Many are buttressed. The understory of shrubs and small trees is between 5 and 15 m tall. Epiphytes and lianas are abundant through all layers of this formation. *Alfaroa mexicana* Stone, *Ardisia densiflora* Krug & Urban, *Dendropanax arboreus* (L.) Decaisne & Planchon, *Ilex brandegeana* Loesner, *Meliosma matudae* Lundell, *Oecopetalum mexicanum* Greenman & Thompson, *Oreopanax xalapensis* (Kunth) Decaisne & Planchon, *Quercus corrugata* Hooker, *Q. insignis* Martens & Galeotti, *Synardisia venosa* (Masters) Lundell, *Turpinia occidentalis* Don, *Ulmus mexicana* Liebmann, *Zunila alba* (Lundell) Lundell are some of the common forest trees. In the understory one finds the following: *Acalypha macrostachya* Jacquin, *Chamaedorea concolor* Martius, *Eugenia rhombea* (Berg) Krug & Urban ex Urban, *Lozanella enantiophylla* (J. Donnell-Smith) Killip & Morton, *Mollinedia guatemalensis* Perkins, *Myrcianthes fragrans* (Swartz) McVaugh, *Myriocarpa longipes* Liebmann, *Parathesis donnellsmithii* Mez, *P. leptopa* Lundell, *Rapanea juergensenii* Mez, *Siparuna nicaraguensis* Hemsley, *Trophis mexicana* (Liebmann) Bureau, *Urera alceifolia* Gaudichaud.

COLD COUNTRY VEGETATION (1800–2900 M)

At the present time much of this area is covered by Pine Oak Forest. Some of this forest is second growth with many fewer species of trees. *Abies guatemalensis* Rehder, *Pinus ayacahuite* Ehrenberg, *P. oaxacana* Mirov, *P. pseudostrobus* Lindle, *Quercus crassifolia* Humboldt & Bonpland, *Q. crispipilis* Trelease, *Q. laurina* Humboldt & Bonpland, and *Q. rugosa* Nee are the principal trees of this zone. A striking characteristic of the plants of this region is the predominance of north-temperate genera at all levels of the vegetation from herbs to trees. Three vegetational formations have very limited distribution in cold

FIGURE 3.—Landscape northwest of Yaleb Taiv, 1977. (Photo by John Swope.)

country. (1) Bunch Grassland occurs on a few high ridges with the following clump-forming grasses: *Festuca amplissima* Ruprecht, *Muhlenbergi gigantea* (Fournier) Hitchcock, *M. macroura* Kunth, *M. robusta* (Fournier) Hitchcock, *Stipa ichu* (Ruiz & Pavon) Kunth, *S. virescens* Kunth, and *Trisetum irazuense* (Kunze) Hitchcock. This formation may be of secondary origin; however, it appears stable and is probably maintained by grazing and harvesting for thatch. (2) Evergreen Cloud Scrub is limited to a few wind-swept ridges near the highest peaks. It is composed of a dense mat of thick-leaved shrubs. Common plants are *Acaena elongata* L., *Gaultheria cumingii* Sleumer, *G. odorata* Willdenow, *Gnaphalium salicifolium* (Bertoloni) Schultz-Bipontinus, *Lycopodium* spp., *Oxylobus oaxacanus* Blake, *Pernettya ciliata* (Schlechtendal & Camisso) Small, *P. hirsuta* (Martens & Galeotti) Camp, *Ternstroemia lineata* ssp. *chalicophila* Loesener, *Ugni myricoides* (Kunth) Berg, *Vaccinium confertum* Kunth, *V. geminiflorum* Kunth, *V. haematinum* Standley & Steyermark. (3) There are a few locations in the high valleys with boggy land or standing water that have a characteristic Herbaceous Marsh. The common plants are *Carex* spp., *Cyperus* spp., *Lythrum vulneraria* Schrank, *Rhynchospora* spp., *Scirpus* spp., *Typha latifolia* L.

EVERGREEN CLOUD FOREST.—On the tops of the highest peaks and ridges, on steep north-facing slopes, and at the heads of canyons at elevations of 2300 to 2900 m occurs this plant association. It is superficially similar to Montane Rain Forest and elsewhere in Chiapas it has a broad range of intergradation with Montane Rain Forest. In Zinacantán the stands of Evergreen Cloud Forest are isolated from other optimum formations and intergrade with Pine Oak Forest. Precipitation in some form falls in every month; however, that which falls in the dry season (February through May) is mostly through condensation from the daily fogs. This forest has one or sometimes two layers forming the canopy. The trees are closely spaced and up to 40 m tall. Epiphytes are abundant and are mostly ferns and bryophytes. There is a dense understory of shrubs. The common canopy trees are *Abies guatemalensis* Rehder, *Chiranthodendron pentadactylon* Larreategui, *Clethra lanata* Martens & Galeotti, *Drimys granadensis* L., *Meliosma matudae* Lundell, *Microtropis contracta* Lundell, *Olmediella betschleriana* (Goeppert) Loesener, *Oreopanax capitatus* (Jacquin) Decaisne & Planchon, *Persea donnell-smithii* Mez ex J. Donnell-Smith, *Photinia matudae* Lundell, *Pinus ayacahuite* Ehrenberg, *Quercus benthamii* A. de Candolle, *Styrax ramirezii* Greenman, *Weinmannia pinnata* L., *Wimmeria chiapensis* Lundell. In the understory the following plants are common: *Cavendishia crassifolia* (Bentham) Hemsley, *Celastrus vulcanicola* J. Donnell-Smith, *Chusquea foliosa, Cyclanthera*

FIGURE 4.—Landscape northwest of Yaleb Taiv, 1989. (Photo by Robert M. Laughlin.)

langaei Cogniaux, *Daphnopsis selerorum* Gilg, *Deppea grandiflora* Schlechtendal, *Dryopteris wallichiana* (Sprengel) Hyland, *Fuchsia paniculata* Lindley, *F. splendens* Zuccarini, *Gentlea micranthera* (J. Donnell-Smith) Lundell, *Greigia oaxacana* L.B Smith, *Marattia weinmanniifolia* Liebmann, *Miconia oligotricha* (de Candolle) Naudin, *Rapanea juergensenii* Mez, *Saurauia oreophila* Hemsley, *Smilax domingensis* Willdenow, *Symplocos breedlovei* Lundell, *Ternstroemia lineata* ssp. *chalicophila* Loesener.

TEMPERATE RIPARIAN FOREST.—This association borders all streams above 1400 m regardless of the surrounding vegetation. It is composed of genera of temperate plants that can tolerate roots in water most of the year. Most of the trees are deciduous and lose their leaves in the dry season when the water in the streams is at the lowest level or dry. Aside from mosses, these forests have few epiphytes. The trees vary from 10 to 30 m tall. The most common trees and shrubs of this formation are *Acer negundo* ssp. *mexicanum* (de Candolle) Wesmael, *Alnus acuminata* ssp. *arguta* (Schlechtendal) Furlow, *A. jorullensis* Kunth, *Berchemia scandens* (Hill) Trelease, *Cornus excelsa* Kunth, *Crataegus pubescens* (Kunth) Steudel, *Cuphea hyssopifolia* Kunth, *Platanus mexicana* Moricand, *Salix bonplandiana* Kunth, *S. chilensis* Molina, *S. taxifolia* Kunth, *Taxodium mucronatum* Tenore.

Into the Whirlwind

Robert M. Laughlin

San Lorenzo Zinacantán, a prosperous Mayan township in the highlands of the state of Chiapas, Mexico, has been the focus of intensive anthropological and linguistic research for 30 years. Responding to the cultural vitality of the Zinacantecs, Evon Z. Vogt chose this community to be a laboratory for the study of social and cultural change. His Harvard Chiapas Project fielded over a hundred students who investigated many aspects of Zinacantec life, from a wide variety of perspectives. Shortly after we began our ethnobotanic research in 1963, their publications confirmed our conviction of the importance of plants in Zinacantec culture and provided us with a substantial foundation for further study.[1]

The encyclopedic presentation in "The Flora" of myriads of discrete ethnobotanical details gives no hint of the whirlwind of change that has beset Zinacantán in the past 25 years.

During this period the population has swelled from roughly 8000 to nearly 20,000.[2]

In 1963 most Zinacantecs lived in one-room houses with wattle-and-daub walls and high-pitched thatch roofs. The number of plant species known to have been used for the construction of a traditional house is impressive:

House Component	No. of Plant Species	
wattle	23}	
pole wall	10}	106
mainpost	61}	
roof	55}	
lashing	34	
thatch	25 (9 commonly)	

These picturesque houses have all but disappeared. The loss of wattle-and-daub walls and thatch roofs means a great reduction in the variety of plants used for house construction. The roof structure now is essentially built of pine. Those people with sufficient resources build 1–3 room adobe or brick houses with tile roofs. A few are building flat-roofed cement or cement block structures. Far down the economic scale, and usually in the temperate hamlets, are pole-walled houses with galvanized metal or laminated cardboard roofs.

Inside the house the most dramatic changes have been caused by the introduction of electricity: light bulbs, a radio, a tape recorder, possibly a record player, a television set, and a clothes iron. Also new are tortilla presses, metal pots and bowls, and plastic containers. Frequently the pole beds have been replaced by plank beds, sometimes enclosed by brightly colored plastic sheeting.

The most noticeable change is in the clothing. The woven palm hat was largely replaced by one of woven plastic, before it, too, gave way to Texas-style sombreros, and then bare heads. Factory-made pants, belts, shirts, and sweaters, jackets, shoes, sneakers, and boots for men now predominate. The neckerchief is disappearing, leaving only the pin-striped red tunic to mark a man from Zinacantán, but that tunic, once plain, now sports an ever more exuberant display of floral embroidery. Women's blouses and shawls, too, are growing bright flowers. Wide ribbon bows perch on their heads. Earrings and plastic sandals are becoming fashionable.

The past 25 years have witnessed a profound change in the economic, social, political, and religious structures of Zinacantán, spurred by the economic boom of the 1970s, and now modified by a much tighter economy.

In 1963 Zinacantán was populated by relatively independent peasant corn farmers. A small minority was comprised of growers and merchants of flowers and fruits, as well as salt merchants.

The principal agent of change was improved transport. In the highlands a network of rough roads was developed to connect the hamlets to the highway, and in the lowlands the remaining forests were made accessible for felling and conversion to cornfields.

Previously, Zinacantecs had descended the mountains on foot, with their mules, to rent *ladino* lands on either side of the Grijalva River. Each year Zinacantec intermediaries, who knew a bit of Spanish, would renew contracts with the same landowners to parcel out the land and agree on the rent. But these *ladinos* now were turning their property into pasture land for cattle. So, the hours spent on foot were replaced by hours standing on trucks, followed by perhaps another hour on foot to reach an unfamiliar landlord. The farmers, too, had to deal with often unfriendly *ladino* truck owners to transport their harvest. Their difficulties eased in the 1970s as Zinacantecs themselves became truck owners.

Rapid transportation, however, had mixed blessings, for there is now a whole generation of men who are ignorant of the plants that grew along the foot trails to the lowlands; plants useful for food, medicine, and construction. "I only know a quarter of what my father knows," is a frequent refrain.

The prosperity of the 1970s spawned multiple government development programs.

Milpa Production

Many varieties of hybrid corn and beans were introduced. The Mexican Department of Agriculture (SARH) periodically

19

FIGURE 5.—Thatched roof house, Zinacantán Center, 1977. (Photo by John Swope.)

FIGURE 6.—Household accoutrements, 1977. (Photo by John Swope.)

22

FIGURE 7.—Young weaver, 1977. (Photo by John Swope.)

FIGURE 8.—Weaving palm hat, 1977. (Photo by John Swope.)

24

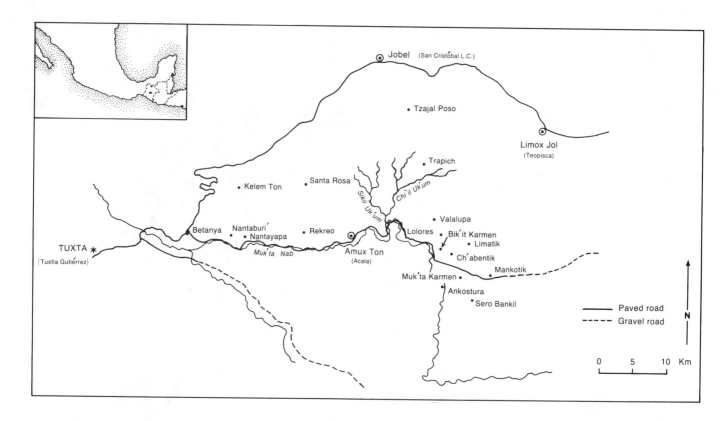

MAP 3.—Grijalva River Valley.

donated seed corn impregnated with pesticide. Herbicides and chemical fertilizers were offered at very low prices, their purchase stimulated by constant promotion on the government "Indian" radio, by bank credits and insurance policies.

Farmers were quick to abandon the planting of local varieties of corn and beans. They also abandoned the *ejido* lands on the mountain slopes, which could only be reached on foot and which gave low yields. The billhook, particularly useful for weeding on the rocky slopes, became an obsolete tool, replaced by its companion, the machete. But other traditional farm tools such as digging sticks, flails, hoes and axes (both requiring handles), provided an unchanging inventory of tree species in use: 74. The wide spread of barbed wire inevitably reduced the number of plant species employed in fencing. Here, too, the variety was extreme: (1) posts, rails, stiles—143; (2) lashing—24.

Traditionally Zinacantec farmers prepared their lowland rented fields with a team of Zinacantec and Chamula laborers whom they fed and paid wages in corn and cash. Weeding by hoe was acknowledged to increase the humidity of the soil, but could take weeks. When confronted with rising salaries and food costs, the farmers chose herbicides, which could be applied by a small team of workers in a short time.

This meant an end to the friendships between Zinacantecs and the neighboring Chamulas that had been renewed every year by joint labor. The introduction of plastic water bottles and the use of weed-killer also greatly reduced the cultivation of gourds. Edible wild plants found growing in the milpa and previously protected by the farmer, now received their dose of lethal spray.

A further novelty was the rental of tractors for cultivating in Zinacantán Center and in the flat, humid lands surrounding the Presa Angostura. Here milpa was replaced by fields devoted exclusively to corn.

The establishment of government (ANDSA) warehouses for corn assured the sale of harvests.

Fruit Culture

The cultivation of peaches was greatly expanded as was that of apples, pears, and plums. Zinacantecs were trained to graft and to spray apple trees with pesticides.

Truck Gardens and Flower Culture

The building of stone and cement water reservoirs and the laying of long sections of hose permitted the irrigation of cabbages, radishes, and coriander. To stimulate early flowering, irrigation was applied to fields of carnations, gladiolas, feverfew, and baby's breath. Chemical fertilizers, replacing compost and animal manure, and herbicides soon were in wide use. Pesticides became popular in the cultivation of cabbages and carrots, and fungicides for potatoes.

FIGURE 9.—Cold frames for chrysanthemums, Pat Osil, 1989. (Photo by Robert M. Laughlin.)

SARH was responsible for the introduction of greenhouses, i.e., cold frames devoted to the cultivation of fancy chrysanthemums. Materials and seeds were donated on condition that the first year's profits be shared with the department. This program was adopted speedily, especially in Zinacantán Center and the hamlet of Pat Osil.

In the temperate hamlets peanuts, sweet potato, and sesame culture were introduced on a small scale.

Marketing

Zinacantec capitalist ventures began in the late 1960s, encouraged by the National Indian Institute (INI). The cantina-dry goods stores in Zinacantán Center had all been the property of *ladinos*. INI set up a CONASUPO store and placed it under the direction of a local Indian. At the same time an Indian established a corn mill. In the 1970s, cantina-stores, blaring *rancheros* from their loudspeaker, and corn mills popped up in the hamlets.

For the tourist trade, women and children sat along the roadside in Naben Chauk, selling flowers and fruits. They also made and sold yarn Huichol "god's eyes" seen by some Zinacantec in the National Museum of Anthropology in Mexico City! Before long these "god's eyes" were replaced. Now the roadside was decorated with long-stemmed, outrageously bright flowers, woven with plastic cord.

Zinacantecs, famous in the nineteenth century as muleteers, took to the wheels: The local conveyance of corn farmers and their crops was expanded to include purchase of corn in the government warehouses at reduced cost, and transport to Tabasco and Veracruz where sales could be made at inflated prices.

As early as 1944 the hamlet of Naben Chauk had been a center for the commercial cultivation of fruit trees (peach, avocado, sweet lemon, lime, and coffee), vegetables (cabbage, field mustard, potatoes, chayotes, watermelon, and pumpkin squash), and flowers (geraniums). These had been marketed in Chiapa de Corzo, Tuxtla Gutiérrez, and as far distant as Arriaga on the Pacific Coast. It was no wonder, then, that the people of this hamlet were to become the leaders in extending trade routes to the Pacific Coast, to Juchitán, and to many towns throughout the state. It was they who dared to venture as far north as Mexico City to purchase gladiolas and football chrysanthemums for sale in Chiapas. Bootleg Chamula cane liquor was also taken to the coast, hidden under bundles of flowers.

A permanent nucleus of Zinacantec traders settled in the state capital. Zinacantecs continued to control the sale of corn in the San Cristóbal market, as well as the sale of tortillas and flowers. Weekly markets were established in the hamlets of Na Chij, Naben Chauk, and Sek'emtik.

Trucks, and later vans, linked Zinacantán Center and many hamlets to San Cristóbal. The multiplication of native ownership of trucks is indicative of Zinacantec prosperity, from 2 in 1970, to 20 in 1975, to 69 in 1981.[3]

Reforestation

Highland and temperate forests in Zinacantán were disappearing at an alarming rate. Even steep-forested slopes were being stripped to make cornfields, to supply timber for house construction, and to supply the average 16 kilos of firewood used daily to feed and warm homeowners. The gathering of firewood now demanded even longer trips. Religious officeholders, who required great quantities of firewood for the preparation of festival meals, had their wood brought in by the truckload. An experiment in breadmaking soon folded for lack of available wood.

The government responded to the stripping of forests by initiating reforestation programs in every hamlet. Teams of young men were offered attractive salaries to plant just two kinds of trees: pines and cypress.

A side effect of reforestation was commented on by a man of Sek'emtik when he was asked what his neighbors in Chaynatik planted around their houses: "Oh, they can't be bothered to plant anything much there anymore since they are getting paid for reforestation."

Construction

For many years, youths had done part-time work on the roads. Now the building of roads connecting hamlets to the highway enlisted the labor of the whole adult male population. The same was true for the introduction of piped water systems, schools, and chapels.

The conversion of native housing from thatch-roofed houses to tile-roofed ones swept through the whole township, again occupying the efforts of the male population. To this was added the restoration of the Church of St. Sebastian and the rebuilding of the Chapel of Lord Esquipulas and the Church of St. Lawrence in Zinacantán Center, the last gutted by a mysterious fire. The courthouse in Zinacantán Center was also remodeled.

At the same time the state capital of Tuxtla Gutiérrez was remodeled and three major hydroelectric projects were set in motion, demanding a vast force of Indian peon laborers. More adventurous Zinacantecs traveled to construction projects as far distant as Villahermosa, Tabasco, and the nuclear plant of Laguna Verde in Veracruz. Although many were employed to carry the buckets of cement, others were trained to become skillful masons.

Economic and Social Consequences

This vast array of new opportunities for gaining wealth had a strong impact on Zinacantán.

In 1967 in the hamlet of Na Chij, virtually every adult man (96%) grew corn. By 1983 the number had shrunk to 59%, and of these only 23% restricted their labors to corn production. Now 14% were merchants, 7% truck owners, 5% masons, and 5% worked for the government, mainly in reforestation.

A subsistence economy had become a money economy. Increased wealth and diversity of occupation meant that a large sector of the population had "become heavily dependent on trends in the regional and national economies."[4] Managerial skills "of a capitalistic nature" were now required to keep families solvent.[5]

In 1967 roughly half the population of Na Chij was of higher economic means. By 1983 this proportion had dropped to 40%, but the wealthy entrepreneurs were much wealthier. The emergence of class differences had become apparent. But the changes in internal social structure went deeper for, previously, young wage earners had become corn farmers in their maturity as corn had been "the only road to prosperity."[6] Consequently Zinacantec society was dominated economically, socially, and politically by older men. But now the wealthy young truck owners and merchants were seizing positions of power. Formerly, wedding godparents had been chosen from among the older men "of reason," who could counsel bride and groom in formal couplets. They were being replaced by young truck owners able to provide eloquent counsel.

Previously, young men courted their fiancées for two years in a process of extended gift-giving that made them heavily indebted to their parents. Bride service, too, was the rule. But with increasing frequency youths now eloped and marriages were settled for a fee considerably less than the cost of a traditional courtship. Parents and in-laws could no longer count on the young man to aid them economically. This, too, contributed to the development of class differences where the families were divided into those who hired fellow Zinacantecs and those who were hired by their neighbors.

Retrenchment

The boom of the 1970s was followed by the economic crisis of 1982. Gasoline prices spiraled, and so the cost of transport made farming in distant locations unprofitable. Reports flooded in of *ladino* landowners who told the Zinacantec farmers after they had cleared strips of forest for their cornfields, "Get out, I'm bringing cattle in!"

Construction projects were suddenly terminated in midstream. Wage laborers who had ventured to the Gulf Coast tropical region saw their return bus tickets cut deeply into their earnings. After working in the industrially contaminated environment many came home with lingering illnesses, and others returned penniless, victims of knife-point gang robberies.

As alternative means for gaining a living shrunk, there was a return to local corn farming. Although 66% of household heads in the hamlet of Apas grew corn in 1981, their percentage had risen to 79% by 1987. Farmers began to cultivate the *ejido* lands that had lain fallow for years on mountain slopes. Mules, by this time rare, were suddenly a valuable possession. Wage earners also turned to the cultivation of flowers and fruit.

Leases were signed authorizing heavy timbering in the pine forests, activities that extended roads down the slopes. In 1987 a German company was converting a section of the cloud forest on the sacred mountain overlooking Zinacantán Center to charcoal for shipment abroad—this at the price of $5 a tree!

Despite the economic retrenchment, trading continues vigorously. In Apas 26% of the married men are merchants, and 66% are part-time wage laborers ranked in descending order socially: (1) mason, (2) *milpero*, (3) peon.

Responding to the huge influx of tourists, "regional clothing" stores have sprung up along the highway in Naben Chauk and Na Chij, the latter identified as such in English! Women have organized to establish a similar store in Zinacantán Center.

The wealthy continue to flourish: a truck owner in Apas irrigates his vegetable garden with his own electric pump and hires 25 of his neighbors to work in his cornfields.

Class differences, then, are becoming even sharper as more and more Zinacantecs must work for other Zinacantecs.

Politics

Many of the same trends visible in the economic and social spheres can be seen in the political structure of Zinacantán.

Under national government orders the civil officials, who had traditionally served for one year without pay, were required to serve for a paid three-year term. Community service, with religious overtones, became a secular salaried job, but the salary was sufficiently low to promote constant complaints of corrupt political practices.

Traditionally the *presidente* was more of a magistrate than a mayor, responsible for the settlement of all major disputes, except those involving murder. But in the 1970s many Zinacantecs were able to communicate with *ladinos* in Spanish and some became very sophisticated in dealing with the *ladino* world. Self-trained Zinacantec "lawyers" served as intermediaries, skirting the magistrate and bringing local disputes to the attention of the political and judicial authorities in San Cristóbal and even Tuxtla. These new opportunities for a larger voice, however often have proved to be very costly, supplying a rich livelihood for unscrupulous *ladino* lawyers and bureaucrats. This pattern of decentralization was extended by the creation of *agencias,* or subordinate political units, in nine hamlets. In 1963 the total number of hamlets was 15. By 1987 there were 15 highland hamlets, 14 temperate hamlets, and 6 colonies in the temperate and lowland zone. The increase in the number of hamlets was due in large part to fragmentation as a result of political disputes between groups of neighbors. The lowland colony of Santa Rosa was wrestled away from *ladino* owners after years of judicial struggle.

Just as outside interests promoted economic changes, the national parties, PRI and PAN, seized on local contests to advance their cause. But then Zinacantecs internalized their political skills, prolonging the life of long-standing factions under the name of *"Camioneros"* (truckers) and *"Campesinos"* (farmers), whose descriptive terms are only suggestive of the nature of the parties. They even split the single organization of shamans into two: those seeking divine support for the "truckers" and those for the "farmers!"

Religion

Here, too, a monolithic structure has been affected similarly by outside pressures. For several centuries the Mayan Catholics of Zinacantán have directed a religious hierarchy of rotating, unpaid servants of the various aspects of Christ, the Virgin Mary, and a host of saints. Service in this hierarchy, based primarily in Zinacantán Center, brought personal prestige and supernatural life insurance and, because of its cost, tended to reduce class differences. In 1963 it had this form:

2 scribes	2 alcaldes	judge ordinary
2 musicians	4 prefects	ritual tutors
4 sacristans	14 ensign-bearers	
	26 stewards and	
	8 constables	

In the 1970s, however, responding to the efforts of the bishop and a vigorous Dominican friar to extend the church's doctrine and catechistic activities, chapels were built in many hamlets. A new church was constructed in Naben Chauk and a new Christ figure installed. This decentralization, which required the establishment of 14 new positions at the bottom level, helped the hierarchy cope with (1) the expanding population, and (2) the new segment of wealthy entrepreneurs.

In this decade, despite the conversion of a relatively small number of townspeople to evangelical Protestantism, and the refusal by many of the nouveau riche to participate, the religious hierarchy continues to flourish, though positions are not in the high demand of the mid-sixties.

Education

Traditionally, it was the role of the children to aid in shepherding and gathering of firewood. During their hours in the meadows and forests, with their mothers and older sisters, they gained considerable knowledge about the plants and trees that surrounded them. A compulsory elementary education, first for boys and later for girls, also, has undoubtedly lessened their familiarity with the flora.

The education system in Zinacantán in the 1960s included bilingual training in Tzotzil and Spanish, but when this was abandoned by the National Indian Institute (INI) it was never

28

replaced by the federal or state school system. Education has been strictly in Spanish. Schools and basketball courts were constructed in every hamlet in the 1970s. A few secondary schools, boasting *"tele-educación,"* are now in operation, expanding opportunities for more highly paid wage labor. At the same time an experimental school in Tzotzil literacy has aroused great interest among young and old, men and women, eager to become "smart."

Health

Although the construction of a hospital in San Cristóbal, providing free service for Indians, has improved the quality of modern medical care, this has been balanced by the extreme rise in the cost of medicines available in pharmacies. A national interest in herbal medicine is beginning to reach Zinacantán.

There has been no restudy of traditional medicine, but shamans, bonesetters, and midwives are still active in great numbers. Although many continue to perform their services in exchange for comestible goods, others have joined the money economy, charging cash fees.

Contact with the *ladino* world has caused important dietary changes. Traditionally, Indian food was boiled. Now much is fried in lard. The Zinacantec diet was essentially that for "a small planet": corn, beans, greens, chili, squash, occasionally mushrooms, bread, eggs, chicken, fish and snails, pork and beef. The proportion of pork and beef in the diet has increased greatly. Thirty years ago there was only one fat individual in Zinacantán, a man who was known to be sick! Overeating was not a general problem here. Whereas Zinacantecs consider skinniness ugly or a sign of illness, when they saw enormously fat people in the United States they asked with amazement, *"What* do they eat?" Now, with the change of diet and the loss of exercise, obesity, particularly among men, is a frequent sight. Visions of ancient Mayan lords sitting stupendously on their thrones have been replaced by the modern Mayan truckers seated imperiously in the cantina, before metal tables studded with beer bottles. Cane liquor, once a necessary ingredient of any significant social event, is drunk with more moderation. Once it was unthinkable for a young man, whether Indian or foreign anthropologist, to refuse a drink when it was offered in a formal ceremony. Now, a shake of the head is accepted. The recent inroads of evangelical Protestantism have also reduced drinking. An exasperated Catholic exclaimed, "They just say they're not feeling well today, and who of us has not said that?" (The traditional Catholics are exasperated because the "proper way" to conduct a social event is with liquor.) The increased consumption of soft drinks has brought to Zinacantecs gold and silver-plated smiles! The health of babies, always a perilous situation, has been endangered by the adoption of bottle feeding. Could it be that in response to the new burden of anxieties, many older people's hair is turning gray—a rare sight in the 1960s!

The Future

Although Zinacantecs have survived many periods of extreme hardship and have capitalized on moments of prosperity, and whereas they hold their heads up with pride, eager to gain the next advantage, there is an underlying fear of what the year 2000 will bring.

A few Zinacantecs are aware of the negative effects of chemical fertilizer, how the land demands ever more fertilizer to produce, but the vast majority champions their use in all three ecological zones. Very few recognize the danger of herbicides and pesticides to their person or to their environment. It is a common practice to use old paraquat containers to hold drinking water! Pesticides may be applied to beans for storage, requiring a thorough rinsing before cooking. Seed corn impregnated with pesticide sometimes is taken to market for sale.

The production of corn is now largely limited to the cultivation of hybrids. In the face of declining profits, and lured by the promise of rich rewards, some farmers clandestinely raise and/or sell marijuana and opium poppies.

The huge population increase, coupled with deforestation and reduction of naturally fertile land at home and afar, has aroused concern. People wonder if hunger is on the horizon.

"Economic diversification and a greater dependence on institutions of the larger society"[7] have increased internal conflicts. Everyone is aware that their own town has become a hotbed of never-ending disputes, and many recognize that this problem is shared throughout the world. "Reason has ended, people are turning into dogs!"

Possibly economic retrenchment will have a positive effect. The outside world is losing its glamor as opportunities for jobs decrease steadily. Internal political disputes, arousing fever pitch excitement, are becoming wearisome to many, especially to the women. A period of consolidation may emerge, a reaffirmation of traditional values, a reinforcement of the conviction, always present, that the Zinacantecs are, in the eyes of their ancient gods, second to none.

Unlike the rest of Mexico, economic pressures had not forced the inhabitants of Zinacantán to join the international wage labor market, but in 1988, two grandsons of Xun Vaskes, the late leader of Naben Chauk, were alerted by a radio announcement of job opportunities in the United States. Motivated partly by a spirit of adventure and partly by heavy indebtedness, they determined to cross the border as "wetbacks." One week after their arrival in Salem, Oregon, where they picked and canned strawberries, Chep Vaskes, at the age of 29, died mysteriously in his sleep. His body was returned to Naben Chauk. Chep, his flowered tunic and neckerchief covering the mortuary-provided tie and jacket, was interred on the mountaintop. His grave, with a green carpet of aromatic pine needles, was adorned with the daisies and chrysanthemums he had planted months before. His family keeps asking how this could be the result of the flowering of man.

Throughout Zinacantán young men, apprised of Chep's fate, are wondering about the alternatives, how to make a living in the future.

Notes

[1]Because of this vast amount of reliable information we feel free in the following introductory chapters and in "The Flora" to restrict our anthropological commentary to previously undescribed details, referring the reader to the splendid general ethnography of Evon Vogt (1969), to his study of Zinacantec religion (1976), to the studies of Zinacantec economies by Nicholas Bunnin (1966), Frank Cancian (1965, 1972), George Collier (1975), and Jack Stauder (1966), to the discussion of Zinacantec medical practices by Horacio Fábrega and Daniel Silver (1973), and to Zinacantec architecture by James Warfield (1966).

Much of the material for this chapter has been drawn from the restudies by Frank Cancian (1986, 1987), and George Collier and Daniel Mountjoy (1988), which confirm and pinpoint present reality. Na Chij census figures are taken from Cancian (1987) and Apas census figures from Collier and Mountjoy (1988).

[2]The population of Zinacantán in 1960 as recorded by the national census was 7650 (Collier 1975:158). In the 1980 census it had grown to 13,006 (Instituto Nacional de Estadística, Geografia e Informática, 1983:1, 89). Private censuses taken by Cancian in Na Chij and Collier in Apas suggest that the figure of 20,000 for 1988 is a reasonable estimate.

[3]Cancian (1986:484).
[4]Cancian (1987:134).
[5]Cancian (1986:494).
[6]Cancian (1987:135).
[7]Cancian (1987:138).

Where Have All the Flowers Gone?

Robert M. Laughlin

The early history of Zinacantán has been gleaned almost exclusively from the reports first, of Dominican friars, and later the secular clergy living among the Indians in Chiapas. The principal historian of the 16th century, the Dominican friar Tomás de la Torre, who lived in Zinacantán shortly after the Conquest (1545), was quoted extensively by Antonio de Remesal and Francisco Ximénez, whose reliability is seriously questioned in a forthcoming study by Jan de Vos. The 16th-century Dominican lexicographer who gives us much information about plants is anonymous. The reports of the parish priests cited below are frequently the only record of their writers' existence. We must let them speak for themselves!

In 1545 when Bishop Bartolomé de las Casas and his troupe of exhausted friars reached the interior of the New World, they "were stopped by the Indians of Chiapa who received them with many flowers and roses, placing garlands over their heads and giving them bouquets to carry in their hands."[1]

Their reception was recorded at first hand:

And this is the custom of the Indians, and whoever lives amongst them must suffer it. Every time we arrive at the towns they adorn us this way and they are skillful in gathering different flowers and fashioning handsome bunches. When they are able, they promenade with flowers and other perfumes in their hands because they are great admirers of fragrance. In the beginning we were greatly mortified to be walking so bedecked and right away we thought of the priests who had trained us and how they would laugh if they saw us like this; but now we do not care a whit. We wear the flowers into the church and there we leave them on the altar and this way we please and edify [the Indians]. [The friars] discovered that to receive them those Indians had newly built three or four huts decorated with many flowers. And they were given a generous luncheon; great quantities of fine fresh fish, melons of Castille and pineapples, all of which abound in this town.... [The elders] spoke to the priests in their tongue I do not know what gabble. Behind them came a crowd of men, many with gourds full of native cherries which are very fine and in great abundance.... There is the greatest wealth of native fruits, pineapples, bananas, jicamas, sweet potatoes, avocados, cherries and so forth. From here the whole area is furnished. Except for figs there are few fruits from Castille. But this is the motherland of melons, of citrons and oranges. Sweet basil plants grow so large that I do not know if they could not be described as shapely trees. To grow eggplants, cabbages, radishes and all other pot-herbs you

have only to toss down the seeds and with no assistance they produce, especially the onions. The common herbs of the meadows and communal lands are amaranths and purslain. I strongly believe that there are not elsewhere in the Indies towns so richly provided with the necessities for the maintenance of mankind. Wheat also grows in irrigated fields. There is a handsome sugar mill.[2]

From Chiapa the missionaries advanced painfully up the steep mountain trail to Zinacantán, the same trail that brought Aztec merchants in disguise, a century earlier, to barter for jaguar pelts, quetzal and cotinga feathers, and amber—also to spy.

Earliest contacts with the Spanish conquistadors had proven the loyalty of the Indians of Zinacantán. Their timely aid in the battle of Chamula, in 1524, had prevented the decimation of the Spanish force, as reported by Bernal Diaz del Castillo. Four years later the Zinacantecs traveled 30 leagues to welcome the next Spanish army with gifts of food and drink. They contributed their manpower first for the domination of the Zoques and Tzeltales, and then for the foundation of Spanish settlements. They even accompanied the Spaniards in their conquest of Honduras and El Salvador. But once the Spaniards had established their control, the Zinacantecs' "loyalty and obedience" did little to ward off their masters' cruel exertion of power.[3]

Arriving in Zinacantán, the missionaries' devotion to peace and poverty speedily won the Indians' support, and so the friars chose Zinacantán to be their headquarters in the highlands.

This town of Sinacantlan, which is large and the capital of all that Nation, is a league and a half from the City [Ciudad Real]. It is seated in a valley with many arroyos. It is near the high mountains, and it is in a depression, although it is at as high an altitude as the City.... It has a very cold climate although milder than the City and lacking morning mists. It is an impoverished land, only it abounds in many wonderful very cold springs. There is a spring here which pours out with the force of an ox.

And there are innumerable pine and oak trees. There are many lime pits and an alabaster quarry.... The people of this town are born more noble than the others of their Nation, and all or most are merchants, and they are known for this far abroad. They have salt wells in their towns. [The salt] from here is used in the whole area, as white salt does not occur elsewhere. They are common wells; whoever wishes makes salt for himself or for sale. Although this Town is barren, it abounds in many things. Since they are

32

merchants the others have recourse here for buying their necessities and also selling all that they bring.

These people also presume greatly and they do not value planting, nor employment, because they say they are merchants. The Spaniards call all those of this Nation *Quelenes,* because the youths the Indians gave [the Spaniards] for service, they called *Quelen* [*kelem*—boy]. But they are called Sinacantecas in Nahuatl, and in their own language they are called *Zotcil vinic* [*Sotz'il vinik*] which means "bat man." This is because their ancestors appeared in the plain [surrounding] the City before the sun existed.[4] They discovered a stone bat and they took it to be God and worshipped it.

They walk naked and when the cold or a fiesta forces them to dress, they put a cloak over their shoulders, with two knots on the right side. The women dress like those of Yucatan because both share much in their languages and customs.

They had many idols, they worshipped the Sun and sacrificed to it, as to full rivers, springs, heavily foliaged trees, and high mountains they gave incense and gifts.[5]

From scattered sources one learns that the chiefs had adobe houses, that the nobility had large numbers of wives, that 3–4 chiefs from the most noble lineages shared civil authority, and that the subject towns of Zinacantán had caciques. Chiefs owned land privately; laborers were employed on land that was not their own. "Patriarchs" seem to have been guardians of the rights of commoners as against those of the chiefs.

Three or four days after their arrival in Zinacantán the friars built a refuge for themselves:

The cloister and the garden with rosemary from Spain, carnations, basil, lilies, roses of Castile and Alexandria, all so beflowered and fragrant as Paradise.... This was the first building that the Order had in the Province.

The town agreed with great willingness and in just three days of work finished the job from the foundation to the roof, designing it wittily with cloister, bedroom, cells, studies, all with a string so it was a pleasure to watch.[6]

The construction of this idyllic retreat was described in different terms by another friar who was witness to the event:

In those times when the friars arrived at Zinacantán they were lodged in a little house which bore the name of House of the Town Leader. But as they do not respect anything there, after the last Mass the priests left in anger. Then they agreed that it would be more peaceful to build a hut next to the church so that in the rainy season they would not be obliged to go outside. They did not like being placed in the house of someone in the town. Until then they had not dared to ask the Indians for a house.... In three or four days they built the little house which they put next to the church, but it was built so badly, it was as poor as the poorest [house] of the saddest Indian. It had two rooms, and a little shelter. On the other wall they put stakes for a corral where they planted many flowers, as carnations, lilies, and fennel

which Fray Jordán sent them from Oaxaca.... The house has miserable poles covered with mud. Fray Pedro de la Cruz became angry because the Indians did not make the wall straight, and he alone, with the strength of his arms could straighten it.

In one of the rooms they made a dormitory that was ten feet wide, or two meters wide. It was so humid one could not sleep there. "It would be better if we moved to the other room," we said. The windows were just holes and the door of the hut was covered with mats.

The house was not fenced in and whatever animal could have entered to break the wall and eat the thatch of the roof, so that it would not offer protection from the sun or the rain. We felt very happy, just thinking that we had a house....

The wall poles that were next to the bed of Fray Tomás de la Torre began to sprout. When the house had dried out, the next day it was filled with puddles of water. More than four springs came up inside the house and now it seemed as if it were a lake. Truly, the church was in the worst part of town, humid and full of arroyos.[7]

From this wellspring came forth the evangelization, indoctrination and instruction of the Indians of highland Chiapas!

Tomás de la Torre commented that "[the town] has pine trees of marvelous height and girth and other hardwood trees that they call *Quitzizté* [*k'isis te'*] which is the cypress, *tendoc* [**ten toj**], *cotoc* [**kot toj**], the juniper: *nuculpat* [**nukul pat**], oaks and other trees whose names in plain Spanish I do not know."[8]

Zinacantán was a regional intermediary in the trade of luxury goods. It also had control of cotton and cacao in the subject lands. Shortly after the Conquest, Pedro de Estrada, *encomendero,* "established a sugar mill with the Indians of Canacantlan [sic] and its subject towns. He spent over two thousand gold pesos until he had it running and in order, and the said Indians have served him according to the taxation the governor and bishop made."[9]

Recalling the military support provided by Zinacantán during the early years of the Conquest, the Spaniards called upon the town once again in 1595 to aid in their grandiose, but ill-starred expedition against the Lacandón Indians.

There were also six hundred Indian warriors from Chiapas [sic; the town's correct name is Chiapa], and two hundred from Zinacantlán.... A great many Indian bearers from Chiapa and Zinacantlán were provided to carry the baggage, and the Indians of both villages named their own captains. The assigned captains got their men ready, along with showy and elegant flags, drums, and trumpets. The men were well dressed and helmets nicely plumed. Arms were made for everyone: lances, bows and arrows, shields, armor—all at the cost of the villages. These Indians were so adept in bearing and in using these weapons, and so well in step in their formations and musters they looked like veteran soldiers in some of the more disciplined armies of Europe. All the Chiapas [sic] companies passed through Zinacantlán, marching behind the sons of Indian chiefs—

young, adventuresome men arrayed with fancy weapons and their arquebuses.

Each one of the soldiers, in addition to his weapons, carried a large gourd in order to have water in the uninhabited and mountainous places, or to use as a buoy in swimming the rivers and lakes, should the occasion arise.

The Zinacantlán companies were mustered before the priests, and together with the Chiapas [sic] companies they marched in perfect order, like an army, to the city of Guatemala where all together they made a very impressive display.

…In addition to the Indian bearers, more than a thousand Indian warriors came from the city of Guatemala, valiant and strong men—though poorly dressed, something which annoyed the Spaniards who recruited them, when they saw those of Chiapas [sic] so finely clothed.[10]

The Spanish army was "guided by the Chiapanec Indians who swam more than three hundred paces and also carried little reed bundles on which they rested in the water."[11]

It was probably at this very time that an anonymous Dominican friar compiled a monumental dictionary of the Tzotzil language spoken in Zinacantán. The dictionary includes a treasury of botanical, agricultural, and culinary terms that provide a vivid description of Zinacantán in the early colonial period.

The friar was careful to qualify his definitions, e.g., "corn wine, it is not here, but if it were they would call it…."[12] And so one is led to believe that what is not qualified in that way in fact was present in Zinacantán. There are some surprises: cork tree (undecipherable Tzotzil), olive tree, dates (no Tzotzil provided), and flax. Other plants introduced in the colonial period that are no longer known by Zinacantecs include jasmine, dill, rosemary, rhubarb, lentils, leeks, and piñons.

The process of naming plants unfamiliar to the Indians can be seen at an early stage—as in **castillan potov** (Spanish guava) for apple, **castillan ixim** (Spanish corn) for wheat, **castillan makum** (Spanish blackberry) for mulberry and pomegranate, **castillan tuix** (Spanish onion) for leek, **castillan toj** (Spanish pine) for piñon, and **castillan ich** (Spanish chili) for pepper and spices. Another method was to pluralize the Spanish name—**higos** for fig (later becoming **ik'ux**), **peras** for pear (later becoming **pelex**), **ajos** for garlic (later becoming **axux**).

From the vocabulary one learns of silk and cochineal culture, but especially of vineyards and wine production. There was dry season corn and rainy season corn as well as 60-day corn. Indians were taught to plow with oxen, to fertilize with horse manure, to graft and to prune fruit trees.

They witnessed the introduction of many kinds of bread, Easter cakes, pancakes, taffy, spices, molasses, nougat, vinegar, olive oil, walnut and parsley sauce.

"Night after night" the Indians wove tribute cloth for their Spanish masters.

Though their wooden idols had been burnt on St. Francis'

Day, 1548, the anonymous lexicographer provided names for the reed shields they hung in the church and for painted images of a flower with a jaguar-dragon in the center.

In 1616 the Zinacantecs were levied a tribute of cacao that "all Seville would have had difficulty in paying."[13]

Shortly thereafter (1625), the English Dominican Thomas Gage journeyed to the region. He passed through San Felipe, which belonged then to Zinacantán. Here he was met by the Prior of Ciudad Real, "a merry fat Fryer."[14]

…the whole village of St. Philip waited for us both men and women, some presenting unto us nosegaies, others hurling Roses and others flowers in our faces, others dancing before us all along the street, which was strowed with herbs and Orange leaves, and adorned with many Arches made with flowers and hung with garlands for us to ride under untill we came to the Church.[15]

Santo Domingo Zinacantán received mention again in 1708 when a *ladino* mystic preached from a hollow oak tree, drawing crowds of Indian worshippers. In 1710, after the friars expelled him from his pulpit, he built a chapel. On the altar stood an image of the Virgin to whom the Zinacantecs offered candles, cacao, eggs, and tortillas. "The Chapel was decorated and lined with *petates*. The woods around have been cleared, fenced, and planted with milpas."[16] When a friar tried to dissuade the Indians from their beliefs and "idolatry" and attempted to set fire to the chapel, "they said in their language that we were burning the house of God and they began to rebel."[17] Whereupon the friars quickly torched the chapel and banished the mystic.

In 1748, reporting to the bishop on the state of his parish, the priest of Zinacantán remarked that "this town was formerly heavily populated…."[18]

Its natives are proud and some are moderately religious. They are inclined to drunkenness, caused by the wretched cane liquor which they bring from Ciudad Real and elsewhere. And even they have learned to make it. But more commonly [their drunkenness] is caused by a drink they produce called *chicha* which they make from corn, from apples and other fruits or from pulque which is prohibited as they use it immoderately, and commit great crimes. If it were not for that, it is very healthful, as it is cold, and they are of hot complexion, and it is so diuretic that neither the cider of Viscalla nor the beer of the North are better. They are inclined to steal, and to engage in business and trade with the other provinces. As is well known this is hurtful both spiritually and temporally. Spiritually, because taking them from their provinces at an early age, makes it extremely difficult for their education. Temporally, because, as said above, being inclined to steal, they cause great damage in the provinces, practicing one robbery after another, and with this absence failing to cultivate their good land, and they are always hungry, and for many months are wandering in search of provisions and carrying out their robberies.[19]

The priest recorded that there were 280 married people, 20 widowers, 55 widows, 108 boys, 112 girls, and many young children.

> Formerly the natives' houses were built of tile and plaster, but few of these remain, and most are of thatch. In their yards they have apple trees, pippins, pears, walnuts, clingstone peaches, free stone peaches, quinces, and other native fruit trees. In their gardens; roses, spikenards, carnations, stock, and other flowers both from Castile and native ones. Their forests are well-stocked with different kinds of pine, *pinaveto,* oaks [*ensinas, robles*], cedars, very large sage [*salvia*] with fine wood, cherries and very plentiful wild trees. They have many medicinal plants, as speedwell, angelica, violet, *lengua de siervo,* sarsparilla, *algafita, mataliste* and other herbs whose medicinal uses are known to the natives.[20]

After describing the mineral resources of Zinacantán, the priest concludes:

> Surrounding the town are five ranches settled by inhabitants of Ciudad Real. They are so close that they intrude on the very plots and yards of the town. Their nearness causes much sorrow, and many inconveniences, as they are compelled to provide saddle horses to travellers for five or more leagues of the king's highway to the inconvenience both of the natives and the travellers.[21]

Because Zinacantán was one of the few highland valleys to be deprived of its ancient patrimony, its inhabitants were forced to plant their corn and beans on the surrounding rocky slopes. And so the majority of men became bearers and muleteers.

In the middle of the eighteenth century 5 native religious brotherhoods (*cofradías*) were functioning. In addition to 4 stewards, each brotherhood had a prioress, elected annually, whose duty it was to beg alms one day a week in the name of the saint she represented. Gifts of corn, beans, cacao, cotton, and eggs, etc., were turned into money for the stewards. The prioresses swept the church, burnt incense, and decorated the altar with flowers for Mass. In 1793 they celebrated 24 fiestas annually.

Other religious activities were anathema to the governor:

> The most serious mischief is provoked by the meetings which the natives customarily hold in private houses on the occasion of their festivities which in some towns are called *Flowers,* wakes for dead infants, and others in the same category at which they commit horrible excesses and [sink into] drunkenness....
>
> Therefore, I absolutely prohibit such wakes and I order the governors never to permit them and [I order] them to punish vigorously all those who would oppose this resolution. I likewise order that none of the above mentioned meetings be held without the strict attendance of the governors, or at least without their permission, and in those which are held in the houses of the so-called cofradias, the governor or a judge must be present to oversee and avoid the said disorders which shall be punished with the same modera-

tion applied in other cases.[22]

In 1797 the priest reported:

> Sinacantan...has more than two thousand natives whose language is Tzozil; they are all corpulent, strong, agreeable, courteous and polite. They know their antiquity from early times, and are scarcely ignorant of their privileges. They did not resist Spanish arms, and helped to conquer the Chamulas. Despite the fertility of their land, they are extremely dedicated to trade and wander outside their land, penetrating the whole province and also that of Tabasco. Bernal Diaz del Castillo wrote: "The Zinacantecs are good people and great traders." Naturally friends of fiestas, they have one follow the other, announcing the future one before the present fiesta is concluded, perhaps lest they lose a bit of joy and distraction, falling asleep [the fiestas] make them feel less the weight of their great misery. Because with this recourse and perhaps with the absolute privation of other pleasures, their strength must endure hard and constant labor, bearing the weight of the day, and the cold up to seventy, eighty, and ninety years, at which age the Prophet only announces pains to us. These flee from the Indian who never lends his lips to complaint. I have seen that a minor stomach pain or a fleeting temperature are all they suffer from. The bark of *palo xiote,* taken in a decoction, pellitory to refresh the head and honey to soothe the breast are all the drugs they need. This appears to be due to the sweatbath in which they enter periodically and frequently....
>
> On the ranges of small mountains is cut a great multitude of wood sufficient to supply the City, although the natives are not very dedicated to timbering.
>
> Pine, oak (*encina*), *ramajo,* fat pine provide wood for the fire, fir (*pinabete*), cypress, and a white cedar provide boards for the houses, oak (*cantulan*) [*k'an-tulan*], hawthorn, *tepegua,* and others are very strong and incorruptible, willows, bald cypress (*sabino*), pines (*juncia,* and *chilca*) [*chilkat*] provide shade to part of the arroyos, large and small that cut into the neighboring hills, and circling and cutting across each other fertilize the land. It is true that they sow several bushels of wheat which when well-cared for will produce more than a hundred, using three or four laborers who are inhabitants of the neighboring village. They have competent irrigation and a single plot which the priest planted produced 16 bushels from 3 quarts, what more can one say? They fence in their houses and their yards have wonderful fruit trees. These are, and in this order: cherry, which is the first to become green, peach, both large and small, white and yellow, and so abundant that in the town they pick annually at least two million. The fig grows much taller than in the other towns of the kingdom although usually it is not the best. The walnut whose root is used succesfully for black dye in painting, whose branches provide charcoal for drawing and whose fruit is one of the most marketable among these Indians. There are scarcely any for many leagues except here. They pick them when

they ripen, and although they could be used at the end of the dog days, or in September they only sell those that they have kept from the previous year, and they are better. There is a wild walnut that has a very small nut. The pear, although small also has a good flavor and produces abundantly. The apple is truly the best that this province boasts, aside from the great number of these trees, their fruit is enormous. They weigh up to six, seven, eight ounces, and (the Indians) pick many of this type and size.

Enchanted with this abundance and beauty of fruit trees they see that a host of medicinal herbs bursts forth at their feet. The Indian is not ignorant of their virtues and knows how to use them successfully. Borage is a good cathartic for them, speedwell they use to refresh the head, willow for quinsy. I advise you here that there are two kinds of willow, false and true, that both are mixed in the yards and fields; one has a larger leaf that is less green, and this one has a broader flower. The thistle is a purgative, and the wild one has a root of great activity and strength for this. It has a purple flower and otherwise is like the cultivated one. Pennyroyal clots the blood. Dill is for wind, rue for the ear. I see them apply four leaves to the eyes although it is powerful for throat sores. *Yerba del toro* is for the flux, *alfilerillo* for quinsy which from time to time is epidemic among these people. Above all *palo mulato* is for burning fevers.

If one speaks of dyes, a small vine which spreads at the beginning of spring, and has a yellow color, gives this color to the thread. Dodder that they call *canác [k'anak']* gives the flesh color for the head ribbons. The black earth which is dug up at the edges of the town provides black for the wool which is fixed with the leaf of a plant named *hisbón* [*isbon*] which is also here. For tanning they also use *timbre*. With its bark they give body and strength to their cane liquor. And it is this same tree to which attaches and fattens the *age* which provides oil for Chiapanec lacquer. I add a dye that I just discovered in a fruit of wild grape of the plant named *lobuluec* [*lo'bol vet*] which gives a fast dark purple.[23]

The priest speaks of the two salt wells in Salinas lined with hollow cypress trunks, and how on the Fiesta of Our Lady of the Rosary it was said that a man, after fasting for a day, was lowered head first into the trunks to clean them. The priest did not witness this, but watched them briefly lower a small image of the Virgin on a tray with candles and incense into the wells. After this they covered the projecting trunks with new *petates*. Commenting on the profit made by mining the salt he said it compared favorably with the 2 peso monthly salary of a peon.

In 1793 the former wealth of Zinacantán is touched upon again: how once they had superabundant mule trains that reached New Spain, and how they took bread and native products to Tabasco, returning with cacao. They had been famous for their abundant harvests of wheat, corn, sheep, vegetables, and fruit. But "now they drink and show no respect for the priest."[24]

Shortly after, in 1806, Zinacantán, with 404 tributaries (family heads), was the third largest town in Chiapas, following only San Bartolo and Chamula. But the Zinacantecs were so widely dispersed that the bishop urged, in 1819, that they be "reduced," i.e., concentrated.[25]

More than half the Zinacantecs lived in hamlets near Chiapa de Corzo and Acala where they worked as day laborers, sharecroppers, and tenants. They were given tools and clothes on credit. After the harvest they paid the landholder with cacao, cochineal, cotton, and weaving. Returning from Tabasco they paid money or cacao. The parish priest wrote, "they do not possess enough land in the ejidos and unclaimed areas around their town because those which they own are absolutely sterile."[26]

The priest described the depths of their distress:

He who does not arrive home naked, dies by drowning on the road from the winter rains, and in the summer frozen by the ice, so that there is no old Zinacantec man, bachelor or boy, nor even woman who is not drunk the whole year. When not in the morning, in the afternoon or at night. They are forced to swindle and many to rob, and they are always poor, and pursued by tributes. Their sons and daughters are naked, and their women whom they mistreat cruelly, setting a bad example for them in every kind of vice, and very bad education, like those who live far from reason and wisdom. Worse, they go frequently to that city to sell their daughters. I mean to set them up as maids…many of whom return home violated and pregnant.[27]

The priest concluded plaintively that all the people had breakfast before Mass and were still idolators, "as I have found in the woods, in caves, in hollow trees, and beneath boulders, dead chickens, candles, and incense burners."[28]

In 1829 four hundred more Zinacantecs had been displaced to the lowland farms. Others continued trading in tropical Tabasco "whence they return only to die."[29]

The parish priest in 1848 complained that Zinacantán was a town "composed entirely of idiot Indians without a single artisan nor anyone who knows any other means or industry. They are all subjected to farming."[30] Then, with more sympathy, he spoke of "the frightful dispersion to which they are compelled, abandoning absoltely their town, moving to other jurisdictions, to serve as peons or as day laborers in the haciendas and ranches that are now so abundant."[31] He pointed out that by the law of 1844 their land was measured and sold to *ladinos*. Arguing that "land is the only cause of their unhappiness," he plead for a donation of land lest the Indians be tempted by revolution "as we begin to fear,"[32] and join towns with "a less pacific spirit."[33]

The plight of the Zinacantecs grew only more desperate. By 1855 nearly half of the households were headed by widows. Traders now shortened their routes, reaching only Pichucalco and Ixtacomitán at the Tabasco border, Simojovel, Tonalá on the Pacific Coast, and Chiapa and Acala in the Grijalva River

Valley. A cloud of locusts had devastated the crops. Again the priest complained of drunkenness, how in "their festivities especially it is sure they will get drunk, usually the first to do so being the individuals who are members of the town government."[34]

In 1856 Zinacantán was composed of 15 hamlets including Paste', Xul Vo', Na Chij, Apas, Naben Chauk, Jok' Ch'enom, Sek'emtik, Muk'ta Jok', Salinas (Atz'am), and X'ukun.

Two decades later the male inhabitants of Zinacantán had largely abandoned muleteering for coffee labor. Long past the Mexican Revolution they were still working as peons and sharecroppers in Grijalva River Valley cattle ranches.

In 1902 the volcano Santa Maria erupted in Guatemala, dropping a handspan-deep coat of ash on Zinacantán, toppling the Church of St. Lawrence and causing many sheep and horses to sicken and die. At this time, as a child, Xun Vaskis used to collect mushrooms with his grandmother under the giant pines that skirted the pond of Naben Chauk, where horned guans once called. "Long ago the huge trees weren't ever touched."[35] Corn, beans and squash flourished on the valley floor. But when Xun reached manhood, around 1912, the *ladino* owner of the ranch of Yaleb Taiv gave permission to the Chamula squatters on his land to fell the forest. Charcoal, burnt logs, and topsoil, he explained, washed down and stopped up the sump, so the pond became a lake, flooding the ancient cornfields of Naben Chauk.

In 1918–1919 the whole area was struck by famine and by the influenza epidemic. A year later the Carranza army waged war in Zinacantán. They had been preceded by bands of ravaging Villistas from 1914 to 1917, and were followed by the Obregón army in 1924. Few lives were lost, but the town felt besieged from all sides. So determined was the government to suppress the Church that Zinacantecs hid their saints in the heavily wooded mountains.

Agrarian reform was very slow to reach the highlands of Chiapa. The Zinacantecs' first petition in 1925 was promptly forgotten. The second, in 1933, was not approved until 1940 when there were 26 *ladino* ranches within town borders, comprising over 17,000 acres. In the twenty years from 1940 to 1960, when the land was finally donated, there were repeated invasions and counterinvasions of property. Before 1960 only 16% of the principal hamlet land was cultivable; 40% of the *ejido* land was cultivable, but when it was distributed it was apportioned not among the expected 20% of the population, but a mere 11%. At least the communal land was doubled.

The Zinacantecs' struggle to regain their land was not easily won. In 1961, the wife of a *ladino* landholder wrote to the president of Mexico, pleading with him to intervene "with your good heart and your influence…because I have no idea how we are going to deal with these stupid kids."[36]

Although Zinacantecs no longer "wandered in the provinces" trading, at the beginning of this century they did sell peaches, chayotes, watermelon squashes, and potatoes in Chiapa de Corzo. After the construction of the Pan-American highway in 1947 they extended their trade to Arriaga on the Pacific Coast and later traded in Juchitán. The flower trade began in the late 1940s when neither the buyers nor the sellers knew the names of the daisies and gladiolas that were being marketed: From that inauspicious beginning, only those familiar with Zinacantec history would have predicted that forty years later Zinacantán would be the home of the Chiapa flower monopoly.

Notes

[1] Ximénes, 1929, vol. 1:348.
[2] Ibid., 348–350.
[3] De Vos, 1985:89.
[4] Linguistic and archeological evidence suggests that the Tzotzil speakers moved into the Chiapa highlands during the Middle Classic period, ca. A.D. 500, but the earliest potsherds found in Zinacantán date from the Late Classic and Early Post-Classic, ca. A.D. 1000, cf. McVicker, 1972.
[5] Ximénes, 1929, vol. 1:359–360.
[6] Remesal, 1932, vol. 2:128–129.
[7] Ximénes, 1930, vol. 1:422–423.
[8] Ibid., 424–425.
[9] Chamberlain, 1948:181.
[10] Comparato, 1983:53–54.
[11] Ibid., 57.
[12] Laughlin, 1988, vol. 3:764.
[13] Remesal, 1932, vol. 2:73.
[14] Gage, 1655:95.
[15] Ibid., 95.
[16] Ximénes, 1931, vol. 3:264.
[17] Ibid., 264.
[18] Monrroy y Calçadillo, 1748:2.
[19] Ibid., 3.
[20] Ibid., 4.
[21] Ibid., 4.
[22] Hurtado, 1788.
[23] de Leon y Goicoechea, 1797:1–3.
[24] de Morales, 1793.
[25] Samartin, 1819.
[26] Wasserstrom, 1983:104.
[27] Escarra, 1819.
[28] Ibid.
[29] Wasserstrom, 1983:135.
[30] Correa, 1848b.
[31] Ibid.
[32] Correa, 1848a.
[33] Correa, 1848b.
[34] López, 1855.
[35] Laughlin, 1977:128.
[36] Edel, 1966:170.

Eating and Drinking

Robert M. Laughlin

I strew Thy lordly sunbeams,
    I scatter Thy lordly shade.
Thou it is who knowest,
    Thou it is who seest,
How I eat,
    How I drink.
I ask nothing of my father,
    I ask nothing of my mother,
I ask nothing of Thy child,
    I ask nothing of Thy offspring.
I watch not at dusk,
    I watch not at dawn,
At the edge of their fire,
    At the edge of their ashes,
My beauteous Father,
    My beauteous Lord.
I ask not for their corn,
    I ask not for their beans,
I ask not for Thy cross,
    I ask not for Thy passion,
My beauteous Father,
    My beauteous Lord.

        Romin Teratol (common prayer)

In Zinacantán the gods watch as their children exhaust their supply of corn. The righteous ones, the worthy ones bear no jealousy for their neighbors' corn, their neighbors' beans. They do not ask for riches, they wish only their fair share.

It is a rare day in a Zinacantec household when no beans are eaten, and so basic is corn that when one says, "My meal is finished," he is saying, "My corn is gone," and, "Will you fold a tortilla?" means "Will you have a meal?" Not only are tortillas the staple, they are also the cutlery. And so, people who do not eat tortillas must live at the ends of the earth. It is they who gulp down their food like wild animals. And back home a "corn swallower" is one who brags about what he, in fact, does not have. The importance of corn and beans may be measured by the extraordinary number of native "species" of these two crops cultivated by Zinacantecs: 29 of corn and 42 of beans.

Although there is little variation in the preparation of beans, corn is eaten in many forms. There are 8 ways to cook corn kernels and corn on the cob. There are 8 kinds of tortillas and 7 kinds of tamales. There are 9 flavors of corn chowder and 7 of corn gruel, as well as posol and pinole.

Next in importance are greens of many kinds, potatoes, squashes, and tomatoes.

Salt is the blessing of the meal and so is an obligatory seasoning. Most meals are seasoned with dry chilis or accompanied by fresh chili. Wild onions, Mexican tea, mint, coriander, and ground squash seeds are common condiments. Spices such as cloves, cinnamon, pepper, allspice, and ginger are used to season meat and corn gruel. Other important condiments include lime, husk tomato, piper, and marsh marigold. Brown sugar, and now, increasingly, refined sugar are added in quantities to coffee. Corn gruel, pinole, and mature squashes are sweetened.

Fruit forms a large part of the diet, but is never eaten at a meal. Included as snacks are chayotes and corn on the cob. On All Souls' Day these are the graveside offerings: chayotes, plantains, corn on the cob, oranges, and sugarcane. Less frequent are bananas, sweet lemons, apples, and pears. These are the fruits that the soul of a person who dies on All Souls' Day carries to the dead.

In the magical mountainous world of the summit of Muk'ta Vitz thrive tropical fruit trees: mangoes, mamey sapotes, sugarcane, and pineapples, but only those favored by the tutelary gods can see them. The fruits may be enjoyed on the mountaintop, but he who takes them home and eats them will die in an instant.

Care should be taken not to eat fruits that have grown together, lest you have twins. They should be divided up among many or only eaten by old people.

A tally of the plants that form a part of a Zinacantec's diet presents an extraordinary variety (Table 1). Of the 211 plants, 68 are more than occasional. Perhaps it would be more correct to say, "very occasional," for most days of the week the diet seems extremely limited. Despite the availability of many fruits in the San Cristóbal market only a few are purchased with regularity by Zinacantecs.

Because of the men's trips to the lowlands to prepare their milpas, they have a much broader diet than women, but now that travel to the lowlands is mainly by truck, corn farmers pick many fewer temperate and lowland fruits.

According to the 1970, census most Zinacantecs eat bread once a week, fish less frequently, meat and eggs two days a week.

When an individual falls ill the heat quality of the foods he eats is of importance. Most plants are classified as "hot," "medium," or "cold." It is a general rule that roots, tropical fruits, and greens are "cold," but the rule may be modified by a number of considerations. A hot-tasting root, such as a radish, is classified as "hot." A red stem, as of some sugarcane, is

TABLE 1.—Diet: vegetables, fruits, etc.

Food	Cultivated	Wild	Total
Greens	6	0	
Occasional greens	8	18	
Subtotal	14	18	32
Other cooked food	15	0	
Occasional cooked food	11	10	
Subtotal	26	10	36
Grains, nuts	6	2	
Occasional grains, nuts	3	8	
Subtotal	9	10	19
Fruit	30	3	
Occasional fruit	16	45	
Subtotal	46	48	94
Occasional other raw food	8	6	14
Seasoning	23	3	26
Food wrapper	3	8	11
Drink	9	5	14
Candy	5	0	5
Total	143	108	251
Minus repeats	111	100	211

"hot." A bitter green, as watercress or mustard, is also "hot." A young pumpkin squash is "cold," but a more bitter, mature squash is "hot." A fresh chili is "cold," a dried chili, "hot." Coffee sweetened with refined sugar is "cold," that with brown sugar, "hot."

These factors are weighed differently by each person. One stresses the aquatic, green quality of watercress, and classes it as "cold," whereas another stresses its piquant, bitter taste and have it "hot." There is endless room for disagreement!

In the past, Indian food was boiled, but Ladino food was fried. Though this distinction is still recognized, frying with both lard and oil has become common in Indian cuisine.

In the preparation of food it is acknowledged that cooks have different "hands." One will use up all the corn dough on a few tortillas, but another will make a little dough stretch far. Or one woman's amaranth greens will always be bitter, whereas another's always sweet. In the preparation of tamales for a ritual meal special procedures are taken so that nothing will go amiss, for example, so that a cook's pregnancy will not spoil the tamales. Ritual corn gruel also is protected from pregnancy. In both cases 3 rounds of cane liquor provide a final safeguard.

Food and drink reign supreme in the consciousness of Zinacantán. Returning from a visit: "What did they give you to eat, what to drink, how much?" In the old days no serious business was carried out without a gift of cane liquor, the amount measured very closely by the importance of the occasion.

The interaction between people is mirrored by their communication with the gods who are fed offerings of candles and indirectly partake of the ritual meals served at any significant event, whether it is for a birth, a baptism, a wedding, a funeral, a curing ceremony, or a religious official's banquet. Very often the banquet and accompanying libations seem to take precedence over all other activity, and so a religious official's inability to pray properly is overlooked if he is a generous provider of food. This was demonstrated recently by a *ladino* religious official whose ignorance of ritual Tzotzil was forgotten when he provided not one, but two cows for a meal! As everyone knows, a stingy official who provides sparingly for his guests will run out of corn and pesos in a moment's notice, but the cash and corn of a generous man will stretch and stretch.

Recalling the birth of his child, Romin Teratol paid little attention to the actual birth; instead, he described at length the meal he served afterwards. A man who troops along behind a procession of religious officials is said to be waiting expectantly for a handout, like an old dog.

Little is more satisfying to a Zinacantec man than to sit down at a long table with a peppermint cloth rolled out, a bottle of cane liquor at the head, bowls of chicken or beef broth before every person, and in the middle, salt bowls and towering stacks of tortillas. To be served more than you can eat—this is the good life!

And for the women who have been sitting around the fire all day or all night, preparing the food, commenting on just how it should be done and how others failed to provide their guests as they should have, all the while slipping generous handfuls of food into their mouths until it is their turn for the repast—this, too, is the good life!

These visions of bountiful meals are not restricted to "the earth's surface." Frequently a dreamer will recount in the greatest detail the ingredients of a meal that was just served him. The pleasure of eating and drinking in a dream is almost invariably awarded a dark interpretation. To eat good food is to be sold to the Earth, to get stomach ailments. Conversely, to eat meager fare is to eat abundantly on the earth's surface. To eat fruit is to get worms. The drinking of cane liquor, chicha, and corn gruel usually portends a common cold or stomach distress.

Throughout a Zinacantec's life he or she prays:

> May there not yet arise,
>   May there not yet pass,
> The seeming good,
>   The evil,
> The eater,
>   The drinker.

With these words, a Zinacantec begs that there be protection from witchcraft, that one's days may continue on this earth.

FIGURE 10.—Scarlet runner bean harvest, October 1977. (Photo by John Swope.)

FIGURE 11.—Metate platform, 1977. (Photo by John Swope.)

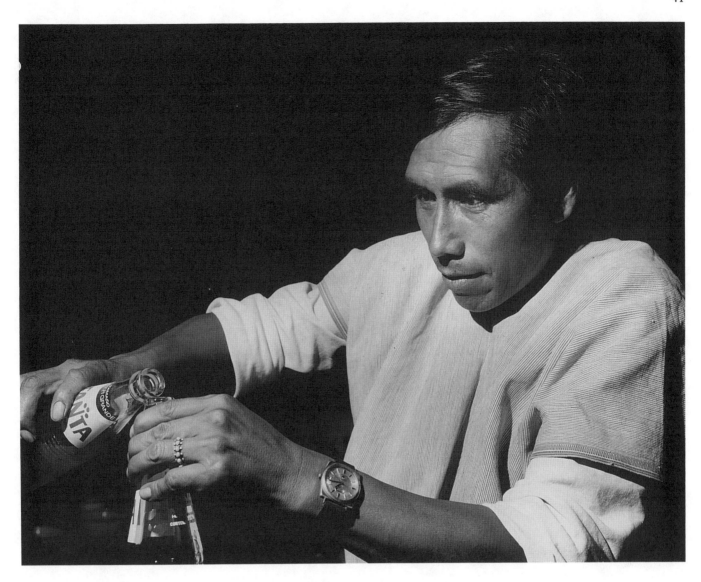

FIGURE 12.—Decanting cane liquor, 1977. (Photo by John Swope.)

On the Mend

Robert M. Laughlin

Three hundred and eighty-eight Linnaean species of plants with medicinal use in Zinacantán are recorded here:

Plant	Cultivated	Wild
"Vines"	9	33
"Trees"	27	87
"Plants"	27	205
Total	63	325

This would seem to offer dramatic proof that herbal medicine is the key to Zinacantec curing practices, but that is not so, for the basis of restoring health in the most serious cases is always through communication to the gods via prayers and offerings.

A shaman discovers his or her power through dreams that authorize the shaman to serve, as in this dream of installation:

When I came out, it seems—when I obeyed the command [on the earth's surface], Our Lord arrived. He arrived. Our Lord arrived. "Well," he said, "Are you there?" he said.

"I'm here," I said.

"Fine!" he said. "Let's go! They say you are to learn your orders," he told me. Hm!

I arrived at the house of Our Holy Father, Esquipulas. I went in there. "Are you there?" I asked.

"Have you come?" they said to me.

"I've come, sir," I said. I bowed to them. They looked like the elders with their red turbans. "Are you here, sir?" I bowed to them. "Sir!" I said.

"Well," [one of them] said, "Have you come then, son? As for you, you will serve," he told me. "You will serve," he said. "Here is your little present," he said. Thi–s many flowers—I was given flowers. Flowers. Yes!

They were beautiful, all Easter lilies, and so forth. "Here, see!" he said. "Receive these, please!" he said. Yes!

"Walk with these!" he said. Hm!

[Later] when they went to escort me [they gave me] two gourds, ceremonial gourds, as we say. For pinole, as we say. They are held [wrapped] in a cloth. Yes!

Two gourds and a quart bottle of cane liquor.

Then there was a staff. And, "Here, take this with you!" they told me. Yes!

I took the staff with me. I took it with me. Yes!

It was probably the bamboo staff. Yes!

That's the way it is when I walk, where I walk. Yes! Wherever I walk, that's how Our Lord gave me [my power]. Yes!

That's why I dreamt that way when Our Lord installed me. That's the way it was, indeed! Yes!

Herbal remedies may form a part of a curing ceremony, but, except in the mending of bones, they take a secondary part, if present at all.

Knowledge of herbal cures is widely shared by men and women. It is not a prerogative of shamans though they and hypochondriacs seem to be the best informed. A shaman who is not known for administering such cures nevertheless listed 45 species that he had used. Many local and some internal illnesses may be cured by home remedies without the aid of a shaman.

The restoration of health through herbs most often is viewed as a restoration of the proper body heat. Just as food is classed as "hot," "medium," and "cold," so are illnesses and their corresponding remedies. Again, as with food, the preparation of the herb may alter its heat. So, if it is boiled and the broth drunk, it may be "hot," but if it is crushed in cold water and the infusion taken it may be "cold." Some herbs' heat quality is not effected by their preparation.

After a major curing ceremony no "cold" food may be consumed for the prescribed period of time the patient is being "cared for." After taking "hot" medicine the patient should be careful not to drink cold water, nor to step in mud or cold water lest swelling be induced.

When the stems and leaves of plants are picked for medicinal purposes care is taken that they be the young tips. When the various plant parts are gathered, prepared, and administered they seldom are accorded special treatment, nor are they mentioned in prayers.

A medicinal herb, **spoxilin,** "its medicine," **jtunel,** "useful one," or **nichim,** "flower," is often specific to one illness, but some, such as chamomile, feverfew, and fennel are cure-alls.

In addition to the herbs that simply act to restore the proper heat, to dry out infections, to reduce swellings, etc., there are a number of herbs with distinctly magical properties. These are used in cases of witchcraft and soul-loss. The principal magical plants are tobacco, garlic, camphor, elderberry, and rue. Their strong odor is a powerful means for discouraging witches and Earth Lords from assaulting or retaining one's soul. They serve to "close their eyes."

For the medicinal treatment of animals, Zinacantecs do not call upon the services of a shaman, though a bonesetter may be sought.

Preparation of medicinal herbs consists of the following:
1. Peeling
2. Mashing raw between the palms of one's hands

3. Mashing raw between two stones
4. Grinding on the metate
5. Soaking
6. Spraying with cane liquor
7. Boiling
8. Mixing in cold water
9. Straining
10. Placing in the night dew
11. Toasting
12. Burning and pulverizing
13. Wilting on the fire (if in the field) or on the griddle. When prepared for animals the modes of preparation are limited to 1–3, 7–9, and 13.

The means of administration are as follows:

1. Drinking
2. Chewing
3. Applying to eyes, ears, or nose
4. Bathing or shampooing
5. Exposing to steam
6. Smoking body or clothes
7. Bandaging
8. Pressing leaves on body
9. Rubbing or "sweeping"
10. Striking body with nettles
11. Striking earth to recall soul
12. Calling soul
13. Wearing medicine
14. Burying medicine

For animals the means of administration are limited to 1, 4, 7–9, and 13.

A particular remedy is often confined to one plant, but it may consist of several plants. Not infrequently salt, sugar, chili, or cane liquor are added. For animals salt, sugar, or cane liquor may be added. The size and frequency of dosage varies greatly, but some medicines are known to be delicate.

The "steam cure" is a complicated remedy. This treatment is given to reduce swelling or follows bloodletting. A fire is set in a round hole that has been dug in the floor of the steambath. Thirteen brown river pebbles are put in the fire and a variety of plants are placed on top. Sometimes the bones of a black vulture are added. A large gourd of urine (half the contents from one of the male assistants and half from one of the female assistants) is poured over the rocks. The patient sits on the leaves, covering himself with a blanket, enveloped in the steam.

Despite the frequent lack of what we would call medicinal herbs in the treatment of patients, no shaman can cure without "flowers": an array of 10 or so plants used in the ritual bath and for decoration. To become a bonesetter a man is ordered in his dream to mend and erect a splintered tree. A midwife receives her "flowers" and is ordered to accept babies without scorn. A shaman receives his bamboo staff, ceremonial gourds, and "flowers."

Indeed the major curing ceremony is called **muk'ta nichim,** "great flower," and the minor ceremony, **bik'it nichim,** "little flower." These ceremonies have been carefully described and illustrated fully by Vogt (1976), who points out the multiplicity of life force symbolism throughout the ceremonies; from the green pines, tender "flower" shoots, to the long-lasting blood red geraniums. Two corrections should be added. Following a curing ceremony the "flowers" may be placed in *any* tree (not specifically a **tulan**) next to the nearest shrine. Through interviews with Antzelmo Peres, Vogt discovered that the plants used as "flowers" possessed an inner soul, characterized by heat, color and strength (Vogt, 1976:89–91). Subsequently, Antzelmo Peres has denied the existence of such souls or their attributes, claiming that someone in that interview must have been drunk!

It is no coincidence that the "flower" of the man's kerchief is a fuschia red pompon, that the "flower" of the fire is a spark, and the "flower" of cane liquor, the highest proof. Indeed, the naked Christ on the cross, wears nothing but a cloth flower to cover his loins.

Dressing Our Lords

Robert M. Laughlin

To change the pine and floral adornments at the household altars, the chapels and churches, and at the crosses that mark gravesites and sacred points in the landscape is to "dress Our Lord," **stz'akubtas kajvaltik**.

In 1977 when the sacristans were shown photographs of the interior of the Church of St. Lawrence taken in 1960, they were astonished and close to tears over the luxuriant floral decoration. In addition to the many familiar vases of lilies, gladiolas and daisies rising step by step on the altar, each and every tabernacle was enclosed in its dark green arch of bamboo palm fronds festooned with bright red bunches of geraniums. Of course the nave was carpeted with sweet-smelling pine needles.

They say it was the priest who ordered that the pine needles be removed lest they rot the cement floor when it was newly laid. No one can recall when the arches disappeared. Since the mid-1980s the chancel floor and benches have been clothed in a thick, fresh cover of pine needles.

During the past quarter of a century the old hamlet chapels of Atz'am and Sak Lum and the old ranch chapels of San Mikulax and Kelem Ton were joined by a new Chapel of Lord Esquipulas, and chapels in Apas, Bik'it Joyijel, Chak Toj, Elan Vo', Na Chij, Naben Chauk, Paste', and Sek'emtik. An examination of these 12 chapels and the chapel of Muk'ta Jok' shows that 100 different plants are used for religious decoration. Of these, 55 are cultivated and 45 are wild.

Plant	Cultivated	Wild
"Vines"	4	2
"Trees"	16	18
"Plants"	35	25

The majority are also used in the Church of St. Lawrence, but some substitutions are made in the temperate and lowland chapels. Bamboo palm arches and pine decorations occur in all but one hamlet. Generally two pines flank the chapel doorway and three, the cross, and in the official's house three are also for the cross and two flank the altar. Pine needles carpet the floors of eight chapels. The flowers of the **bal te'** or basic flower change are uniformly similar. Geraniums are absent only in the lowland community of Kelem Ton, which is also the only community lacking yellow marigolds for All Souls' Day. Chamomile and roses are widely used during Lent and red marigolds for Our Lady of the Rosary.

Except in Elan Vo' and Kelem Ton, the Christmas decorations are the most lavish, with trees and an abundance of citrus fruits, bananas, sugarcane, popapples, **chuchu'**, squashes, sedum, mosses, and bromeliads. Paralleling the minor creche in the Church of St. Sebastian with the procession Christmas Eve to the major creche in the Church of St. Lawrence are the creches in the hamlets with their processions from the rustic creche in the woods to the munificent chapel creche. The wild trees used in the framework of the mountain creches vary widely from one hamlet to another.

Only in Atz'am and Sak Lum is **k'oxox te'** used for processional paths supplanting, or in addition to, the usual wax myrtle and rapanea. Fan palms are used frequently for decoration and palm fronds are distributed on Palm Sunday in many hamlets.

Responsibility for providing the necessary decorations varies greatly from one hamlet to the next. In Apas, Muk'ta Jok' and Paste' only the officials are responsible. In Bik'it Joyijel the men take turns, becoming stewards for a single fiesta. In San Mikulax four men are selected each year to provide the flowers. In Na Chij both the officials and the deputy provide, whereas in Atz'am, it is the officials, the fiesta committee, and anyone who pleases. In Sak Lum and Sek'emtik the officials are aided by the fiesta committee. In Elan Vo' the officials, a palm man appointed by the deputy, and anyone may provide. Most complicated is Naben Chauk, where some decorations are supplied by the officials, some by the fiesta committee, some by the deputy, some by the flower merchants, some by the reforestation committee, and some by the godparents of the Christ Child. At the opposite extreme are Chak Toj and Kelem Ton, small communities that lack religious officials and whose chapels are decorated communally.

The most eloquent testimony to the human and divine importance in maintaining the beauty and fragrance of the houses of Our Lords is given by Palas Muchik, chief musician of the stewards-royal, who is in charge of the Chapel of Lord Esquipulas. One night he had this dream:

> First a man came here to my house. He came in by my gate. "Are you here, Pancho?" he said.
>
> "I'm here," I said.
>
> "Ah, fine," he said. "You are supposed to go, because someone is going to talk to you here. You will be spoken to here above your house," he said.
>
> "All right," I said. I went.
>
> Then, I arrived there.
>
> "Have you come?" said the bishop.
>
> "I've come, *padrecito*," I said.
>
> "Ah, fine," he said. "Well, how are you?" he said.
>
> "I've nothing wrong. I'm all right," I said.
>
> "Ah, I want to ask you a favor. Won't you please take the shoulder bag here?"
>
> "Ah," I said. "What's it for?" I asked.
>
> "Please, scatter this for me, yourself. You're ahead of

46

FIGURE 13.—Household altar, Zinacantán Center, 1977. (Photo by John Swope.)

FIGURE 14.—Christ on Good Friday, Naben Chauk, 1984. (Photo by John B. Haviland.)

me, scatter these pine needles for me that you see here," he said.

"Sure, why not," I said.

"Let's go enjoy ourselves!" he said.

"Let's go!" I said. So I started out on the highway here, the road that goes to Muk'ta Vitz. We went. I scattered the pine needles. This many pine needles, not a lot, but the amount remained the same. Oh, I scattered them. The bishop was right behind me. It was he who stepped on the pine needles I scattered.

We went along. We came to a ridge up the–re.

"Well, we've arrived here," he said.

"All right," I said.

"Look down in this direction!" he said.

Well, I looked down at the lowlands. "You all say the lowlands are far away. You all say your friends have gone far away for the bean planting, but no, they're nearby," he said.

"Maybe they're near," I said.

"Yes, near, take a look!" I looked do–wn. The lowlands were nea–r, they were near now. I loo–ked down. Our friends were working. They were in the midst of planting. Some were hoeing, others were doubling corn, but they were near now. I was looking at them from just this distance. "See! Those who are working, those who are traveling, we'll get to see from here, see!" he said.

"Ah, fine," I said.

"The lowlands are near. As for me, I can see down from here," he said. "Take a look, you can see all the lowlands well. Take a look!" he said. I looked, but I could see—all the lowlands. Oh, it was rea–lly visible, where rivers flowed, where the tall forests were, it was really visible.

"Well, let's go!" he said. We had been standing there for maybe five minutes. "Let's go!" he said.

"Let's go then!" I said. I scattered the pine needles still. We we–nt to the mountain. I arrived at the mountaintop.

"Well, see here!" he said. "Scatter all the pine needles here now!" he said.

"All right," I said.

Then I scattered the pine needles.

Then, "Thank you," he said. "Thank you for doing me the favor. This is fine," he said.

"Well, don't mention it," I said.

"See the beans, look!" he said. "Look at the corn!" he said. There were just **ibes** beans, just yellow corn.

"Ah, fine," I said.

"See!" he said. "I'm going to tell you to go say a few words. Why is the house of Our Lord Esquipulas so terrible? I don't think it is at all good any more. It hasn't any flowers any more. You don't hear anything good any more. Who is in charge?" he asked.

"It's the shamans," I said.

"Ah," he said. "But why?" he said.

"Who kno–ws why. That's what they decided," I said.

"But it didn't use to be that way," he said.

"No, *padrecito,* but now pine needles aren't used," I said.

"Ah," he said. "No," he said. "You tell them, you give orders, have pine needles given at the house of Our Lord Esquipulas. Pine needles are wonderful. It is pine needles that are wanted so much by Our Lords," he said.

"I don't know if I'll be obeyed," I said.

"Of course," he said. "Never mind if you give a command, never mind if you let them know, it isn't your fault. Whoever doesn't respect you, whoever doesn't obey, never mind," he said. "Tell them!" he said.

"All right," I said. "Can I tell them?" I asked.

"Yes, why not," he said. "Our Lord is unhappy that there aren't pine needles, no pine needles," he said.

"All right," I said.

"Then, I say thank you, go along!" he told me. I returned, it was my soul.

"God, My Lord, what could it mean?" I said to myself.

Then, who knows how long it was, maybe it was three or four weeks, I chatted about it when I went, too [to the shamans' meeting]. The shamans heard me talking about it. "Is it true that you had a dream, is it true that you dreamt about something?" they asked me.

"Yes," I said. The shamans were gathered together. "Yes," I said.

"What was it about?"

"Like this. See, it was like this," I said. "He came by to escort me like this, but I don't know if it's just the madness of my dream. I don't know if I'm telling lies, because I don't know, but that was what I saw, indeed, but who knows if it is true or not. You, who are shamans, haven't you dreamt about it? You, who have souls, who have been sworn in at the foot of Our Lord Esquipulas, how about you? But me, I'm ignorant, but that's what I saw," I said.

"Ah," they said. "But as for that, we have dreamt about that, too. We didn't want to talk about it. We certainly did talk that way, but we didn't believe ourselves. 'Forget it!' we said to ourselves," said [one of the shamans].

"You other shamans, have you seen it?" asked the senior shamans.

"We've seen it, indeed, but we didn't want to say, but it isn't a joke, for Mr. Francis is probably telling the truth, because that is bad, it isn't a joke, it's true Our Lord here was used to having pine needles, but now there aren't any. It's bad that we've lost [the custom]," said the others.

"Yes, that's true, indeed!" they said.

"Well, but it would be good if we gave them, if we obeyed that. It's bad if we go out and don't obey. It's bad. But Mr. Francis is giving good advice. It isn't that he's getting drunk, he isn't a drunk, he's speaking like a real man. Why don't we accept? It would be good," they said.

Pine needles are put there now. They are placed there on Saturday. They're there on Sunday, Monday, Tuesday, Wednesday, Thursday, Friday.

Then on Saturday they are taken out. They sweep out the pine needles. They scrub [the floor] with soap. The inside of Our Lord's house is left good and clean. One week there are pine needles, one week no pine needles. That's how the year passes. That's how it has been left.

Well, on New Year's, the day before the swearing in, it is the outgoing [officers] who give the pine needles, on the last day of December. The outgoing [officers] give them early on the thirty-first of December.

Then at dawn on the first of January it is the new [officials] who give them. At midnight they give them. The outgoing [officials] take them out late on the thirty-first. The inside of Our Lord's house should be left we–ll swe–pt.

Then, early on the first of January, at midnight when the bells are rung…

Then the bells are rung, the rockets are fired, candles are lit, mortars are exploded, then the pine needles are sca–ttered. The year is new, the pine needles are ne–w on the first of January. That's how it has been left.

For a Handful, a Fistful

Robert M. Laughlin

At the celebration of Holy Cross Day in early May, kinsmen and neighbors who share a common waterhole travel to their wellspring, clean it, and offer flowers and candles, words and song, incense and libations there at the neighborhood shrines. The importance of this rite in preserving family and community solidarity has been thoroughly demonstrated (Vogt, 1969, 1976). The ceremony's explicit purpose is revealed by the prayers intoned by the shaman in charge, who reaffirms the sacred bond between men and gods, man and nature, between farmers and their sustenance, maize. These prayers are invoked in remembrance and anticipation of the agricultural activities that consume the interest and lives of the members of that community.[1]

The shaman,

> "I who am an utter dog,
> I who am an utter pig,"

explores the whole panoply of deities and cosmic forces, beginning with Jesus Christ, together with heaven and earth, kings and angels, snakes and thunderbolts, six holy Fathers, six holy Mothers, the Virgin Mary, Lord Esquipulas, the Savior, St. Lawrence, St. Dominic, St. Sebastian, and St. Michael to still watch over, for him, the young and the old,

> "Shouting at dusk,
> Shouting at dawn."

He offers their meager gifts and asks,

> "May I prod Your lordly noses,
> May I prod Your lordly ears,"

so that, in one accord, in unison, without anger, the gods will favor his clients,

> "Wherever they leave their filth,
> Wherever they leave their rubbish."

He asks that nothing harm them, nothing befall them, that they not yet be struck or frightened,

> "Wherever they walk,
> Wherever they travel,
> Wherever they borrow,
> Wherever they share,
> Your back yard,
> Your side yard."

He addresses the holy wellspring, the holy headwater,

> "Your bathing place,

> Your shampooing place,
> Where it is used,
> Where it is consumed,
> By Your lowly children,
> Your humble offspring,
> Where they wash off their filth,
> Where they wash off their dirt."

Foreseeing his clients' need for corn to keep them alive, he asks for protection,

> "Wherever they may get the pittance,
> Wherever they may get the trifle."

Specifically he asks the gods to shield his clients from deadly serpents, which he refers to cryptically as "seeds," "kernels":

> "For my sake, still set aside,
> For my sake, still push aside,
> Your one seed,
> Your one kernel."

He asks for protection when the corn is planted:

> "Where their ten toes ache,
> Where their ten fingers ache,
> Where they scatter,
> Where they strew,
> Your lordly sunbeams,
> Your lordly shadows."

And he begs them to provide the rain necessary for their crops:

> "For my sake will You sprinkle in unison,
> For my sake will You water in unison,
> In holy accord may it be spilled,
> May it be pured now,
> ...the water of Your faces,
> The water of Your countenances."

Looking farther to the future, he asks that next year they may be the same, seem the same, so they may meet once again on this Holy Cross Day.

At the house cross (translation of Holy Cross Day prayer; see Appendix 8 for Tzotzil original):

> "In the holy name of the holy God,
> Jesus Christ, My Lord,
> How much is it now My Father,
> How much is it now, My Lord?
> My lowly earth has returned,
> My lowly mud has returned,

50

Here, beside You,
   Here, before You.
This many will I ready now,
   This many will I prepare now,
The pittance,
   The trifle,
The cause for Your lordly fear,
   The cause for Your lordly shame.
The holy day has arrived,
   The holy hour has struck has struck,
For Your great fiesta,
   For Your grand festival,
Together with the flowery holy earth, holy
   heaven,
   Holy ground, holy land,
Holy king, holy angel,
   Holy snake, divine thunderbolt,
My great holy Father,
   My great holy Lord.[2]
How much is it now, My Father,
   How much is it now, My Lord?
Will it be well-accepted,
   Will it be well-received,
However much comes,
   However little comes?
They arrived with anxious heads,
   They arrived with anxious hearts,
Your lowly children,
   Your lowly offspring.
Will You watch for me with care their lowly
   backs?
   Their lowly sides?
Shall nothing yet harm them,
   Shall nothing yet befall them,
Wherever they walk,
   Wherever they travel,
Wherever they climb down,
   Wherever they climb up,
At dusk,
   At dawn,
Before Your flowery faces,
   Before Your flowery countenances,
Wherever they may find,
   Wherever they may get,
The pittance,
   The trifle,
Of the cause for Your lordly fear,
   The cause for Your lordly shame.[3]
Divine name of the holy God,
   Jesus Christ, My Lord,
For this my lowly earth has returned,
   My lowly mud,
 Now beside Thee,
   Before Thee,

My Lord,
At the table:
In the holy name of the holy God,
   Jesus Christ, My Lord,
Take heed, holy tabletop,
   Take heed, sacred tabletop,
However long, holy torches,
   However long, holy candles,
Have You awaited here my lowly earth,
   My lowly mud,
However many,
   However few You are,
However many of You, My lordly Fathers,
   My lordly Mothers,
However many of You I ready now,
   I prepare now.
Are You well-readied now,
   Are You well-prepared now,
Will You be well-accepted now,
   Will You be well-received now,
By the holy earth,
   By the holy heaven,
By the holy ground, the holy land,
   The holy king, the holy angel,
The holy snake, the divine thunderbolt?
However much I beg holy pardon now,
   I beg holy permit now,
For the backs,
   For the sides,
Of Your children,
   Your offspring.
We have reached the hour,
   We have reached the day,
Of Your great fiesta,
   Your grand festival,
Holy Cross of May,
My great holy Father,
   My great holy Lord,
For as many of Your great fiestas,
   Your grand festivals,
Flowery holy earth, holy heaven,
   Holy ground, holy land,
Holy king, holy angel,
   Holy snake, divine thunderbolt,
Will You watch for me with care,
   Will You observe for me with care,
All the backs,
   The sides,
Of Your lowly children,
   Your lowly offspring?
Will nothing yet befall them,
Will their lowly backs not yet be struck,
   Will their lowly sides not yet be struck,
Will their lowly backs not yet be frightened,

Wherever they walk,
   Wherever they travel,
Wherever they share,
Your back yard,
   Your side yard,
Your lordly shadow,
   Your lordly cover,
Wherever they leave their filth,
   Wherever they leave their rubbish,
At dusk,
   At dawn,
Before Your flowery faces,
   Before Your flowery countenances,
My great holy Father,
   My great holy Lord.
Will the holy words be now in unison,
   Will the holy lips move now in unison,
With the great holy Fathers,
   The great holy Mothers?
Will You be accepted by all,
   Will You be received by all,
My great holy Father,
   My great holy Lord?
Take heed, My Father,
   Take heed, My Lord!
For this my earth has returned,
   My mud,
Beside Thee,
   Before Thee,
My great holy Father,
   My great holy Lord.
Addressing the candles:
In the holy name of the holy God,
   Jesus Christ, My Lord,
Take heed, My great holy Father,
   Take heed, My great holy Lord!
However much there is now, My holy Father,
   However, much there is now, My holy Lord,
Before Your lordly faces now,
   Before Your lordly countenances now,
Great holy Fathers,
   Great holy Mothers,
Great holy oceans,
   Great holy Lords.
I ready the pittance,
   I ready the trifle,
Of the cause for Your fear,
   The cause for Your shame,
One lowly torch,
   One humble candle,
One lowly chunk of incense,
   One humble cloud of smoke,
One lowly flower,
   One humble leaf,

Of Your lowly children,
   Your humble offspring.[4]
For them I beg holy pardon,
   For them I beg divine forgiveness.
The holy day has arrived.
   The holy hour has struck,
For Your great fiesta,
   For Your grand festival,
The holy cross of May.
My great holy Father,
   My great holy Lord.
Take heed, My Father,
   Take heed, My Lord!
Will the words be now in unison,
   Will the lips move now in unison?
Will it be accepted now in holiness,
   Will it be received now in holiness,
The pittance,
   The trifle,
Will the holy tabletop now arrive,
   Will the divine tabletop now arrive,
Will the holy carnations now arrive,
   Will the holy lilies now arrive,
Beside You,
   Before You?
May You bear the hardship,
   May You endure the suffering,
To watch for me now with care,
   To observe for me now with care,
All the backs,
   The sides,
Of Your lowly children,
   Your humble offspring.
May nothing yet harm them,
   May nothing yet befall them,
Where they leave their filth,
   Where they leave their rubbish,
Where they borrow,
   Where they share,
Your back yard,
   Your side yard,
Your lordly shadow,
   Your lordly cover,
My great holy Father,
   My great holy Lord,
For how long, My Father,
   For how long, My Lord,
How much now, My Father,
   How much now, My Lord,
Will You be able to watch for me,
   Will You be able to observe for me,
Will You not yet frighten their backs, for me,
   Will You not yet frighten their sides, for me?
May their backs not yet be struck,

May their sides not yet be struck,
Beside You,
    Before You,
For as long as they walk here,
    For as long as they travel here,
For as many dusks,
    For as many dawns,
Before Your flowery faces,
    Before Your flowery countenances,
My great holy Father,
    My great holy Lord,
Take heed, My holy Father,
    Take heed, My holy Lord!
May You talk now in unison,
    May You speak now in unison,
With the flowery holy earth,
    With the flowery holy heaven,
Flowery holy ground, holy land,
    Holy king, holy angel,
Holy snake, divine thunderbolt,
My great holy Father,
    My great holy Lord.
However much there is now, My Father,
    However much there is now, My Lord,
I shall give up now,
    I shall leave now,
The pittance,
    The trifle,
Beside You,
    Before You,
You who are My holy Fathers,
    You who are My holy Mothers.[5]
Take heed, six holy Fathers,
    Take heed, six holy Mothers!
Will You talk now in unison,
    Will You speak now in unison,
With the holy wellspring,
The holy wellspring,
    The holy headwater,
Your bathing place,
    Your shampooing place,
Where it is used,
    Where it is consumed,
By Your lowly children,
    Your humble offspring,
Where they borrow,
    Where they share,
Where they wash off their filth,
    Where they wash off their dirt,
At dusk,
    At dawn,
Before Your flowery faces,
    Before Your flowery countenances?
May You talk together now in unison,

May You speak together now in unison,
    May Your lordly heads not yet grow angry,
    May Your lordly hearts not yet grow angry,
For as long as they walk,
    For as long as they travel,
Your lowly children,
    Your humble offspring,
The young, shouting,
    The old, shouting,
Beside You,
    Before You,
And the flowery holy earth,
    The flowery holy heaven,
And the flowery holy land, holy ground,
    Holy king, holy angel,
Holy snake, divine thunderbolt,
    My Lord.
Take heed, My holy Father,
    Take heed, My holy Lord!
May You accept for me now, with care,
    May You receive for me now, with care,
The little,
    The bit,
The cause for Your fear,
    The cause for Your shame.
There is nothing to arrive in piles now,
    There is nothing to arrive in heaps now,
A pittance arrives now,
    A trifle arrives now.
Your lowly children,
    Your humble offspring,
They were worried,
    They were fretting,
How would it pass,
    How would it take place,
Your great fiesta,
    Your grand festival,
You who are Our great holy Fathers,
    You who are our great holy Mothers.
Will they still be the same,
    Will they still seem the same,
Next year, before Your flowery faces,
    Next year, before Your flowery countenances?
Will they still beg holy pardon, just the same,
    Will they still beg forgiveness, just the same,
For their lowly backs,
    Their humble sides?
Will You still stand erect,
    Will You still stand firm?
In the holy name of My great holy Father,
    My great holy Lord,
Take heed, My Father,
    Take heed, My Lord!
May You talk now in unison,

May You speak now in unison,
With Lord Esquipulas, great holy man,
  Lord Esquipulas, great holy Caucasian!
Take heed, My Father,
  Take heed, My Lord!
For how long now, My Father,
  For how long now, My Lord,
May I prod Your lordly nose,
  May I prod Your lordly ears, now?
How long for the pittance,
  How long for the trifle,
The lowly torch,
  The humble candle,
Of Your lowly children,
  Your humble offspring?
With these I beg holy pardon,
  I beg divine forgiveness,
For the backs,
  The sides,
Of Your lowly children,
  Your humble offspring.
So it may pass,
  So it may take place,
Your great fiesta,
  Your grand festival,
With the sacred, holy cross of May,
My great holy Father,
  My great holy Lord,
Take heed, My Father,
  Take heed, My Lord!
In unison accept for me the pittance,
  In unison accept for me the trifle,
There is nothing in piles,
  There is nothing in heaps,
Just for Your great fiesta,
  Just for Your grand festival.
Take heed, You who are My great holy Fathers,
  Take heed, My holy Mothers!
Will You still watch in unison,
  Will You still observe in unison,
All the backs,
  All the sides,
Of Your lowly children,
  Your humble offspring.
For my sake You have not yet lost them,
  For my sake You have not yet discarded them,
For my sake give to them still, above Your lordly
      feet,
  Above Your lordly hands,
May nothing yet harm their backs,
  May nothing yet harm their sides,
May their backs not yet be struck,
  May their sides not yet be struck,
By the holy kings,

By the holy angels,
By the holy snakes,
  By the divine thunderbolts,
May their backs not yet be frightened,
  May their sides not yet be frightened,
By one of Your seeds,
  By one of Your kernels,[6]
Flowery holy earth,
  Flowery holy heaven.
Take heed, My holy Father,
  Take heed, My holy Lord!
Talk together, in unison,
  Speak together, in unison,
For my sake, still set aside,
  For my sake, still push aside,
Your one seed,
  Your one kernel.
For my sake do not frighten the backs,
  For my sake do not frighten the sides,
Of Your lowly children,
  Your humble offspring,
For as long as they walk,
  For as long as they travel,
At dusk,
  At dawn,
Before Your flowery faces,
  Before Your flowery countenances,
Wherever they borrow,
  Wherever they share,
Your back yard,
  Your side yard,
Your lordly shadow,
  Your lordly cover,
Wherever they leave their filth,
  Wherever they leave their rubbish,
Downhill,
  Uphill,
At dusk,
  At dawn,
Before Your flowery faces,
  Before Your flowery countenances,
May nothing yet harm their backs,
  May nothing yet harm their sides,
Where they walk,
  Where they travel,
Where they climb down,
  Where they climb up,
Where their ten toes ache,
  Where their ten fingers ache,
Where they scatter,
  Where they strew,
Your lordly sunbeams,
  Your lordly shadows,
    My Lord,[7]

54

Will there still be talk in common,
   Will there still be speech in common,
For my sake will You sprinkle in unison,
   For my sake will You water in unison,
One of Your lordly sunbeams,
   One of Your lordly shadows?
Shall we borrow,
   Shall we share,
The water of Your faces,
   The water of Your countenances,
Your bathing place,
   Your shampooing place,
   My Lord?
In holy accord may it be spilled,
   May it be poured now,
However much,
   However little,
However much, My Father,
   However much, My Lord,
Of the water of Your faces,
   The water of Your countenances,
   My Lord.
May You still watch over them for me in divine
      accord,
   May You still observe them for me in divine
      accord,
Will they still get,
   Will they still receive,
The pittance,
   The trifle,
The cause for Your fear,
   The cause for Your shame,
Your lordly sunbeams,
   Your lordly shadows,
   My Lord?
May You watch over them for me in divine
      accord,
   May You observe them for me in divine accord!
Take heed, My Father,
   Take heed, My Lord!
May You talk in holy unison now,
   May You speak in holy unison now,
With the holy Father, St. Lawrence,
   Father, St. Dominic,
Heavenly woman,
   Heavenly lady,
Flowery holy purchaser of heaven,
   Holy purchaser of paradise,
   My Lord.[8]
However much, My divine holy Father,
   However much, My divine holy Lord.
Will the talk be in unison now,
   Will the speech be in unison now,
Will it be accepted in divine accord,

Will it be received in divine accord,
However much appears,
   However little appears,
The torch,
   The candle,
Of Your lowly children,
   Your humble offspring?
Will the holy tabletop be proper now,
   Will the divine tabletop be proper now,[9]
 Beside You,
   Before You,
And the flowery holy earth,
   The flowery holy heaven,
The holy land, holy ground,
   Holy king, holy angel,
Holy snake, divine thunderbolt?
How long, My holy Father,
   How long, My holy Lord,
Will You still watch for me with care,
   Will You still observe for me with care,
All the backs,
   The sides,
Of Your lowly children,
   Your humble offspring?
May their backs not yet be lost,
   May their sides not yet be lost,
Still stand erect,
   Still stand firm,
May their backs not yet be struck,
   May their sides not yet struck,
By the holy king,
   By the holy angel,
By the holy snake,
   By the divine thunderbolt,
Take heed, My Father,
   Take heed, My Lord!
May their backs not be frightened,
   May their sides not be frightened,
By the holy earth,
   By the holy heaven,
My great holy Father,
   My great holy Lord,
May You still watch for me in divine accord,
   May You still observe for me in divine accord,
Their backs,
   Their sides,
For as long as they walk here,
   For as long as they travel here,
Your lowly children,
   Your humble offspring.
At dusk,
   At dawn,
Your flowery faces,
   Your flowery countenances,

You who are My holy Fathers,
  You who are My holy Mothers,
Take heed, My Father,
  Take heed, My Lord!
Talk now together in unison,
  Speak now together in unison,
With the flowery holy Martyr, My Father,
  Flowery holy Martyr, My Lord!¹⁰
Take heed, My Father,
  Take heed, My Lord!
 Will they be watched carefully now,
  Will they be observed carefully now,
All the backs,
  All the sides,
Of Your lowly children,
  Your humble offspring?
For this their heads are anxious,
  For this their hearts are anxious,
With this pittance,
  With this trifle,
This many of their torches,
  This many of their candles,
I beg holy pardon,
  I beg holy forgiveness,
For their lowly backs,
  For their humble sides.
How will it pass,
  How will it take place,
Your great fiesta,
  Your grand festival?
Perhaps next year Your flowery faces,
  Perhaps next year Your flowery countenances,
If, just the same, they still gather together,
  If, just the same, they still join together,
If, just the same, they still see with their faces,
  If, just the same, they still see with their
    countenances.
They beg holy pardon,
  They beg divine forgiveness,
For their lowly backs,
  For their humble sides,
You who are Our holy Fathers,
  You who are Our holy Mothers.
Take heed, My Father,
  Take heed, My Lord!
May You bear the hardship now,
  May You endure the suffering now,
Talk together now in divine accord,
  Speak together now in divine accord,
With the holy Lord, Our Saviour,
In the center of the holy heaven,
  In the center of the holy paradise,
How much is it, my holy Father,

How much is it, my holy Lord,
How much is it now, My Father,
  How much is it now, My Lord,
Will the words be now in unison,
  Will the lips move now in unison,
With the Lord, St. Michael Archangel, My Father,
  With the lord, St. Michael Archangel, My Lord.
How much, You who are My holy Fathers,
  How much, You who are My holy Mothers,
Will You accept for me now in holiness,
  Will You receive for me now in holiness,
However much,
  However little,
Arrives beside You,
  Arrives before You,
And the flowery holy earth,
  And the flowery holy heaven,
And the flowery holy ground, holy land,
  Holy king, holy angel,
Holy snake, divine thunderbolt?
How will it pass,
  How will it take place,
Your great fiesta,
  Your grand festival,
  My Lord?
You shall still stand erect,
  You shall still stand firm.
May nothing yet harm the backs,
  May nothing yet harm the sides,
Of Your lowly children,
  Your humble offspring,
For as long as they walk,
  For as long as they travel,
For as many dusks,
  For as many dawns,
Before Your flowery faces,
  Before Your flowery countenances,
Wherever they borrow,
  Wherever they share,
Your back yard,
  Your side yard,
Wherever they leave their filth,
  Wherever they leave their rubbish,
Wherever they use,
  Wherever they consume,
The water of Your faces,
  The water of Your countenances,
Your bathing place,
  Your shampooing place,
Flowery holy king, holy angel,
  Holy snake, divine thunderbolt.
How much is it, My holy Father,
  How much is it, My holy Lord?
May You talk now in divine accord,

May You speak now in divine accord,
May it be accepted in divine accord,
    May it be received in divine accord,
The pittance,
    The trifle,
By the holy kings,
    By the holy angels,
By the holy snakes,
    By the divine thunderbolts,
By the flowery holy earth, holy heaven.
Take heed, holy wellspring,
    Holy headwater,
    My Lord!
May You accept for me in divine accord the
        pittance,
    The trifle.
It does not arrive in piles,
    It does not arrive in heaps,
Beside You,
    Before You,
It is just a pittance,
    it is just a trifle,
A drop now for Your lordly mouths,
    A drop now for Your lordly lips,
Say Your lowly children,
    Say Your humble offspring,
Beside You,
    Before You,
My great holy Father,
    My great holy Lord.
With this has ended Your great fiesta,
    Your grand festival.
Take heed, My holy Father,
    Take heed, My holy Lord!
How much is it now, My Father,
    How much is it now, My Lord,
Are the words in unison,
    Do the lips move in unison,
My great holy Father,
    My great holy Lord?
May I pass before Your faces now,
    May I pass before Your countenances now,
I have just prodded Your lordly noses,
    Your lordly ears,
My holy Father,
    My holy Lord,
Take heed, My Father,
    Take heed, My Lord!
How much is it now, My Father,
    How much is it now, My Lord,
Take heed, holy torch,
    Take heed, holy candle!
However much, My Father,
    However much, My Lord.

My lowly mouth has returned,
    My humble lips,
From Your lordly forum for talk,
    Your lordly forum for speech.
Are the words now in unison,
    Do the lips move now in unison,
Are You accepted in unison,
    Are You received in unison,
By the holy heaven,
By the holy ground,
    By the holy land,
The holy king, the holy angel,
    The holy snake, divine thunderbolt,
And the holy wellspring,
    And the holy headwater?
How much shall I give up now,
    How much shall I leave now?
Will You watch for me with care,
    Will You observe for me with care,
All the backs,
    All the sides,
Of Your lowly children,
    Your humble offspring,
That they may not yet be lost,
    That they may not yet be discarded,
That their backs not yet be struck,
    That their sides not yet be struck,
That, for my sake You not yet frighten their backs,
    That, for my sake, You not yet frighten their
        sides,
By Your seed,
    By Your kernel,
Watch over them now for me with care,
    Observe them now for me with care,
May You not frighten the backs,
    The sides,
Of the young,
    The old,
The round ones,
    The perched ones.[11]
For as long as they walk,
    For as long as they travel,
Shouting at dusk,
    Shouting at dawn,
Beside You,
    Before You,
Borrowing,
    Sharing,
The water of Your faces,
    The water of Your countenances,
Your bathing place,
    Your shampooing place,
    My holy Lord,
Talk now in divine accord,

Speak now in divine accord,
Watch still for me in divine accord,
    Observe still for me in divine accord,
All the backs,
    The sides,
Of Your lowly children,
    Your humble offspring,
Take heed, My Father,
    Take heed, My Lord!
May I pass before Your face,
    May I pass before Your countenance,
May You grant me holy pardon,
    May You grant me divine forgiveness,
When I am right,
    When I am not right,
When I reach,
    When I do not reach,
 Your lordly forum for talk,
    Your lordly forum for speech,
I, who am an utter dog,
    I, who am an utter pig,
My great holy Father,
    My great holy Lord.
Take heed, My Father,
    Take heed, My Lord!
May I pass before Your faces,
    May I pass before Your countenances,
In the holy name of the holy God,
    Jesus Christ, My Lord."

It is customary for a group of farmers working together in the lowlands to request that a shaman intercede for them; and so the Holy Cross Day rites may be preceded by a ceremony given before the clearing of the trees, undergrowth, or corn stubble, so that the farmers will work happily, without fear, protected from the threat of snakes. This field ceremony is no longer practiced with frequency, but the Holy Cross Day prayers are still generally followed by a set of three field ceremonies.

In each case if there is no shaman in the group then one of the farmers is asigned to call on a shaman. Presenting him with a bottle of cane liquor, they decide how many crosses should be made. The major shrine may be in the center of the cornfield, at the foot of an old tree, especially a fig (**mutut**), that is believed to have "soul" (**ch'ulel**), or at a nearby cave. A date is set and agreement is made to pay for the shaman's transportation and food.

One person per group is sent to bring the candles and flowers, and one to bring food and liquor. Two wax and two tallow candles are brought for each cross, two pine tips, two geranium flowers, and pine needles. Sufficient aguardiente must be brought for the three rounds drunk at each cross.

A shrine is also prepared at the campsite where offerings are made after returning from the other shrines. Here they eat a meal, usually of chicken.

There is no need for the same shaman to serve at each of the ceremonies. If a shaman cannot be found, then all the older farmers pray together as best they can.

The first ceremony in this set is held just prior to planting. As in the Holy Cross Day prayers, the shaman requests that his clients be protected from all danger, including snakes. He asks that water be granted for their crop so they may gain a handful, a fistful of the corn on which they depend for life.

"Despite their filth,
    Despite their rubbish,
The nothing can not be,
    The nil can not be."

"In the holy name of the holy God,
    Jesus Christ, My Lord,
Take heed, My great holy Father,
    Take heed, My great holy Lord,
However much, holy earth, holy heaven,
    Holy land, holy ground,
Holy king, holy angel,
    Holy snake, divine thunderbolt,
Will it be well-accepted now,
    Will it be well-received now,
However much,
    However little,
Of the cause for Your fear,
    The cause of Your shame,
However many of our torches,
    However many of our candles?
Our heads were anxious,
    Our hearts were anxious,
How long shall we borrow,
    Shall we share,
Your back yards,
    Your side yards?
Shall nothing yet harm our backs,
    Shall nothing yet harm our sides,
Have You not yet frightened our backs,
    Our sides,
Have our backs not yet been struck,
    Have our sides not yet been struck,
However much here beside You,
    Here before You?
Here we scatter,
    Here we strew,
Your lordly sunbeams,
    Your lordly shadows,
Here in Your back yards,
    Here in Your side yards,
Here where our brushhooks descended,
    Here where our digging sticks descended,
Here where we leave our hardship,
    Here where we leave our suffering,
Beside You,

Before You,
My great holy Father,
  My great holy Lord.
Take heed, My Father,
  Take heed, My Lord!
Will You talk in unison,
  Will You speak in unison,
Will You decide for me now with one accord,
  Will You consider for me with one accord,
Will we borrow equally,
  Will we share equally,
The water of Your faces,
  The water of Your countenances,
Your lordly bathing places,
  Your lordly shampooing places?
For my sake will You sprinkle with divine care,
  For my sake will You water with divine care,
One of Your sunbeams,
  One of Your shadows,
Which now we scatter,
  Which now we strew,
Beside You,
  Before You?
Shall we still get,
  Shall we still receive,
A handful,
  A fistful,
Of Your lordly sunbeams,
  Your lordly shadows?
Despite their filth,[12]
  Despite their rubbish,
The nothing can not be,
  The nil can not be,
The cold hunger can not be,
  The cold thirst can not be,
A single one can not be,
  A half one can not be.
We can walk,
  We can travel,
With our fathers,
  With our mothers,
With our elder brothers,
  With our younger brothers,
Until our bellies are full,
  Until our hearts are full,
 Until we have received,
  Until we have possessed,
Your lordly sunbeams,
  Your lordly shadows,
You who are Our great holy Fathers,
  You who are Our great holy Mothers,
Take heed, My Father,
  Take heed, My Lord!
May the words be now in unison,

May the lips move now in unison,
May it be accepted in divine accord,
  May it be received in divine accord,
However much,
  However little,
With the lord, Our Saviour,
In the center of heaven,
  In the center of paradise,
However much, My holy Father,
  However much, my holy Lord,
Will You accept for me in unison,
  Will You receive for me in unison,
The pittance,
  The trifle,
Will the holy tabletop arrive,
  Will the divine tabletop arrive,
There, beside You now,
  There, before You now?
Will You talk together now in unison,
  Will You speak together now in unison,
With St. Michael Archangel,
  In the center of heaven,
With St. Michael Archangel,
  In the center of paradise?
However much, my holy Father,
  However much, My holy Lord,
Will You decide for me now with one accord,
  Will You consider for me now with one accord,
For my sake will You still sprinkle equally,
  For my sake will You still water equally,
Your lordly sunbeams,
  Your lordly shadows?
Here where we leave our hardship,
  Here where we leave our suffering,
We brush off our sweat,
  We brush off our water,
Beside You,
  Before You,
Our ten fingers ache,
  Our ten toes ache,[13]
Here beside You,
  Here before You,
You who are Our great holy Fathers,
  You who are our great holy Mothers,
Will You still favor our backs for me,
  Will You still favor our sides for me,
Will they still be spilled,
  Will they still be scattered,
All our ashes,
  All our dust,[14]
We, who are Your lowly orphans,
  We, who are Your humble foundlings,
Your ashes,
  Your dust.

May You bear the hardship, My Fathers,
  May You bear the hardship, My Lords,
To watch still for me with care,
  To observe still for me with care,
All the backs,
  All the sides,[15]
Of Your sunbeams,
  Your shadows,
You who are Our great holy Fathers,
  You who are Our great holy Mothers,
  My Lord.
For my sake will You still sprinkle them,
  For my sake will You still water them,
My great holy Father,
  My great holy Lord?
May You talk together in divine accord,
  Speak together,
With the flowery holy earth,
  Flowery holy heaven,
Holy land, holy ground,
  Holy king, holy angel,
Holy snake, divine thunderbolt.
Take heed, My Father,
  Take heed, My Lord!
Is the divine talk in accord,
  Is the divine speech in accord,
May nothing harm our backs,
  May nothing harm our sides,
May You not frighten our backs,
  May You not frighten our sides,
Here beside You,
  Here before You,
For my sake still set aside with care,
  For my sake still push aside with care,
Your seed,
  Your kernel.
May You not frighten our backs,
  May You not frighten our sides,
You who are Our great holy Fathers,
  You who are Our great holy Mothers.
So we have left the pittance
  We have abandoned the trifle,
For this we have come with anxious heads,
  For this we have come with anxious hearts,
However much,
  However little,
The cause for Your fear,
  The cause for Your shame,
Here beside You,
  Here before You,
Grant a little pardon.
  A bit,
Our torch,
  Our candle,

Our chunk of incense,
  Our cloud of smoke,
Our lowly flower,
  Our humble leaf,
We have nothing in piles,
  We have nothing in heaps,
We, who are Your lowly orphans,
  We, who are Your humble foundlings,
We, who are Your ashes,
  We, who are Your dust.
Holy name of the holy God,
  Jesus Christ, My Lord.
May I pass before Your faces,
  May I pass before Your countenances,
You who are My great holy Fathers,
  You who are My great holy Mothers.
May You stand erect in divine unison,
  May You stand firm in divine unison,
Holy name of the holy God,
  Jesus Christ, My Lord."

Drinking cane liquor:

"In the holy name of the holy God,[16]
  Jesus Christ, My Lord,
Take heed, My Father,
  Take heed, My Lord!
However much now, My Father,
  However much now, My Lord.
There is still a pittance,
  There is still a trifle,
Of the cause for Your fear,
  Of the cause for Your shame,
The first of Your shot glasses,
  The first of Your pitchers,
  My Lord.
The dew of Your lordly mouths,
  The dew of Your lordly lips,
However much I give up now,
  However much I leave now,
Of our lowly torches,
  Our humble candles,
Beside You,
  Before You,
Flowery holy earth,
  Flowery holy heaven,
Flowery holy land, holy ground,
  Holy king, holy angel,
Holy snake, divine thunderbolt.
May I pass before Your face,
  May I pass before Your countenance,
I receive it first, My Father,
  I receive it first, My Lord!"

The second ceremony is given at the time of the second

weeding (if two weedings are still carried out), usually around the Fiesta of St. Dominic (4 August), when high winds are frequent. The shaman implores the same host of deities to be ever watchful, to protect his clients from the witches who wish to play in their cornfields. He asks the gods to deflect the winds, lest his clients' labor, their hardship and suffering be in vain. Finally, he asks,

"That nothing harm,
    Nothing befall,
Your lordly sunbeams,
    Your lordly shadows."

"In the holy name of the holy God,
    Jesus Christ, My Lord,
Take heed, My great holy Father,
    Take heed, My great holy Lord!
How much is it now, My Father,
    How much is it My Lord,
Flowery holy earth, holy heaven,
    Holy ground, holy land,
Holy king, holy angel,
How much is it, My Father,
    How much is it, My Lord,
Will it be well-accepted now,
    Will it be well-received now,
However much,
    However little,
I give up now,
    I leave now,
Here beside You,
    here before You,
Here where our ten toes ache,
    Here where our ten fingers ache,
Here, beside You,
    Here, before You,
    My Lord,
Take heed, My Father,
    Take heed, My Lord!
Will You stand erect in divine goodness,
    Will You stand firm in divine goodness,
Will You still watch for me with care,
    Will you still observe for me with care,
Your lordly sunbeams,
    Your lordly shadows?
Will nothing yet harm them,
    Will nothing yet befall them?
May it not yet arise now,
    May it not yet pass now,
earthly seeming good,
    The earthly evil,
The fiery heart,
    The crimson heart.[17]
With divine care still shield them from it, for me,
    With divine care still deflect it from them, for

me,
May it still pass by on high,
    May it still pass by aloft,
The seeming good,
    The evil,
Over the backs,
    Over the sides,
Of Your lordly sunbeams,
    Your lordly shadows,
Watch over them still for me at dusk,
    Watch over them still for me at dawn,
My great holy Father,
    My great holy Lord.
For my sake divert from them still the path,
    For my sake divert from them still the course,
Of the seeming good,
    The evil,
The fiery-hearted,
    The crimson-hearted,
By a distant mountain,
    By a distant ridge,
    May it pass.
My great holy Father,
    My great holy Lord.
Not yet now over the backs,
    Not yet now over the sides,
of Your lordly sunbeams,
    Your lordly shadows,
My great holy Father,
    My great holy Lord.
For this I beg now holy pardon,
    For this I beg now divine forgiveness,
Beside You,
    Before You,
Flowery holy earth,
    Flowery holy heaven.
Take heed, My Father,
    Take heed, My Lord!
Talk now in divine accord,
    Speak now in divine accord,
With the holy Father, holy St. Lawrence,
    My great holy Father,
Father St. Lawrence,
    My great holy Lord.
However much, My Father,
    However much, My Lord,
However many of Your shining faces,
    However many of Your gleaming counte-
        nances,
My holy Father,
    My holy Lord,
I reach with talk,
    I reach with speech,
However much for my pittance,

However much for my trifle,
Our lowly torches,
    Our humble candles,
With which we beg holy pardon,
    With which we beg divine forgiveness.
Will nothing harm the backs,
    Will nothing harm the sides,
Of Your lordly sunbeams,
    Your lordly shadows,
That we have scattered here,
    That we have strewn here,
On top of Your flowery faces,
    On top of Your flowery countenances?[18]
You who are Our great holy Fathers,
    You who are Our great holy Mothers,
Here in a distant land,
    Here in a distant place.
But may Your flowery faces not be far away,
    But may Your flowery countenances not be far
        away.[19]
In unison watch over them for me,
    In unison observe them for me,
In unison shield them from it, for me,
    In unison deflect it from them, for me,
The seeming good,
    The evil,
The fiery-hearted,
    The crimson-hearted.
May it not pass, the seeming good,
    The evil,
Over the backs,
    Over the sides,
May they not provide the playground,
    May they not provide the amusement place,[20]
Of the seeming good,
    The evil,
However many beside,
    However many before,
Your lordly sunbeams,
    Your lordly shadows.
My great holy Father,
    My great holy Lord,
Watch over them for me with care,
    Observe them for me with care,
My holy Father,
    My holy Lord.
For my sake will You still favor here our backs,
    Our sides.
We are satisfied with a handful,
    A fistful,
Of Your lordly sunbeams,
    Your lordly shadows,
My holy Father,
    My holy Lord.

May it not be in vain that we bear the hardship,
    May it not be in vain that we endure the
        suffering,
May it not be in vain that we brush off our sweat,
    May it not be in vain that we brush off our
        water.
For my sake, favor our backs,
    For my sake, favor our sides,
May it not play,
    May it not rejoice,
The seeming good,
    The evil.
May it pass by on high,
    May it pass by aloft,
Over a distant mountain,
    Over a distant ridge,
May its path be detoured,
    May its course be detoured,
You who are Our Holy Fathers,
    You who are Our holy Mothers,
Take heed, My Father,
    Take heed, My Lord!
May You talk together now in unison,
    May You speak together in unison,
With the holy lord, Our Savior in the center of
    heaven,
    With the Lord, Our Saviour in the center of
        paradise.
However much now, My Father,
    However much now, My Lord,
Your faces are shining,
    Your countenances are gleaming,
However much we beg holy pardon,
    We beg divine forgiveness,
Beside You,
    Before You,
With the flowery holy earth,
    Flowery holy heaven,
Flowery holy land, holy ground,
    Holy king, holy angel.
However much, My holy Father,
    However much, my holy Lord.
Will You accept for me now in unison,
    Will You receive for me now in unison,
The pittance,
    The trifle?
Nothing comes in piles,
    Nothing comes in heaps,
We are a pittance now,
    We are a trifle now,
We beg holy pardon,
    We beg divine forgiveness,
Here, beside You,

Here, before You,
Will You watch for me with care,
  Will You observe for me with care,
Your lordly sunbeams,
  Your lordly shadows,
That nothing yet harm,
  That nothing yet befall them.
May it not yet arise,
  May it not yet pass,
The seeming good,
  The evil,
The fiery-hearted,
  The crimson-hearted.
May it not yet be the playground of the seeming
    good,
  May it not yet be the playground of the evil,
By the backs,
  By the sides,
Of Your lordly sunbeams,
  Your lordly shadows,
Stand erect in goodness,
  Stand firm in goodness,
Watch over them for me with care,
  Observe them for me with care,
My great holy Father,
  My great holy Lord,
May You bear the hardship,
  The suffering,
Deflect for me,
  Divert for me,
However much the seeming good,
  However much the evil,
My great holy Father,
  My great holy Lord,
Pardon, My Father,
  Pardon, My Lord.
However much now, My Father,
  However much now, My Lord,
Flowery holy earth, holy heaven,
  Holy ground, holy land.
Will it be well-accepted now,
  Will it be well-received now,
The pittance,
  The trifle,
Our lowly torch,
  Our humble candle,
Our chunk of incense,
  Our cloud of smoke,
Our flower,
  Our leaf,
That we have come to give up,
  Come to leave,
Beside you,
  Before you.

So, our heads are anxious,
  Our hearts are anxious,
Over the pittance,
  The trifle,
That nothing harm,
  Nothing befall,
Your lordly sunbeams,
  Your lordly shadows,
You who are Our holy Fathers,
  You who are Our holy Mothers.
Take heed, my Father,
  Take heed, my Lord!
In unison watch over for me,
  In unison observe for me,
Where our brushhooks have descended,
  Where our digging sticks have descended,
For this we came with anxious heads,
  For this we came with anxious hearts,
With our elder brothers,
  With our younger brothers,
With My Father,
  With My Lord,
  My Lord.
May You bear the hardship,
  The suffering,
Protect for me Your lordly sunbeams,
  Protect for me Your lordly shadows,
For my sake do not discard them, My Father,
  For my sake do not discard them, My Lord.
For this we beg holy pardon,
  Divine forgiveness.
Take heed, My Father,
  Take heed, My Lord!
Grant a little holy pardon,
  Grant a bit of holy pardon,
Here, beside You,
  Here, before You.
We have brought nothing in piles,
  We have brought nothing in heaps,
We are a pittance,
  We are a trifle,
So we beg holy pardon,
Beside You,
  Before You.
Holy name, holy God,
  Jesus Christ, My Lord,
May I pass before Your face,
  Before Your countenance,
My great holy Father,
  My great holy Lord."

The third ceremony is celebrated before the harvest. Mindful
of the necessity of bearing bags of corn on steep slopes where
a fall could be fatal, the shaman pleads again for protection for

his clients. He asks that the gods not be angry, that they not let the corn hide itself from his clients' hands, that the gods not permit the witches to carry off what is the rightful due of his clients.

"Give to our feet now,
   To our hands now,
The pittance,
   The trifle."

"In the holy name of the Holy God,
   Jesus Christ, My Lord,
Take heed, My great holy Father,
   Take heed, My great holy Lord!
However much now, My Father,
   However much now, My Lord,
Flowery holy earth, holy heaven,
   Holy ground, holy land,
Holy king, holy angel,
   Holy snake, divine thunderbolt,
However long now, My Father,
   However long now, My Lord,
That I come kneeling,
   Come bowed low,
Beside You, now,
   Before You, now,
Will it be well-accepted now,
   Will it be well-received now,
However much the pittance,
   However much the trifle,
The cause for Your fear,
   The cause for Your shame,
Our lowly torches,
   Our humble candles,
With which we beg holy pardon,
   With which we beg divine forgiveness?
However many we carry away now,
   However many we take away now,
Of Your Lordly sunbeams,
   Your lordly shadows,
Holy Father,
   My holy Lord,
Will You deliver to our ten toes,
   To our ten fingers?
Will You favor our backs,
   Will You favor our sides,
Will You favor for me our backs,
   Our sides,
You who are Our holy Fathers,
   You who are Our holy Mothers?
Take heed, My Father,
   Take heed, My holy Lord!
Will we get from here,
   Will we take from here,
The handful,

The fistful,
Of Your lordly sunbeams,
   Your lordly shadows,
My great holy Father,
   My great holy Lord?
Take heed, holy earth, holy heaven!
 For this we beg holy pardon,
   For this we beg divine forgiveness,
So we come now with a pittance,
   So we come now with a trifle,
With our elder brothers,
   With our younger brothers,
With my father,
   With my mother,
However much now, My Father,
   However much now, My Lord.
We have reached the hour,
   We have reached the day,
To carry away,
   To take away,
Your lordly sunbeams,
   Your lordly shadows,
Here, beside You,
   Here, before You,
My holy Father,
   My holy Lord.
Take heed, My Father,
   Take heed, My Lord!
However much now, My Father,
   However much now, My Lord,
May You bear the hardship,
   The suffering,
To release for my Your lordly sunbeams,
   To release for me Your lordly shadows,
To give them to our feet,
   To give them to our hands.
May You not set them aside,
   May You not hide them from me,
You who are Our holy Fathers,
   You who are Our holy Mothers,
Holy earth,
   Holy heaven,
Holy ground, holy land,
Take heed, My holy Father,
   Take heed, My holy Lord!
So we are a pittance,
   So we are a trifle now,
However much, My holy Lord,
Will You watch over them for me in unison,
   Will You observe them for me in unison,
Where we pile them up,
   Where we set them down,
Your lordly sunbeams,
   Your lordly shadows,

May seeming good not appear,
  May evil not appear,
May the fiery-hearted not appear,
  May the crimson-hearted not appear,
Shield them for me with care,
  Deflect them for me with care,
Divert them for me with care,
 However much, My Father,
  My Lord.
However much the pittance,
  However much the trifle,
For my sake give them not to their feet,
  For my sake give them not to their hands,
However many of Your lordly sunbeams,
  However many of Your lordly shadows.
Give to our feet now,
  To our hands now,
The pittance,
  The trifle,
For this I come kneeling,
  For this I come bending low,
So we come to carry,
  Come to take,
Come to gather Your lordly sunbeams,
  Come to gather Your lordly shadows,
Here, beside You,
  Here, before You,
However many we have scattered here,
  However many we have strewn here,
However much we bore our hardship here,
  However much we endured our suffering here,
Here, where we brushed off our sweat,
  Here where we brushed off our water,
My great holy Father,
  My great holy Lord.
Take heed, My Father,
  Take heed, My Lord!
May Your head not grow angry,
  May Your heart not grow angry,
Now for this comes our pittance,
  Now for this comes our trifle,
For this come our lowly torches,
  For this come our humble candles,
For this comes our chunk of incense,
  For this comes our cloud of smoke,
For this comes our flower,
  For this comes our leaf,
However much before Your faces,
  However much before Your countenances,
We carry away Your lordly sunbeams,
  We carry away Your lordly shadows,
  My Lord.
Will You release their backs for me,
  Will You release their sides for me,

May You not hide them from me, My Father,
  May You not hide them from me, My Lord.
For this we beg holy pardon,
  Divine forgiveness,
For this our heads were anxious,
  For this our hearts were anxious,
For this comes our pittance,
  For this comes our trifle,
 Beside You,
  Before You.
Talk in one accord,
  Speak in one accord now,
With the holy center of heaven,
  With the holy center of paradise,
However much now, My Father,
  However much now, My Lord.
Will the pittance be accepted in one accord,
  Will the trifle be accepted in one accord,
With the Lord, holy Saviour, My Father,
  Lord, holy Saviour, My Lord?
Will the holy tabletop now,
  Will the divine tabletop now,
The pittance,
  The trifle,
Our lowly torches,
  Our humble candles,
With which we beg holy pardon,
  Divine forgiveness,
Here before Thy flowery faces,
  Here before Thy flowery countenances,
My great holy Father,
  My great holy Lord?
Take heed, My Father,
  Take heed, My Lord!
Will the words be now in unison,
  Will the lips move now in unison,
For my sake wilt Thou favor our backs,
  Our sides,
However much before Thy faces,
  Before Thy countenances,
We take Thy lordly sunbeams,
  We take Thy lordly shadows,
We gather them together,
  We set them together,
  My Lord.
Will our poverty be watched over in holiness,
  Our scraps,
Now will we take them away,
  Now will we carry them off,
The pittance,
  The trifle,
  My Lord?
For my sake wilt Thou favor our backs,
  For my sake wilt Thou favor our sides,

Will our ashes fall off here,
  Our dust?
We who are Your orphans,
  We who are Your foundlings,
Your ashes,
  Your dust,
However long at dusk,
  However long at dawn,
Before Your flowery faces,
  Before Your flowery countenances,
My great holy Father,
  My great holy Lord!
Take heed, My Father,
  Take heed, My Lord,
Grant a holy pardon now, in unison,
  Grant divine forgiveness now, in unison,
We brought nothing in piles,
  We brought nothing in heaps,
With a pittance,
  With a trifle,
A drop now for Your mouths,
  A drop now for Your lips,
Holy name of the holy God,
  Jesus Christ, My Lord.
Take heed, My Father,
  Take heed, My Lord!
However much now, My Father,
  However much now, My Lord,
May I pass before Your face now,
  May I pass before Your countenance now.
I have just finished giving up,
  I have just finished leaving,
The pittance,
  The trifle,
Beside You,
  Before You,

Holy name of the holy God,
  Jesus Christ, My Lord."

Notes

[1] This, and the prayers that follow were intoned at lightning speed by Antzelmo Peres Peres in my house. Had they been recorded on site they would have been infinitely longer, but their content would have remained essentially the same. See Tzotzil original in Appendix 8.

[2] This verse refers to the Earth Lords.

[3] This is corn.

[4] Flower and leaf refer to cane liquor.

[5] These are the tutelary gods.

[6] Seeds and kernels are snakes.

[7] Sunbeams and shadows are corn.

[8] Heavenly woman, heavenly lady is the Virgin Mary. The purchaser of heaven, of paradise, is Christ.

[9] The tabletop refers to the offerings on the table.

[10] The martyr is St. Sebastian.

[11] The round ones, the perched ones are children.

[12] Even though people defecate and dirty the gods' yards, they must eat tortillas.

[13] This is literally, "ten hands" and "ten feet."

[14] Will his clients die?

[15] As if they had human form, the shaman refers to the backs and sides of the corn plants.

[16] After a brief pause, the shaman takes the glass and, holding it, recites the following lines. The last verse is a toast, after which he swallows the cane liquor.

[17] This verse refers to witches.

[18] This is the earth's surface.

[19] Here the shaman pleads that although the cornfields are far from home the gods remain with them.

[20] May the witches not make sport with their cornfields by sending wind.

Lordly Sunbeams, Lordly Shadows

Robert M. Laughlin

The techniques and economics of Zinacantec corn farming have merited three monographs (Cancian, 1965, 1972; Collier, 1975). Here I offer a handful of personal views. The first two are drawn from Xun Teratol, a young corn farmer, who describes the hardships and care required by milpa agriculture. The second and third come from my field notes, which tell of bean planting and corn harvesting with my *compadre*, Petul Vaskes, a man no longer young. (I do not mention here how, doubled over with stomach pain, I endured the bean-planting trip only three days before fleeing to the highlands). Whereas Xun Teratol spoke of the physical hardship and the details of handling corn and the natural environment, these accounts show the demands made of Zinacantecs by farming in the lowlands that are owned and controlled by a dominant *ladino* society. The fourth view is provided by Petul Vaskes' ancient father, Xun, as he reminisces about the famine of 1918—divine punishment, he believes, of "Everyman's" ill-treatment of holy corn.

Learning to Grow Corn
(Xun Teratol)

"We'll tell what cornfield work is like.

"When I first went to work, I went to clear the forest. My late father sent me and a worker to a place west of Acala. And we carried our tortillas and our *posol*. But it was terribly far away, as we went on foot. We started from Zinacantán Center and continued on to the lowlands.

"When we arrived, it was about three o'clock in the afternoon.

"We ate. When we finished we went to look for wood for our billhook handles, because my worker knew what kind of wood was strong. But as for me, I didn't know what was the strongest for a billhook handle. We went into the forest to look for billhook handles because, 'Tomorrow we'll start working early,' said my worker.

"Well, I went, went to look for the billhook handle. My worker told me that the best was **kanéla te'**. It was **kanéla te'** that we used. But (the handle) was stuck in very tight, and a nail was driven in at the back of the billhook.

"The next day we began work. But the land was very steep.

"We began at the bottom, because you can't work from the top down, you have to work upwards.

"As there were large trees they were felled by ax, but the small ones were felled with a billhook.

"But the underbrush was cleared first carefully. When we finished clearing the underbrush then came the ax. We just worked with axes. But yes, indeed, it's harder with axes, less so with billhooks, because the billhook is just for the brush under the trees.

"Then I found the ax very hard. I told my worker that and he felled the big trees. But one day of work was very difficult. My hands got terribly blistered. The second day was even harder, but by the fifth or sixth day it was all right. (My hands) just got used to it. The two of us cleared for 11 days.

"Then [the wood] dries out for four weeks. And then we went to burn the wood. We went to light the fire underneath, but we had a good fire lane around the sides of the cleared land. When the fire came along it burnt well, but the fire didn't run away. But it was very scary. When we finished burning that was the end of the clearing of the forest. But the weeding is more difficult then [on newly burnt land]. It was finished. Then it was planted. Five to six seeds per hole. The clearing took 11 days for only two quarts of seed. When the planting was finished we returned. Again I went with just the same worker.

"Then it seems we returned home. We arrived to eat together. But we ate chicken. Because that is what the proper way is, it can't be any old meal, because they say that is the way corn will be planted well. Because, you see, chickens have long toes. And [with the meal we had] one shot of cane liquor apiece. That's all.

"But when that was over we went for the replanting, because so much of the seed corn doesn't come up. But I was the only corn farmer [around], there weren't many corn farmers. But it was terribly scary, because I didn't have many companions.

"The replanting of the cornfield was over. I waited for the weeds to grow. When the weeds got thick, then I went to the weeding. I looked for a worker again, but it was just the same worker. But he was very strong-hearted, he wasn't ever scared. But we went again on foot. But the toasted tortillas and the *posol* were just carried on tumpline. It's true that trucks reached Acala, but we would have to climb back up and walk very far. That's why it would be about the same if we went the whole way on foot.

"Well, we arrived, we looked for wood for our hoe handles. My worker looked for **tux-nuk' te'**, but I looked for **akit**. But it was no good, it was very soft. It only lasted four days, but the **tux-nuk' te'** is harder. I just changed my hoe handle, it couldn't finish the work. But I thought this was very hard, too, as this was the first time I learned how to work. But it was because my

68

FIGURE 15.—Breaking ground in Zinacantán Center, 1977. (Photo by John Swope.)

worker was kind and showed me how to do the work. But my father never showed me what the clearing and the planting were like. I never saw. So I asked my worker to teach me. But he worked very fast. But, as for me, I couldn't keep up with the way he worked. But my worker hurried terribly. But I, who was supposed to be the boss, just fell way behind. Then he worked slowly, he would rest from time to time. But no matter what, I couldn't keep up, because I had never learned before how to work. But it was so painful, too. That's how it was. We worked at the weeding for two weeks. But my father also said, 'Go double the corn, plant beans under the corn!' When the cornfield had dried out well, that was when the time came for bean planting. I looked for a companion, or a worker, as we say.

"We went and doubled the corn. But the bean planting was not so hard. The work is easier.

"First we doubled the corn, when that was over we scraped the ground for beans. We did the scraping one week before we planted. But the beans are planted closer together, not like corn. Three or four beans are planted together. But that wasn't so hard. Planting beans is easier work. Then we came back up. That's the way the bean planting ended. And then we went again when the beans and the corn had dried well. We went to look. But then we did the harvest and then we flailed the beans. But first we pulled up the bean plants, because if the bean plants are sitting there and the corn harvest is first, that's not right, because we musn't step on the beans or the pods will pop open. That's why the bean-pulling comes first. But the bean-pulling must be done early. It can't be done the whole day, because the sun gets too hot and the pods pop. It should be stopped at 10 or 11 o'clock and then the bean-flailing starts. That's the way it is every day until it's finished. When that is over then we can begin the corn harvest.

"Then we began the corn harvest. But it was difficult, too, because the land was so steep. We just carried half a bag of ears of corn.

"We were in the lowlands for three weeks. But it was hard to finish the harvest, it was so slow, because [the land] was so steep. When the ground is level then it's much better. We can walk easily with a whole bag. But the way that was, you couldn't, you were afraid you would fall with it. But little by little it was finished.

"Well, when all the corn was ready, then we carried it to the side of the highway, there near Acala. But it was terribly hard to bring it out, because we just brought it out by tumpline. The beans and the corn were just carried out on our heads. But it took a long time, because there were just two of us, me and my worker, the one who started the clearing. And it was he who worked until the corn was harvested and until it arrived at my house. But we did our best with the burden. We tried to get horses, but no luck. In Acala there are oxen that pull carts, but the cart couldn't get [to the field]. A horse could get in if there were any, but there weren't. That's why it came out with such difficulty on our heads. We borrowed the house of a *ladino* there on the roadside near Acala.

"When we were ready we looked for a truck to go to the

FIGURE 16.—Farmer with herbicide sprayer, 1983. (Photo by John B. Haviland.)

house. Well, that's how I worked to the west of Acala. But I found it very hard, and besides, this was the first time that I tried out to see what the work was like. When that was over I just abandoned the land. Then I went to the west of Concordia. And I went to see where beans grew well, where the land was good. But then it was fine. I learned how to do all the work. Now I know how to clear the forest, and how to plant corn, weeding, or bean planting. Now it's fine. But the clearing and the weeding is harder. Weeding by hoe is hard. But now I can take the clearing. I just do the weeding with weed killer. But that's not so hard. It's not like where a hoe is needed. Everyone who works in the cornfield does it the same way, because now we've seen how weed killer works."

How to Grow Corn
(Xun Teratol)

"Well, we'll talk about the right way to work; the clearing, the planting, the weeding—the way I prepared my cornfield to the west of Ocozocuautla this year.

"Well, I got ready. I looked for my workers. Three workers and two of us, too, with my younger brother, five of us in all.

"We went together, two Chamulas and one countryman. But first it was the clearing, but it wasn't big trees, no, just small ones that can be chopped with a billhook or a machete. My workers just used billhooks, but I used a machete. But if the trees are bigger a billhook is needed.

"When we started to work, it's the boss who takes the lead, it's he who watches how the work is going. Because it was my work, I watched carefully to see how my work was going. We began at the bottom of the work, not at the top or the sides, at the lower ground because the land was a bit steep. But if it's level we can work wherever we want, but that was a bit steep, but just a little bit. It was flat enough so we could work on it. We cleared as we went up, but not very fast and not very slowly, the work was at a good pace. I directed my workers [to stand] at my side. I was the first, then the others lined up. But the paid workers don't want to work too hard; they learned how I worked. If I worked slowly, they would work slowly, too. But they didn't want to do the work well, just when they felled [a tree], that's all. 'But no, that's no good,' I told them. 'But work well, cut up the trees well!' I told them. But some wanted to obey me and some didn't. But if the boss isn't there, the workers don't care at all. The clearing needs to have [the trees] chopped well and cut up into small pieces, not just lying on their branches. No, the trees should be pushed to the ground. If the trees aren't cut up into little pieces they won't burn. But if they are left well-chopped, then fine! Then they will surely burn, so that they turn to ash. But if they are chopped carelessly, then they won't burn at all.

"One day I went to work for the owner [of the land]. I went to fix his fences. But the next day [when I came back] I looked at my work. But it was terrible; they hadn't chopped [the trees] properly. Some of the trees weren't cut. But it was me who took a second look. I cut them so they would burn well and dry out quickly. But if they are just felled, they won't dry out quickly. But if the boss doesn't care, the workers are delighted by it. But that's the way it is. The trees should be pushed well to the ground and cut into pieces, with their branches lopped off.

"When the clearing was over, we came back [home]. And then we went to do the burning, but we went together with the other corn farmers. We did the burning together. But first we set fire to the top. Two of us lit the fire, and one at each side of the cleared land. But we began at the top. The others just had fun watching. Because first there should be the firelane fire around the cleared land. Then when it is set afire at the bottom, then the fire gets going, then the fire gathers strength. Gradually it gets strong. But if it gets strong, the smoke grows black and it burns well. Where the fire didn't pass by, I lit it again, but it caught well, because it was well-chopped. If it isn't properly chopped, it is left poking up, but that's bad. But when it is chopped correctly, then it burns indeed. That's how the burning ended.

"Then we went to do the fencing. Any kind of tree will do if it is planted when the moon is full. We made the fence. The posts were an armspan apart, and the posts were two meters tall.

"When the fencing was finished we went to do the planting. We took our seed with us. I got workers, too. I told them how many seeds should be planted [per hole], just four or five corn kernels. But each hole should be a meter apart, and the rows the same distance apart. But some people plant quickly and some don't. As for me, I can just plant a quart a day, but some can do more than a quart. Each has his own way. But one quart *has* to be planted. But there are workers who don't know how to work, they plant too close, but that's bad, they're crowded together. And there are others who plant too far apart, but that's wrong, too. It should be done just right. Well, that's all.

"Then there is the weeding. But the weeding wasn't too hard, because it was rocky and hoes couldn't be used. I just put weed killer on it. But where the land is good, a hoe is fine. But there is a correct way with hoes, too. Where we find good land, fine, if we do the work, but some people don't care about their work. But no, as for weeding with a hoe, there are those who just turn the ground over, roll it over and don't scatter it. And it can be well-scattered, too. There are three ways. One kind is just pulled up and pulled up, it just lies sitting. And also there is the kind if the [ground] is well-scraped up at the foot of the corn plants and they don't scrape it up in the middle. But they leave it well-covered. But no, that's not right. What is good is if the weeds are shaken out, so long as the whole [field] is hoed, not just around the foot of the corn plants. The weeds [should be] shaken out properly and left lying on the ground. But it isn't necessary to leave them piled up in the middle, no! They can't be left scattered, but so long as they are well-shaken out. Then if they feel the sun for a minute they'll die right off. But if they are with their dirt they won't die, because, you see, the weeds' roots are still clinging to the dirt. Then if a nor'easter comes, they'll revive right away, they won't die. They'll stay the same. But it wasn't worth a thing. It's true it was worth it for a little while, but not for long. [The weeds] just change places. But that's no use. It's better if the weeds are well-shaken out. But they should be left lying on top of the ground. That's really good, and it suits the corn better. And people also use a billhook, but that's if the ground isn't good. But the billhook isn't used just on little [weeds], it's for when they are already big, when the weeds have reached our knees. Then it's better, but just a little. Weed killer is still better, but just a little bit, too. What is best is the hoe. Well, that's all.

"For bean planting a hoe must be used, it is better. But the weeds are scraped up well. They are left in the rows of corn stubble, but not between the rows. It's good if there are no weeds at all. That's better, indeed. But there are just three or four beans per hole, the same distance as the corn stubble. Two rows of beans are put in. But they are not weeded. Just the place is weeded and planted, that's all. Then if [the bean plant] dries out, when it dries out it is pulled up. [The beans] are pulled with their stems and their leaves. They aren't picked. It is the pole bean that is picked, as it can't be pulled out, because it is fastened to the corn stubble. Now the kind that is pulled out with its leaves is called bush bean. When it is pulled out it is left in little piles. It is gathered up later. But first a threshing floor is made, where the beans will be flailed. When it is ready, we pile them up at the edge of the threshing floor, when we have finished gathering them up.

"A burlap bag is spread out on the threshing floor. When that is done, then the beans are scooped up and flailed. But just two people to a threshing floor. Then when we see the beans are well flailed we shake them out. The flail is rather thin, not very thick. If they are well-flailed we toss out [the pods], as many as we get in a day. And then we gather the beans when [the flailing] is over. Then they are winnowed. But they are not winnowed in a basket, just on a piece of plastic or a burlap bag, whatever there is. They are just spread out there on the threshing floor. We feel which direction the wind is coming from. We pay good attention to that. Wherever the wind lands, that's where we stretch out the plastic or the burlap. But we are behind the beans. They must be thrown up. When we throw them up, the dirt doesn't land with them, but between us or where we are standing, throwing [them]. But they should be tossed up with a gourd. Then when they are winnowed well, they are put in a burlap bag. As much as there is is gathered up.

But that is the way it is every day until it is finished.

"Now when the bean pulling is over, then the corn harvest begins. If it is dry, if it isn't raining it is good for the harvest. Then it is fine to gather it up and make a pile of all [the corn]. But if it is raining [the corn] should be stacked in burlap bags and protected from the rain. It can't be put in piles, because it will sprout if it gets wet. But it needs a good threshing floor first, too. Because where I grow corn there it rains so much, that's why it just has to be stacked in burlap bags. But if there are several workers, we can divide up; some harvest and some flail, so that the ears of corn don't pile up. Because if it's just corn kernels they need less space. But when the harvest begins it's done two rows at a time, because if it's too many [rows] a lot of corn may be left behind.

"Now when the flailing is begun, first one looks for the posts for the sieve, and they are stuck in. Four cross poles [are needed] for where a rope is tied around the sieve. And there are four tall, but thin trees from which to hang the plastic or blanket or whatever is used to hold in the corn kernels. And a good ladder is needed because it is set up high.

"Now when they finish making [the platform], then the corn can be flailed. But because there are so many nor'easters there where I work, the corn to be flailed must be gathered up very

FIGURE 17.—Flailing corn in the highlands, 1976. (Photo by John B. Haviland.)

quickly. But where there are no nor'easters it's better when it accumulates. But where I work the corn kernels are gathered up as soon as they jump out. But just the same they must be quickly stuck in the bag. But the rotten ones must be selected out from the seed corn for the next year. But my corn is not winnowed in the lowlands, just at home, because people say that if it is winnowed in the lowlands its soul will remain there. So I have it arrive home to be winnowed.

If all the corn is ready, then one has to get a truck that will come all the way home. But it comes together with the corn, and that's all."

Lowland Bean Planting, 18–20 September 1980
(R. Laughlin)

"We left Naben Chauk at 7:30 A.M., Petul Vaskes, his son, Antun [my godchild], and their group leader, Mario Iyen [Guillén], a local *ladino* fully integrated into the culture.

"Three hours later, mostly by paved road, we reached Revolución Mexicana, where a few staples were bought, then on to the San Angel turnoff where we drove for about ten minutes before leaving the VW Safari. In the rainy season the next two leagues must be traveled on foot or by oxcart or horse.

The San Pedro river must be forded 5 times.

"At San Angel Mario asked a woman to pass the word to Petul's son, Manvel, who was coming by bus, that we had already arrived. He tossed a head of cabbage on the ground for her daughter to pick up.

"Then we met the wife and daughters of the *finca* owner on their oxcart. Mario gave them a bag of rolls and asked that they bring our bags of toasted tortillas, *posol*, etc., later in the day. We were given two *papausas,* left our bags at a neighboring house and were told that Manvel was already ahead of us. At the house where we left the car Mario had deposited a peach tree slip for the owner's son.

"At the first river crossing we met Manvel and Matyo, a compadre of Mario's. They had lit a fire to warm their tortillas. We ate both black and white tortillas, mashed beans, previously fried egg, and lead tree beans.

"We then stopped at a house where Mario gave the *ladino* owner a slug of cane liquor and a bag of bread, asking him to show us a small waterfall there.

"As we walked along, Mario identified tree after tree for my benefit. We finally arrived at Finca San Vicente, a tile-roofed house with a main room and a bedroom at each end. The parlor had an altar to St. Anthony, but was otherwise bare except for

FIGURE 18.—Lowland field house, corn harvest, 1976. (Photo by John B. Haviland.)

streamer-decorated ceiling and walls adorned with a mirror, old newspapers, and hardware store calendars boasting nude women. Wide corridors ran the length of the house. There was a cook house and small hut close by. Many chickens and a few turkeys ran up and down the front corridor.

"The old owner, his legs sticking out of torn pants, and his feet stuck in broken rubber boots, accepted a bag of bread and two plastic liter bottles of cane liquor that were given by Antun in request for a piece of forest and a guided tour of the spot. The old man, nearly toothless, was not eager to make the deal because a previous group of Zinacantecs had refused to cooperate in fixing the road or in giving him any field work. He demanded one day of labor.

"After the agreement was made we walked on towards Mario's fields, passing the house of one of the *finca* owner's sons where we left a bag of cookies. We passed through pine forest, and in the arroyos, tropical rain forest.

"Mario's fieldhouse was about 20′ long, 11′ wide, and 7′ high, thatched with palm. It was equipped with a metal wheelbarrow, a set of chairs, a metal cot, a radio, and a wide variety of household articles, even sheets!

"Petul's house was not so large, roofed with plastic sheeting. The floor had a gutter around it. The hearth, just wood, was at the entrance. From the roof pole hung 2 bags of toasted tortillas, 1 of *posol,* cotton blankets, extra shirts, pants, and tunics, hats, small bags of beans, dried chilies, and salt. The furniture was limited to 1 chair, 4 stools—one in the shape of a frog with mouth and eyes cut in it, and 1 petate.

"On the ground were scattered the agricultural implements: herbicide [4 cans of Transquat, 1 can of Hierbester], 4 axes, 3 machetes, 1 brush hook, 3 digging sticks, whetstones, flashlights, 3 tumplines, 2 plastic sheets, 1 large gourd, plastic bottles, one 5 gallon jerry can, plastic nets for carrying clothes, small nets and 1 plastic box for seed beans, bags of seed beans. There were 2 pairs of shoes. Cooking implements included 1 enamel pot, 3 clay pots, 3 enamel bowls, 1 large and 1 medium enamel spoon. There were several packs of cigarettes. The food supplies lying on the ground were limited to peaches, lead tree pods, small tomatoes, 1 head of cabbage and 1 onion. Later the food transported by oxcart arrived: 2 more bags of toasted tortillas, 3 bags of *posol,* 1 small bag of potatoes, 2 cabbage heads, 1 bag of salt, and a bunch of coriander.

"Before supper Petul's house was extended at the front so that the hearth area which had been outside could be covered with thin plastic sheeting.

"Mario's group consisted of his young son, Romin, a boy from Petz Toj, and 3 *ladino* brothers from the *barrio* of San Diego in San Cristóbal. They had all been there a month and were anxious to leave. Mario's *compadre* slept and ate with us, but worked with Mario.

"Most of Mario's corn, planted on 15 May, had been doubled. Black *jamápa* bush beans had just been planted in 2 rows between the corn rows, 4 to 5 beans in open holes that should not be more than an inch deep.

"Supper was a pot of tomatoes, eventually seasoned with onion and chili.

"The rain poured down just after we arrived and continued off and on all night.

"The next morning Mario turned his radio on at 5 A.M., breakfast at 5:30 after we had all gone up the hill to the spot chosen for our toilet needs where there was a pile of corncobs for our use. Breakfast was tomatoes and beans.

"We were in the bean field around 6:15. It had been cleared and sprayed with weed killer. The brush was left in 3 rows across the hillside as it was too wet to burn. We started at the top right hand corner and worked across, first planting a liter of white beans, then a liter of black *jamápa*. The holes are made about 8″ apart [a handspan]. The digging stick is always held in the right hand, stuck in, pushed forward and turned to make the hole wide enough to toss the beans in without bending over. Each planter starts a couple of holes ahead of the planter to his right [descending] or to his left [ascending or returning].

"In mid-morning we stopped for *posol*. At noonish we had lunch: a can of sardines, shrimp, beans, and ground squash seeds.

"When the planting was near its end the workers began racing each other amid much joking and laughter. Mario's calculation of the amount of beans needed to plant the irregularly shaped plots of hillside was exactly right [as he pointed out].

"We then went to a field still covered with cut brush and with our digging sticks piled it up into rolls, which we pushed down the hill. We abandoned this around 3 P.M. when the rain came down in sheets, soaking all of us. We waited awhile in the *finca* owner's corridor, then continued on to Petul's house, leaving Mario behind as he had a change of clothes there and was reading to the owner's daughters, while we were shivering in the corridor.

"Beans and tomatoes for supper. These were supplemented by ears of corn that were roasted on the fire [after being snitched from the owner's corn fields].

"On the third day Mario and his son fumigated between the rows of doubled corn while the others planted *jamápa* beans in the rows ahead of them. Transquat kills only grass, whereas the Hierbester is for broad-leaved plants. The two are mixed together. A small chili can of herbicide is mixed with 20 liters of water. Beans are not affected by it, but squash and chili are easily damaged.

"I helped the *finca* owner's son double his corn. Care must be taken to bend the stalks between the joints so they won't break off. Poisonous caterpillars are a peril in this process.

"Because it often rains here in the mid-afternoon Mario expects his workers to work until 6 P.M. on a clear day.

"The beans planted here are the same as those planted in Acala, but because it is more humid here they produce better.

"Cooked beans only last a day here before turning sour. If they are poured into another pot that has been rinsed with cold water they will sour much faster. This can be arrested by

74

boiling them immediately.

"Supper—beans, also a soup made of cabbage, potatoes, tomatoes, seasoned with coriander, chili, and later a squeeze of lime juice."

Lowland Corn Harvest, 11 November 1980
(R. Laughlin)

"I drove Petul Vaskes' wife, daughter, and granddaughter to the corn harvest. Petul and his son, Manvel, were already there, camped at the side of a stream. On the other side of the stream was a large encampment of Naben Chauk people, including a grandmother, three or four young women, and a baby. No shelters had been put up. One fellow was lying in a hammock. The harvest had been very poor, because it had not rained sufficiently in August. Also, the people of Acala, living nearby, had come into their fields probably on All Souls' Day when they were in the cemetery, and had stolen both corn and pumpkin squashes. Not only was the land steep, but strewn with river pebbles that increased the drying effect of the sun.

"Because of the steepness Petul did not harvest two rows at a time as is done on flat land, but started at the bottom and harvested the whole bottom area first. He held the ear, inserted the metal corn shucker that was slung around his right wrist and pulled it down from the tip of the ear to the middle and then away to the side so that the ear would pop out. Then he would break off the tip and pull off the silk. He carried a net on his back. Because much of the corn had been knocked down by wind and covered with morning glory vines it was often difficult to find the ears of corn. The runty ears were also hard to shuck because the husk was so thick and tough.

"Petul's group had only had two ceremonies; one for Holy Cross Day and the other on 25 July for wind protection, but the latter had done no good because there was a heavy rainstorm with wind that knocked down a couple of large trees, frightened the people, and was held responsible for the death of a baby.

"The threshing platform had already been set up. It consisted of four stakes, three of them projecting about three feet above the net. The platform was 5′ x 6′, with four horizontal poles fastened at shoulder height.

"Although some of the women helped with the harvest most just sat around talking, embroidering tunics and cooking. Petul's women seemed to think it was a lark. They had brought down cabbage greens and fresh tortillas for us to eat. They cooked a pumpkin squash, but were apologetic that they had no sugar to sweeten it. Later, Xun Teratol told me that women now are less inclined to go to the lowlands than they used to. If they enjoy providing their men with soft tortillas, they may go down at any stage of the corn farming.

"The group was having a hard time getting the *ladino* landowner to lower his rent. Instead of going out and inspecting the fields as he had promised to do, he just sat by his truck and drank while they tried to convince him to be fair, considering the bad harvest. Apparently he starts drinking early in the day.

The Famine
(Xun Vaskes)

"Long ago the famine came. Ooh, the famine, hell, it was a punishment from Our Holy Father!

"Those who had sold a lot of their corn nearly died. They ate [tortillas made of] banana roots and fern roots.

"The poor…ooh, you came here to San Cristóbal and there weren't any tortillas. They were just thi–s big! One roll for two bits. But that's if there were any, and there weren't.

"But it was some chastisement!

"You see, the rain didn't come, none. The lowlands were laid waste by the sun. You couldn't see anything anymore. Nothing was left. Me, in the past…I had gotten a binful plus fifteen bushels of flailed corn, but I hadn't sold it. If I had sold it I would have died. The Ixtapanecs went crazy, then. [They sold it for] five pesos a peck, but just solid money, not paper like it is now.

"Five-peso pieces, but just round silver pieces if there were any, but there weren't. Me, I sold some after the corn had lasted a while. I sold several bushels.

"As soon as the corn fields flowered with tassels the other poor people pulled them a–ll off [to eat]. They paid one quart [of corn] for a week's [labor] if they had any, but they didn't. The other poor people didn't ask for pay anymore. The Chamulans, if they had two ceremonial gourds or one ceremonial gourd [filled with] a ball of weed leaves, greens, amaranth, they left—wherever it was they went looking for an employer. The Chamulans who weren't given [jobs] were just stretched flat, lying on their backs, dead on the road. Face up, they died. They died. It made no difference if it was an older man or a woman or a girl, still they perished. They died on the road to Zinacantán Center, of course, the Zinacantán Center road. An awful Chamulan girl passed by our house. There beneath the red-berried hawthorn, in the tiny gully, she died. She passed by my house. 'Eat!' she was told by my mother. But she didn't want to work, she did nothing. 'Work in the corn field! Fluff wool!' she was told.

"'I don't want to,' she said. When she arrived, then, she had two ceremonial gourds [each filled with] a ball of amaranth greens and spider flowers.

"You see she didn't want to fluff wool. She didn't want to. She just lazed about. My parents ate banana root.

"Because it pleased me, and I had my own [supply], I supported them. My older brother and my father went as far as Chix-te'tik [Cherry Trees]. They found only eight ears, eight ears of dried corn. That was all!

"I said to my father, 'Never mind, father, I have some. Don't go again! It costs so much effort. I will support you,' I told him, because I was living separately, apart already. To my older sister I gave three pecks. But that was because I had some myself. [The corn growing] in my little yard was already ripening. It grew. The holy corn was turning yellow.

FIGURE 19.—A walk in October 1977. (Photo by John Swope.)

"'Well, give me two or three pecks of your corn and take the land here,' said my father.

"'Fine, take it!' I told him. Me, what else could I do, because they were my parents?

"Well, sir, I supported them. The Ixtapanecs, ooh, they asked favors. Hell, they had the money, but what good was it? Me, I had planted irrigated fields at Vunal.

"So then I went to guard my corn with a shotgun and a machete. There were two or three friends, long-panted ones [Ixtapanecs]. I was standing guard with them. The corn ripened. I carried it [still] on the cob. But the robbers were killing people. If you met Ixtapanecs on the way they killed you.

"Me, I didn't want to be killed. Because I was prepared when I traveled. There were three or four of us. We got together when we traveled during the famine. Not even here [in San Cristóbal] was it [any better]. God, it was punishment!

"Now the *ladinos* here, they haven't taken it to heart yet. Punishment will come, you'll see when, what year, it comes again. They step on the corn. They throw it out. They eat it on the cob.

"You see we had grown arrogant because we came to offer them [corn] for the money we could get.

"Well, you'll see, on whatever day it is, the chastisement is yet to come, you'll see!

"Me, I felt the punishment. But tortillas, they weren't for sale anywhere then, 'That's the end of them, some other day.' There weren't even wheat buns or rolls. Ooh, [they sold them] for two bits, but they were this big! But we couldn't get filled up with those, either. We couldn't eat tortillas anymore. You would eat them, but on the sly. You would eat secretly, yes indeed! There wasn't anybody who ate. Everybody [ate] corn tassels. The Chamulans [ate] fern root. Twice my parents ate banana root.

"'Do you want to eat?' my mother asked me.

"'Hand it to me, I guess I'll eat some,' I told her.

"'But it isn't edible. Don't eat any more, you'll just die,' I told my parents, because I had some [corn] of my own. Me, I was kind to my parents. I was kind to my older brother. I was kind to my older sister, all of them, because I had some [corn] of my own. Me, I had a lot stored away. That's why! But I wasn't punished. My father sold his. He wasn't careful. Me, I was scared. Long ago, then, it was a stiff punishment. Ooh, for everybody! Whoever had any [corn], then, pai–d one quart for a week [of work]. Who knows if a quart would give enough to eat for two days. Who knows if it would be eaten in one or two [days] with as much as is eaten at each meal. Once it was a very stiff punishment. It will come again, you'll see, some day, some year! The holy rain isn't good like this. Some years it falls and some years it doesn't. But the price of corn will rise here, you'll see, because they spill it and step on it all the time. Ehh, the holy corn suffers so much here. I saw it. I saw it this morning. It suffers so.

"The trouble is, it is offered up because the money flows out here. Here is where they keep buying things. But corn is so hard to raise. It is so much work. There is exhaustion. There are, ooh, long trips to where the holy corn is harvested. The holy corn takes so many days!"

Flowers for a Price[1]

John B. Haviland

Why the Valley of Naben Chauk Is Flooded[2]

Old Mol Xun was sitting in the sun, picking the hard kernels off a pile of corncobs that lay on a plastic sheet by his front door, and pitching the seed corn into a large basket. He told the following story about the origins of the village.

Long ago, when people had not yet come to live in Naben Chauk, "The Lake of Thunder," tall pine trees covered the valley floor. Deer wandered through this forest, and jaguars and monkeys, too; and when the heavy summer rains came, ducks swam on the small lake that formed in the lowest corner of the valley, by the limestone sinkhole.

Then the holy earth decided it should make this place attractive to human beings, and the sinkhole began to run free. The lake receded. The forest became deeper.

Then came the Zinacantecs, first just three families, then their relatives, and in time their children. They cut clearings in the forests on the valley wall to build their houses and to plant their cornfields. Corn, beans, squashes, and melons grew well in the fertile soil; and people gathered firewood, hunted game, and collected fruits and mushrooms in the woods.

The people of Naben Chauk multiplied, and they began to clear more land for their milpas. Distant relatives came from the lowlands and, bargaining with the new settlers, bought land on the flat valley floor to build more houses. The hillsides were left to the pine trees.

Other people went to work as squatters on the nearby ranch at Yaleb Taiv, "Where frost has fallen." The *ladino* owners were greedy for more cornfields, so they sent these squatters down towards the Naben Chauk valley, to clear the forests. They chopped the giant pine trees, and they slashed the grasses and the undergrowth, and they set fire to the cleared land to fertilize the fields they would plant.

The people of Naben Chauk saw the soil and the ashes and the charred wood wash down the mountain sides towards the sinkhole, when the summer rains began again. But they also saw the white corn, and the beans, and the squash that the Yaleb Taiv squatters harvested on the newly cleared land. There were also fruit trees—peaches, plums, and apricots—that people began to plant, by their houses and on the edges of new fields as they, too, cleared more forest. Soon, the fields yielded good harvests of beans and

corn and squash; and the household gardens began to grow abundant peaches, chayotes, and apples.

But the sinkhole began to fill and clog with the silt, with the debris from the cleared fields, with the waste from house compounds. And once again the lake began to grow, filling the flatlands in the center of the valley each summer, rotting the cornfields that were foolishly planted nearby, driving people from their houses which suddenly sprouted springs in the middle of the hearth, or under the bed platform.

What was once a forest became a village and then a small town. The jaguar and deer and wild ducks were hunted, chased away, forgotten, replaced by domestic turkeys and chickens, sheep, and finally by trucks and VW mini-buses. The peach trees grew old, had grafts, sprouted plum blossoms or fell to the axe to make way for newly discovered species. The cornfields were planted with potatoes, with cabbage, with herbs, and, finally, with flowers.

So that was the result: the holy earth wanted its children to settle the valley of Naben Chauk. They came to live. They cleared the forest. They planted their corn, their chayotes, their peaches. And the lake grew and grew, wider and wider, filling the valley, pushing back the houses, seemingly reclaiming from the flat lands what the people chopped from the hills.

Corn, Mules, and Traders

When one thinks of Zinacantecs—perhaps even when they think of themselves—one thinks of corn. Vogt (1970:48) writes: "The Mayas have been maize cultivators par excellence for some 4500 years, and the Zinacantecs are no exception." Anthropologists have, understandably, seen Zinacantec life as revolving around the cultivation and consumption of corn, taken as an ancient and honorable pursuit for human beings. Maize is ubiquitous. Riding up the Pan-American Highway through Zinacantán, in the fertile days of the Fiesta of San Lorenzo in August, can seem like a trip through one long, continuous cornfield, stretching from the valley below Muk'ta Jok' to the edge of Huitepec, near San Cristóbal. Passing the valley of Naben Chauk, one will often lose track of the houses—patches of red tile, amidst oceans of corn leaves. Even the poorest Zinacantec house has a stash of corn; the richest will be stacked to the rafters with it. Two Zinacantecs, meeting for the first time and striking up an acquaintance, are likely to

John B. Haviland, Department of Anthropology, Reed College, Portland, Oregon 97202.

78

ask, politely, "Where is your cornfield?"

Nonetheless, one must not be misled by this conceptual preoccupation with corn. Zinacantecs, since the arrival of the Spanish, have worked more than their own cornfields.

Old Mol Xun himself farmed corn in the valley of Naben Chauk, where his grandmother remembered the deer roaming before men inhabited the place; and he farmed in hot country up and down the Grijalva River valley. The memories from his youth, however, were filled not with the hoe and the digging stick, but with leather, pack saddles, and mules. Unlike his sons—whose dedication to corn has kept them, for most of their lives, in the constant cycle of cultivation, moving only between their highland home in Naben Chauk and a succession of lands rented from lowland non-Indian ranchers, and investing what surplus they had in distinguished careers in Zinacantán's religious hierarchy—Mol Xun was a traveler. His career, both in the service of the saints and the town, was likewise distinguished. He made his living, however, not by growing but by trading, both selling his own goods and hauling those of others. He carried corn and liquor to Chiapa de Corzo from the highlands. He brought coffee and cane from the far reaches of Tzeltal and Chol country up to San Cristóbal. He bought barrels from the Tojolabales, and ventured into the lowland Tzotzil regions of Soyaló and Bochil, buying their pigs and becoming acquainted, in the process, with their talking saints. He matched wits with the famous witches of Totolapa. He once carried the mail to Comitán, and took forty days to accompany his mule train to Tonalá, on the Chiapas coast, with a cargo of highland bootleg.

Mol Xun was a master of the cornfield, as well, and he spent a part of nearly every day up to his last hoeing "inside his fence,"[3] somewhere on his ample lands in Naben Chauk, but his career illustrates a pattern in Zinacantec life that predates the reliance on agriculture that settled onto the community after the provisions of Revolution and Land Reform—Chiapas style—made Zinacantecs into the highland's premier "growers of milpa." In the last century, and up to the Revolution, Zinacantec muleteers were the teamsters of central Chiapas, known throughout the highlands as vendors of salt[4] and as consummate traders. It is only men younger than Mol Xun's son, Petul—now in his seventies—who grew up "without knowing how to load a horse."

By the nineteen-sixties, many people in Naben Chauk made their livings by other than the cultivation of corn. Young men worked for salaries: building roads, mixing concrete for *ladino* masons, guarding construction sites and buildings against thieves, writing texts for Harvard anthropologists, and so on. Somewhat surprisingly, many such people simply farmed *no corn* at all. They had, in their own words, "forgotten about the hoe." If Zinacantec life depended centrally on the cultivation of corn, the existence of such people seemed to suggest the beginning of the end for Zinacantec culture. In the terms of Mol Xun's story, most of these non-farmers were recreating in modern form the activities of their ancestors: trading (now not

salt but flowers), and hauling (no longer with mule teams but now with trucks and minibuses). They had not, though, ceased to be Zinacantecs; indeed, their approach to these activities has an unmistakable Zinacantec stamp.

Now let me describe some of the activities, practiced by Naben Chauk's "flower re-sellers,"[5] activities that they qualify under the general rubric of **chonolajel** (from the verb **chonolaj-** "practice selling"), known in Zinacantec Spanish as *negocios,* "business." It will begin, however, with Petul—old Mol Xun's son—a man who retreated from his father's trading profession to dedicate himself to the cultivation of corn, but who still practices small-scale trading.

Mi mu xlaj tana, ta jk'elanbe: "If they don't get sold later, I'll give them away."

The Indians who engage largely in corn farming include hosts of casual sellers, Zinacantecs who sell their seasonal produce and home-grown flowers, or who occasionally supplement their incomes by limited re-selling. In the village of Naben Chauk almost every household has someone setting out once or twice a month to try his (or her) hand at selling some fruit, grain, or leaf in a *ladino* market. Petul's household can illustrate the sorts of activities involved.

The simplest venture involves transporting one bag at a time of the household's corn hoard into market to meet current needs for cash. Clearly, those who can keep their corn through the plentiful time after the harvest until the time of highest prices, during the following growing season, will realize the most profits—but demands for hard cash will not always wait. Petul has sold corn in San Cristóbal—his favorite market is the small plaza in San Ramón where he can usually fetch a better price and get home earlier than by selling in the San Cristóbal central market—in January, when prices are low, to pay for curing ceremonies; or in April, when prices have not risen yet as high as they might, in order to fund his own upcoming farming operation or to pay for fertilizer. The procedure is always the same: haul out a sack of corn from the house the previous afternoon to winnow and clean it; remeasure it into a new burlap sack; then hump the load down to the road before dawn the next morning, to load it onto a truck or combi. Arriving in town, one unloads the corn in the selected market place, and pays the freight. There is then a further choice to make: whether to sell the entire load, wholesale as it were, to one of the corn resellers, many of whom are also Zinacantecs, or whether to spend hours in the process of "small-selling," by weight or dry-measure, to individual buyers. The latter process nets more but can require many hours standing in the market waiting for customers and haggling out the price with each one.

Selling to the corn resellers, who often have their agents waiting by the combi stops, has the advantage of getting the whole business over with quickly, and producing all the proceeds in a single wad of bills. The wad is, however, none too fat, for the market price of corn, in terms of its comparative buying power, has dropped steadily over the past decade. An eighty-kilogram bag of corn that fetched US$14 in the San Cristóbal market in 1976 (just before the first modern devaluation of the Mexican peso), and that could still be bought for a bit over US$15, two years later in 1978, would bring only about US$13 from the corn resellers at the same market in January 1988. In the same span, for example, the cost of bus or truck fare from Naben Chauk to town, converted to its US dollar equivalent, has nearly doubled,[6] and other prices have followed a similar inflationary curve.

A decade ago, Petul had surplus beans to sell as well, often hauling them, in a similar routine, to Tuxtla. There he also usually sold them in bulk to market shopkeepers for resale. Their markup, in turn, might be thirty percent (in 1976, from Petul's price of US$0.36 per kilo to the Tuxtla vendor's selling price of US$0.48). In 1988, Petul's farming operation had changed, and he had beans only to eat, not to sell. The price of beans had risen somewhat, but was still reputed to be ridiculously low.[7] In January of that year, Zinacantecs could be seen on the streets of San Cristóbal walking door to door hawking them.

Corn and beans are the staple foods in Petul's house compound, and they are also his staple commodities in commerce. But from time to time his commercial ventures include flowers, fruits, and sometimes other plants from the neighboring forests. Indeed, as real income from corn diminishes it becomes increasingly necessary for Petul to try other means for bringing cash into the household. In the mid and early 1970s, Petul's family sold the products of their gardening rather casually. Neighbors would sometimes come to buy a few bunches of the family's kale, favored by Petul's wife. Occasionally a daughter would gather especially plentiful coriander and sell a few bunches of it during a trip to town, or in the Naben Chauk Saturday market. Once the entire family took greens, squash, spices, and some spare clothing, and made the trip to the hamlet Chikinibal Vo'. This village lies down the mountains from Naben Chauk, in somewhat hotter country where such crops do not grow and where the women, because they spend much of their time hauling water instead of weaving, find it hard either to garden or clothe themselves. Although the women sold their heavy produce and second-hand clothes in the center of the village, Petul carried greens from door to door. Finally, with their profits, the Naben Chauk family not only paid the truck fare, but also bought coffee from their warm-country countrymen.

Other small-scale selling ventures depend on both changing seasons and changing fashions. When the peaches ripen in Naben Chauk—those same peaches that were planted in the early days of the hamlet—their owners have always harvested them and taken them to town, or at least to the highway, to turn them into cash. In the early 1980s, people in Naben Chauk discovered that their tired old peach trees could have plums grafted onto them, producing an earlier and richer crop; a rage of grafting has transformed peach blossoms to plum blossoms.

Petul, who sold his peaches, and sometimes the few apples that the worms didn't get, in August—usually in Tuxtla where the prices are better—now also sells his plums there in June. This is free money: it grows on trees, if you have the time to lug it to market. The only variable is how soon your fruit ripens, or how late it lasts, and thus whether you avoid the seasonal glut and get a better price.[8]

Other fashions have also come and gone through Naben Chauk. In the early 1980s, when Petul had a couple of regular hired workers from Chamula, he turned their expertise at growing potatoes to his advantage by getting them to plant some for him. There followed several tumultuous seasons trying to work out the marketing strategies for potatoes, especially given the seemingly irrational preferences of the market. Petul's daughters quickly discovered that red-skinned potatoes "cook up better"; inexplicably, *ladino* customers in Tuxtla roundly preferred the white-skinned variety.

Other casual selling trips are governed by the calendar of fiestas rather than the seasons. There are times when Petul needs extra money, and thus tries to sell whatever can bring in some cash. This happens routinely before one of Zinacantán's major fiestas—for example, the festival of St. Lawrence in early August, when Petul often tries entrepreneurial flower-selling ventures. He may launch a trip that combines selling the bulk of his peach crop with harvesting and marketing whatever flowers are ripe, supplementing these commodities with bunches of greens or herbs from the garden. For such occasions, Petul is likely to rent a space on the market streets, or even a stall as yet unoccupied by its late rising Tuxtleco owner, to sell his own produce in smaller but more profitable quantities.

There are also several crucial points in the year when selling suddenly becomes especially lucrative, or when demands for produce make selling especially attractive. An example is the period of the year around All Saints' and All Souls' Days (1–2 November), when *ladinos* and Indians alike decorate graves and prepare feasts. Petul will again harvest and take to market (these days, usually Tuxtla) all the available flowers, garden produce, and any ripe chayotes. He will even lop off the tips of the cypress trees planted for shade and privacy around his yard, to sell them as adornment for household altars or flower garlands. On such occasions, Petul will leave for Tuxtla at 10 P.M. the night before, sleeping on the truck in the Tuxtla market, so as to stake out a good space in the market during the wee hours of the morning. Even then the glut sometimes reduces hoped-for profits to a minimum.[9]

At the Christmas season Petul's daughters will make a special trip to the wildest Naben Chauk forests to search out plants that he can add to his wares when he goes to sell in Tuxtla. They bring back various bromeliads (**kilkil ech'**, **uma' ech'**, and **uchul ech'**), moss (**tzon te' ta ton**), the fragrant leaves of Hierba Santa (**jabnal**), and even young palm plants (**unen xan**)—all things that can be sold to ladinos as decorations for creches. At Christmas, too, Petul sometimes

FIGURE 20.—All Saints' Day at the cemetery, Zinacantán Center, 1977. (Photo by John Swope.)

makes experimental trips with his flowers to other markets around Tuxtla, to try his luck at milking the season for some extra profit. He has explored the bus network that links Tuxtla with a series of small colonies in the area, selling produce in the town plazas of new settlements such as Copoya, on the south, or towns near the Chicoasén dam on the north. It was on such a trip that Petul remarked that any flowers he didn't manage to sell he would simply donate to the local saint, to insure at least some non-material benefit from produce that could not be turned into cash.

This casual "flower selling"—the family's cover term for all this commerce in flowers, fruits, and assorted garden and forest produce—is normally a supplement to Petul's normal profession, which is raising milpa. Nonetheless, from time to time, like his neighbors, Petul has engaged in such business more seriously. When one of his old-maid goddaughters was orphaned a few years ago, she took up active flower selling, despite the scandalous gossip that circulated about her for traveling alone by truck to such uncontrolled places as Tuxtla. Petul, seemingly inspired, also decided to try his hand, in the slow agricultural season between final weeding and harvest. He put together a small amount of capital and invested it in perishables, which he transported to the northern city of Pichucalco, on the Tabasco border—a place he chose, apparently, because it was not already claimed by other Zinacantec vendors. He made weekly trips for almost two months, at which point he was robbed on the bus home, losing his "starter" capital. Harvest was, by then, nearly upon him, so he abandoned the venture, perhaps with some relief.

The Flower Sellers of Naben Chauk

For several decades, Naben Chauk has been a center of floral commerce. Travelers to and from San Cristóbal on the Pan-American Highway routinely stop on the edge of the valley to buy bouquets of flowers, or small buckets of fruit, from children hawking them with shouts and waves to passing cars. Whereas these children once ventured up to the road only sporadically, or when there was an abundant harvest of fruits, trying for a few chance pesos, there are now permanent tin-roofed flower stalls, staffed with adults.

A study of the flower business in the early 1960s[10] reported that most of the heads of household in Naben Chauk were "growing" flowers for sale, a practice begun by a few entrepreneurs in 1949, which grew rapidly throughout the 1950s with the advent of cheaper seeds and bulbs. By 1963, there also existed a group of flower "sellers." Some grew their own produce, but most bought flowers from their hamlet neighbors, or from other Indians in San Cristóbal. They transported these flowers, by bus and truck, for resale in the markets of Tuxtla Gutiérrez, in the lowlands. Most of the flower growers in this period were average corn farmers, like Petul, who filled their free time with the small scale but relatively lucrative flower crop. The flower vendors, on the other hand, were largely youths who were structurally "emigrants left behind"—that is, Zinacantecs in the position of those landless Indians who leave their village and their society permanently, but who, in this case, still could spend half or more of their time in their villages—between selling trips—and who could thus maintain "many aspects of a normal life in Zinacantán."[11] That this situation was fragile, and that the flower vendors could bring major changes to Zinacantán was something students of the time foresaw.[12]

Flower selling represents one obvious way in which the changing economics of plants have altered Zinacantec productive life. The range of flower varieties bought and sold evolves continually, but this is only one of a set of rapid shifts that hold great interest. The flower merchants of Zinacantán experience (and engineer) constant and dramatic changes in markets, costs, sources, methods, and in an emerging understanding of market forces and non-Indian flower-buying patterns, in a variety of places throughout the state and, indeed, the *República Mexicana.*

Each year has brought something new in the business: permanent flower shops in Tuxtla, standing transport orders that have funded the purchase of trucks; weekly trips to the old Jamaica Market and lately the *Central de Abastos,* or Central Market, in Mexico City, as well as to Oaxaca and Puebla, to buy exotic flowers; and even air-freighted shipments of flowers arriving in Tuxtla in response to telephoned orders (sometimes in Tzotzil!). The ripples from these changes rebound off the social edges of village life, as well. The crucified figure of Christ, at Easter, is offered strange flowers with whose names the people of Naben Chauk—except for the flower sellers who bring them from Puebla—are unacquainted. The owner of Tuxtla's *Florería San Lorenzo*—a flower shop named after the patron saint of modern Zinacantán—is rumored to have a three-story concrete house in Tuxtla for his non-Indian wife there, and to be building another identical dwelling in Zinacantán for his "real" wife. One flower seller now sports the same acrylic towel and plastic sandals in his Naben Chauk house that he wears when he sells flowers in the Tonalá market.

Moreover, the flower trade has produced further economic gradations within the hamlet of Naben Chauk. Some merchants—the richest ones, often truck owners themselves—earned their money *entirely* from buying flowers in bulk from distant markets and reselling them to other Indian retailers. Others enhance their reselling profits by cultivating their own flowers and fruit on highland land formerly dedicated to corn, thus turning otherwise idle time at home in the village into cash at the market. At the other end of the spectrum, some Zinacantecs engage in flower trading on a tiny and haphazard scale, only supplementing other sources of income (corn farming or wage labor, for example) by experimenting with small markets, or by contracting out their flower crop to regular merchants. The business has also produced a new class of peripheral Zinacantec wage laborers: truck drivers whose salaries buy both their mechanical and navigating skills;

82

otherwise underemployed "hired hands," who sit and do the selling at somebody else's flower stall; even specialized flower haulers who pick up a few pesos hanging around on street corners near the markets waiting to help deliver a bundle, by tumpline, to its owner's market stall.

Lavie chiyojtikin xa skotolik: "By now, everybody knows me."

Selling flowers in the markets of Tonalá and Arriaga, on the Chiapas coast, is both adventure and drudgery for the men from Naben Chauk. The place is hot, and, for most highlanders, incommodious. There's not a decent tortilla in sight, and bed is an egg carton laid on the sidewalk. But the coastal towns are also free from the prying ears and eyes of neighbors, the fences and the walls of the hamlet, the jealous intrigues of relatives, and the party politics of the Naben Chauk town hall. Here one's business is simple: first guarding, and then selling, one's load of cargo. At night, with money in your pocket, you can buy a meal, or see a movie, and no one is the wiser.

For most vendors, the pattern is the same, week after week.[13] Take Lol, for instance. Early Thursday morning he arises early, as usual, perhaps in time to make the half-hour walk down the mountain to his woodland properties, where he has a field of daisies planted. He surveys them to see whether he can get a gross or two of the flowers ready for market that weekend. If so, he tells his wife to cut them during the day, along with two or three dozen calla lilies from inside the yard. Then he heads out to the highway in order to catch a minibus into San Cristóbal before seven o'clock. He needs to meet with the flower vendors from Chamula, as well as his countrymen, regular suppliers from Zinacantán Center and Pat Osil, to arrange for his cargo the next day. He finds most of these people in the market in town, though he takes a municipal bus out to San Felipe to track down another of his regular suppliers who still owes him a bundle of one hundred dozen carnations that he had paid for in advance the previous week. He finds the man coming down the path from his house, and he arranges to pick up the flowers the following morning, there on the highway.

Business complete, Lol flags down a Zinacantec truck passing through San Felipe on its scheduled trip from San Cristóbal to Tuxtla. He clambers into the cabin to gossip with the driver during the short ride back to Naben Chauk. He has the rest of the day to cut and bundle his own flowers, using the branches of the wax myrtle (**satin**) which has the singular virtue for this task that "it doesn't dry out, or wilt right away." He also prepares his plastic sheeting, his tumplines (which double as ropes), his hot-country clothing (packed carefully into an airline bag), and his "starter"—a wad of bills representing his capital for the next day's purchases.

Friday is market day, so it requires an early start: Lol is up and on the road, with the other flower vendors, taking a truck to town by three A.M. Their regular ride to the coast is on a truck owned by Lol's brother; but that vehicle spends the night in Na

Chij with the driver, so the vendors pay for another ride into San Cristóbal. It is still dark, and cold. The men have covered their lightweight clothes for the coast with sweaters, their woven tunics, even stocking caps.

Out behind the San Cristóbal market the flowers have begun to pile up. Lol takes delivery of the ones he had ordered the previous day. A Chamula grower had brought forty-four bunches of lilies, and Lol strikes a quick bargain for another thirty-three bunches, to complement those he had ready at home. He decides to pass up several offers of baby's breath, being sold by Zinacantecs from Sak Lum, because the flowers look suspicious and damp; he thinks they will begin to rot and stink in the Tonalá heat.

Finding rather few marketable flowers for sale—probably because of the rain, he thinks—and knowing that he has a load of about forty dozen chrysanthemums waiting for him in San Felipe, Lol turns to the vegetables, looking for a bargain. He buys an entire sack full of radishes from another Chamula, guessing by hefting it that it holds about three hundred bunches. The same man offers him "mustard greens," which upon inspection turn out to be watercress. Lol bargains him down and buys the Chamula's entire supply, secretly reckoning them to be cheap; he rushes off to find a couple of cardboard cartons to pack them in.

By now the truck has arrived, and other vendors begin to load their things aboard. Lol remembers that he has taken orders for toasted tortillas, from a woman who sells them in her Tonalá shop, so he buys several bagsful near the market. He also stops a non-Indian man with whom he has dealt before to buy two kilos of small plastic bags, of the proper size for holding one kilo of beans. He left beans in Tonalá the previous week, and he wants the bags to be able to finish selling them this weekend. Partly because of this previous investment, and partly because of the poor quality of the flowers and vegetables for sale because of bad weather, Lol decides that he has enough cargo for the week. The other people on the truck buy carnations, daisies, feverfew, stock, both white- and lilac-colored; also freshly dug Chamula potatoes, a few cabbages, and several huge bags of spices: thyme, in tiny little dried bunches, and fresh coriander. One lone vendor from Zinacantán Center sells a bundle of small purple carnations, which a Naben Chauk man snaps up.

It is 10:30 A.M., time to set out. The Tonalá cargo has been loaded first, towards the front of the truck. The Arriaga load, to be removed first, is towards the back. The ladder is hauled inside, and the truck is off, Lol riding up front with his brother—the truck owner—and the driver, the rest of the vendors sitting on their flowers under the tarpaulin in back. It is a large white five-ton truck, with slat sides in the rear, covered against the damp morning air.

Two more stops—one by the road in San Felipe to pick up the pre-ordered flowers: more lilies, a bundle of small carnations, and some *Agapanthus* or "Lily of the Nile" flowers, called simply **yaxal nichim** "blue flowers," but known to the *ladinos* as *agapango* or *cien-en-uno* "one hundred in one," and the other at home in Naben Chauk. Here everyone picks up the last bundles readied by waiting wives and children. Lol has his own daisies and lilies, and also a few large watermelon squash culled from a brother's cornfield. Somebody has a boxful of aberrant out-of-season *chayotes* and a bundle of cypress tips. Another flower merchant loads a small bunch of straw flowers, known as *siempre viva* "always alive," which he has grown and intends to try selling.

Lol is handed a small woven bag, full of fresh tortillas and a piece of fried egg to eat on the road, which he stuffs into the airline bag.

Everyone relieves himself in the ditch: it will be four or five hours on the truck, and often roaming police patrol cars make it inconvenient and costly to stop and disgorge passengers on the road. This is a produce truck, officially not permitted to carry passengers—in fact, not permitted to carry more than three in the cabin, so that the four people riding there routinely duck below the dashboard when passing intersections where police are known to sequester themselves.

The ride down the mountain begins, twisting through the lower hamlets of Zinacantán, past the turnoff to Ixtapa, down towards Chiapa, where it begins to get hot. The truck stops for gasoline, and the people in the cabin remove their Zinacantec tunics. Sweltering under the canvas, which has been securely tied down to keep out the prying eyes of police, the vendors stretch out to sleep upon bumpy beds of flowers. One Chamula kid who begged a ride, mistaking this truck for one of the regular Zinacantec trucks that work the San Cristóbal-Tuxtla run, pays his fare and exits on the outskirts of Tuxtla, amid guffaws from the Zinacantecs who imagine him humping his bag of who-knows-what all the way into the market in the midday sun.

Once, when the patrol cars were fewer, the flower trucks would make a routine refreshment stop on the way through Tuxtla: a cold Coca Cola or a plastic bowl full of what among Tuxtlecos passes as **ul,** a corn drink, typically flavored here with slightly burned chocolate. But now the truck owner wants to hurry on—there is too much chance of meeting a police car. In fact, just on the outskirts of town, one appears, lights flashing. The policemen signal to the driver to pull over, then speed on to stop another truck farther down the road. One policeman walks back towards the Zinacantecs.

Lol curses and extracts a wad of bills from his pocket, peeling off a thousand-peso bill[14] and handing it to the driver.

The cop sticks his head in the window. *"¿Cómo estamos?"* he asks indifferently, "How are we?"

The driver hands over the bill, silently.

"Orale pues," says the cop, and saunters back to the patrol car to join his partner.

Passing through Ocozocoautla, the truck makes a detour through town. Though normally another Zinacantec truck brings flowers and produce to this market, one of the Naben Chauk people who sells there had sent for a supplementary load. The large vehicle lumbers through the narrow streets by the Ocozocuautla market, scraping mirrors against awnings, and passing close enough to some street vendors that Lol buys a mandarin on the fly. Two Zinacantecs appear, wearing only their plain white woven shirts, and celeste-colored trousers. They receive a bundle of flowers and what looks like a forty-liter plastic bag full of Chamula cane liquor—wrapped in newspaper and unsuccessfully hidden in one of the ubiquitous egg cartons. Then they disappear again into the market.

The journey continues, out again on the open road. Lol suggests a soft-drink stop in Cintalapa, but the driver, not used to this route because he is only filling in for his brother, decides to press on. No more police cars appear, and after several more hours down the twisty coastal range, the truck arrives in Arriaga, the first flower stop.

Four people on board plan to spend the weekend there selling: two Naben Chauk men with long-term histories selling in Arriaga, another boy who is the employee of this truck's owner—also a long-time Arriaga flower vendor who now stays with his truck rather than sitting for three days in the market, preferring instead to pay someone else to sell for him—and, surprisingly, a woman who says she is from Chenalhó but whom all recognize to be a Chamula in disguise, who has managed to secure a regular ride with the Naben Chauk truck. The truck makes its way to the market, now quiet and largely deserted in the late afternoon, and the Arriaga cargo is unloaded.

Lol steps off the truck and is immediately accosted by an old *ladino* man who asks him to promise to bring five liters of cane liquor down with him the following week. "My uncle is having a birthday," he explains. As Lol waits, another man comes up to the truck from the market. Before it can even be unloaded to the ground, he puts both hands on a large watermelon squash and starts to bargain for it. He wants it for *taverna*—a sweetened beer fermented inside the squash and known to pack a knock-out punch. Perhaps it will be someone else's birthday.

Several of the Naben Chauk men go into the Arriaga market and pick up more bundles of flowers there. These are the exotic varieties, delivered, the previous night, from Mexico City by yet another Naben Chauk truck.

Now the last half-hour ride down the road, past the fruit fly inspection station, and up behind the Tonalá market. It is just beginning to get dark, and everyone wants to unload the flowers, which are by now feeling as tired as their owners.

First Lol and the others unload the cargo that goes inside the market. All the flower sellers help each other in the process, with one man staying on the truck to hand bundles down, and the rest hauling one bundle after another up the back ramp and into the market. Despite the lateness of the hour, there is lots of activity in this part of the market, because another huge truck, filled with vegetables and fruits, has arrived from Puebla and is beginning to unload. As the Zinacantecs carry their flowers—wrapped in leaves, old pieces of plastic sheeting, and tied up with tumplines—the local merchants unload wooden crates of mandarins, and fiber bags of cabbages and potatoes, all delivered to their stalls by youths with wheeled carts. These same youths make joking remarks to the Zinacantecs, jostling them and grabbing at their loads as they pass. All seem to be old friends.

Soon the Naben Chauk truck has unloaded half its cargo, and it moves around by the covered outside stalls where the younger Zinacantec vendors will sell. As the last flowers are unloaded, the driver stretches out on the sidewalk to rest up for the ride back to the highlands. Xun, the truck owner, takes up a broom and sweeps out the flatbed, then wanders around the truck, tying up the tarpaulin and brushing bits of debris from the paintwork. He has yet to collect the fares for both vendors and flowers. He is planning to return to Arriaga to see what produce he can carry back to Tuxtla—perhaps watermelons. Because of the poor weather, there was a smaller cargo than usual this week, and Xun is vaguely worried about his profits on this trip. He will charge the flower sellers just less than the price of a kilo of meat for their own fare down to Tonalá, and the same amount for each of their bundles; but with the small load this week, the total will not amount to much. A recent dispute between the flower sellers has produced a competitor: another Naben Chauk truck now makes a flower run to Tonalá, and Xun is beginning to wonder whether his weekly trip, with a reduced load, is still worthwhile.

Once he has moved all his cargo inside the market, Lol stops to have a look at the things for sale from the Puebla truck. He has dealt with the owner—a fat Mexican woman with a clipboard in her hand—before, and he knows how much she is willing to bargain on her prices: not much. He decides to buy two dozen gigantic cabbages from her, as well as a bag of potatoes. The tangerines, though attractive, he figures to be too expensive, even though he is beginning to think that he has brought too little produce with him and will not have enough to keep selling for the whole weekend. He takes his new purchases back and sets to work preparing his wares.

A few of the Zinacantecs, who have been selling in Tonalá for several years, have regular spots within the market—not normal stalls, but conventional spaces in the aisles where they display their produce on Saturdays and Sundays. Lol, in fact, has a whole closetful of equipment, stored in various locked rooms around the market. For the moment, what he needs are his buckets and tubs, which he extracts from the market storeroom where he left them the previous week. The flowers first: they must be unwrapped and set in water to recover. "They must come to life, their souls must return," after being tied up so long. The other Zinacantecs who have positions inside the market do the same. The carnations and daisies, cut with long stems, are put directly into tubs that have been filled with water, taken from one of the fish stalls inside the market. The feverfew must be trimmed with a knife first, as must the lilies, for their stems have gotten crunched during transport. Lol also tears away the blackened petals of the lilies. The chrysanthemums must be untied and spread, so that they will regain their rounded shape. Lol divides the whole cargo of flowers in half, and he sets part aside, also in large water tubs, to hold until Sunday. Tomorrow he will have to drain and replenish the water, for it will turn black by morning. He may also have to add a headache tablet—*Mejoral* or aspirin—to the water if the flowers look droopy.

Lol turns his attention, finally, to the vegetables. The watercress also has a very tired look about it, so Lol shakes out each bunch and lays them out on the floor on a cardboard box so they will not be so tightly bunched. He is afraid they will turn yellow before he can sell them. The radishes, packed tightly in a bag, seem to be just fine where they are.

He decides to leave the Puebla cabbages and potatoes alone, too, and he strolls out to see how the others are doing. One of the Naben Chauk men has brought Chamula potatoes, freshly dug and red-skinned, and Lol examines them closely. No good, he reckons, too young and too damp. And the Chamulas sent them covered with dirt. They need to be washed, and then they are likely to start rotting straight away—not like the fancy imported potatoes that he has bought from the Puebla truck. They are ready to sell, straight from the sack. Another has had a disaster: the bagful of fresh coriander that he bought in San Cristóbal turns out to have been packed wet, and it is already beginning to rot. Against the protests of his fellows he hoists the entire bag onto his shoulder and carries it to the refuse heap, where he dumps it out. He will have to recoup these costs with something else.

There is some discussion about the carnations. Most of the flower sellers have brought carnations from the highlands—small, fragrant, red ones, tied up in bunches of about fifteen each. But included with the fancy Mexico City flowers are also red carnations, these much fuller blossoms, tied up by the "dozen" (which, on inspection, turn out to have only eleven flowers each). One vendor, Maryan, has the idea that to distinguish these "finer" flowers further he should attach a sprig of cypress bough to each bundle, so he sets to work making this little adornment.

Lol, however, has finished preparing his cargo, as it is now nearly 10 P.M. He has thought of trying to wash, but he decides that he won't be able to convince the market caretaker to open the toilet room where the water is. Instead, he decides he is ready to eat and go to sleep. Tonalá is a hot place, and at night, when it is merely warm, the people swarm on the streets. They stay up to hours unheard of in the chilly Chiapas highlands—and likewise they arrive at the market long before dawn, unlike the people of San Cristóbal, who wait until it is light to venture, well bundled up, to the market. Leaving a couple of flower sellers who are still working on their loads, to guard the goods, Lol and a couple of companions set out for supper.

There are currently two eating places favored by the Zinacantecs at night: one regular restaurant where one can get a plate of chicken and a soft drink for about the cost of the truck fare down, the other a twenty-four hour taco joint, with a television, and a sour-faced waitress, where one orders by the piece. Lol elects the latter because of the late hour. Around the corner from the tacos there is a boxing match in progress, in what looks like a makeshift ring in someone's patio. As they gulp down eight tacos apiece, the Zinacantecs can hear the shouted bets, even over the din of the Mexican variety show on the television, and the steady chopping of the taco-maker's cleaver as he works over a pig's head by the entrance. By now, everyone has been awake for almost twenty hours, and it is time to get back to the market and go to sleep.

There are several choices here, too. The market is locked up at night, except for one rear entrance; but sleeping inside is stuffy and unpleasant. Sleeping outside on the empty market counters is better, and there one can keep an eye on the otherwise unprotected flowers and vegetables; but near the building, under the trees, there are always swarms of mosquitos. It seems best, tonight, to stretch out on the sidewalk, across the street from the market, where one can both sleep better and still watch the goods. There is only one worry: a crazy man, half naked and muttering to himself, who has suddenly appeared near the market. The Zinacantecs lay out their beds—again, folded egg cartons—on the street, side by side, remove their sandals, loosen their belts, and stretch out to sleep. Lol carefully hides the huge stones that one of the Zinacantecs uses to weigh down his plastic sheeting, so that neither madman nor thieves can use them to crush his head during the night. Thankfully, the madman finds a step near the market and himself nods off.

In the morning, he has gone. It is four o'clock and the Saturday market begins to come to life. Trucks filled with local produce draw up to disgorge their contents, currently mostly oranges and melons. The *ladino* shopkeepers arrive to uncover their stands and lay out their wares: plastic shoes, bags, belts, razors, flashlights, acrylic garments. They dislodge one of the Zinacantecs who, worried about the madman rifling his vegetables or upsetting his tubs of flowers, had moved up to sleep on one of their tables during the night. The other Zinacantecs unwrap the blankets that had protected them from marauding mosquitos and wander back to their own cargo, setting out mats and plastic bags and preparing for the day's sales.

Lol's setting up is more complicated. First he must retrieve some additional equipment, which he has stored in the locked back room of one of the butchers, near where he sells his flowers. He has a stool and several wooden crates, which he fashions into a makeshift table, covered with a piece of plastic. He also has a wooden cashbox, with a supply of change. His complicated system of accounting means keeping the proceeds from different sales separate, and the different compartments of the box serve this end. He also has a five-kilo scale, which he extracts from the box to inspect. It has taken to working badly, sticking instead of balancing smoothly, and he fiddles with its adjustments and thinks of trying some oil.

Finally he has a half-empty sack of black beans, and a metal measuring can. He purchased the beans the previous week from another Zinacantec, and he intends to sell what remains over the next two days.

He begins to arrange his wares by pouring a heap of beans out onto his table and measuring a few kilograms into plastic bags. Then he stores the flowers and packed vegetables for Sunday's sales in the butcher's back room, and arranges the rest of the produce on and around his stand: the expensive flowers in their tub, on the wall behind him, the rest arranged in bunches next to the beans, and the vegetables stacked to one side. The radishes are arranged in a circle with the red tubers on the outside and the leaves meeting inside. Lol strips the yellow leaves from the watercress, and does a last minute touch up to any blackened lily petals or withered daisies. Although all the cabbages came at the same price from the Puebla truck, he selects 10 of them and sorts them into two categories—large and small. He will sell the two groups at different prices.

Almost immediately he has his first sales, but not from ordinary customers—some of the regular vegetable vendors have been attracted by his handsome radishes, and ask him to sell them some on the cheap so that they can, in turn, sell them at their own stalls. What's more, they want them on credit. Lol obliges, carefully noting down in a small, tattered notebook their names and the numbers of bunches they carry away.

Soon the first marketers begin to appear, and quickly Lol is busy selling flowers, beans, cabbages. He has a stash of old newspapers—bought there in the market—and string which he uses to tie up the bundles of flowers. The plastic bags he bought in San Cristóbal are for the beans, which he first measures either by the kilo or in a liter measuring cup before deftly tying them up in the bags. The exact measurements here are critical, because Lol's profit margin on beans is tiny and depends on a level measuring can or a perfectly balanced scale. One man, a regular customer with a ten thousand peso debt from the previous week, stops by to pay what he owes. At the same time, however, he orders another ten kilos of beans—also on credit—and says he will send his helper along for them later in the morning. Many of his customers call Lol by name, and banter with him as they complain about his prices. "Here," says Lol, "everyone knows me. They all look for Lorenzo."

The coffee woman, from a restaurant on the second floor of the market, comes by to take breakfast orders. Lol decides on two pieces of sweet bread and a glass of **ul,** a thick hot gruel, but *ladino* style, made from rice or cornstarch, rather than corn dough. He has by now discovered that his lilies appear to be inferior to those of his neighbor; and that the cabbages simply will not fetch a price that will render him a profit. Only the watercress, which though still looking wilted, is not to be found elsewhere in the market, seems to sell well, and Lol stands firm on his price. He steps across the aisle to consult with the neighbor, another Naben Chauk man called *Chaparrito,* "Shorty."

"I didn't think you could sell those Puebla cabbages," says Shorty. "The only way you can make a profit on cabbages is to buy them from Chamulas. The best thing to do is cut them up and sell halves." Shorty also has a suggestion about the beans, which appear to have been dusted with a pesticidal powder. "Rub them off between your hands," he urges, "and then they will look blacker." The two men agree not to go below a minimum price for the lilies, and Lol asks Shorty to keep an eye on his stall while he goes outside briefly.

The other Zinacantecs are doing a brisk business in the open air. Crowds pass on the street. Young boys, hauling loads for stall owners, call at Lol and threaten him with mock punches as he sits down to relax with a Naben Chauk friend, selling beets (brought from San Cristóbal) and mandarins (bought in Tonalá the night before). They watch with curiosity and make appropriate comments as a peanut vendor, apparently himself a Tzotzil-speaking Chamula, walks past. The sun is up and it is beginning to get hot.

Back inside the market, the meat vendors are also beginning to work up some energy. Their selling style is aggressive and strident, perhaps because the meat itself has a limited life on the counter, and the best cuts go fast. Lol is sandwiched between a beef lady, whose husband appears only to cut the major joints, leaving the piece-by-piece selling to her, and a chicken lady, who sets up a table next to Lol's tubs of carnations. Both talk directly to almost everyone who passes by, sometimes trying to clutch at them to catch their attention. Lol sits silently, only occasionally brandishing an old broom handle when a dog comes too near where he sits. His regular customers come to him, and he usually waits until a prospective customer has finished pawing through the radishes or shaking the bunches of daisies, before he offers her a price or ventures a suggestion. He bargains only minimally, having decided on his prices the night before in consultation with the other Naben Chauk people.

Little by little his piles begin to diminish. Lol carefully puts the beans proceeds in a plastic bag, and the money from the sale of the daisies—products of his own gardening—under a piece of cardboard in his cashbox, so as to keep these accounts separate. There is a constant commerce in small bills, as the vendors begin to call on each others' cash supplies to make change, as the day wears on. The restaurant lady comes by to collect her glass and the price of the corn drink, and to see what Lol will have for lunch, there at the stall. The chicken lady sells her last battery hen, and leaves temporarily to bring more from the main stall of which she is only a satellite. The beef lady begins to spread sea salt on the remaining pieces of meat hanging from the rack in front of her. She also calls out to Lol to save her several bunches of watercress and radish, and she sends her daughter across the aisle to pick out four bunches of flowers, which Lol gives her for nothing.

Outside the Zinacantecs are now in direct sunlight, and they pull back their wares into the shade of the trees or erect emergency tents made out of plastic sheeting and woven fertilizer bags. The crowds have thinned, fleeing the midday heat. The flowers, and their owners, are beginning to wilt, but they eat their lunches there at the stalls, hoping to catch some late shoppers. Lol emerges again, this time to gossip with the other Zinacantecs about political machinations within the market. Some of the Tonalá stall owners have, it appears, lodged a complaint about the growing number of Zinacantecs who are selling vegetables that they buy in Tonalá instead of highland produce. The market administrator is being asked to prohibit them from the market, but Lol scoffs at the business. "They want to be the only ones who eat," he says, "but this is a public market." No one has said anything to him, in any case, and it is only the newer vendors, selling outside the market without established positions, who have been criticized.

Throughout the afternoon sales are slow. Lol, in fact, packs up everything but a few tired-looking flowers and—ever hopeful—the cabbages, and settles back to read the latest issue of *Kalimán,* a superhero comic, which he borrows from Shorty. The butchers close up shop, admonishing Lol to be sure to lock the storeroom after he puts his things away. The chicken lady goes into a frenzy of hawking to rid herself of the last wings and feet and herself departs. The fish vendors, with whom Lol has had several long conversations about market politics, stack the remaining fresh fish on an ice-filled wheelbarrow, and head for home. It appears to be time to prepare for the evening.

Tonalá's three movie theaters, closed for many years, have once again become an attraction in the town. Shorty proposes that they go to the only decent picture in town, a kung fu movie showing near the central plaza, and he asks the watchman to give him access to the washroom to take a bath. Lol stores his flowers and follows suit. Lol quickly reviews his take for the day and discovers that he has managed to earn back his costs and has a small profit, after one day of selling. Both men take the money for their evening meal and the movie ticket from their cashboxes, and set out, returning to find the other Zinacantecs already asleep on the sidewalk.

The next day, Sunday, proceeds much like Saturday, except that Lol and his companions begin to feel anxious to head for the highlands by early afternoon. Lol manages to sell nearly everything except the poorest of his daisies, a bunch of extremely haggard-looking calla lilies, and the wretched cabbages, which he has been trying to sell at a loss. Finally he trades the lot, with much obscenity and mutual criticism, with one of the Zapotec ladies from Juchitán, who also sells flowers and fruits. She gives him two watermelons, which he stuffs inside his airplane bag, and she reminds him that he still has not brought her the bootleg cane liquor he has promised for months. He threatens to come back and marry her, husband or no husband (and, in his case, wife or no wife).

Then he stores his tubs and boxes away, hides his wad of bills on his person, and leaves the market, giving farewell greetings to the several Naben Chauk men who are still trying to sell their last bunches of flowers or a final watermelon squash. A couple of *ladino* women call after him, "Adios, Lorenzo!" He heads for the first-class bus station. He hopes to be in time for the 4 o'clock direct bus to Tuxtla, where he can get a second-class bus home to Naben Chauk, and go to sleep in his own bed before midnight.

The History of the Flower Business

Lol and his companions have organized their lives for nearly twenty years around weekly trips to lowland markets, selling flowers and fruit, and occasionally supplementing their income with other related ventures. Lol undoubtedly gave the watermelons he smuggled back from Tonalá to his children to eat—they had to be smuggled because fruit is not permitted past the fruit fly checkpoint on the outskirts of Tonalá, and Lol ran the risk of confiscation as he carried them home on the Cristóbal Colón bus. At certain seasons of the year, however, it is worthwhile bringing larger quantities of hot country fruits back from the coast, to sell at fiestas in the highlands. Sometimes watermelons, lemons, or mangos are cheap and plentiful in Arriaga, and the flower vendors arrange with their truck driver to carry quantities home for resale. And Lol is just one among many; flower resellers ply their trade in Tuxtla Gutierrez and Chiapa de Corzo, in Cintalapa and Ocozocoautla, in Arriaga, or even as far as Huixtla and Pijijiapan, on the Chiapas coast.[15]

However, the Zinacantec flower trade has not always been so elaborate. According to Bunin (1966), the flower business began in Naben Chauk sometime prior to 1950, doubtless aided in its early growth by the construction of the Pan-American Highway, which linked Naben Chauk and its neighboring hamlets directly by road to markets in San Cristóbal, Tuxtla, and beyond.[16] This is when an increasing number of Naben Chauk people began to grow flowers for sale, furthering the process that, in Mol Xun's recollections, began with the felling of the forests and produced Naben Chauk's lake. Indeed, many farmers planted their flower fields on the flat, damp valley floor, and even on the very edge of the lake (or, at least, where they calculated the lake would reach during the wet season), to simplify irrigation. Commercial flower growing, then, appears to have nearly a forty-year history—long enough that for most people in Naben Chauk, flowers, like peaches, have *always* been there.

The personal reminiscences of both Petul, now in his seventies, and Lol, thirty years younger, show us how the business has evolved from a casual supplement to household ready cash to a personally transforming profession. Moreover, the progression from Mol Xun, the muleteer, to his son Petul,

FIGURE 21.—Arranging flower stall at the market, Tuxtla Gutiérrez, 1983. (Photo by John B. Haviland.)

the corn farmer par excellence, to his nephew Lol, the *comerciante* or "businessman" with a shadowy other life in Tonalá, demonstrates the genealogy of economic and social change in Zinacantán.

Finding Jalisco

Lol had mentioned that Petul, his uncle, was one of the oldtimers who used to go to Tonalá, and who were selling there when he took up the business as a youth. Petul, in turn, attributes his start in Tonalá[17] to one Antun T'ot'ob, who was the first to discover the road down to the coast, sometime around 1949 or 1950.

Before that, during peach season, Petul and his father, Mol Xun—along with others from Naben Chauk—used to sell their peaches, their hawthorns, their chayotes, and watermelon squash to a *casero*, a man from Chiapa de Corzo, named Juan Xantis (Sánchez). They would set out with their mules from Naben Chauk before dawn, arriving in Chiapa about noon, with their peaches all packed into big bags. Often Juan Xantis would ride up the road to intercept them above Chiapa, not far below Ixtapa, probably to avoid competition from other peach buyers. Petul says they used to do this for many years. They would often sell all their cargo on the road and then turn around and come straight home. This Xantis had over a dozen horses, and he would take the produce back to Chiapa himself. When asked what he did with the stuff, he would say that he sold it in a place too far away for the Zinacantecs to get to. "Jalisco," he called it.[18]

At some point, Antun T'ot'ob, unsatisfied and curious, decided to find out where this place was. He made an expedition with one of the *ladino* men from Naben Chauk, who had moved there from Salinas after the new Pan-American Highway had replaced the old road from the lowlands. The highway already passed through Naben Chauk at that point, although it was not yet paved. The two men went to Chiapa de Corzo, then took a truck to Tuxtla, walked to the far edge of town, and from there made their way by truck or bus to Arriaga—which is where they discovered the *casero* had been selling the peaches all along.

When Antun came back to Naben Chauk, he told the others that they were being robbed by the Chiapanec. They decided to mount an expedition as a group to the newfound market. Petul himself decided to take four sacks of peaches.

They stacked their loads up by the first curve, where the highway passes through Naben Chauk, and they waited all night for a truck that would take them. Finally a huge truck responded to their calls of "Arriaga!"[19] The truck driver agreed to take them but told them the charge for their bundles would be very high: three pesos per sack of peaches. He refused to bargain the price down to 2.50 pesos. Each person paid a fare of fifteen pesos.[20] They left about dawn and got to Arriaga in late afternoon, piling their stuff up by the side of the road.

Antun asked whether they might want to go on to Tonalá, a place he had never been but only heard about. He suggested they could simply ask where the market was and try their luck at selling. So they flagged down a bus and went down the road to Tonalá. The fare was 2.50 pesos per person and another 3 pesos per sack.

When they arrived, all the townspeople gathered around to see what they had brought, and they sold almost the entire load the first afternoon. They slept overnight. The next day, the remaining peaches were quickly sold, with people asking when they would be back next with more of the same. Petul remembers that this first trip was near the end of peach season already, so they didn't have many more trips left that year. He also remembers that on that first trip he came home with the almost incredible sum of 2500 pesos, which would have been a small fortune in those days.

They saw the *casero* Juan Xantis in Arriaga on that trip, and Petul remembers speaking with him. "Have you arrived, Petul?" asked the Chiapanec. "Where is my load of peaches?" "Well, that's all finished now," Petul replied, "since I have seen the road for myself." After that Petul never remembers seeing that *casero* again.

For the next seven or eight years, Petul made regular trips to Tonalá, and elsewhere on the coast. He always preferred Tonalá, because that's where he seemed best able to sell his peaches. Other men of his generation from Naben Chauk also traveled regularly to the coast: Antun, who had first made the trip, as well as Petul's brothers-in-law and friends. They made the trip to Pijijiapan about twice, doing very well, and on to Pueblo Nuevo, where they didn't sell much because of competing fruit coming down from the highlands of Motozintla. Once they also set out for Tapachula, but never got that far, having been warned that there were already plenty of peaches there.

Petul remembers that they always used to go down to Tonalá in their traditional short pants and their beribboned hand-woven palm hats, called **semet** "griddle" for their flat, wide-brimmed shape. As a result they underwent lots of ribbing: "your penis will be visible," people joked, "and your legs will get sunburned." People urged them to wear long pants. Petul's father, Mol Xun, when he came to hear of this new fashion, mercilessly mocked the people involved for "making themselves into non-Indians." He also criticized Petul for wasting his money on storebought trousers.

During this period of selling peaches, old Mol Xun never went to the Chiapas coast, although Petul remembered his father's telling him of going there long ago to deliver cane liquor, by horse, taking forty days for the round trip. The tradition of Zinacantec commerce, first by mule and foot, later by bus, and most recently by trucks owned by Zinacantecs, themselves, thus has a long tradition.

Why did Petul stop going to Tonalá to sell? Too many young men, he says, who had gotten their starts following the trail blazed by men of Petul's generation, started to take over the business—people like Lol. These young men wouldn't give the older men space any more, because they began to set up a more or less permanent trade there (unlike Petul and his companions, who used to go only once or twice a year during the peach season). The advent of flowers totally transformed the business.

Jun vwelta chiyelk'an xa ox li aktavuse: "Once, I remember, the passing bus tried to steal me."

How, then, does Lol remember his own path to becoming a flower seller? His story[21] gives a clear picture of the evolution of the life of the new Zinacantec flower sellers.

Lol began selling flowers, on the highway at the edge of the Naben Chauk valley, when he was a boy, barely into his teens. When he began to sell flowers, however, he was already experienced in the world of *ladino* work. Never attracted to corn farming in the lowlands, where his father routinely took him, as soon as he was old enough to travel on his own, he began to earn money for the family by working on paying jobs, such as road building and construction.

Lol began to learn Spanish, not in school—which he attended for a total of one half day—but rather doing road work in the lowlands, smuggled onto the job by his older brother who, like Lol, preferred earning some money to sitting in a classroom. Lol was, he remembers, still too young to drink the tequila that the Mexican road workers offered, although little by little, though, he learned to read from them.

It was when he worked on construction sites in Tuxtla that Lol also began to enter the fringes of market life. Sometimes early in the morning, sometimes in the afternoon, after finishing his daily quota of trenches dug or bricks laid, he would go to the Tuxtla market and sit around on the street corners where people unloaded their cargo. There he could often pick up a few centavos hauling fruits and flowers from the trucks to the market stalls, or even carrying some lady's shopping bags.

Back in Naben Chauk, Lol began commerce in flowers himself, buying them from neighbors and hawking them to passing vehicles on the Pan-American Highway. The only flowers to be had at that time were red geraniums, ubiquitous in Zinacantec ritual and grown for profit mainly by two Naben Chauk brothers, who made their living this way. Lol would buy a small quantity, whenever he had time free from the cornfield or the construction site, and set himself up in a small makeshift flower stall on the edge of the Pan-American Highway. Sometimes alone, and sometimes with a few friends, he would hold the flowers aloft to passing cars and buses, selling to whoever "had the urge to buy them."

Little by little, Lol began perfecting his trading techniques. He first added red gladioli, bought from a new flower grower whose fields were on the valley floor. He would find some thick sticks, and tie the geraniums to them so that they would stand up in an eye-catching display. Then he would array the gladioli against a horizontal pole and wait for passing Mexicans to buy them. The profits were meager, but they were sufficient for him to continue with the business for several years,

whenever his obligations to his father's cornfields left him free time.

Once, he remembers, a passing bus tried to "steal" him. Stopping apparently to buy his flowers, several Mexicans, who Lol was convinced were going to abduct him, got off the bus. He ran away in terror, leaving his flowers lying where they were, and finding them gone when he finally returned to have a look. Soon thereafter, disillusioned with the roadside business, Lol began to look for other ways to make a living.

Although people from Naben Chauk were, by this time, growing large quantities of commercially saleable flowers, few were actively involved in selling the flowers in *ladino* markets. They might sell a few flowers to hamlet-mates who needed them for curing ceremonies or for offerings at the church, but only a few specialists were, in those days, carrying flowers for resale to the markets of Tuxtla and San Cristóbal. One of these was Maryan P., whom Lol approached in conversation, begging to be taken along on a selling trip to Tuxtla. Maryan agreed and set Lol to work going house to house in Naben Chauk buying daisies for resale in the Tuxtla market. People had, according to Lol, perhaps seen a daisy here or there being sold in a marketplace. They had begun to start cultivating them, though most of the growers "didn't know how to sell them." Maryan P., now with Lol as his apprentice, began taking quantities of daisies to Tuxtla to sell.

Lol began making the trip himself, throughout the week, selling his daisies on the Tuxtla streets near the old central market. The flowers came exclusively from Naben Chauk, and Lol remembers clearly the price spiral of the early years. A load of one hundred bunches of daisies went from three *tostones* (half-peso coins) to two pesos, to three pesos. Lol's profit on such a bundle would, in turn, be two or three pesos. With particular clarity he recalls one spectacular success on a New Year's day when he chanced to be the only flower seller in the market. On that day he sold the flowers retail at three bunches for "two bits" (twenty-five centavos), or eight pesos per hundred bunches. This profit was cause for celebration when he brought it home to his family.

All during Lol's youth he remembers Naben Chauk's peaches. The older men, of his father's generation, used to sell the fruits during the height of the season. His uncles, including Petul, were part of the group of men who went regularly to Tonalá. Lol's father had many peach trees, and he would ordinarily sell his entire crop to a neighbor, Mikel Buluch, who would pay him five centavos for two peaches, the variety called *karera,* which used to be planted throughout the Naben Chauk valley before fancier new peach varieties, along with plums, pears, and apples, were introduced.

By this time, old Maryan P., Lol's first mentor, had also begun to carry flowers to Tonalá. Again Lol asked to accompany him, and again the old man agreed to take Lol on as apprentice. The first trip took place in the early 1960s. The two men traveled by second-class bus to Tuxtla, changing there for another bus to Arriaga. Before entering the town they got off at the Tonalá crossroads to flag down a passing vehicle on the short, gravel-paved stretch to Tonalá. On this trip the two men took only two bundles of flowers, one of white daisies and the other of small white carnations.

Arriving at the Tonalá market, Lol and his guide faced another problem: where to set themselves up to sell. The problem was that another pair of Zinacantecs, also from Naben Chauk, was already in Tonalá. They, too, were regular flower vendors who left the highlands in order to arrive with their flowers late on Fridays. Lol's guide, Maryan P., had calculated the schedule so as to get to Tonalá about the time their rivals would be finishing their loads of flowers. The plan was sound, but at first, early on Saturday morning, there was simply no place for them to set up, because the other Zinacantecs had claimed all the available flower-selling space. By around ten o'clock, one of the Naben Chauk men finished selling all he had. As he prepared to go back to the highlands, he spoke to Lol and Maryan, offering them his place at the market. They set up their wares and themselves began selling, staying until late the next day, Sunday, long after the other Zinacantecs had gone home.

This was Lol's first visit to the coast, and apart from flower selling, which was diverting albeit slow, he found the experience frightening and unpleasant. Worst of all was the heat: a hot sun that meant one felt like drinking one soft drink after another, day and night. In those days the market sat behind the municipal *palacio,* to one side of a large movie theater at one edge of the town square. The Zinacantecs slept out in the open, or under the roof in front of the town hall where, Lol remembers, the soldiers "watched after them" at night, also making it unnecessary to sleep right in the market with the flowers.

When the flowers were finished, Lol and his partner returned to the highlands by flagging down a truck at the gasoline station on the outskirts of Tonalá and seeing how far they could get before taking a bus. This happened about 1961, four years before Lol married, although the exact dates are lost in Lol's memory, as are the costs, long ago, of flowers or transport.

Lol accompanied Maryan P. on several more trips, until he saw for himself that it was "worthwhile," and gained the confidence to try for himself. The old man continued to sell, and Lol would accompany him to Tonalá, but carrying his own cargo. He experimented with selling in other places. In Cintalapa, between Tuxtla and the coast, Lol found the people unpleasant. In Arriaga, the first stop on the coast, where Lol also tried selling, people wouldn't pay good prices for his produce. In those days he could buy fruit in Naben Chauk at the rate of fifty large peaches for between two and three *tostones* (fifty-centavo coins)—an average, say, of three centavos each; in Arriaga he could resell the peaches for at most three for 20 centavos, or worse, at five centavos apiece. In Tonalá, by contrast, people gladly paid ten centavos each. Lol also tried selling farther away, in Tapachula, before he established himself in Tonalá.

Thereafter, he began to make regular trips to the coast every Friday, returning to the highlands on Mondays after selling all he could. Sometimes when he had left-over cargo in Tonalá, he would go early on Sunday mornings to Pjijiapan, farther down the coast, to try to hawk the left-over produce near the train station, or walking from door to door. Once he had a regular routine, he thereafter rarely missed the weekend trips. During peach season, he sometimes made two trips in a week, returning to Naben Chauk late on Sunday in order to buy more fruit in San Cristóbal before going back down to the coast on Monday.

By this time, by his own reckoning, Lol was beginning to get smarter. There was a large group of elder Zinacantecs, including several of Lol's uncles, who banded together to carry the peach crop to market in Tonalá and Arriaga. They were, as Lol puts it, the one who gave the orders for Arriaga and Tonalá. They had made a regular arrangement with the owner of a pickup truck from Chiapa de Corzo to take them down to the coastal markets every week, or every three days, depending on the season. Lol asked them if they would take him with them on these trips. "No room," was the reply. These men wanted no one else to invade the market.

Lol did follow a couple of these senior men on their buying trips to San Cristóbal. They would buy peaches from non-Indian women from town, who would sell their crop in the small plaza at the foot of the church of Guadalupe in town. Sometimes they would contract with a Zinacantec to climb the peach trees and harvest the fruit himself. Zinacantec resellers competed with each other to corner the peach crop, intercepting potential vendors as they walked into San Cristóbal on their way to market.

Unsuccessful in finding a ride to the coast with the older men from his hamlet, Lol decided simply to set out on his own. He would transport his cargo of peaches and flowers home from San Cristóbal by truck. Then, despite the relatively high cost, he would stop the second-class bus as it passed through Naben Chauk, and make the trip to Tonalá in that way. He discovered that he could get to Tonalá before the others. They would arrive and greet him angrily when they found that he was already in the market selling.

This was clearly a time of much competition and animosity between the Zinacantecs who engaged in reselling. Lol quickly found a companion, another man who could not capture a ride from the Naben Chauk elders. This man was called Juan Goat, an evil-tempered man with a scraggly beard, which stuck out in clumps like a goat's. He had come from another hamlet to take a Naben Chauk bride. His father-in-law was one of the Naben Chauk elders who sold peaches in Tonalá, but he had a falling out with the other men and no longer was included in the pick-up group. He and Lol began to transport their loads to Tuxtla by truck, then making their way to the far side of the city in order to try to flag down a ride to the coast on the large corn-transport trucks. Juan Goat was experienced at this business, knowing which trucks tended to charge exorbitant fares—and cursing them as they passed. Lol followed the older man's lead, learning the details of the complicated network of transport between highland and coast.

Lol's memories of his growing involvement with the flower trade focus, in fact, on transport. After he and Juan Goat got tired of flagging down trucks on the road out of Tuxtla, they started investigating bus schedules in more detail. There was the green bus, known as "Corzo," that left Tuxtla for the Coast at 9 A.M.; there were slower second-class buses to Arriaga; and from Arriaga there were several different trucks that would carry the Zinacantecs to Tonalá, in particular a very large corn-hauling truck belonging to a Chiapanec called Belisario, with whom Lol often rode.

It was through Belisario that Lol met old José, another *ladino* from Chiapa de Corzo, who had a small flatbed truck with wooden slat sides. José would drive from San Cristóbal, where his wife had a house, down to Tonalá to buy fresh shrimp and fish, which he then transported back to the highlands for sale. Sometimes he would take a small quantity of fruit or flowers with him—Lol remembers that even though he owned a truck he was still wretched enough to try peddling the flowers on the Tonalá streets—but his principal interest was the fish. Lol made José's acquaintance and begged a ride for Juan Goat and himself; the fare was three pesos for each bundle of flowers and five pesos for each person. This arrangement lasted for a long time, giving way finally when one of José's brothers-in-law, a certain Humberto who had a larger truck, began to take the Zinacantecs on a regular basis. At first, Humberto arranged to take Lol and his Zinacantec friends in another small pickup, taking them to Arriaga and Tonalá and dropping them off once or twice a week, depending on the season.

About this time, Lol reports, his fortunes began to change. Before he had been the apprentice, watching the older people sell and learning from them how to travel, how to sell, how to negotiate the Tonalá marketplace. Now, however, people began to come to *him*. "Do you have a truck?" they would say. "I do," he would tell them. "Let's have a drink," they would say, "we want to go too. Take us with you." From learner Lol was transformed into boss. He began to have, as he put it, his own men—his own followers. As some of the old timers began to give up the business, some of the other elders themselves started coming to Lol, begging to be included in his trips.

Lol also began to establish contacts in Tonalá. An elderly woman, near whose stall he often set up his flower stand at the market, became his friend and adviser. She gave him hints about how to display his wares, and how to set prices. She gave him space for some of his marketing paraphernalia—clothes, a money box, measures and weights—and she often let him sleep over at her house. After she retired from the market stall, she remained a resource for him, letting him bathe at her house, and from time to time advising him about some of his more dubious enterprises (such as selling bootleg cane liquor, smuggled from the highlands to coastal cantinas).

During this period, Lol also decided to marry, putting together the necessary capital during a year-long courtship. He would take his prospective wife's family's chayotes with him to the coast, and deliver the profits to his in-laws-to-be.

Humberto did so well with his transport business, that he ultimately bought a brand new seven-ton Dodge truck. Now he could really hold cargo! Humberto also acquired a woman partner who sold radishes, lettuces, and tomatoes in Tonalá. The truck would leave from San Cristóbal each Friday, and then return from the coast on Sunday or Monday, leaving Lol and his partners off at home in Naben Chauk. The cost was higher—five pesos per load of cargo and ten pesos per person—but still less than the bus fare, and clearly both more secure and more convenient than standing by the roadside. The added cargo capacity, and also the need to fill the truck to make the journey profitable, meant that more of Lol's "friends" began to join the regular weekend trip to the coast—with flowers, with fruit, sometimes with the vegetables that could be found in the San Cristóbal market.

Lol reckons the crucial dates from this period with a genealogical calendar, anchored to a transport milestone: the shift from a dependence on non-Indian transport to the use of a Zinacantec-owned truck. The social details are complex, although the economics are simple: Lol and his friends calculated that it would be both cheaper and more reliable to organize their flower business around a fellow Zinacantec's truck, once Zinacantecs began to own their own vehicles. The chronology, as Lol reconstructs it, was as follows. Lol married in 1965, and his first two children, sons, were born in 1966 and 1969. During that time he was "working with Humberto," that is, transporting his cargo of flowers to Tonalá on the Chiapanec's truck. By this time, the flower business was changing. The elders from Naben Chauk, including Lol's uncles, had gotten too old and had started to withdraw not just from regular trading but even from seasonal peach selling, leaving the rigors of distant travel to the younger men who dedicated themselves to the trade, and who, like Lol, had acquired both linguistic and practical expertise in negotiating a non-Indian world.

The case of Xun Martines was typical: like many elder men of his generation, he would invest large amounts of cash in buying and transporting peaches to Tonalá during the fruit season, which normally came just as the cornfield weeding season finished. The quick profit on peaches could thus offset the costs of intensive cornfield labor. A single disaster, however, could wipe out one's investment and sour one's enthusiasm, and this is what happened to Martines. One entire load of peaches, perhaps packed wet, perhaps mishandled on the road, arrived damaged in Tonalá. There ensued a massive argument with the other peach vendors, both Zinacantecs and natives of Tonalá. Unable to sell the fruit to the Tonalá resellers, the hapless Xun had to throw the entire load onto the market rubbish heap. "Forget it," he said—according to Lol—and "went back to the milpa."

At the same time, younger men from Naben Chauk—men

with neither their own land nor much experience at farming corn—began to approach Lol, now known as an expert at "business," for help in launching their own flower selling careers. Most of these youths were unmarried or newly married; many were Lol's cousins or childhood playmates. None of them knew "where to sell or how to sell," but all were anxious to learn. Coming to Lol with a bottle, they would beg for the chance to join Lol's group. "Let's drink," they would say, "take us down with you to sell. Show me the road." Lol claims credit for giving most of the Naben Chauk flower vendors their start in Arriaga and Tonalá.

It was as the group of "his people" grew that Lol became friendly with one of the first Zinacantec truck owners, a man from Na Chij. The fares on other trucks and buses had begun to rise; from five pesos per person, the cost had risen to seven, and then to ten pesos. Lol took his own bottle to his wealthy countryman, proposing a deal in which the truck owner would make a regular weekly trips to Tonalá, just as the Chiapanec had been doing. Within a year, by 1971 or so, Lol had sealed this arrangement by making the truck owner his compadre, convincing the man to serve as baptismal godfather to his third child, a daughter, and later to the sibling who followed thereafter.

The flower sellers were agreed that it was better to travel with a countryman, especially when he had his truck sitting there ready and waiting. More than municipal loyalty was at work however: with the Na Chij man the vendors could travel on credit, leaving payment for a trip until after the selling was complete and profits were in hand. Lol recalls, in fact, that before he made the truck owner his compadre they occasionally had drunken arguments:

"Sometimes we would ask to ride on credit down to the coast. We wouldn't pay him when he left us off, but only after we had finished selling. Then sometimes he would get drunk, the poor old fellow, and he would say to me, 'You bastard, are you ever going to pay your debt?'

"'I'll pay it, of course,' I would say, 'but I don't have it now.' We used to fight with each other, when he would get drunk.

"But when he was sober, he'd always just say, 'Let's go.' He knew we'd all pay sooner or later. Anyway, my compadre made a success of it, in the end. He really made most of his money by hauling flowers to Tonalá and Arriaga."

In fact, from a tentative beginning with a rickety second-hand truck, which ultimately broke down entirely on the road to Arriaga, this Na Chij truck owner progressed to a new three-ton truck, and later to a huge seven-ton truck, which carried enough cargo that Naben Chauk flower sellers who traded in Ocozocoautla and Cintalapa also joined the weekly trip from the highlands. A few people from other hamlets, particularly Apas, joined the trip from time to time. Again, Lol was the boss; people who wanted to join the journey negotiated with him.

Lol's regular trading in Tonalá thus now spans more than twenty years. From an irregular beginning, selling seasonal fruit from a curb-side stand, Lol has gradually incorporated himself fully into the Tonalá market. Each Naben Chauk man now has a well-defined spot at the market where he, or his designated replacement, sells every week. There was a time, however, when a scrambling competition for space threatened the unity of Lol's "group."

"You see, I didn't always go every week. I occupied myself with other things sometimes, you see. But then when I would go back the next week, well I didn't know where to set up my stand. That Chep Tojtik had seen my spot before, and he never failed to go down, every single week. So I would arrive on Friday, and I wouldn't have any place to set myself down. Well that's because Chep had told his brother Maryan: 'Here. Take this spot; it's unoccupied.' But that's where I would have gone to set up my stall. So we were about to start fighting about it, trying to steal each other's spot. We were going to become enemies over it.

"But then I decided—just forget it. Never mind. And I found another spot."

Finding a good spot at the market had been a matter of getting to Tonalá early and staking one's claim. Moreover, the competition involved more than Zinacantecs. Lol remembers that the *ladinos* from the nearby ranches would often storm into the market early on Saturday mornings and chase the Indians away, in order to set out their own produce. However, once the Zinacantecs established a regular system of transport, the rest of the organization—places to sell, prices on common produce, cooperation over watching cargo, eating, and entertainment—became similarly regimented. Each Zinacantec now pays a standing market rent on his place, which is accordingly reserved for him by the market administrator. Most of the regular vendors, like Lol, have an arrangement with one of the stall owners for storing buckets, scales, boxes, plastic sheets. Most, too, have their regular customers, week after week.

Lol's memories of his flower-selling career end, however, with a lament. He thinks with envy of old José from Chiapa de Corzo, the man who used to give him a ride to the coast.

"And that old José that I told you about, the guy with the little truck. Today he has a house of two stories. There's a big house there, with a sort of arch, on the corner near the gasoline station, on the road out towards San Cristóbal.... That's where José's house is. It's a very nice house, two stories. He even has a car. That's all from his selling, that's how he made it. And he used to do that, too: when he couldn't sell all his fruits and flowers at the market, he would go out hawking them from door to door."

Worse, Lol looks around at the other Naben Chauk men whose flower-selling careers he helped to start, and he compares their circumstances to his own. His brother, his cousin, his nephew, and several of his earlier apprentices, have all gone from flower vendors to truck owners. Indeed, Lol currently transports his own flowers on his brother's truck, bought, Lol calculates, on the brother's profits from selling flowers in Arriaga (a task the brother now contracts out to a younger man, while he himself stays with the truck). Worse still, another flower-vendor's truck has recently[22] started a competing weekly trip to Tonalá and Arriaga, prompting a bitter division within the group of Naben Chauk men who sell flowers there.

Despite his brick house with a concrete roof in Naben Chauk, and despite his political career as a hamlet official, Lol compares himself unfavorably with his fellows in the flower business.

"They have made a success out of it. But not me—I drink too much liquor! I never managed to save any money. Can't afford a truck."

Jamaica

Lol's reminiscences bring us close to the present day, but omit what is in some ways the most noteworthy aspect of the recent flower business in Naben Chauk: its expansion into distant markets, and the concomitant expansion in knowledge and experience, social and otherwise, among the flower sellers. In the late 1970s, a group of Zinacantecs began to look beyond the San Cristóbal markets, and their own or their neighbors' gardens, for the flowers they would sell in lowland markets.

Around 1980, one enterprising Naben Chauk flower vendor, Maryan K., now himself a truck owner, introduced an innovation into the business. He had been involved in selling flowers for some years, and being an inquiring fellow (Lol says he has "a clever and lively head"), he had made the acquaintance of some of the other flower traders who arrived in Tuxtla. This group included some who knew of the flower markets in Mexico City. Once he got wind of the possibility of buying flowers more cheaply in distant markets, he decided to investigate, traveling by bus and asking around in Puebla and Mexico City.

Maryan made one trip entirely on his own to Mexico City, and then he invited his friend Lol, and together they made two more trips by bus, arriving at the huge Jamaica flower market in the center of Mexico City. They hired commercial transport trucks to haul their flowers back to Arriaga (whence Maryan went to Tuxtla to sell them, and Lol to Tonalá). Then they decided to find a truck of their own, and Lol contracted with his compadre, the truck owner from Na Chij, who at that point had never been to Mexico City. It was Maryan K. himself who guided that first truck into the city.

By the mid 1980s, men from Naben Chauk had a flourishing trade in exotic flowers, which were acquired on weekly trips to Mexico City, in several Zinacantec trucks. These trips continue to the present day, and as I noted at the beginning of this

FIGURE 22.—Zinacantecs loading flowers at the Jamaica Market, Mexico City, 1985. (Photo by John B. Haviland.)

chapter, they are now supplemented by telephoned orders and airfreight delivery from the *Distrito Federal* to the Tuxtla airport!

The trips to Mexico City have furthered the practical and social education that spending long periods selling and living in *ladino* towns had already begun for these Zinacantecs. The following brief sketch of a typical trip[23] may suggest how the commerce in flowers is changing, and has the potential further to change, the foundations of Zinacantec life.

The trip began in Naben Chauk about 3 A.M. on a Tuesday. The ride to Mexico City was simply a longer version of the weekly ride down to the Chiapas coast. The food was worse, the fatigue more intense, and the police bribes more costly. These costs were, in turn, calculated into the overall price—in 1981, about 5000 pesos,[24] split among the ten flower buyers—set for the trip by the truck owner. The Zinacantecs, alternately standing and dozing in the back of the empty truck, made their way across the Isthmus of Tehuantepec, through rural Veracruz, and into the center of the country, arriving about nightfall at the toll highway leading up into the mountains near Orizaba.

As the truck wound up the highway, the fog rolled in, night fell, and it began to rain. Tarpaulin beds became tarpaulin roofs, as the truck began the nightmarish ride up the two-lane toll highway into Orizaba. The road was bumper-to-bumper with traffic, mostly gigantic trucks competing with each other to leap into the left-hand lane and pass the cowed passenger cars that had the misfortune to be on the road. "Damned little cars," muttered the Na Chij driver as he slammed the gears and passed about half a dozen of them on a blind curve. He had now been driving almost non-stop for nineteen hours—having left his bed before 2 A.M.—and he had another four or five to go before reaching the Jamaica Market.

About midnight, somewhere on the toll road beyond Puebla, the truck again pulled to the side of the road. Another Zinacantec truck was there, waiting. Another was expected. Because there were only a few people who knew how to navigate the complex route from the toll-road exit in Ixtapalapa into the bowels of the Federal District where the flowers were to be had, the owners were waiting to distribute the competent pilots among the three Zinacantec trucks. Finally, the three trucks set off in tandem, into the city.

The roads were deserted at this hour—almost 1 A.M. on Wednesday morning—and Lol's truck wove its way to the market, where there was still parking space in the Zinacantecs' favorite street. It was now very cold, and it would be several hours before the market would begin to stir. The driver claimed the cabin as his bedroom, and immediately plunged into a desperate sleep. The rest of the Zinacantecs accommodated themselves among the bedrolls in the rear—each man carefully putting his airline bag, which contained his bankroll for purchasing flowers, under his head.

At three o'clock, a light-skinned, blue-eyed *ladino* from Michoacán popped his head over the side of the truck and shouted: "The flowers have arrived!" The Jamaica Market had been transformed. All the neighboring streets—still lit with streetlamps—now teemed with people. Trucks jammed with flowers were parked in every available space. Bundles, on backs and on wheeled carts, were hurried to and fro.

Instantly the Zinacantecs were on their feet, digging in bags for their tumplines and their wads of money. It was time to survey the goods and check out the prices. Lol and his brother clambered down off the truck, and began to confer on what sorts of flowers they were after. Then they set out in different directions to survey the week's offerings, planning to meet again at the truck to compare prices. The unit of flowers was the *gruesa*—a dozen dozen—and soon Lol and his companions were hauling carnations, chrysanthemums, and several varieties that, according to Lol, had "no name" back to their growing stacks of cargo. Other Zinacantecs contracted men with pushcarts to bring the goods to the truck.

By the time it was light, Lol had spent almost 8000 pesos[25]

on his flowers. As each new load of flowers appeared, Lol pulled a wad of banknotes from his pocket, and, in consultation with his companions—sometimes disguising the normal Spanish number words with archaic vigesimal locutions in Tzotzil—he compared prices and quantities. He still wanted to buy a few more things, but he now was planning a trip into the center of Mexico City where he knew a man who would sell him bullets for his .22 rifle back in Naben Chauk.

Later, the Zinacantecs stacked the truck high with the flowers they had bought, preparing for the return trip to Chiapas. The driver, who had slept without moving since arriving, roused himself about 10 A.M. and went off in search of some food. Within the hour they would set out again on the highway, and he would put in another twenty-four hour shift without sleep. All together, the Naben Chauk buyers had spent more than 30,000 pesos—the equivalent of two-and-a-half months' wages for a skilled Zinacantec mason, back in Naben Chauk. The truck was filled to overflowing, and the Zinacantecs prepared themselves for the tight squeeze as they rode another twenty hours back to Arriaga, atop this floral bed.

Their schedule was carefully timed. They had left Naben Chauk so as to be at the Jamaica market early on Wednesday for the arrival of fresh flowers. They would leave before noon, hitting the hottest part of the return journey only after sunset, passing through the scorching lowlands of Veracruz and Oaxaca at night. They would deliver the flowers to Arriaga, and then to Tuxtla and Chiapa de Corzo during Thursday. Vendors could thus begin to sell the produce on the following weekend, picking up the flowers and transporting them to their final markets on Friday for sale on Saturday and Sunday. During a seven day week, as Lol put it: "I only get one day free, on Monday."

Mother's Day

At some seasons of the year, Lol does not even get to rest on Mondays. An especially active season for the flower trade comes at All Saints' and All Souls' Days (1–2 November), when most Mexicans make elaborate offerings, including food and flowers, to their deceased relatives. At this season, many Zinacantecs take what flowers and produce they can harvest from their gardens and fields, and head for *ladino* markets to try to turn the traditional All Souls' ritual into cash.

However, the real professionals among Naben Chauk's flower sellers say that they sell the most flowers on another day, the 10th of May. In Mexico this is the *Día de las Madres*, "Mother's Day," a highly commercial national celebration of Mexican-style motherhood. This is a time when the professional flower sellers make a special effort to procure a plentiful supply of top-quality flowers.

When there is an extraordinary market for flowers, the regular sources of supply—including the vast Jamaica market or, in recent years,[26] the central produce market in the capital—are insufficient to meet these Naben Chauk vendors' needs. In the same spirit of entrepreneurial adventurism present throughout the evolving flower trade in Zinacantán, Naben Chauk traders have in recent years made special forays to other markets, in search of cheaper and better flower varieties.

To give a final example, an abortive but instructive expedition in search of more flowers took place a few days before Mother's Day in 1984. Almost as an experiment, Lol and his companions set out to Oaxaca in search of flowers, a bit unsure of the exact whereabouts of the village, but trusting to their business expertise to guide them. They ultimately found their way to the community of San Antonino, known by Lol as San Antonín—a place that he had visited the previous year at All Saints' Day.

Huge fields of flowers, being tended and watered, were visible along the road. However, as the Naben Chauk merchants ate in the little plaza, an Apas truck drove up. The other Zinacantecs had already been in the town a few hours, and they furnished the black news that there were no flowers to be had. They were leaving, they announced, although the sceptical Naben Chauk merchants did not trust their words.

Members of the Naben Chauk group began to fan out, asking random people passing in their horse-drawn carts: *"¿Vende flor?"* "Do you sell flowers?" Some even knocked on people's doors. Someone produced a couple of telephone numbers, apparently belonging to former flower vendors from a previous trip, while others walked around the parched back streets of the town, trying to find addresses that people on the plaza suggested.

It was evident that there *weren't* any flowers after all. Most of the apparently abundant crop had been pre-ordered and paid for by other people—not Zinacantecs. The few flowers that were stacked in people's patios were rather poor. Lol went out to the fields, on the north edge of town—flat and fertile looking land. Instead of the endless beautiful flowers he expected, however, he found only a few planted fields, of rather tired aspect. Some kind of worm had ruined the crop.

Lol immediately began to hatch new plans. He thought of trying to get a telephone message to his sons in Naben Chauk to tell them not to give away his own crop of feverfew. (He had been planning to share it with other merchants, confident that he would be able to replace it with better flowers from afar). There was now no time to strike out to Acasingo (in Puebla) or to Mexico City to get an adequate load. Lol had been planning to make a killing during this selling spree, and he had almost twenty-five thousand pesos[27] to spend on cargo. But at this rate, he wouldn't be able to *find* that many flowers, let alone buy them.

When I left the Naben Chauk party, Lol was in a quandry, about to mount a house-by-house search for flowers, with approaching rain clouds promising to ruin the plan of going to the fields themselves, in the cool of the night, to cut flowers from those vendors who still had crops to sell. In the end, Lol and his companions tried to rescue the trip by buying flowers in the central Oaxaca market the following day, returning to Chiapas with a fairly massive loss.

Ikuch xa yu'un, li prove: "He made a success of it, the poor fellow."

This trip to Oaxaca makes plain a central feature of the Naben Chauk flower business: its riskiness. Flowers are inherently an uncertain commodity, both because of their obvious perishability, and because—unlike much edible produce—both the supply and demand are evanescent and unpredictable. The business therefore depends on a precise sense of timing, and on a good dose of luck. Lol and his companions had counted more on luck than on good business sense when they set out in search of Oaxaca flowers, to find the crop already sold or promised to others. Similarly, more than one Naben Chauk merchant has squandered a small fortune in start-up capital investing in a load of flowers from Mexico City that either dried out on return or rotted unsold in a lowland market town.

At All Saints' day in 1983, one Naben Chauk flower seller lost forty-five thousand pesos[28] in a single weekend when the truck returning from Mexico City broke down at Tapanatepec, still on the hot coastal plains of Oaxaca, ruining almost the entire load of flowers. On this occasion, the Zinacantec had sent his partner to buy for the two of them in Mexico City, while he himself set out in the other direction, towards Comitán near the Guatemalan border, also in an optimistic search for cheap flowers. Both ended up with nothing but an empty purse.

During that same season, Lol made major trips both to Mexico City and to Puebla, buying huge loads of flowers that he ended up selling at a loss—falling several thousand pesos short of covering his initial investment, his travel costs, and his running expenses. Another Naben Chauk flower vendor reportedly spent over one hundred thousand pesos[29] in the Jamaica Market during the same weekend, and no one doubted that he would suffer a severe loss.

On the other hand, the economics of flower selling are clearly such that its most successful practitioners gradually transform themselves into truck owners, some of Zinacantán's richest citizens. This is Lol's own observation: that people who have "survived" the rigors of selling end up rich men, who thereafter make their livings "sitting down," i.e., riding shotgun on their own trucks.

The small-scale or casual flower vendor relies on transforming each load for sale into a profit sufficient to cover running costs and to contribute something to his household economy. For a man who farms corn, both cultivating and selling flowers can supplement income that is otherwise limited to post-harvest boom and pre-harvest bust. But when the "starter," the pool of capital required to maintain the trade, disappears in a disaster—the broken down truck or the robbery in Pichucalco—people like Petul simply give the business up. Lol, a full-time flower vendor, insulates himself against such temporary setbacks by investing his profits, not only in houses with concrete roofs, but also in loans to his fellow Zinacantecs. Money loaned when Lol is flush becomes reserve savings when, tapped out, he calls the loans in again. Lol's contacts with flower growers, with people in the Tonalá market, with truckers, all represent part of the cultural capital that allows him to survive the vicissitudes of the market. He also diversifies his trade, hauling liquor and corn, and living always on the lookout for something he can sell at a profit if he just carries it to the right market.

At the big-time end of the scale, there are no fewer than six truck owners in Naben Chauk who have been active for years as flower sellers. Lol's brother, the man who now hires a youth to sell flowers for him in his old spot in Arriaga, is one. Another, the man with whom Lol avoided a fight over who had rights to a good spot in the Tonalá market, has *two* trucks. Two or three additional trucks belonging to Naben Chauk flower sellers make, or have regularly made, the weekly run to the *Central de Abasto* in Mexico City—a trip that by January 1989 cost the merchants over two million pesos[30] for truck fare alone. A couple of the owners of these trucks are major suppliers of flowers in Chiapa de Corzo and Tuxtla. The economics of Zinacantec truck ownership require detailed study. But it seems clear that participating in this large scale floral enterprise, as well as hauling Zinacantec corn, beans, and bodies, has contributed to the efflorescence of Naben Chauk trucking, a latter-day, gasoline-powered analog of the mule teams that, according to Mol Xun, once grazed in the Naben Chauk valley.[31]

It remains to try to quantify what Lol means when he says that someone "has made a go of it,"[32] or that selling flowers "is worthwhile."[33] The changing value of the peso, and rampant inflation, have made calculating costs and prices a complex matter. In what follows I will try to render values in the relatively more stable US dollar equivalent. I will also venture some comparisons with such relevant costs as the price of meat.

Petul reported that first trip to Tonalá to sell peaches, which cost him $1.40 in truck fare, and $0.50 per bag of peaches, yielded the astronomical profit of $200; having no other fixed guide to purchasing power or wages in that period, we observe that, if we believe Petul, the total earnings from a trip were roughly 140 times the cost of one-way transport. Put another way, Petul's remembered profit was $100 per bag of peaches, 200 times the cost of transport (which, in this case, was the only cost, as they were his own peaches). Even by the early 1960s, when an agricultural worker's daily wage was only about $0.50, this would have been an astounding haul, even for only one such weekend in a year.

Bunnin (1966) writes that, in 1963, a dedicated flower vendor from Naben Chauk reported his own average earnings as about $8 per month, whereas Bunnin estimated that he could be earning up to about $5 for a four-day trip to Tuxtla. Again, this is to be compared with a daily wage for Indian laborers of about $0.50.

In February 1976, the Zinacantec trucks still charged about $1.60 to take a flower seller to Tonalá, and each bundle of flowers (or bag of peaches, etc.) cost $3.20. The difference between the selling price and the cost of 100 bunches of carnations (which were bought in San Cristóbal for $12 per hundred) was only about $4. (In that same period, Zinacantecs were paying their milpa workers about $1 per day, though laborers in Tuxtla and Chiapa could earn about three times that.) In this year, Lol would carry flowers, peaches, cabbages, and earn a profit of about $20 per weekend, after all his costs were paid. Lol's earnings were thus well above those of corn workers, but not appreciably better than those of laborers in higher-paying jobs.

By 1985, the figures were inflated and the profits were much better. On a flower-selling trip in April of that year, I calculated Lol's total outlay to be about $130, including $8 for truck fare.[34] On the flowers he sold during this trip, his profit (by my calculation) was about $150, and he also earned about $120 selling his own plums and hog plums, bought in Chiapa. Thus his total profit for the week was $270, about twice the value of his original investment.

To put this sort of wage in perspective, workers on government development projects (road building or reforestation, for example)—the best jobs Zinacantecs could find in those days—in 1983 earned a weekly salary equivalent to the cost of about 30 kilos of meat. An experienced Zinacantec mason, in 1981, could earn a daily salary equivalent to about four-and-a-half kilos of meat. Lol's weekly earnings, from this flower trip at least, equaled about 80 kilos of meat, or over ten kilos per day.

I should add that on this same trip, in 1985, Lol made a further profit of about $53 on a load of 200 liters of cane liquor, which he transported to Tonalá on the flower truck—that's another sixteen kilos of meat.

In January 1988, times were hard again, for flower sellers as well as for nearly everyone else in Chiapas. Now a bridge worker's weekly salary would buy only twenty kilos of meat, a skilled mason's only about ten kilos, and a truck driver's only six kilos. Selling flowers (seventy-five dozen lilies, as well as thirty-three dozen carnations) and vegetables (mostly radishes and cabbages), Lol's profits for the weekend were about $90, or about forty-five kilos of meat. He was still earning more than laborers (or truck drivers), but in terms of buying power, flowers were paying half as much as they had three years before.

As a final note, it is worthy comparing how floral prices have fluctuated over the period of the Naben Chauk flower industry. Bunnin's 1963 study showed the following prices (per 100 bunches, converted to equivalent US dollars) for a variety of retail flowers in the Tuxtla market:

1963 (Bunnin, 1966)

Lily	$12.00
Gladiolus	$ 8.00
Carnation	$ 1.20
Daisy	$ 0.80

It is not clear what size bunches these were; similarly, the fancy grade flowers from distant markets had not yet reached the Zinacantec vendors.

In 1976, when the peso still had the same parity against the dollar, carnations cost ten times as much, and made a handsome profit when sold in Tonalá.

1976 (February)	Buy	Sell
Carnations	$12.01	$16.02

In 1983, after several devaluations, the selling prices in Tonalá had hardly changed at all when converted into dollars, although the Tuxtla retail prices were low. Daisies continued to be cheap.

1983 (August)	Sell Tonalá	Sell Tuxtla
Carnations	$16.25	$3.25–$6.50
Daisies	$0.65	

In 1985, flowers had the following prices in different retail markets.

1985 (April)	San Cristóbal	Tonalá
Carnations	$4.00	$10.00
Daisies		$13.00
Gladiolus		$ 4.50 (per dozen)
Chrysanthemums		$82.00
Feverfew	$3.27	$ 9.22
Cypress boughs	$2.05	$ 6.83
Calla lilies	$6.15	$16.39

Finally, in 1988 I recorded the following prices for the flowers that were carried to Tonalá in January.

1988 (January)	San Cristóbal	Tonalá	(Mexico price)
Lilies	$13.15	$36.00	
Chrysanthemums	$ 8.77	$16.00	(10 dozen)
Carnations	$11.00	$22.00	
		$66.00	$29.00
Lilies of the Nile	$65.80	$87.70	
Feverfew	$ 8.80	$22.00	

Since the early 1980s, when business was booming, there has clearly been massive inflation in flower prices, coupled with a fairly severe reduction in real profits for the Zinacantec flower sellers. At least some of the people who were "surviving well" during the rapid expansion of the flower business during that earlier period have now gone on to become truck owners, apparently by taking advantage of windfall profits. But the days of those profits have gone. Zinacantecs who stayed in the business or who were lured into it by seemingly easy money have been disappointed. Present day flower merchants—or at least the small-scale retailers—cannot reproduce the high levels of income of that earlier period. Perhaps this is why Lol, working harder than ever down in Tonalá, laments the fact that he "drank away" his profits from past years, and that nowadays "he feels himself poor."

Yik'al chkom li bak'ine: "Perhaps sooner or later I'll leave her."

Bunnin's 1963 study of the Zinacantec flower business divided it into two social universes: the flower growers, who were on his analysis merely extending practices of normal Zinacantec life to the cultivation of a new cash crop; and the flower sellers, who were the residue within the community of extreme external pressures towards change—in his words, "emigrants left behind." Unlike those who respond to economic and social pressures inside Zinacantán by leaving the community entirely, this group of largely young men do spend more than half of their time outside the municipality, buying and selling flowers; but they keep their homes and families in Naben Chauk. According to Bunnin (1966:232):

> Since they maintain their place inside the community while at the same time developing new links with the outside world, they are marked—unlike the flower growers—as carriers of penetrating change in the pattern of life in Zinacantán.

I said at the outset that the flower sellers of Naben Chauk have not ceased to be Zinacantecs. This is certainly true, as far as it goes; but there is little doubt that the flower sellers have already done much to transform the notion of what being a Zinacantec means. The transformation continues. Let me end this extended essay with a personal vignette, from a trip to Tonalá with my Naben Chauk friends and compadres in January 1988.

Manvel, who has been selling in Tonalá nearly as long as Lol, is a handsome man with a large family back in Naben Chauk. His eldest son, Xun, a frail lad who was often sick as a child, frequently accompanied him on his weekly trips to the coast.

Some years ago his mother-in-law came to gossip at my house, and she had nothing but harsh words for Manvel. "You see he's building a new house," she said. "When that is finished he will leave his wife [the speaker's daughter] and move alone into the new house."

The following year, Naben Chauk bubbled with rumors that Manvel's wife wanted to leave him. Even as we trudged up the mountainside on a major, expensive curing ceremony for her, Manvel confided to me that she always seemed angry with him: this hot condition was part of what the ceremony was designed to cure.

The next year, when I arrived in Naben Chauk after a nine-month absence, the women of the house compound where I live couldn't wait to blurt out the latest scandal. Over fresh tortillas, I was regaled with tales of Manvel's misdeeds: people said he had another wife, down in Tonalá. He had, reportedly, spent thousands of pesos on a truckload of beer for the wedding celebration; and he even had a child with the new woman. Everybody said it was true, but Manvel continued to deny it.

I was curious, but not convinced. Neither Manvel nor the other flower sellers had said a thing. When I went down to Tonalá, Manvel seemed normal; he followed his usual routine, and we even traveled home to Naben Chauk together on the same first-class bus.

Nonetheless, in January 1988, having joined my friends as a "fellow Zinacantec merchant," and after we had all prepared our flowers and vegetables for sale the following day, and were laying out our egg-carton beds on the sidewalk, Manvel said to me, "Well, sleep well. I'll see you tomorrow."

"And where are you off to," I asked, unthinkingly.

"I have to go over there," he said, gesturing vaguely with his head, and quickly trotting off into the night.

The following day, as I chatted with a fat *ladino* woman who sold chicken in the market, conversation dwelt on current hard times. "No money," she said, "and the government doesn't care about us. We can't even support our families anymore." She looked around. "And for Manuelito it's worse," she continued, "since he has two families to support now. And that new wife of his is always asking him for money."

So there it was. Brazenly, I asked Manvel to present me to his new wife, and, after a moment's hesitation, he took me home with him for lunch. A handsome woman, whom I had seen for some years selling *atole* in the market, cooked us fish, garnished with cabbage and radishes from Manvel's own market stall. She sat silently and watched us as we ate and talked in Tzotzil, which she clearly did not understand.

How was it, then? I asked Manvel. What did his wife back in Naben Chauk have to say?

"Oh, I still deny it to her," he told me, "even though my mother-in-law is always accusing me. But this arrangement isn't working out too well, anyway. This woman always complains that I don't give her enough. Her brothers may beat me, but, perhaps, sooner or later, I'll have to leave her."

Back in the market, preparing to go back to the simpler world of Naben Chauk, I sat for a while, in the slack selling hours of an early Sunday afternoon. Xun, Manvel's son, had been waiting in Tonalá when we arrived the previous Friday afternoon, and I asked him when he had come down from the mountains.

"Oh, I have been here a month," he said. "I don't like to go home much: it's too cold." He rearranged a pile of mandarins on his stand, and I noticed that he was selling exclusively fruits and vegetables that could be acquired right there in Tonalá. "Sometimes my father brings me some things to sell, but mostly I buy my load right here. Right now the only things I have from home are some beans, which I sell little by little."

What did his mother have to say about his father's new wife? "Well, we don't talk about it. But I give her money myself when I go home."

A group of uniformed Tonalá school children walked by, looking without much interest at Xun's avocados and bananas. He glanced at me with haggard eyes—he still didn't look well, I thought. "You know," he said, "I would like to go to school here, too. But I have to keep working."

"Do you know any people here in Tonalá?"

"Well, there's this girl. Her father runs that refreshment stand just by the steps inside the market. He has given me permission

to talk to her. But she isn't here today, otherwise I would take you by so you could see her."

It was getting close to 4:00, when the bus would depart for the highlands, so I said good-bye to Xun, bidding him, in Tzotzil, to be strong as he stayed behind, selling his vegetables, and the last of his father's flowers.

Notes

[1] My thanks are due especially to my compadres Lol Vaskes, Natil Xun Vaskes, and Mol Petul Vaskes of Naben Chauk, for their friendship and companionship, at home and on the road; to Leslie K. Devereaux for mutual fieldwork; to the Australian National University, the Instituto de Investigaciones Antropológicas of the Universidad Nacional Autónoma de México, Reed College, and the National Geographic Society for financial and logistic support; to Robert M. Laughlin and Frank Cancian for comments on various drafts; and to Lourdes de León for everything else.

[2] See the tale of this name, in the words of my late *compadre* Mol Xun Vaskes in Laughlin (1977:126–129), and the introductory chapter "Where have all the flowers gone?" My version of this (hi)story is also due to Mol Xun, especially to conversations with him around our house compound during an idyllic stay in Naben Chauk between January and June 1976.

[3] ta yut (s)mok

[4] Even as late as 1967, on my first trip to the township of Chenalhóo, in the company of a Zinacantec cargoholder in search of cheap meat, we were greeted by locals, who recognized our Zinacantec costumes, with the question, "Do you have salt to sell?"

[5] j-'ekel-nichim

[6] In 1976, a truck ride to Tuxtla from Naben Chauk, for example, cost 6 pesos (= US$0.48). In 1988, the same truck ride costs 2000 pesos (= US$0.88), and the bus costs 2700 pesos (= US$1.18).

[7] In Tonalá, Zinacantecs were selling black beans at 1200 pesos (= US$0.53) per kilo, and a bagful in San Cristóbal was reputed to cost about 100,000 pesos (= US$43.86), which would average out to about US$0.50/kilo.

[8] In the first years of the plum rage, a box of early plums could fetch the equivalent of US$6. In 1987, in the early part of the season (the first week of June), a box was worth about US$3.80, but a few weeks later the price was about half that.

[9] At All Saints' Day, 1983, Naben Chauk people bought carnations in San Cristóbal for resale in Tuxtla, but because of the number of flowers that appeared, and the especially hot weather, flowers that had been bought for 25 pesos a bunch (= US$16.25 per hundred) were unloaded in Tuxtla for only 10 pesos (= US$6.50 per hundred). Cypress boughs dropped from 10 pesos to 2 pesos a bunch during the week before the All Saints' Day, and Petul's take on the 60 bunches he carried to Tuxtla was the equivalent of US$1.30.

[10] Bunnin(1966).

[11] Bunnin(1966:231).

[12] Bunnin (1966:232).

[13] I sketch a composite view, based on trips to Tonalá in February 1976, August 1983, April and July 1984, April 1985, and January 1988.

[14] The ethnographic present here is January 1988. Exchange rate, US$1 = Mex$2300.

[15] By 1988 there were separate trucks making regular flower deliveries to four different zones: in addition to the two weekly trucks (which sometimes went twice in a week) to Tonalá and Arriaga, there was another for Cintalapa-Ocotzocuautla, another for Pijijiapan and Huixtla, and then the regular run of hourly trucks on the route between San Cristóbal and Chiapa de Corzo and Tuxtla. I have not included regular trucks bound for Mexico City and Puebla to buy better flower varieties, which I describe in a later section.

[16] Bunnin's researches, in 1963, were confined to Zinacantec flower selling in these two nearby cities, and do not mention flower selling in more distant markets on the Chiapas coast, for example.

[17] The following section is drawn from my field notes of 12 April 1984.

[18] Jalisco was the name of the community where the train station was located. By the 1930s the community had been absorbed into an expanding Arriaga.

[19] Petul recalls that Antun T'ot'ob had stopped calling it "Jalisco" now that he knew the name of the real destination.

[20] This would have made Petul's cost 27 pesos, at a time when the daily wage a corn farmer paid a worker would have been less than four pesos.

[21] The following notes are drawn from Tzotzil conversations with Lol recorded in April 1984. The description offered here is considerably less fluid than Lol's own narrative and dialogic presentation, whose flavor is retained in only a few passages in what follows.

[22] In early 1988.

[23] Based on my notes from May 1981.

[24] A little over US$200 at 1981 rates.

[25] More than US$300 at the exchange rates of the time, though this money included investments from several of the other Tonalá flower sellers who had given Lol their money and sent him to buy for them all.

[26] The regular vendors at the Jamaica market were evicted by force and the market was razed in a series of moves by the municipal government in 1986 and 1987 to centralize food and produce distribution in the Distrito Federal. Flower selling has been relocated in the *Central de Abasto*.

[27] At the time, almost US$150, and all of this money Lol's.

[28] About US$288.

[29] More than US$600.

[30] Almost US$900, split among ten flower buyers. In addition, each man had between 800,000 and 1.5 million pesos (US$350–$650) to invest in flowers in Mexico City.

[31] It has also produced a most interesting new category of Zinacantec: the truck driver. Sitting on the curb in Tonalá, in January 1988, as the last of the flowers were being unloaded from a Naben Chauk truck, I had a long conversation with our driver, a youth in his early twenties from Na Chij, who told me that he had never hoed corn in his life. His father, one of Zinacantán's first truck owners, had put all his sons to work as drivers, and this youth, from the time he learned to handle a stick shift and an overdrive button, had made his living with vehicles. At the time he was earning 120,000 pesos, or about US$50, a month at this full-time job. He did not help with the unloading.

[32] ikuch xa yu'un

[33] xlok' kventa

[34] Lol worked out his costs a different way: he figured he had brought about $60 worth of flowers (feverfew and daisies) and fruit (plums) from home in Naben Chauk, but he didn't count this as cost—this is simply what it would have cost him to buy similar produce. Similar, he did not count into his own outlay the $20–$30 worth of flowers that he "borrowed" from his hamlet mates, to replace at a later date with equivalent flowers of his own.

Poetic License

Robert M. Laughlin

The Zinacantecs' recognition of physical similarities has generated a scientific classification of plants—a plant taxonomy. But this same perceptivity and attention to shared shapes and colors, sounds and smells, textures and movements also creates a poetic association between the flora and man, between the flora and the cosmos.

Tzotzil terms for plant morphology demonstrate the use of human or animal anatomy and clothing to name plant parts (Tables 2 and 3).

The process of applying human anatomic terms to plant morphology may be reversed so that plant parts contribute to the labeling of human morphology:

snichimal yut k'obol, lit. the flowers of the inside of the hand, i.e., palmar lines
yanal eal, lit. the leaf of the mouth, i.e., lips
bek' atil, lit. the seed of the penis, i.e., testicles
bek' satil, lit. the seed of the eye, i.e., eyeball

Less static, infinitely progressive is the association provided by adjectives and verbs to give a comparison, often surprising, often humorous, of plants and man. Frequently these associations are not consciously recognized until the appropriate moment, though some have become universally known analogies, i.e., the chubby legs of a healthy child and the thick cornstalks of a healthy young corn plant; a useless man and

TABLE 2.—Tzotzil anatomic botanical terms.

Head	**sjol**	tuber, heart, head, disk, florets, stamens, and pistil
Hair	**sjol**	corn silk
	stzatzal	down, fiber
Forelock	**stz'utujal**	chaff
Eye or face	**sat**	clove, grain, grain of wood, kernel, bean, berry, burr, fruit, nut, pod, bulbule
Ear	**xchikin**	wing, tepal
Nose	**sni'**	top, tip, end, sprout
Mouth	**sti'il**	edge
Whisker	**yisim**	root
Neck	**snuk'**	neck of fruit, section of trunk chopped all the way around
Arm	**sk'ob**	branch
Claw or toenail	**yich'ak**	tendril
Milk or breast, nipple	**xchu'**	milky sap, eye of potato, nipple-like protrusion at end of fruit
Belly	**xch'ut**	middle section
Belly button	**xmixik'**	calyx
Back	**spat**	upper surface, shell, skin, pith
Penis	**yat**	stamens and pistil
Ass	**xchak**	basal end, large log
Leg	**yakan**	stem, internode, pedicel
Foot	**yok**	stem, trunk
Skin	**snukulal**	skin
Grease	**svuntoal**	inner skin, membrane
Heart	**syol**	kernel embryo, pit, hilum, core, basal scar, disk florets, stamen and pistil, heartwood
Intestines	**sbikil**	stringy pulp
Flesh	**sbek'tal**	pith, soft wood, nut meat, edible part of fruit
Joint	**ska'av**	node
Blood	**xch'ich'el**	red sap
Pus	**spojoval**	milky sap
Breath	**yik'**	odor
Fart	**stzis**	citrus rind oil

TABLE 3.—Tzotzil raiment botanical terms.

Skirt	**stzek**	skin, sheath, bare fruiting stalk
Pants	**svex**	sheath
Stockings	**smeriax**	large, leafy stipules
Purse	**xchuival**	seed membrane
Bag	**svorxail**	skin
Spurs	**yexpuxal**	prop root
Machete	**smachitail**	seed pod

scattered corn and beans; well-dressed people and cornstalks laden with beautiful ears.

The majority of associations listed below were offered during the compilation of a general dictionary, lacking a specific focus on botany (Table 4).

It is hardly a great leap from here (Table 4) into male joking speech to reduce men to bananas and women into chayotes!

After examining the wealth of analogy in everyday conversation, it is not surprising to find analogies extended to ritual speech, including prayer. Indeed these poetic substitutions are so pervasive that they render the couplets nearly unintelligible to the foreign initiate.

The tutelary gods are described as **ch'ul-yij**, **ch'ul-k'on**, holy ripe, holy yellow. Each of the deities is addressed **lanichimal ba**, **lanichimal sat**, Thy flowery visage, Thy flowery face. Christ, together with the male saints, is addressed, **nichimal jtot**, **nichimal kajval**, my flowery father, my flowery lord.

Children, too, have their metaphoric denominators: **snich**, **sk'elom**, his flower, his sprout; **p'ejel**, **luchul**, round, perched; **nichim**, **lavaléna**, flower, pink, **asaséna**, **lavaléna**, lily, pink.

TABLE 4.—People and plants: mutually descriptive terms.

STEM, TRUNK, PLANT

bak-'ok	thin-legged (person)—skinny-stemmed (plant)
bix-'akan	long-legged (person)—long-stemmed (plant)
xchak'ak'et	jingling (money)—rustling (reeds)
xchivan	bare teeth or wrinkle nose in disgust—put leafless branch in fire
ch'etel	messy (woman's hair)—stalky (cabbage)
ik'-lusan	black (grimy old hat)—(frost-bitten and wilted plants)
ik'-te'an	black (erect penis)—(large standing tree partially consumed by fire)
ik'-telan	dark (dirty legs)—(fallen burned trees)
jetzel	cross-legged, sitting with legs tucked under—not yet headed (cabbage)
juljul	tall and skinny (person)—branchless (standing tree)
jumul	barely sprouting (pubic hair of virgin)—(weeds)
xkoch	become loose (tooth, fingernail, toenail)—flake off (bark)
k'an-tilan	glossy brown (legs after being rubbed with a stone and oiled for fiesta)—(sugarcane)
xliklajet	in tatters (clothing)—dangling and swaying (Spanish moss, torn banana leaves)
slin sba	grow healthily (child)—(tree)
xlip'ip'	toppling over into ravine (person)—(tree)
xli'vluj	splitting open suddenly (virgin's vagina)—(straight-grained wood)
xmolib	grow old (man)—(tree)
xni'et	rocking back and forth slumped forward (drunken woman, person on horse)—swaying (heavily laden branch)
nitil	drawn (face), clinging (infant who clings to mother's blouse and refuses to be set down)—clinging (vine, bean plant)
pajal vo'	stomach juices that rise to one's mouth when nauseated—chicha, "sour water"
petzpetz	stocky (person)—low and heavily foliaged (tree)
potol	in motionless group (people)—in a clump (bush bean plants pulled up for flailing)
sak-ch'alan	pale (thighs)—(bamboo)
sak-julan	white (bone)—(barkless trunk)
sak-la'an	white (person with clean clothes)—(split wood)
sak-metzan	white (fallen drunk)—(lumber)
sak-pisan	white (buttocks of person defecating)—(potato, cabbage)
sayson	walking feebly (sick person)—weightless (trunk)
taman	too widely spaced (teeth)—plants
tomol	dripping (mucous)—protruding (sprout, saguaro cactus)
tzonol	thick (beard)—thick (moss, bromeliads)
tz'uyul	bowed (head of drunk)—bowed down (heavily laden tree)
vanal	sitting or standing dumbly—sitting (large log)
xvechlajet	recovering (sick children)—wiggling (fence posts, trees in wind)

TABLE 4.—*Continued.*

STEM, TRUNK, PLANT (continued)

vutz'ul	with neck pushed into shoulders by heavy burden—bowed down (small, heavily laden tree)
xotajtik	curly (hair)—crooked (sticks)

LEAVES

ik'-chexan	black (fallen muddy drunk)—(palm for hat)
ik'-tz'uyan	glossy black (hair of young girl)—(black dyed palm)
xkokoj	fall out entirely (teeth)—fall off entirely (leaves), drop off (fruit)
xlebebet	glistening (face, legs, greased or oiled hair)—glossy (leaf)
xlininet	running in crowd—rustling (leaves, fruit)
tzopol	puffy (face of person from the cold)—in a small pile (pine needles)
yax-k'o'an	black and blue (bruise)—green (grass stain)

FLOWERS

xjulav	wake up (person)—open (evening primrose, cut flower after it is watered)
lusul	floppy (hat brim)—withered and drooping (flowers)
moch'ol	curled up (sleeping person)—(closing flowers, leaves, bean pod)
sak-potzan	white (mouth of drunk with spittle)—(double roses)
sak-yoman	white (face of invalid)—(flowers)
tom-jol	conical-headed (Chamula wearing traditional hat)—capitate (onion flower)

FRUIT

chak-bojan	red (virgin's urethra)—(inside of watermelon)
chak-juban	red (blood)—(chili water)
chak-voch'an	red (face from sunburn)—(chilies on plant or in sauce)
chinkul	bumpy (face of person suffering acne)—(pineapple)
ik'-tz'uyan	glossy black (hair of young girl)—(cherries in cluster)
ik'-vojan	black (scrotum)—(grapes, cherries)
kaval	wide open (anus)—split open (base of chayote, overripe papausa)
pajpaj	long and pointed (tight pants)—(pear, avocado)
pitajtik	staring wide-eyed—swollen (healthy **ibes** bean pod)
xpuk'tzaj	become sunken (cheeks)—become mushy (fruit)
sak-pak'an	white (face with sickness or fear)—(inside of unripe watermelon)
te'-tzinan	hard (penis), constipated, unable to urinate, immobile (foetus that won't descend)—hard (banana or avocado that won't ripen)
t'ijil	sitting in the sun (hatless person)—large and ripe (squash)
tzisil	flatulence—spray of citrus rind
xamal	squashed (excrement)—(fruit)
yalal matzal	beautiful (girl's eyes)—peeping forth (young squashes, gourds or chayotes)
yax-set'an	green (insufficiently dyed wool of sash)—(sliced white sapote)
xyayij	be wounded—be damaged

CORNSTALK, PLANT

chak-pujan	red (blood-stained clothing, clothing stained with red dye, tunics worn by men of Apas)—brown (stunted corn plants)
ja'al t'omol	fat and healthy (baby)—thick and healthy (cornstalk, stem of squashes, gourds, reeds, sugarcane)
xjochochet	scraping sound (drunk dragged by the arms)—(corn stubble dragged on the ground)
skejan sba	kneel (person)—grow upwards (flattened corn plant)
k'an-ch'etan	brown (dirty clothes)—yellow (cornfield ruined by rain)
k'an-loman	brown (muddy clothing)—yellow (seared cornfield)
smechan sba	stand or project crookedly (broken leg or arm)—(corn beaten down by the wind)
snach'an sba	peek (person), peer (prisoner)—peep out (corn plant that sprouts and withers)
p'osajtik	chubby (legs of child or girl)—thick (young cornstalks)
xtomk'ij	break (leg, arm)—(cornstalk in wind)
xiket	moving (girl's tangled hair in wind)—(corn stubble in wind)
yax-balan	blue (legs of woman stained with newly dyed skirt)—green (cornfield)

TABLE 4.—*Continued.*

CORN LEAF

valalik	curled up (beautiful eyelashes)—(leaves of corn plants just beginning to be seared)

CORN FLOWER

sbal sba	roll over and over (fighting people)—be in flower

CORN EAR, KERNELS

chak-ch'etan	brown (hair)—(corn silk)
chak-nexan	brown (hair)—(corn silk)
chak-vitan	brown (single hair), red (nose of person in cold, clitoris)—brown (corn silk)
xchik'inaj	sweat (person)—(ripe corn)
k'an-bek'an	brown (brush burn, nearly bald head)—yellow (corn kernels)
k'an-jeman	yellow (excrement)—(corn in large piles)
k'ojoj	acrid (burnt hair)—(burnt corn gruel)
xpu'klij	scattering suddenly (people)—spilling suddenly (corn)
sak-bek'an	clean (clothing)—white (corn kernels)
sak-let'an	white (semen)—(spilt corn gruel)
tan pukuk	lit. ashes and dust, i.e., useless man—corn or beans scattered around floor
xin	smelly (body odor)—sour (corn dough) corn or beans scattered around floor
xin	smelly (body odor)—sour (corn dough)
yalal matzal	well-dressed (people)—beautiful (young corn ears)

LAND

ch'aj	lazy (person)—unproductive (land)
ik'-butan	black (fallen drunk wrapped in robe)—(fire-burnt hill)
kankan	bald (person)—denuded (land)
oy yip	be strong (person)—be productive (land)
sak-bajan	white (white-haired and bald on top)—(denuded land)
sak-juxan	bare (whiskerless face)—(land)
t'ant'an	naked (person)—denuded (land)

The paired terms **snichim ba**, **snichim sat**, his flowery visage, his flowery face, extends dramatically to include days, the day of one's life, the day of one's service (in the religious hierarchy), the floral decoration of an office holder's altar, as well as a steward's chaplet.

The crucial elements of a religious service are similarly identified:

floral decorations and cane liquor—**nichim, yanal te'**, flower, tree leaf

cane liquor and meal—**xi'obil, sk'exobil**, the cause for dread, the cause for shame (before Our Lord)

cane liquor—**stz'utujal, snak'obal**, His dew, His shade

candles—**ch'ul-toj, ch'ul-kantela**, holy pine, holy candle

incense—**j-p'ej yo jpom, j-p'ej yo jch'ail**, a chunk of my lowly incense, a cloud of my humble smoke

Money is termed **j-sil akrusil, j-sil apaxyonal**, a splinter of Thy cross, a sliver of Thy passion. Corn is **xxojobal, snak'obal**, the sunbeam, the shadow (of Our Lord). As if corn plants had human form, the gods are implored to watch over

All the backs,
All the sides,
Of Your sunbeams,
Your shadows.

The snake is **latz'unubike, lavovolike**, Your seed, Your kernel.

Finally, to rejoice is **xmuyubaj, xnichimaj**. The former term is derived from **mu**, fragrant, whereas the latter is to flower. Not surprisingly, **nichimajel** is Paradise.

The seminal importance of analogy extends to the field of medicine, where a quick examination of the giant tuber of the wild yam, or the long, fleshy pseudobulb of a terrestrial orchid, or the pendulous finger-like projections of the cecropia flower provide conclusive evidence of why these particular plants are employed for penis enlargement!

To stimulate hair growth, cattails and certain lushgrowing vines are used. The father of an unmarried girl may soak the vine for her shampoo so the boys will fall in love with her, for they think that long hair makes a good pillow. Her father will also be happy to receive her suitors' cane liquor.

Similarity between plants and man is not limited to surface qualities. Although the Zinacantec dialect of Tzotzil distinguishes between the birth of animals and man, **x'ayan**, and plants, **xvok'**, the Chamulan dialect includes man under **-vok'**. Man and plants grow, **xch'i**, are subject to sickness, **chamel**, and die, **xcham**. Fruits are wounded or damaged, **xyayij**, and an old tree that is cut down and sends forth new shoots, rejuvenates **xcha'-kremaj**. Plants and man are weak, **k'un,** or strong, **tzotz**.

Digging still deeper, both plants and man are ascribed a soul, **ch'ulel**. This term, derived from the now-forgotten, archaic word for god, **ch'u**, has more than one meaning. Strictly speaking, a foetus receives its soul from the tutelary gods, and that soul is fixed more securely in the baby through baptism. In this sense soul is a sacred quality, a mystical force. But it is also possible to say of a child, **iyul xa xch'ulel**, lit. "his soul has returned," i.e., he has become responsible. The same phrase may be applied to a grown person, meaning, he has come to his senses, or to a drunk who had passed out, or to a sick person regaining consciousness.

Pursuing the subject of souls, it must be remembered that Zinacantecs are not prone to holding philosophical discussions either among themselves or with anthropologists. Information gleaned from chance remarks or from observations made in the context of work, worship, or play are likely to be denied in a formal interview. As there is no formal training, a great variety of belief and conviction exists. Some objects are ascribed souls, with no reason given, whereas the presence of a soul in other objects is given a specific rationale.

Briefly, deities, the Earth Lord, the saints' images, crosses, fire, and salt have souls. Named rocks, cliffs, and caves bear the soul of the Earth Lord. A new house receives its soul through a shaman's offering of prayers and candles. Bells have souls, as do cars if they have been blessed by a priest. Musical instruments have souls as do corn gruel pots, being recipients of cane liquor. Furniture has no soul, but tools acquire the soul of their owner. It is widely believed that if you leave your tool in the field or the woods overnight the weeds or the trees will beat it so that the next day you will feel too exhausted to work. Like tools, clothes assume their owner's soul. They are censed when their owner is sick and some are burned when he dies. Candles, incense, and cane liquor have souls. Food has a soul as it keeps us alive.

All plants have a soul; they know when to flower even though they have no father and no mother. Plants and trees talk to each other. But there are those who claim that only useful plants have souls, while others explain it this way: "weeds do not have good souls," they are not sensible, not responsible— "they are like people who pay no attention to what you say to them."

A specially strong soul is the property of medicinal plants and the "flowers" of a curing ceremony, for they defend us. At a curing ceremony the flowers, incense, pine, cross, cane liquor, and candles talk together (**tzobol k'op**) and are then united to Our Lord.

Before the introduction of herbicides and the devastation of the forests, it was believed that the souls never departed from weeds and trees, as the vegetation always sprouted back up. But they do feel pain when cut. The sap is their blood.

At night the souls of plants interact with man "beneath the earth's surface," when he dreams, when his soul sees.

Analogies are embedded in the visions of the soul in a systematic way. Sometimes they are interpreted straightforwardly, sometimes stood on their head to provide an explanation for one's nocturnal adventures. And so, to see or eat a cabbage head gives warning not to set out on a trip, lest one be murdered on the trail. To gather firewood is to die, for green wood is used to line the grave. To hoe is to dig one's grave. To receive a tortilla gourd and a waterjug is to receive a girl's soul, to foresee the birth of a girl, and agricultural tools signify a boy's birth. To receive a female visitor is to become prosperous, to receive the corn's soul, but to give corn away is to lose its soul. The reverse logic, though, is just as predominant, so, to see heaps of corn is to become poor, to eat or drink well, to become sick, to eat meager fare, to eat abundantly.

Via this system of interpretation, this nighttime vision of the flora, shamans, midwives, and bonesetters receive their power from the gods. Shamans are given their bamboo staffs, shamans and midwives their gourds and flowers, whereas bonesetters are ordered to set upright a tree that has fallen in smithereens.

By analogy, too, is explained the origin or the names of various plants. The first woman was created from a watermelon squash. Of a noticeably pregnant woman they joke, "now she has a watermelon squash!" Because the Virgin Mary had no breasts Our Lord gave her the mammiform **chuchu'** fruits. From the milk of Mary's breasts sprouted potatoes, claim some, while others tell how she boiled three river pebbles. Chili sprouted from the drops of Christ's blood. Christ rubbed his wounds with white corn and so created the red form. Or, too, Thunderbolt's daughter was struck by her husband and wiped her nose with an ear of corn. Magueys are the product of Christ's spit, which he rubbed on the rocks with his finger. The prickly pear, **petok**, was created from clouds, **tok**. The glossy black avocado, **tzitz**, is derived from the egg of the junco, **tzitzil ul**. And everyone knows where the apple that stuck in men's throats came from.

The Flood stories tell of how squirrels received their tails from "squirrel tail grass," and how coatimundis received theirs from "coati tail" bamboo because they were eating "coati's white sapote" fruit, and squirrels were eating "squirrel's avocado" fruits. Even earlier, **tontikil ch'aben** provided a mattress for Mary to lay the Christchild on to change his diapers, while they were hiding in a banana grove.

And later, while Christ's back was turned, the Devil created cane liquor by pissing three times around the cauldron of boiling sugar water. Analogies continue as Rabbit dirties the papayas, leaving round, black pellets inside them, and then tricks Skunk into strumming his guitar in the reeds, believing that a wedding party is approaching to the sound of skyrockets. Alas for Skunk, the cracks and pops are the reeds Rabbit had set fire to.

The poverty of Zinacantán is explained, too, by analogy, for when the Indian king departed for Mexico City, the *ladinos* of San Cristóbal strew pine needles at his feet, while the Indians scattered coins.

But most striking of all is the play and counterplay of images when a man discovers a beautiful dahlia, which, as he stoops to pick it, turns into a hideous, fat snake, and then is transformed into the dazzling daughter of Thunderbolt.

Equipped with blood and soul, plants also express their emotions and reveal their personality. This statement should not be taken literally, "for plants have no faces, how can we see them talk? When we say that a plant cries, that is just a figure of speech."

How do wild plants, trees, and vines figure in the panorama?

Both **ximo'** and **xut**, the ancestors' corn and beans, were so fussy and complaining that Our Lord banished them to the wilds. When weeds are left uncut, but bowed down to be cut the next day, "they suffer." Weeds that are weeded and trees that are felled "get angry." The weeder is considered by his victims to be a "murderer," **jmilvanej**, and should he leave his tool out overnight they will "beat it," **chmajvan**. Oak wood, **tzajal tulan**, which sparks in the fire is said to "get angry," and "scold." Weeds that have felt the blade of the hoe are "jealous" of those next to them that are still untouched. Weeds that overgrow a cornfield "laugh."

A tree such as **tzajal kachímpa te'**, having very dense heartwood extremely difficult to cut, is "so stronghearted." When weeds survive a weeding, the frustrated farmer may exclaim, "they don't feel the hoe, the fuckers rebelled." The soul of a tree that is girdled and refuses to die, always producing scar tissue, is known to retaliate, **chyaluvan**, and cause the death of its persecutor. The soul of any large tree that is cut may chase, **snutzvan**, and frighten, **ssibtasvan**, the axeman.

This is what is said of "stupid" or "useless" vegetation.

Many of the negative personality traits seen above are shared by useful plants. They may be "rebellious," as **koko'on**, which will not grow again after a lot has been pulled up. Or they may be "uncooperative sometimes" as **unen mu**, which is always bitter when cooked by some people, or a fruit tree that does not fruit. White bush beans are known to be "small-" or "weak-hearted," i.e., unpredictable, sometimes producing well, sometimes not, regardless of the planter. Red and black bush beans are "strong-hearted." A plant may be "distracted in heart" and fail to grow in the dry season. It may become "lazy" and stop growing altogether. Or it may be very discriminating and "see who will treat it well," as tobacco that will not grow in everyone's yard.

Of course, useful plants, just as weeds and wild trees, "suffer." Bean plants "suffer" if they are left unpicked. Beans "suffer" when spilled and stepped on. Plants do not "grow used" to some regions where they are cultivated, they do not "feel at home." Plants have "two hearts," are unhappy if they are not cared for, or if they do not grow well. They become "depressed" if they are planted on unproductive land or are not weeded. Unweeded plants "cry."

But a well-weeded plant, a plant that flourishes, is of "one heart." It is happy. If it grows fast and robustly it is "industrious." A plant such as **pimil anal**, a succulent that usually flourishes, "doesn't disobey" or "doesn't know how to disobey." Some plants are known to "endure," as an herb that is stored inside and retains its flavor when dry. Other plants "know two ways," as a medicinal herb that is a remedy for two kinds of sickness, or a food plant that is cooked in two different styles. Squashes and chayotes "learn from" or "picture" the stars so as to produce many fruit. Corn and beans "visit" among themselves, mixing strains of different colors.

Corn's personality is no different from that of the rest of the flora. It "suffers" when unweeded or spilled and stepped on. It "grows tired of" its place on a steep slope and turns yellow. It "gets angry" and "rebels" when it is not weeded. If planted in poor soil it "gets lazy" and stops growing. Corn "cries" if it is not weeded or if it is sold to a government warehouse. But it "endures" if it grows even when it is weeded only once. Of course it "feels better" when well-weeded.

There are forms of corn ears, however, which, acting in consonance with their name and shape, are thought to be threatening to people, or to have souls that even consume the souls of the neighboring corn. Figures of speech, maybe, but once the grain has been removed, their cobs are speedily broken.

In this world of personified flora the Zinacantecs have also personified many of the major elements of the universe. The sun is Christ, Our Holy Father, and the moon is the Virgin Mary, Our Holy Mother. The Thunderbolt, an aspect of the Earth Lord, is addressed, "Holy King, Holy Angel, Holy Serpent." The Earth Lord is also envisioned as a wealthy *ladino* rancher, in charge of distributing rain and wind, lord of the land and the forest. **Me' Ik'**, Mother Wind, is the embodiment and origin of wind. With her hair a tangle of leaves and twigs, she is said to emerge from caves, when mist and drizzle are especially thick, to steal the soul of corn. **Me' K'inubal**, Mother Nor'easter, the rainbow, is a cold Chamulan female devil who also steals corn's soul.

When giving a new house its soul, the shaman prays to Our Lord, the tutelary gods, the saints, and the Earth Lord, that the inhabitants of the house may prosper. At the Holy Cross Day ceremonies and the agricultural ceremonies these same deities are importuned to protect the farmer from injury and snakebite, to provide sufficient rain, to protect the cornfield from wind and to grant a decent harvest.

For many, the stages of the moon are of critical importance. When the moon is full or waning slightly, all trees, corn, and all flowers except carnations should be planted. Fruit trees planted at this time will not grow too tall and will fruit earlier. Rafters and houseposts, lashing vines, thatch, and highland fence posts are cut so they will not become wormeaten. Corn is doubled and flailed.

When the moon is young, fruit trees should not be planted lest they (1) not root firmly, (2) grow tall and be blown down by the wind, (3) have flowers fall, (4) fruit later. Posts should not be planted lest they rot. Carnations should be planted so they will grow tall. Corn flailed during a waxing moon will be weevil-eaten.

Nothing should be planted when there is no moon, for the seeds will "picture" or "imitate" the moon and grow underground.

If a person is drowned, the river is said to have "gotten its meal," **ista xa sve'el**, and will no longer flood. The same expression is used if the sky clears after constant rain, presuming that a horse or other animal has perished.

Attention is paid to birds as weather omens. If a buzzard's wings whir or grackles flock, a nor'easter is coming, but if the swallows flock it will lift.

To influence the natural elements, a variety of magical means may be employed. To bring rain at weeding time you should place three gourds half-filled with water at the eavesdrop of your house, or you should toss 13 empty river snail shells in the sky. To stop a rainbow (that signifies the end of rain), a bullet may be fired at its foot. To stop hail, hot coals are tossed at it three times. To lift a nor'easter, eat watermelon squash, or, claim some, cheerfully, drink lots of cane liquor!

Innumerable techniques to enhance and protect the crops can be found scattered throughout the Flora.

Magical means (**metz'tael**) are also used by envious people and witches to damage an enemy's crop. So, a witch may pray in caves, calling forth wind to blow down an enemy's corn crop. Or he may transform himself into a rainbow and stand over an enemy's fruit trees. The rainbow's heat first kills the leaves at the top of the tree.

Simpler methods may also be taken (1) to cause a peach tree to die, bury a stick of pine at its foot, (2) to cause the stems of watermelon squash and chayote to die, boil the stems of **ch'aben** and place them on top, (3) to cause watermelon squash and chayote flowers to drop off, cut the young stems and eat them with a lot of green chilies, (4) to cause bean flowers to drop off, smoke a lot in the field, (5) to cause the blossoms of commercial flowers to die, blow tobacco water on them, (6) to cause a cornfield to die, sprinkle tobacco on it. By prayer a witch may "disorient," **ssokbe sjol**, the Earth Lord so that the beams at the corners of an enemy's house will creak and the inhabitants fall ill.

Unquestionably, much of this "knowledge of the elders" is known more by hearsay than by practice, and is vanishing.

These methods in no way exhaust the repertory of what Frazer (1890) would call "sympathetic magic." The Flora is peppered with activities that recognize and respond to similarities between man and the universe, man and plants, plants and the universe. Man's state of mind is reflected on the plants and the universe so that a grudging planter will have a meager harvest.

A brief inventory of agricultural techniques that rely upon analogy to enhance one's crops suggests the power of association in Zinacantec philosophy. These are what the elders call **smelol**, "the true way":

1. Whistle to produce well-formed gourd tips.
2. Tighten belt to produce gourd with constricted center.
3. Plant chilies barefoot to produce thin-skinned fruits.
4. Piss on chili plants to produce hot chilies.
5. Place chicken feet in seed bag to produce strong-rooted corn.
6. Before planting corn, provide meal of chicken, iguana, or armadillo for strong roots.
7. Do not whistle when planting corn lest one cause wind damage.
8. Plant watermelon squash in the afternoon when the sun is low so that the runners not grow long and barren.
9. Plant watermelon squash at night when there are many stars so there will be many fruit.
10. Plant watermelon squash with a piece of brown sugar, carried on oak bark or a piece of broken pot so squashes will be sweet and have a thick rind.
11. Plant chayotes on fiesta days characterized by an abundance of fruit, such as Christmas and All Souls' Day, so chayotes will bear well.
12. Sit cross-legged when planting chayotes so tubers will be near the surface.
13. Chew coyol fruits, which are always borne in large clusters, and spit the seeds on avocado trees, chili, or watermelon squash plants so they will fruit well.
14. Do not cut down a ceiba or you will swell up and die.
15. Do not scratch your head when harvesting chayote tubers or they will become stringy.
16. Do not plant corn on a Sunday, "dog's holiday," or your crop will be eaten by dogs.
17. Do not harvest chayote tubers or potatoes until the afternoon, when their souls return from their noon bath, clean and white.
18. Do not sell or deny that you have tobacco or mint, or the plants will lose their souls and die.
19. Do not eat beans on Lenten Fridays or in Holy Week or they will turn into flies.
20. Do not plant corn during Holy Week or corn will be infested with corn smut, the smoke of Judas' cigar.
21. Do not plant or cut wood from Holy Wednesday to Easter, lest Our Lord suffer one's pain.

Proceeding from these analogic techniques, there are others that require verbal games. Some plants must be referred to by other names, as castor bean, which is termed Mary's greens, **maruch itaj**, so that the leaves will not be bitter. Certain poisonous plants must be spoken to directly to avoid being blistered, whereas other plants are ordered to grow or to fruit. It is said that people, to protect themselves, dance before poison ivy. Others slash avocado trees to persuade them to fruit.

Zinacantec farmers' poetic techniques in farming do little to reduce the drudgery, the hard work. Of this they are well aware. When corn farmers are about to go to the steamy lowlands to cultivate their fields there is a standard expression to describe their prospects, "then the balls will certainly sweat!"

But their recognition of the pain, exhaustion, and danger in corn farming is tempered by a respect for hard labor in the fields: "There is good food if you know how to work, son!" Coupled with their industry is a respect for careful use of the corn. And so they say disparagingly of a man who spends his resources on cane liquor, "He finished scooping up all his corn." This attitude is often expressed with an added reverence towards corn, their very sustenance: "He doesn't care about his corn, he sells it right off," "they don't care for it anymore, it just lies scattered."

Zinacantecs are often embarrassed, shy, about speaking of these "superstitions," "old wives' tales," as we would call them. But just as a Zinacantec denies belief in one custom, he will swear the validity of another. It must be a very cynical Zinacantec to doubt that disrespect towards corn, ill treatment, will not be repaid with divine punishment, with hunger and poverty, brought down by corn's lament.

Mixed with **pólvo** and **líkido**, powder and liquid, insecticide and herbicide, who is to say whether the poetic license of Zinacantán, binding man and plant to the universe, can persist.

What's in a Name?

Robert M. Laughlin

Scanning the botanical plant names in Appendix 2, it may be seen that many are pan-Mayan; 174 appear in two or more languages. Of these, by far the largest number are for "trees": 97, whereas 51 are for "plants" and 26 for "vines." Considering the small number of species of "vines" as opposed to "plants," the figures demonstrate the cultural importance of the former (including beans), and the relative insignificance of the latter (including "weeds"). The greatest degree of sharing occurs between the neighboring Chiapan languages: Tzeltal, Tojolabal and Chol, as well as the bordering Guatemalan languages: Chuj and Kanjobal. Three terms are borrowed from some Mixe-Zoque language: **kokov**, compare with Zoque **kakawa**, **potov**, compare with Sierra Popoluca **pátan**, and **tzima'**, compare with Zoque **¢ima**. These derive from proto-Mixe-Zoque **kakawa**, **¢ima**, and **pataw**. A dozen Nahuatl loans (not all listed in Appendix 2) may have been borrowed in part from Spanish. These are **amat**, **amolyo**, **jikamo**, **kakaxon** (**jobel**), **makulixkuat**, **met**, **mosote** (**jobel**), **nantzi'**, **otot**, **tempix**, **tzon** (**te'**), and **vamuch** (**te'**). Four terms, **jutuju**, **mukumu**, **nankipu**, and **tuturu**, may possibly have originated in Chiapanec. Some cognates refer to closely related species, whereas others may focus on plant parts or even use, as **tux** for cotton seed, **chi** for maguey fiber, **sakil** for squash seed, **aj** for skyrocket rather than for reed, and **otot** for house rather than for bamboo.

Because of the introduction of plants from Europe, there are a large number of Spanish loan words. There are also native plants, particularly from the Grijalva Valley lowlands, whose names are Spanish in origin or combine Spanish and Tzotzil words.

A comparison of Tzotzil and Tzeltal plant term cognates shows dramatically that cultural significance acts as a strong conservative force. Of the cognates, 87% are cultivated plants, 80% are protected, 45% wild, but useful, and only 17% are insignificant. "Names of plants that are considered to be important are retained over long periods of time, while names of insignificant plants disappear at a much faster rate" (Berlin, Breedlove, Laughlin, and Raven, 1973:163).

In 1963 we introduced a new occupation in Zinacantán that came to be known as **sa'-tz'i'lel**, "plant searching," a name that established **tz'i'lel** as equivalent to flora, or to our general use of "plant," including trees, vines, etc.

LIFE FORM

Under the umbrella of "plant" we discovered three major categories of "life forms": **ak'**, "vine," plants with viny, twining stems; **te'**, "tree," plants with erect, woody stems, generally growing more than two meters tall when mature; **tz'i'lel**, "plant," plants that are neither viny nor woody nor tall-growing. As in Tenejapa, mushrooms and fungi are considered to be members of the fauna rather than the flora, but, unlike Tenejapa, there are no wholly unaffiliated or anomalous plants—every plant is a member of at least one of the three life forms. This does not mean that everyone assigns a plant to the same category. There were differences of opinion between different observers and between the allocations of a plant by the same observer at different times. Woody or herbaceous plants that spread widely may be called "vine." Vines that are more bush-like may be called "tree," or "plant." Shrubs, sub-shrubs, and stunted or young trees may be classed variously as "tree," or "plant." This last is the most frequent overlap, but a few plants have been assigned by different individuals to each one of the life forms. Some kinds of plants are by their very nature anomalous, or, as cacti, have closely related species ranging from plant to vine to tree. Moreover, individual members of the same species may sprawl to varying degrees, or grow to varying heights and sturdiness.

Unlike in Tenejapa, where graminaceous plants are assigned a major category, Zinacantecs subsume these under "plant," sometimes granting them a subdivision, jobel, "grass."

Two, further complications arose: **tz'i'lel** may also carry the connotation of weed or useless plant, while a name, ＿＿ **ak'**, may not refer to a vine, but to a tree whose bark is used for lashing.

SETS AND ISOLATES

The life form is composed of sets of plants and isolates that do not seem to belong to any set. The sets consist of plants that are seen by Zinacantecs as being more similar to the other members of the set than to any other plant. As mentioned before, these gestalt sets usually represent a pattern of shared morphological features, a similar silhouette, though a few are based on a shared single trait, as toxicity, or similarity of use, as commercial flowers.

There are a number of plants whose silhouette seems more important to the Zinacantecs than their life form membership. Columnar cactuses, though classed as "tree," are grouped with the prickly pears, and sprawling or low-growing cacti are classed as "plants." Similarly, datura and hibiscus, though "trees," are most strongly associated with shrubby "plants" bearing trumpet or bell-shaped flowers, as tobacco and four o'clock.

The sets that emerged from our study are not named by Zinacantecs; they correspond in Tenejapa to "covert complexes" (Berlin, Breedove, Raven, 1974:160). For convenience sake we have supplied them with names and ordered them alphabetically in the Flora. Our criteria in choosing the name of one of the members of the set to carry the name for the entire set was (1) if it was the most prominent culturally, or (2) if it had the most number of specific forms, (3) if it was a native Tzotzil term rather than a Spanish loan, or (4) was the least descriptive of a number of descriptive terms.

In addition to the sets that compose a life form are the isolates, or plants that have not yet been associated by Zinacantecs with any other plant. Further questioning may reveal relationships that have escaped us to date.

GENERICS

The generic members of a set may be monotypic or polytypic, i.e., be one of a kind, or have two or more specific components. In some cases, particularly among the "plants," the generic name is a collective noun, generally descriptive, that we have described as representing a non-Linnaean assemblage of morphologically diverse plants, usually sharing a particular trait signaled by the name. Many of these Linnaean species bear an additional name and occur in other sets.

Most generic names of plants are composed of one, two, or three words, with the third word usually **ak'**, **tz'i'lel**, or **te'**. Generic names of two words usually consist of an adjective and a noun, as "white tree," a noun describing a noun, as "cotton tree," or a noun possessing a noun, as "jaguar('s) whiskers." In the latter case the possessed noun precedes the possessor.

When evoking botanical names, two descriptive terms dominated our conversations—**batz'i**, "genuine" or "true," and **yit'ix**, "bastard" or "false." Semantically, **yit'ix** is "the jealous one." In only two Instances, **batz'i te'**, oak, and **batz'i itaj**, kale, is **batz'i** a necessary component of the name. In all others it is a useful means for signaling the true, the basic one of two or more related species. In the Flora we have retained **batz'i** in many instances for the sake of clarity. Tenejapans employ **batz'il** widely as a necessary component, but Zinacantecs add the corresponding descriptive term only when required to for purposes of distinction. The importance of botanical concerns is illustrated by **yit'ix**, a term that could logically be used for the even more diverse realm of insects, or for birds and mammals, but it is restricted to the botanical world. With such a handy term any unknown plant can be easily described. We never included **yit'ix** as a name, though the term was extremely useful in discovering what plants were considered to resemble or be distantly related to a plant. The Latin names of plants designated "**yit'ix**" are entered under the extended range of that particular plant.

Within the broad scope from genuine to false the Zinacantecs use a number of means in the naming system to establish relationship. The commonest is to have an animal possess the plant, so, mouse's chayote is a relative of chayote (see Table 5). Almost always, a plant possessed in this way is wild and of less utility than the genuine form. Although these names usually are used to distinguish generics, occasionally they indicate specifics, as **yuch'ul vo' bolom,** jaguar's orchid. The possessor may also be a spook, Judas or an ancestor.

Another way to express a similar distance is to add the appropriate **ak'**, **tz'i'lel**, or **te'** to the name, so, **xantiya** is a watermelon, and **xantiya ak'** is a wild vine resembling a watermelon, **aj-te'** is a white sapote, and **aj-te' te'** is a wild, lowland tree.

Zinacantecs employ a broad expanse of descriptive terms. Some are applicable to native genera, species and variety, but most focus on the lower two levels.

Most prominent is size: large, medium, small, dwarf, tiny.

Color vies with size. It may be combined with spotting and striping, and variegation.

Most frequently, color and size terms are not attached to the generic in everyday speech. When asked, "What kinds of such-and-such are there?" the individual will answer, "There's a big one and a little one," or, "There's a red one and a white one." Then, in subsequent conversation on the subject he will naturally refer to "big ____," "red ____," etc.

Shape terms are legion, referring to root, bark, stem, leaf, flower, and fruit. Here is an incomplete sampling: pendulous, erect, hollow, flat, thick, thin, brittle, stiff, hard, soft, strong, wide, double, round, long, squat, protuberant, tubular, nippled,

TABLE 5.—Animal possessors.

Animal possessor	Plant names
Horse	8
Mouse	8
Fox	7
Deer (or sheep)	7
Bird	6
Raven	6
Pig	5
Squirrel	4
Cow (or bull)	3
Jaguar	2
Rabbit	2
Opossum	1
Coati	1
Coyote	1
Goat	1
Turkey	1
Buzzard	1
Chachalaca	1
White-tipped dove	1
Mockingbird	1
Groove-billed ani	1
Towhee	1
Snake	1
Rattlesnake	1
Wasp	1
Deer fly	1
Caterpillar (different kinds)	2

curly, cross-shaped, four-sided, inflated, clustered, etc.

Texture is also prominent: downy, downy-tipped, spiny, leathery, bumpy, smooth, bald, slippery, sticky, and milky.

Flavor and odor penetrate the naming process: bitter, sweet, sour, acrid, fragrant and stinky.

Manner of growth is considered, whether ground-growing or vine-like, i.e., bush or pole (bean).

The speed of growth is also noted: forty-day, early and late.

Time of day and time of year is another component: dusk (flowering), Corpus Christi (planting, flowering), All Souls' Day and Christmas (maturing).

Habitat and location may figure in the name: rock-growing, cliff-growing, epiphytic, aquatic, and terrestrial, lowland, temperate, highland, Chiapan, Ixtapanec, San Lucas, Ocozo-cuautla, etc. This leads to foreign, fine, hybrid, cultivated, first cultivated, and wild.

Equally important in the naming process is the use of plants: possession by elders or ancestors indicating former use, remedies for a great variety of illnesses, poisons, cooking herbs, flowers used on specific fiestas as that of Our Lady of Guadalupe or Christmas, gourds for calling souls, holding tobacco, or rubbing the body, thatch for houses or packsaddles, ships, shampoo, edible fruits. But use names are infrequent for vines (16) and trees (24). Remedy names for plants occur very often, particularly as synonyms.

Related to shape and use is the distinction between boy and girl. The female form is thicker and preferred.

With considerable imagination, Zinacantecs name plants for their resemblance to an animal, e.g., shrimp, or to an animal's body part (Table 6).

There are a smaller number of names associated with animals, such as ant path tree, bumblebee perch, hummingbird nest perch, antlion plant, coyote tree, butterfly vine. The association may be one of appearance, as antlion plant, or of use, as ant path tree.

The resemblance of plants to man-made objects is noted: machete, old woman's tumpline, old man's walking stick, rosary, needle, bell, and penny.

A few names compare one plant to another: orange sweet lime, ear of corn bromeliad, custard apple oak, watermelon squash (shaped), pumpkin squash.

There are a few descriptive names that avoid the above categories, as sky pillar, three months, magdalen vine, etc.

Of course many plant names have no descriptive, possessive, use, or association elements. The majority of these consist of a single word or a single word combined with **ak'**, **te'**, or **tz'i'lel**.

Now there is the problem of synonyms, of which we recorded 1134, ignoring the distinction between singular and plural adjectives, as **muk'ta** and **muk'tik**, also ignoring the distinction between terms with identical meanings, as **bik'it** and **k'ox**, "small." When one of the plant collectors, Antzelmo Peres, a shaman, was asked how he could communicate with his patients' families if he told them to bring a handful of X for the cure and they called it Y. "No problem at all, I just describe

the plant to them!"

The majority of synonyms fall into a limited number of categories:

1. Slightly different spelling, e.g., **nankipu, nankito**.

2. Substitution of a Spanish for a Tzotzil term or vice-versa, e.g., **tzo' xulem te', matabey, ch'ix te', kevrajacha**.

3. Addition or subtraction of a descriptive, often referring to size or color, or of **te'**, **ak'**, and **tz'i'lel**, e.g., **sakil karnéro te'**,

TABLE 6.—Animal body part names.

Animal	Body part
Deer (or sheep)	neck
	ear
	tail
	hoof
	burp
Dog	tongue
	tooth
	paw
	tail
	vagina
	penis
Bull, cow	forehead
	horn
	tongue
	tail
Mouse, rat	ear
	claw
	tail
Rabbit	ear
	fur
Pig	penis
	fart
Gopher	ear
	tail
Opossum	whiskers
	fart
Coati	tail
	penis
Rooster	cockscomb
	bristle
Jaguar	whiskers
	tail
Squirrel	ear
	tail
Bird	claw
	shit
Armadillo	ear
Ram	penis
Cat	claw
Turkey	wattle
Crocodile	tail
Rattlesnake	fangs
Horse	shit
Buzzard	shit
Fox	rib
Frog	bone
Firefly	wing
Cricket	spit

"white ____," equals **karnéro te'**, **ajo' te'** equals **ajo'**.

4. Substitution of one descriptive for another, with the same meaning, e.g., **kilon ech'** "pendulous ____," for **kilkil ech'**.

5. Substitution of one descriptive for another, with different meanings, e.g., **tzajal pom tz'unun** "red ____," is the same plant as **muil pom tz'unun** "fragrant ____."

6. Substitution of one animal possessor for another, or one animal's association for another's, e.g., **ne bolom** "jaguar tail," is the same plant as **sne lakarto** "crocodile's tail."

7. Substitution of a descriptive for a use term or vice-versa, e.g., **ik'al ok tzib** "black-stemmed fern," is the same plant as **poxil sarampyo** "measles medicine."

8. Substitution of one use for another, e.g., **poxil sep'** "mange medicine," is the same plant as **poxil chakal,** "boil medicine."

9. Substitution of a generic or specific name by that of a closely related plant, e.g., *Lagascea helianthifolia,* is named both **tzojoj** and **sakil sun,** "white **sun**."

We had thought originally that synonymous names could be traced to particular hamlets, and although this is so for a limited number of names, in most cases the choice appears to be highly individualistic. On one occasion we had Antzelmo Peres and his wife separately identify a number of plants. To our great consternation, we discovered that they agreed on only a quarter of the names—those most culturally significant. We then recalled that Anselmo's wife was an orphan child from Magdalenas who was adopted by a Zinacantec when she was about 8 years old, and indeed some of her names did not sound as if they were from Zinacantán. When a next-door neighbor was questioned, she raised the percentage of agreement to over 60%.

We have no doubt that the number of plant names is limited only by the number of people who were asked to provide names. In the absence of written records the mind is free to play with wonderful ingenuity. An American student, investigating the ethnozoology of Zinacantán, dutifully included as a member of his list of birds, **unen sonso mut** "stupid little bird," and though no one dared in seriousness to provide me with a "stupid little plant," there were times when they surely felt our fastidious search for names deserved such a reward!

The Flora

The Flora

Dennis E. Breedlove and Robert M. Laughlin

The flora is divided into its three life forms: "vine" (**ak'**), "tree" (**te'**), and "plant" (**tz'i'lel**). Each life form is composed of a varying number of sets followed by the isolates, which do not seem to belong to any of the above sets.

Each set is introduced by stating the total of its generic members, followed by a description of its characteristic features.

Regardless of the set name, its generic constituents are listed alphabetically. The Tzotzil name is presented first. If it occurred in the colonial dictionary (Laughlin, 1988) it is starred (*). When possible, an English translation, enclosed in quotes, is provided next, but should one of the component terms of the Tzotzil name be untranslatable or have a variety of references, it is left in Tzotzil. If a plant is known to grow in expanses or large expanses, the suffixes **-tik** or **-altik** may be appended, e.g., **trikotik**, wheat field, **trikoaltik**, large wheat field. This is indicated by (**-tik, -altik**). Next, also within parentheses, the synonyms are listed alphabetically. If they occurred in the colonial dictionary they, too, are starred. The same criteria that was used in deciding set names dictated the choice of which synonym should be given as the major generic name. All synonyms are also listed in Appendix 5 with a translation, when possible. Next in sequence is the common English name, if such exists, followed by the Latin name or names. The Latin name is tagged by numbers, e.g., (1–7), to indicate how many separate times the plant was identified and by how many individuals. Major cultivars that were seen endless times by endless numbers of consultants were simply marked (1–1).

Discussion of the plant begins with a description of its morphology, whether cultivated, adventive, or wild, and its range. Then follows a cultural description initiated by historical or mythological context, cultivation or gathering practices, use (of root, stem, leaf, flower, fruit) for construction, tools, religious decoration, remedy, food, etc., and, finally, sale. Remedies and foods are further characterized as being "hot" (**k'ixin**), "medium" (**lek no'ox**), or "cold" (**sik**). Their temperature may be a quality of their natural state or may be changed by the method of their preparation. Generally speaking, roots, greens, and fruits are "cold," but if they have a spicy or bitter flavor they are described frequently as "hot." There is considerable variation in the ascription of temperature; the determining factors are not well understood.

For the sake of precision, a plant's use is tied to the particular Latin species identified by a consultant as having that application, even though other members of the generic may well have the same use.

The extended range follows. This is an alphabetical listing of Latin names referring to plants identified by consultants as being **yit'ix** or similar to the generic in question.

If the generic is polytypic, the total of specific members is listed.

The nominate form of the specific is presented first. It may be signaled by the adjective **batz'i**, "genuine." The botanical and cultural description adheres to the format for generics.

Most varietals are indented, following the description of the specific. A few, however, show differences that were considered by the consultants as being so minor that they hesitated giving them varietal names. These are simply noted within the description of the specific. The format for the botanical and cultural description of varietals and isolates is identical to that of generics and specifics.

The final tally for the contents of this Flora is as follows:

	Sets		
"Vines"	10		
"Trees"	35		
"Plants"	35		
Total	80		

	Set Members	Isolates	Total
Genera			
"Vines"	88	7	95
"Trees"	220	40	260
"Plants"	253	47	300
Total	561	94	655
Species			
"Vines"	103	7	110
"Trees"	154	39	193
"Plants"	257	39	296
Total	514	85	599
Varietals			
"Vines"	17	5	22
"Trees"	2	6	8
"Plants"	31	6	37
Total	50	17	67
Grand Total	1125	196	1321

CONTEMPORARY SYNONYMS IN TZOTZIL

	Sets	Isolates	Total
Genera			
"Vines"	96	10	106
"Trees"	248	27	275
"Plants"	323	27	350
Total	667	64	731
Species			
"Vines"	82	7	89

"Trees"	184	37	221
"Plants"	281	29	310
Total	547	73	620

Varietals
"Vines"	3	0	3
"Trees"	3	1	4

"Plants"	7	0	7
Total	13	1	14
Grand Total	1227	138	1365

The total of 2686 Tzotzil names for generics, specifics, and varietals refers to Latin determinations of 1484 species with an additional 30 identifications by genus.

"Vines": "Ak' Sets"

aros chenek'
  ik'al aros chenek' — *Vigna umbellata* (Fabaceae)
  sakil aros chenek' — *Vigna umbellata* (Fabaceae)
  tzajal aros chenek' — *Vigna umbellata* (Fabaceae)
botil
  ik'al botil — *Phaseolus coccineus* (Fabaceae)
  sakil botil — *Phaseolus coccineus* (Fabaceae)
  tzajal botil — *Phaseolus coccineus* (Fabaceae)
  tz'ibal botil
    sakil tz'ibal botil — *Phaseolus coccineus* (Fabaceae)
    tzajal tz'ibal botil — *Phaseolus coccineus* (Fabaceae)
ibes
  ik'al ibes — *Phaseolus coccineus* ssp. *darwinianus* (Fabaceae)
  k'anal ibes — *Phaseolus coccineus* ssp. *darwinianus* (Fabaceae)
  sakil ibes — *Phaseolus coccineus* ssp. *darwinianus* (Fabaceae)
  tzajal ibes — *Phaseolus coccineus* ssp. *darwinianus* (Fabaceae)
javas
  k'anal javas — *Vicia faba* (Fabaceae)
  sakil javas
    krem javas — *Vicia faba* (Fabaceae)
    tzeb javas — *Vicia faba* (Fabaceae)
    tzajal javas — *Vicia faba* (Fabaceae)
  javas kajve — *Mucuna pruriens* var. *utilis* (Fabaceae)
kántela chenek'
  ik'al kántela chenek' — *Vigna unguiculata* (Fabaceae)
  k'anal kántela chenek' — *Vigna unguiculata* (Fabaceae)
  te'tikal kántela chenek' — *Vigna vexillata* (Fabaceae)
karvensa
  ik'al karvensa — *Cicer arietinum* (Fabaceae)
  sakil karvensa — *Pisum sativum* (Fabaceae)
manya chenek'
  batz'i manya chenek' — *Arachis hypogaea* (Fabaceae)
  soktomal manya chenek' — *Arachis hypogaea* (Fabaceae)
x'ak'il chenek' — *Phaseolus vulgaris* (Fabaceae)
  chana x'ak'il — *Phaseolus vulgaris* (Fabaceae)
  ik'al x'ak'il — *Phaseolus vulgaris* (Fabaceae)
  ik'al x'ak'il ta olon osil — *Phaseolus vulgaris* (Fabaceae)
  k'anal ton tz'unun — *Phaseolus vulgaris* (Fabaceae)
  k'anal x'ak'il — *Phaseolus vulgaris* (Fabaceae)
  muk'ta ik' — *Phaseolus vulgaris* (Fabaceae)
  sakil ton tz'unun — *Phaseolus vulgaris* (Fabaceae)
  sakil x'ak'il — *Phaseolus vulgaris* (Fabaceae)
  santoal ik' — *Phaseolus vulgaris* (Fabaceae)
  santoal tzoj — *Phaseolus vulgaris* (Fabaceae)
  tzajal x'ak'il — *Phaseolus vulgaris* (Fabaceae)
  tzajal x'ak'il ta olon osil — *Phaseolus vulgaris* (Fabaceae)
  tzo' t'ul — *Phaseolus vulgaris* (Fabaceae)
  tz'ibal x'ak'il — *Phaseolus vulgaris* (Fabaceae)

xchenek' tzajal om — *Rhynchosia pyramidalis* (Fabaceae)
xlumil chenek'
  ik'al xlumil — *Phaseolus vulgaris* (Fabaceae)
  sakil xlumil — *Phaseolus vulgaris* (Fabaceae)
  tzajal xlumil — *Phaseolus vulgaris* (Fabaceae)
  tzo' bail xlumil — *Phaseolus vulgaris* (Fabaceae)
  vayu' xlumil — *Phaseolus vulgaris* (Fabaceae)
  ik'al pat — *Phaseolus vulgaris* (Fabaceae)
  ik'al xlumil
    ik'al pat — *Phaseolus vulgaris* (Fabaceae)
    sakil pat — *Phaseolus vulgaris* (Fabaceae)
    sakil pat ivriro — *Phaseolus vulgaris* (Fabaceae)
  kvarentáno — *Phaseolus vulgaris* (Fabaceae)
  muk'ta ik' — *Phaseolus vulgaris* (Fabaceae)
  muk'ta sakil xlumil — *Phaseolus vulgaris* (Fabaceae)
  sak-vayan xlumil — *Phaseolus vulgaris* (Fabaceae)
  sakil xlumil — *Phaseolus vulgaris* (Fabaceae)
  tzajal xlumil — *Phaseolus vulgaris* (Fabaceae)
  tz'ibal xlumil — *Phaseolus vulgaris* (Fabaceae)
xut — *Phaseolus coccineus* (Fabaceae)
xut ak' — *Galactia acapulcensis* (Fabaceae)
xvet'
  ik'al xvet' — *Phaseolus lunatus* (Fabaceae)
  sakil xvet' — *Phaseolus lunatus* (Fabaceae)
  tzajal xvet' — *Phaseolus lunatus* (Fabaceae)
  tz'ibal xvet' — *Phaseolus lunatus* (Fabaceae)

ch'um-te'
  sakil ch'um-te'
    k'ox sakil ch'um-te' — *Sechium edule* (Cucurbitaceae)
    muk'ta sakil ch'um-te' — *Sechium edule* (Cucurbitaceae)
  t'arax ch'um-te'
    sakil t'arax ch'um-te' — *Sechium edule* (Cucurbitaceae)
    yaxal t'arax ch'um-te' — *Sechium edule* (Cucurbitaceae)
  tzop ch'um-te'
    sakil tzop ch'um-te' — *Sechium edule* (Cucurbitaceae)
    yaxal tzop ch'um-te' — *Sechium edule* (Cucurbitaceae)
  yaxal ch'um-te'
    k'ox yaxal ch'um-te' — *Sechium edule* (Cucurbitaceae)
    muk'ta yaxal ch'um-te' — *Sechium edule* (Cucurbitaceae)
ch'um-te' ch'o
  batz'i ch'um-te' ch'o — *Cyclanthera bourgeana* (Cucurbitaceae)
  ch'ix ch'um-te' ch'o — *Cucumis anguria* (Cucurbitaceae)
    Cyclanthera langaei (Cucurbitaceae)
    Echinopepon horridus (Cucurbitaceae)
    Sicyos microphyllus (Cucurbitaceae)
  ch'um-te' pox — *Cucumis anguria* (Cucurbitaceae)
  juxob-bail ak' — *Luffa cylindrica* (Cucurbitaceae)
  polotz' — *Cyclanthera langaei* (Cucurbitaceae)

xantiya ak'	*Melothria pendula* (Cucurbitaceae)
xavon ak'	*Cayaponia attenuata* (Cucurbitaceae)
	Cayaponia racemosa (Cucurbitaceae)
xenebal pox	*Polyclathra cucumerina* (Cucurbitaceae)
	Schizocarpum attenuatum (Cucurbitaceae)
	Sicyos microphyllus (Cucurbitaceae)

ch'ako'	*Cucurbita galeottii* (Cucurbitaceae)
ch'um	
baril ch'um	*Cucurbita moschata* (Cucurbitaceae)
kornéta ch'um	*Cucurbita moschata* (Cucurbitaceae)
mail ch'um	*Cucurbita moschata* (Cucurbitaceae)
mail	
chij-chon mail	*Cucurbita ficifolia* (Cucurbitaceae)
sak-vayan mail	*Cucurbita ficifolia* (Cucurbitaceae)
sakil mail	*Cucurbita ficifolia* (Cucurbitaceae)
tz'ibaltik mail	*Cucurbita ficifolia* (Cucurbitaceae)
yaxal mail	*Cucurbita ficifolia* (Cucurbitaceae)
melon	
batz'i melon	*Cucumis melo* var. *conomon* (Cucurbitaceae)
chi'il melon	*Cucumis melo* var. *reticulatus* (Cucurbitaceae)
pepino	*Solanum muricatum* (Solanaceae)
sakil	
kornéta sakil	*Cucurbita mixta* (Cucurbitaceae)
setajtik sakil	*Cucurbita mixta* (Cucurbitaceae)
telajtik sakil	*Cucurbita mixta* (Cucurbitaceae)
volajtik sakil	*Cucurbita mixta* (Cucurbitaceae)
tz'ol	
batz'i tz'ol	
sakil tz'ol	*Cucurbita pepo* var. *melopepo* (Cucurbitaceae)
yaxal tz'ol	*Cucurbita pepo* var. *melopepo* (Cucurbitaceae)
kvarentáno tz'ol	*Cucurbita pepo* var. *melopepo* (Cucurbitaceae)
xantiya	*Citrullus vulgaris* (Cucurbitaceae)

makom	
batz'i makom	*Rubus adenotrichus* (Rosaceae)
	Rubus irasuensis (Rosaceae)
ch'ail makom	*Rubus fagifolius* (Rosaceae)
tuxum makom	*Rubus coriifolius* (Rosaceae)
	Rubus sapidus (Rosaceae)
tzajal makom	*Rubus humistratus* (Rosaceae)
tz'unbalal makom	*Fragaria vesca* (Rosaceae)
makom ch'ix	*Buettneria aculeata* (Sterculiaceae)
makom tz'i'lel	*Duchesnea indica* (Rosaceae)
xoto-chak	*Rubus eriocarpus* (Rosaceae)

noch'och'	*Monstera acuminata* (Araceae)
	Monstera siltepecana (Araceae)
	Philodendron hederaceum (Araceae)
	Philodendron radiatum (Araceae)
	Philodendron tripartitum (Araceae)
	Philodendron warscewiczii (Araceae)
	Syngonium neglectum (Araceae)
	Syngonium podophyllum (Araceae)
	Syngonium salvadorense (Araceae)
yat kotom ak'	*Monstera deliciosa* (Araceae)
	Philodendron hederaceum (Araceae)

chenek' ak'	*Calopogonium coeruleum* (Fabaceae)
	Canavalia hirsutissima (Fabaceae)
	Centrosema pubescens (Fabaceae)
	Cologania broussonettii (Fabaceae)
	Cologania glabrior (Fabaceae)
	Nissolia fruticosa (Fabaceae)
	Pachyrrhizus erosus (Fabaceae)
	Pachyrrhizus strigosus (Fabaceae)
	Rhynchosia discolor (Fabaceae)
	Rhynchosia minima (Fabaceae)
epal nich	*Nissolia fruticosa* (Fabaceae)
jikamo	*Pachyrrhizus erosus* (Fabaceae)
jikamo ak'	*Pachyrrhizus strigosus* (Fabaceae)
	Pachyrrhizus vernalis (Fabaceae)
kakaxon ak'	*Gouania polygama* (Rhamnaceae)
katu' ch'ix	*Machaerium biovulatum* (Fabaceae)
	Machaerium chiapense (Fabaceae)
	Machaerium cobanense (Fabaceae)
	Machaerium riparium (Fabaceae)
leb sotz'	*Mimosa invisa* (Fabaceae)
	Schrankia leptocarpa (Fabaceae)
majáva ak'	*Dalbergia glabra* (Fabaceae)
ne saben	*Heteropteris beecheyana* (Malpighiaceae)
ox-'u	*Sageretia elegans* (Rhamnaceae)
pek' me'el	*Canavalia glabra* (Fabaceae)
	Canavalia hirsutissima (Fabaceae)
	Canavalia villosa (Fabaceae)
	Centrosema pubescens (Fabaceae)
yak'il vob	*Cologania broussonettii* (Fabaceae)
yich'ak mis	*Zanthoxylum culantrillo* (Rutaceae)
	Zanthoxylum foliolosum (Rutaceae)
yok' tz'i' ak'	*Canavalia hirsutissima* (Fabaceae)
	Centrosema plumieri (Fabaceae)
	Centrosema pubescens (Fabaceae)
	Macroptilium atropurpureum (Fabaceae)

amolyo	*Ipomoea microsticta* (Convolvulaceae)

bikil tz'i' ak' — *Ipomoea triloba* (Convolvulaceae)

ch'uxuv ak' — *Mandevilla subsagittata* (Apocynaceae)

Mandevilla tubiflora (Apocynaceae)

kámpana ak'
  batz'i kámpana ak' — *Cobaea scandens* (Polemoniaceae)
  sakil kámpana ak' — *Bonamia sulphurea* (Convolvulaceae)

pik'ok'
  batz'i pik'ok' — *Ipomoea hederacea* (Convolvulaceae)

Ipomoea signata (Convolvulaceae)

Ipomoea tyrianthina (Convolvulaceae)

  k'ox pik'ok' — *Ipomoea purpurea* (Convolvulaceae)

  sakil pik'ok' — *Operculina pinnatifida* (Convolvulaceae)

puyu'
  k'anal puyu' — *Merremia umbellata* (Convolvulaceae)

Operculina pteripes (Convolvulaceae)

  k'ox puyu' — *Ipomoea sp.* (Convolvulaceae)

Jacquemontia pentantha (Convolvulaceae)

  sakil puyu' — *Calonyction aculeatum* (Convolvulaceae)

Ipomoea alba (Convolvulaceae)

Merremia aegyptia (Convolvulaceae)

  tzajal puyu' — *Ipomoea pedicellaris* (Convolvulaceae)

Ipomoea suffulta (Convolvulaceae)

  yaxal puyu' — *Ipomoea hederacea* (Convolvulaceae)

Ipomoea lindenii (Convolvulaceae)

Ipomoea seducta (Convolvulaceae)

sakil ak' — *Ipomoea pauciflora* (Convolvulaceae)

karos ak' — *Smilax bona-nox* (Smilacaceae)

Smilax jalapensis (Smilacaceae)

ne inatab — *Dioscorea convolvulacea* (Dioscoriaceae)

Dioscorea floribunda (Dioscoriaceae)

p'uk — *Dioscorea cymosula* var. *cinerea* (Dioscoriaceae)

Dioscorea cf. *dugesii* (Dioscoriaceae)

Dioscorea nelsonii (Dioscoriaceae)

sik'ol ak' — *Smilax domingensis* (Smilacaceae)

t'ut' ak'
  batz'i t'ut' ak' — *Smilax subpubescens* (Smilacaceae)
  k'ox t'ut' ak' — *Smilax mollis* (Smilacaceae)

jay
  k'ox jay — *Lagenaria siceraria* (Cucurbitaceae)
  muk'ta jay — *Lagenaria siceraria* (Cucurbitaceae)
pulum vo' — *Lagenaria siceraria* (Cucurbitaceae)
tzu
  batz'i tzu — *Lagenaria siceraria* (Cucurbitaceae)
  ik'ob-bail tzu — *Lagenaria siceraria* (Cucurbitaceae)
  kornéta tzu — *Lagenaria siceraria* (Cucurbitaceae)
  muk'ta tzu — *Lagenaria siceraria* (Cucurbitaceae)
  nene' tzu — *Lagenaria siceraria* (Cucurbitaceae)
  tzual moy — *Lagenaria siceraria* (Cucurbitaceae)
  sme' — *Lagenaria siceraria* (Cucurbitaceae)
  stot — *Lagenaria siceraria* (Cucurbitaceae)

axux ak' — *Pachyptera hymenaea* (Bignoniaceae)

barsin ak' — *Cydista diversifolia* (Bignoniaceae)

chikin chij — *Fernaldia pandurata* (Apocynaceae)

kánava ak' — *Antigonon guatemalense* (Polygonaceae)

kranata — *Passiflora ligularis* (Passifloraceae)

kranata ak' — *Passiflora filipes* (Passifloraceae)

Passiflora foetida (Passifloraceae)

Passiflora pavonis (Passifloraceae)

Passiflora subpeltata (Passifloraceae)

k'anal ak' — *Gaudichaudia albida* (Malpighiaceae)

lo'bol ak' — *Gonolobus uniflorus* (Asclepiadaceae)

lo'bol kotom — *Gonolobus prasinanthus* (Asclepiadaceae)

mémela ak' — *Anemopaegma puberulum* (Bignoniaceae)

mikulax itaj — *Matelea aspera* (Asclopiadaceae)

pepen ak' — *Stigmaphyllon humboldtianum* (Malpighiaceae)

pojov ak' — *Blepharodon mucronatum* (Asclepiadaceae)

Ipomoea pauciflora (Convolvulaceae)

Mandevilla subsagittata (Apocynaceae)

Mandevilla tubiflora (Apocynaceae)

Matelea sp. (Asclepiadaceae)

Sarcostemma bilobum (Asclepiadaceae)

tz'itesob jolol — *Ampelopsis mexicana* (Vitaceae)

tz'itesob jolol ak' — *Sarcostemma bilobum* (Asclepiadaceae)

tz'usub
  batz'i tz'usub — *Vitis bourgeana* (Vitaceae)
  sakil tz'usub — *Ampelopsis mexicana* (Vitaceae)

Antigonon flavescens (Polygonaceae)

Cissus cacuminis (Vitaceae)

	Serjania triquetra (Sapindaceae)
	Urvillea ulmacea (Sapindaceae)
	Vitis tiliifolia (Vitaceae)
tz'usub ak'	Didymaea alsinoides (Rubiaceae)
uva	Vitis vinifera (Vitaceae)
vako' ak'	Aristolochia maxima (Aristolochiaceae)
	Aristolochia sericea (Aristolochiaceae)
ve'el inatab	Ampelocissus acapulcencis (Vitaceae)
	Cissus cacuminis (Vitaceae)
	Cissus sicyoides (Vitaceae)
	Parthenocissus quinquefolia (Vitaceae)
xinal ak'	Matelea prosthecidiscus (Asclepiadaceae)
yak' xulem	Hiraea aff. fagifolia (Malpighiaceae)
yat vakax ak'	Pithecoctenium crucigerum (Bignoniaceae)

Isolates

ich ak'	Clematis dioica (Ranunculaceae)
	Clematis grossa (Ranunculaceae)
	Melothria pendula (Cucurbitaceae)
	Mikania cordifolia (Asteraceae)
kururin	Cissampelos pareira (Menispermaceae)
k'an-ak'	
batz'i k'an-ak'	Cuscuta corymbosa var. grandifolia (Convolvulaceae)
	Cuscuta tinctoria (Convolvulaceae)
k'ox k'an-ak'	Cuscuta yucatana (Convolvulaceae)

roxa

batz'i tzajal roxa	Rosa chinensis (Rosaceae)
ik''ik-lo'an roxa	Rosa chinensis (Rosaceae)
sak-pak'an roxa	Rosa chinensis (Rosaceae)
sak-vayan roxa	Rosa chinensis (Rosaceae)
sak-vayan tzajal roxa	Rosa chinensis (Rosaceae)
sak-vilan tz'unbalal roxa	Rosa chinensis (Rosaceae)
k'anal roxa	Rosa banksiae (Rosaceae)
k'ox tzajal roxa	Rosa multiflora (Rosaceae)
makom roxa	Rosa roxburghii (Rosaceae)
sakil roxa	Rosa chinensis (Rosaceae)
te' ak'	Adenocalyma apurense (Bignoniaceae)
	Anemopaegma puberulum (Bignoniaceae)
	Antigonon flavescens (Polygonaceae)
	Bunchosia montana (Malpighiaceae)
	Canavalia glabra (Fabaceae)
	Combretum fruticosum (Combretaceae)
	Didymaea alsinoides (Rubiaceae)
	Gouania polygama (Rhamnaceae)
	Hiraea reclinata (Malpighiaceae)
	Passiflora sexiflora (Passifloraceae)
	Petastoma patelliferum (Bignoniaceae)
	Quassia amara (Simaroubaceae)
	Serjania psilophylla (Sapindaceae)
yak' max	Dalechampia scandens (Euphorbiaceae)
yat tz'i' ak'	Bomarea acutifolia (Liliaceae)
	Bomarea hirtella (Liliaceae)

"Chenek' Set"

"Chenek'* (-tik, -altik, or -ultik)" is a set comprising 14 generics, all but three of which are cultivated plants. They are herbaceous vines with 3-foliate leaves, showy, pea-like flowers, and elongate legumes for fruits. Only the peanut is not an obvious "bean." They are all vines or sprawling, twining plants. Most of the generic terms are used without the set marker chenek', although clearly conceptually they are included in chenek'. The two generics representing the common bean Phaseolus vulgaris are subdivided into a vast array of specifics recognizing color markings, size, shape, growth habits, and habitat, producing 26 specific names, which under intense study may prove to differentiate insufficiently or too highly. The term xut, in addition to its generic use, may refer to bean plants that have become adventive and have smaller flowers and beans. These would occur in highland corn fields that have lain fallow. The commonest kinds are xut botil and xut chenek' (muk'ta ik'), though xut ibes is found occasionally.

Seed beans are selected not at harvest, but before planting. They may be taken to the Church of St. Lawrence on Easter to be blessed.

If the bean planter smokes a cigarette while he is planting, the beans will "see" the smoke and will not drop their flowers later if he, inadvertently, or an enemy, deliberately, smokes in his field. Deer may be serious pests, especially for kántela chenek'. Beans are susceptible to excessive humidity, uch, which causes the flowers to drop off and the pods to shrivel. Beans should be picked while the pods are still yellow, k'on, for if they are allowed to dry completely they will become weevil-ridden. If a child has cradle cap it is thought that his father's bean fields will produce well. However, if beans are mistreated, their soul (shared with corn) will cry and complain to the Earth Lord and to the gods in heaven, thus calling down a famine upon mankind. As beans are not partial to sandy soil, they are never planted with dry season lowland corn.

Beans are boiled, seasoned with salt, chili, and sometimes coriander, mexican tea, or onions. They are "cold."

Beans that are left in their pods get less worm-eaten.

Beans that are flailed and left in the sun shrink and later cook slowly, as do beans that are put in cold water, but there are other beans that, for no known reason, also cook slowly. If they do not cook they are ground on the **metate** and drunk like corn gruel.

When cooking dry beans the pot is only half filled to allow for swelling, but when the beans are fresh the pot is filled.

Pich'bil chenek', "clumped beans," consisting of a lump of beans crushed in the hand, is served with two tortillas to shamans at the annual community ceremonies. They are also given to children. For bean tamales cf. **ixim**.

Only white beans may be eaten on Lenten Fridays or during Holy Week, for other beans are said to turn into flies. Beans may not be eaten by a patient after a major curing ceremony.

As a remedy for smallpox (**muk'ta kuyel**) 13 beans and 13 5¢ coins formerly were put in water and left outside overnight to feel the dew. The water was drunk the next morning and also used to wash the affected parts. It was "cold."

As a remedy for an eye disorder, possibly cataract, **jch'ul-me'tik ta sat**, 13 black beans and 13 5¢ coins are put in water together with Ixtapa salt (this information must date from the early 1960s when 5¢ coins were still common). The cup is left outside every night for three nights, and each morning one of the coins is placed against the eye until the heat of the body has warmed it, then replaced with a cool one. A few beans are also placed on the eye (Fabrega and Silver, 1973:245). The water may also be used as an eye lotion. It is "cold." Sheep that eat beans are said to get diarrhea and run away, but bean pods after flailing are fed to sheep. If lowland cows break into the milpa and eat beans, these will swell up in their stomach with fatal results.

Beans may be resold and are sold at market.

1. **Aros chenek'** is the rice bean *Vigna umbellata*, a native of tropical Asia, a twining annual with yellow flowers, which is occasionally cultivated in lowland areas, but very seldom by Zinacantecs. The bean is the same shape as a grain of rice although a little bigger (3–5 mm long). The pods are so small and narrow that they are difficult to pick.

Specifics: 3.

    a. **Ik'al aros chenek'**, "black rice bean," has shiny black beans.

    b. **Sakil aros chenek'**, "white rice bean," has light tan beans.

    c. **Tzajal aros chenek'**, "red rice bean," is the most common form with bright red beans.

2. **Botil** (-tik, -altik) is the scarlet runner bean, *Phaseolus coccineus*, a coarse tuberous-rooted perennial vine with profuse clusters of bright red flowers. The fruits are green, flattened pods, and the 4–5 seeds are large (16–20 cm long) kidney-shaped beans.

Because of its exuberant growth this bean is planted by only a few people in yards or around the edge of corn fields, often with support. It is planted in all the temperate communities except Minax and the lower hamlets of the Atz'am valley, and in all the highland communities, except Apas. Plants often persist for many years, appearing wild as second growth engulfs them. They are not planted together with corn as they break the corn leaves. One to two beans are planted more than an armspan apart in March–May, but they are known to grow for only certain people. These beans produce a small crop the first year followed by two years of great productivity. The fourth year the plant flowers in abundance, but the leaves yellow and few if any beans appear. The harvest is from December to February.

The young leaves and flowers are boiled with young watermelon squash leaves. The beans may be boiled fresh after removing the pods or they are allowed to dry, are flailed, and then are boiled for more than a day, together with chili, salt, and onions. The flowers, beans, and occasionally the tuberous roots of this plant are eaten. Preparatory to boiling, the roots are dried for a week. People uproot the whole plant, wash the roots and dry the plant for a week, at which time it is boiled.

The leaves may be crushed in cold water and the water given to a poisoned dog.

The beans are sold at market. Bean tamales are sold at market in Chamula.

Specifics: 4. Every specific may also have a flat, **latz**, form where the pods are distinctly flattened and narrow, and the seeds are brightly colored or lustrous and closer together, but smaller and shorter, angular and flat on one or both ends.

    a. **Ik'al botil**, "black **botil**," refers to individuals with dark purple-black beans.

    b. **Sakil botil**, "white **botil**," refers to plants that produce light tan beans.

    c. **Tzajal botil**, "red **botil**," has dusty maroon beans. This is the most common variety. It is preferred for wedding and carnival tamales as it does not sour easily.

    d. **Tz'ibal botil**, "spotted **botil**" (**pinto botil, pirik' botil, tz'ibkun botil, tz'ibkuron botil**), has spotted beans. There are two varieties.

        (1) **Sakil tz'ibal botil**, "white spotted **botil**," has tan beans with black spots.

        (2) **Tzajal tz'ibal botil**, "red spotted **botil**," has maroon beans with black spots. These are known to "visit" with the solid maroon form (**tzajal botil**), mixing on the same plant.

3. **Ibes** (-tik, -altik) refers to *Phaseolus coccineus* ssp. *darwinianus,* a perennial tuberous-rooted, coarse cultivated vine with large, thin trifoliate leaves and white flowers. The seeds (4–5 to a pod) are 14–16 mm long, kidney-shaped, and rounded with dark, mottled markings.

This bean is planted in humid fields in all the temperate communities except Minax and in all the highland communities. In temperate hamlets it takes the place of **x'ak'il chenek'**. Two beans are planted with the corn at the foot of a tree or are provided with a single scarlet runner bean or preferably with also a black **paskva** bean or a white **ton tz'unun** bean. The harvest is from November to January. The beans may be picked when young and eaten fresh.

Specifics: 4.

    a. **Ik'al ibes**, "black **ibes**" (**ik'-soman ibes**), has dark reddish black beans. To cure a sheep of "hot wind," leaves of this bean are mashed in cold water, salt is added, and the water is given to the sheep to drink.

    b. **K'anal ibes**, "yellow **ibes**" (**tz'ibaltik ibes**), has yellow-tan beans and a yellowish pod. It may "visit" the reddish podded **tzajal ibes**.

    c. **Sakil ibes**, "white **ibes**" (**vayu' chenek'**), has white beans.

    d. **Tzajal ibes**, "red **ibes**," has reddish maroon beans. This form and the yellow variety are the commonest. These red beans may be used for wedding and carnival tamales, but they sour quickly.

4. **Javas** (-**tik**, -**iltik**) (**castillan chenek'***) is the faba bean, *Vicia faba.* The pod contains 4–5 seeds and turns black when mature.

It is cultivated in Chaynatik, Joyijel, and all highland communities, but in Naben Chauk it has been mostly replaced by the more lucrative flower culture. The beans are soaked for two days and nights so they will sprout in one week rather than two. One to three beans are planted to a hole in May between the corn plants or in rows between the rows of corn after the corn has sprouted. They may also be planted earlier in the corral, two handspans apart and watered.

They may be damaged by aphids, jays, and flickers. The harvest is in early November, around All Souls' Day.

The leaves are applied to burns, either ground and applied when green or burnt and the powder applied.

The beans are seasoned with mexican tea, chili, and salt and may be boiled, roasted, or fried in lard. They are "cold" when young, but "hot" when old.

This bean is classed as a "plant."

Specifics: 3.

    a. **K'anal javas**, "yellow **javas**," has yellowish beans. It is cultivated rarely.

    b. **Sakil javas**, "white **javas**," has white beans. It is the commonest variety. It has two forms.

      (1) **Krem javas**, "boy **javas**" (**chimpu javas**), has narrow beans on a single stalk. Two to three beans are planted in a hole. This bean does not cook well.

      (2) **Tzeb javas**, "girl **javas**" (**muk'tik javas, tranjero javas**), has wide beans and 3–4 stalks. One bean is planted to a hole.

    c. **Tzajal javas**, "red **javas**," has dull reddish brown beans. It is planted infrequently. It is known to "visit" with the white beans, mixing on the same plant.

5. **Javas kajve** (**kaxlan kajve, nes-kajve**) is *Mucuna pruriens* var. *utilis,* a bean imported from Africa as a substitute for coffee. It is an herbaceous vine with large, pinnately trifoliate leaves with large, asymmetric, ovate leaflets, pubescent above and below, 8–15 cm long. The flowers are large,

dark, brownish purple, to about 4.5 cm long. The legume is oblong, densely pubescent with stiff irritating hairs. The seeds are shiny and black 1–1.5 cm long.

This bean, grown in the lowland areas, has not been seen in cultivation by the Zinacantecs who insist on classifying it as a type of coffee rather than a bean. We hope some day they will learn "the truth." It is sold by *ladinos* at market. It is seldom, if ever, bought by Zinacantecs.

6. **Kántela chenek'** (-**tik**, -**altik**), "candle bean" refers to wild and cultivated members of the genus *Vigna*. These are sub-erect to spreading vigorous annuals. The flowers are off-white to yellow, veined with purple. The 7–8 seeds to a pod are almost round although angled in outline and 8–12 mm long. The cultivated form, *Vigna unguiculata,* is the cow pea of Asiatic origin introduced into the area.

These are grown or occur wild in the lowland areas and Minax. The seed beans may be scattered or 1–3 beans planted with the corn, but the plant spreads across 3–4 rows and if the corn is not doubled, the bean plant will pull the corn to the ground where it rots. Some people do not plant it until early August, lest it be eaten by bean beetles. The harvest is in December–January. It is very difficult to harvest because the plants are hard to pull up and the beans break in their pods when flailed and must be picked and shelled individually.

Specifics: 3. Each cultivated specific may have a **latz**, flat-ended form, with beans 7–10 mm long and closely spaced.

    a. **Ik'al kántela chenek'**, "black candle **chenek'**," has dull black, slightly mottled seeds. The **latz** variety, known as **tzo' chij**, "sheep shit," is the preferred form. These are both *Vigna unguiculata.*

    b. **K'anal kántela chenek'**, "yellow candle **chenek'**" (**sakil kántela chenek'**), has dull tan beans. It is the least common variety and is a form of *Vigna unguiculata.*

    c. **Te'tikal kántela chenek'**, "wild **kántela chenek'**" (**kántela ak'**), is *Vigna vexillata,* a wild occurring species similar to the cultivated plants but more pubescent and with smaller flowers. It occurs in lowland second growth. No use is reported.

7. **Karvensa** (-**tik**), (**arveja, arvensa**) refers to the pea *Pisum sativum* and the chick pea *Cicer arietinum*). The latter is very rarely cultivated and only a black form has been seen. **Karvensa** is classed as both "plant" and "vine."

Specifics: 2.

    a. **Ik'al karvensa**, "black **karvensa**," refers to the single occurrence of *Cicer arietinum* observed cultivated by a *ladino* farmer in the Grijalva Valley. Normal white (tan) chick peas when encountered in the market are grouped with *Pisum sativum*.

    b. **Sakil karvensa**, "white **karvensa**," the pea (*Pisum sativum*), is grown in Chaynatik, Joyijel, Sak Lum, and in most highland communities. It is also grown by Chamulans.

Peas are planted in the rainy season, 2–3 to a hole, or in the dry season if irrigated. They are spaced 2–3 handspans apart. They mature in 3 months. They are seldom, if ever, eaten by Zinacantecs.

8. **Manya chenek'** (**-tik, -altik**) is the peanut *Arachis hypogaea,* which is cultivated in temperate areas. Peanuts, especially when they are eaten fresh, are reputed to cause erections. They are fed to stallions when they want them to mate. A bag of peanuts is included in the net of fruit given by the elders to each of the scribes on the fiestas of St. Sebastian and St. Laurence. They are "cold."

Specifics: 2.

    a. **Batz'i manya chenek'**, "real peanut," refers to the small-shelled form cultivated most commonly in Tenejapa and sold frequently on San Cristóbal street corners. This peanut has been introduced recently into Masan, Minax, and Potovtik, where it is cultivated by a few people. The peanuts are planted in the rows between the corn, one peanut to a hole, the same distance apart as the clumps of corn. They are hilled.

    b. **Soktomal manya chenek'**, "Chiapan peanut," is the large hollow-shelled form cultivated in Chiapa de Corzo and formerly sold by a few Zinacantecs in San Cristóbal.

9. **X'ak'il chenek'** "vine bean" (**ak'il chenek', chobtikal chenek', k'ajbenal chenek'**), refers to pole beans, rapid growing, twining plants of *Phaseolus vulgaris.* These all need support either from poles or corn plants. The flowers are in short lax racemes, and the color varies from white fading yellow, to pink and lavender. The pods are slender with 4 to 8 seeds.

In discussing and selecting pole beans a distinction is made between "**xte'-pat**" or "**te'-pat**," "hard pod," and "**xk'un-pat**" or "**xk'un**," "soft pod," or "soft" beans. The former have thin brittle pod walls, whereas the latter have soft, thick pod walls even when dry. Their pods also curl up. They may be cooked and eaten together with the beans even when dry.

In temperate communities a distinction may be made between early, **santoal**, beans (All Souls' Day), and late, **paskva** or **paxku'al**, beans (Christmas). Although Zinacantecs are aware that there are differences between highland and lowland pole beans, i.e., the highland black and red beans are smaller, rounder, and tastier, **mas tot**, "thicker" than lowland beans, some forms seem to cross over in the temperate zone to a much greater degree than bush beans.

None of the red pole beans are used for wedding or Carnival tamales.

Beans are planted throughout the township together with corn: in La Selva and Naben Chauk in the first two weeks of March, in other highland and temperate communities in late April and May, and in the lowlands in late May and June.

If only an **almul** or a liter are planted, the farmer does it himself, first planting a quart of corn then adding the beans, 2–3 per hole, 2 rows at a time. If he plants 3–4 **almul** he gets 2–3 helpers. Two workers plant the corn followed by 1 bean planter. When the last 2 rows of corn are planted only 1 row of beans is planted so that the next day it can be seen where work ended. If there are 6 workers, 4 plant corn, 2 plant beans.

In the lowlands, if 1 or 2 cups are planted the 1–2 workers plant corn till noon then plant the beans. If 1 **kvarto** is planted, even if there are 3 to 4 corn planters there is only 1 bean planter. He plants beans in the 3–4 rows, and falls way behind. When the corn planters have finished, they help him finish. Not everyone plants pole beans because in some places they don't produce. Also, many workers are needed at harvest time or else the cows will eat the beans.

The beans are harvested with the corn.

Specifics: 14.

    a. **Chana x'ak'il** has rounded reddish brown beans 8–12 mm long. It is grown in highland and temperate areas. It is fast-cooking and especially tasty.

    b. **Ik'al x'ak'il**, "black x'ak'il" (**batz'i chenek', paskva chenek', paxku'al chenek', yut mokal chenek'**), has lustrous black beans 8–12 mm long. It is planted throughout the township. There is a "soft pod" form.

    c. **Ik'al x'ak'il ta olon osil**, "lowland black x'ak'il," is the lowland variety.

    d. **K'anal ton tz'unun**, "yellow hummingbird egg," has small 6–9 mm lustrous yellow beans. This is cultivated infrequently in the temperate zone.

    e. **K'anal x'ak'il** (**t'oskin chenek'**) has yellow brown beans. It is planted in highland and temperate communities. The term **t'oskin** refers only to the temperate bean.

    f. **Muk'ta ik'**, "large black" (**lansa vitzal chenek', vara chenek'**), is a long-podded variety with large beans that is grown at all elevations.

    g. **Sakil ton tz'unun**, "white hummingbird egg," has small 6–9 mm lustrous white beans. It is cultivated in highland and temperate zones.

    h. **Sakil x'ak'il**, "white x'ak'il," has dull white beans 8–12 mm long. It is cultivated in temperate and lowland communities. It has a "soft pod" form.

    i. **Santoal ik'**, "All Souls' Day black," is a fast-growing temperate black bean.

    j. **Santoal tzoj**, "All Souls' Day red," is a fast-growing temperate red bean.

    k. **Tzajal x'ak'il**, "red x'ak'il," has lustrous maroon-red beans 8–12 mm long. It is planted throughout the township. A "soft pod" form occurs.

    l. **Tzajal x'ak'il ta olon osil**, "lowland red x'ak'il," has slightly bigger beans than the above. There is a "soft pod" form also.

    m. **Tzo' t'ul**, "rabbit shit" (**vola x'ak'il**), has very round gray-brown beans 8–12 mm long. It is grown at all elevations.

    n. **Tz'ibal x'ak'il**, "striped x'ak'il" (**k'anal tz'irin x'akil, pinto x'ak'il, pirik' x'ak'il, tz'ibaron x'ak'il, tz'ibirin x'ak'il, tz'ibkun x'ak'il**), has tan beans

7–10 mm long with black mottlings. It is grown at all elevations. In temperate communities it is described as fast growing, **santoal**. This white-podded form may "visit" with the black-podded **ik'al x'ak'il**, mixing on the same vine.

10. **Xchenek' tzajal om**, "red spider's **chenek'**," is *Rhynchosia pyramidalis* (1-1) a vine with small yellow and maroon pea flowers about 1 cm long. They are arranged in spikes arising in the axils of the trifoliate leaves. The leaflets are ovate, broad at the base and drawn out at the tip, 5–10 cm long. The seed pods are medially constricted. The pod contains two seeds, which are bright, shiny red with a black spot at one end. It grows in second growth of the lowland area.

The beans of this vine, resembling the color pattern of a black widow spider, serve as an antidote for a black widow bite. To counter the "cold" of the bite, 13 splinters of pitch pine and a handful of **kururin** root are boiled with three beans. The "hot" broth is drunk.

11. **Xlumil chenek'**, "ground bean," refers to non-twining or little-twining plants of *Phaseolus vulgaris*. These bush beans, having 5–6 seeds per pod, do not need corn plants or poles for support. Some claim that the same bean can produce bush or pole bean plants depending on how it is planted, others deny this vigorously. As with pole beans, a distinction is made between "hard pod" and "soft pod" beans. In discussing bush beans a distinction is often made also between seeds that are 7–10 mm long or 10–13 mm long; the former are described as "**vola**" or "**volajtik**," "round," or "**chimpo**," "small," whereas the latter are "**telajtik**," "long," or "**muk'ta**," "large." Lowland black bush beans are given a third distinguishing set of terms: the round, small beans being "**sme'**," "female," and the long, large beans, "**stot**," "male."

A further distinction is made between highland bush beans and lower temperate and lowland beans. The latter are somewhat larger.

Red and black beans are strong-hearted, **tzotz yo'on**, and white beans are small-hearted, **bik'it yo'on**, or weak-hearted, **k'un yo'on**, that is, they are unpredictable, sometimes producing well, sometimes not, regardless of the planter.

Bush beans are planted when the moon is young so the tips will be tender, but beans planted when there is no moon will not come up.

Highland bush beans are planted by only a few people in some of the communities. There is a variety of cultivation techniques. Where irrigation is available they may be planted in the dry season, 4–5 beans to a hole, spaced 20 cm apart in rows 30 cm apart. They are harvested in April–May. If planted in the cornfield, after the corn has sprouted, two rows are planted similarly between the rows of corn. Some people plant two bean plants between the corn plants, too, but that makes weeding difficult. They are harvested with the corn. They may be pulled up or picked by hand, dried in the sun, flailed and winnowed.

In the lowlands and lower temperate communities, bush beans are not planted together with the corn because it is too shady and they grow very scrawnily. Instead, they are planted in September by many people when the corn is ripe and is being doubled. They require fertile land.

The rows between the corn are hoed to remove the weeds, but this hoeing is much easier than mid-summer weeding, for the roots are not so firmly set. It is done prior to the doubling of the corn so as not to disturb the corn plants. The beans are planted in two rows as above, but after they are tossed in the holes they are not covered over. One **kvarto** and one big cup or four big cups can be planted by one man per day. A really fast worker can plant two **kvarto** per day, two **janika** per week. They are harvested with the corn from December to January. Unlike the corn threshing floor that must be accessible to trucks, the bean threshing floor may be in the middle of the cornfield.

Young beans can be eaten fresh or, when mature, dried and boiled. The spent pods are used as fodder for sheep.

Specifics: 14.

Highland:

   a. **Ik'al xlumil**, "black **xlumil**," has solid black beans, more intensely black than the lowland form.

   b. **Sakil xlumil**, "white **xlumil**," has white beans. Soft-podded beans occur. This is planted very infrequently.

   c. **Tzajal xlumil**, "red **xlumil**" (**koxo mol**), has dull red maroon beans, 8–12 mm long, brighter and smaller than the lowland form. Soft-podded beans occur. These beans are used by a bride's family to make the wedding tamales. The cantors feed the spooks bean tamales on Carnival Monday. For Carnival each cantor provides one-half **janika** of beans.

   d. **Tzo' bail xlumil**, "gopher shit **xlumil**" (**vara chenek'**), is a long-podded variety of black bean recently introduced by the government into Zinacantán Center.

   e. **Vayu' xlumil**, "tan **xlumil**," has tan beans. It is planted very infrequently.

Lowland:

   f. **Ik'al pat**, "black pod," has a dark pod, 20 cm long, with the black beans 10–13 mm long and widely spaced within the pod. One **kvarto** produces $1^{1}/_{2}$ **janika**.

   g. **Ik'al xlumil**, "black **xlumil**" (**belakrus chenek'**, **verakrusáno chenek'**), has black beans 7–10 mm long. This form is more productive and cooks faster than **muk'ta ik'**, but it is getting mixed together and lost. One **kvarto** of seed produces $1^{1}/_{2}$ **janika**.

     (1) **Ik'al pat**, "black pod," has a dark pod, 12 cm long.

     (2) **Sakil pat**, "white pod," has a light pod, 9 cm long, with 5–10 closely spaced, flat-ended beans.

     (3) **Sakil pat ivriro**, "hybrid white pod," has a light pod, 15 cm long, with 10–15 closely spaced, flat-ended beans. This variety is the most prized as the top of the plant is covered with pods, and is

undoubtedly the result of recent introduction.

h. **Kvarentáno** is a fast-growing, highly prized black bean that produces two **janika** per **kvarto**.

i. **Muk'ta ik'**, "large black" (**jamápa chenek', muk'ta ik' k'ajbenal chenek', vega chenek'**), has dull black beans 10–13 mm long. Because these plants grow a bit taller, attaching themselves to the corn stubble and fruiting at the top, they take longer to produce a crop. They are also harder to pull up at harvest time, but the beans are heavier than the **ik'al xlumil**. One **kvarto** produces only one **janika**. It may take as many as six pot fulls of water to cook. See **ik'al xlumil** above.

j. **Muk'ta sakil xlumil**, "large white **xlumil**," has white beans 10–13 mm long. There is a soft-podded form.

k. **Sak-vayan xlumil**, "tan **xlumil**," has tan beans. It is cultivated infrequently.

l. **Sakil xlumil**, "white **xlumil**," has white beans 7–10 mm long. There is a soft-podded form.

m. **Tzajal xlumil**, "red **xlumil**," has dull red beans 10–13mm long.

n. **Tz'ibal xlumil**, "striped **xlumil**" (**tz'ibaron xlumil, tz'ibirin xlumil**), has tan beans with black markings, 10–13 mm long. It is cultivated infrequently.

12. **Xut** (**-tik**) (**te'tikal xut**) is the term for wild members of *Phaseolus coccineus,* the scarlet runner bean. They differ from the cultivated forms in having an annual or perennial habit, small leaflets with prominent reticulate veins beneath, smaller, shorter inflorescences, and beans that are dull black with irregular mottling and are 10–12 mm long. They occur in second growth in temperate and highland areas.

It is said that this bean was once cultivated, but it was so fussy, always demanding to be weeded and frequently complaining to Our Lord so that, in exasperation, He banished it to the wilds.

Some people eat the flowers, boiled with beans, meat, or watermelon squash flowers or young fruit. They are "cold." The roots may be boiled and eaten too. Only poverty-stricken people eat the bean. They are gathered by women.

Extended range: *Phaseolus vulgaris.*

13. **Xut ak'** is *Galactia acapulcensis,* a slender herbaceous vine with softly pubescent stems pinnately trifoliate leaves with elliptic to oblong ovate leaflets, 4–8 cm long. The magenta to purple pea flowers are racemose and about 1 cm long. The legume is linear, pubescent, 3–3.5 cm long. It occurs in second growth of lowland and temperate locations.

14. **Xvet'** (**-tik**) (**patax, pataxet**) refers to lima and seiva beans, *Phaseolus lunatus,* annual vines with pale yellowish, pink, and white flowers. The seeds, three to a pod, are 12–15 cm long, flat and angled on the ends.

They are planted in April and May by a few people in about half the temperate communities and in the lowlands. One to two beans are planted to a hole with the corn. They fruit all year. There may be three pickings, but the major harvest is in January–February. They are not a preferred variety of bean because they spread too widely, all stages of flower and fruit occur simultaneously, and their thorns enter one's hands during harvesting.

The leaves and beans are reputed to be fatal to sheep.

To prepare the beans for eating, they are boiled once when fresh and twice when dry. They are "medium."

Specifics: 4.

a. **Ik'al xvet'**, "black **xvet'**," has black beans.

b. **Sakil xvet'**, "white **xvet'**," has off-white beans with scattered black markings.

c. **Tzajal xvet'**, "red **xvet'**," has dull maroon-red beans.

d. **Tz'ibal xvet'**, "striped **xvet'**" (**pinto xvet', pirik' xvet', tz'ibirin xvet', tz'ibkuron xvet'**), has black-and-white streaked beans.

"Ch'um-te' Set"

The "**ch'um-te'** set" contains eight generics, which are herbaceous, mostly perennial vines in the squash family (Cucurbitaceae) with fruits substantially smaller than those in the **mail** set.

1. **Ch'um-te'**, "ch'um tree" (**-tik, -altik**), is the chayote *Sechium edule,* a commonly cultivated vine with many variants. The plant is a vigorous, herbaceous perennial arising each year from thick, fibrous, starchy tubers. These tubers (**ko'san**) are edible and reminiscent of potatoes in flavor. The flowers are small white and in pedunculate axillary clusters. The fruit is ovoid and variously covered with spines. Some strains have no spines at all. The stems and leaves are very like those of squash.

An extraordinary variability and complexity of belief and practice is associated with the cultivation of chayotes.

From one week to one month prior to planting, a hole is dug one meter wide and a meter deep. It may be filled with compost, cow, sheep, or chicken manure, and ashes. Some do not use sheep manure, claiming that it harbors june bug grubs. The ashes, however, are said to kill the grubs. The lime water used to boil the corn for tortillas is tossed in the hole daily.

The proper time for planting is most commonly said to be on St. Andrew's Day (**sk'in jtottik apuxtol,** 30 November) and during the Christmas season when the chayotes are sprouting, either on 20–22 December (**xoj-k'at'ixtik, ventex mamal**) or on Christmas Eve. The chayote will imitate the abundance of fruit, both the hawthorn apples that the dudes string on their necklaces and the fruit hanging on the pine trees flanking the creche. All Souls' Day, with the graves piled with fruit, is also appropriate, as is Epiphany, the Fiesta of St. Sebastian, and Carnival (**xlok' penton**). Planting should be done when the moon is full. Chayotes should be planted in the cool of the dusk so that the vines will not grow long and sterile, or they should be planted when the stars have appeared, ensuring productivity.

To persuade the chayote roots to remain close to the surface, the planter should either sit cross-legged or with his legs outstretched. If he prefers, he may have three girls and one boy sit cross-legged, or have three young girls sit with their legs pointing to the hole. Neighbors' children may be borrowed for this purpose. Also, the planter will know which direction the roots will grow by placing the chayote on its side, with its bottom facing the preferred direction. Two to four, but most commonly three, chayotes are placed in a hole, either touching one another or with the ends of their sprouts in contact. Eight to fifteen chayotes may be lined up in a row, touching each other. To influence productivity, 2–3 or 13 pebbles or 13 kernels of red, white, or yellow corn may be placed with the chayotes. Some farmers place three corncobs radiating out from the chayotes or else, after covering the chayotes with dirt, place them on top. This is to ensure that the tubers will not grow deep. The chayotes are placed 20–40 cm deep in the hole.

An old potsherd may be placed on top of the hole to keep the chickens away. Gophers may become serious pests by eating the roots. Young plants are watered. When the sprouts surface they may be staked, ashes poured on the ground, and the ashes enclosed in a ring of stones. Young plants may be protected with a fence. Some farmers provide an arbor for their vines. To stimulate growth, the vines should be cut back on St. Andrew's Day. The first new shoots in the spring should be pruned to assure abundant fruit. An old plant fruits earlier in the year.

The farmer with a green thumb (sk'abal) will have vines producing fruit in a year. For others, the vines may never fruit or not fruit for two years. One should not point at flowering chayote vines lest the flowers drop off. Nor should one point at young chayotes, squashes, or gourds when they are still on the vine or they will rot. The fruits are harvested from August through November in the highland hamlets, continuing into January in the temperate hamlets. If the vine produces few fruits it is said that it will have many tubers. They may be resold and are sold at market.

To provide extra assurance that the tubers are growing close to the surface the farmer should roll on the ground three times before beginning to dig them up. He may have a child roll on the ground in his stead. Digging may be done early in the morning, but it is preferable to delay until after mid-day when the chayote souls are bathing. By mid-afternoon the souls will have returned and the tubers will be clean and white, with thin skins. Care should be taken not to scratch one's head lest the tubers be fibrous. Chayote tubers are dug from November to mid-January. If dug too soon they will be too young and small; if dug after the plants have sprouted again they will be stringy. They are sold at market.

The "cold" young shoots are boiled and eaten as greens. Chayote leaves are stuck in the top of a pot of chayotes or corn on the cob to keep the steam in. The fruit has two large, starchy seeds with a fleshy covering and is boiled and eaten whole except for the skin. The "cold" young fruits and tubers are boiled, seasoned with salt and chili, and eaten as part of the meal. The young fruits are first peeled, rinsed, chopped into 4–5 pieces, and then boiled with beef or boiled and fried with eggs. The ripe fruits, though they are not considered to be "fruit" (lo'bol), are boiled and eaten cold as between-meal snacks. When the water has evaporated the chayotes are ready to be served. Care should be taken not to let the fire go out beforehand for then the skins will be difficult to remove. The fruits may be smeared with honey. Chayotes are given as essential offerings to the dead on All Souls' Day. In male joking speech they are the standard reference for female genitals. Cf. batz'i ch'aben, sakil ich.

Specifics: 4.

a. Sakil ch'um-te', "white ch'um tree," is a white variety with a uniform covering of thick spines. There are two forms.

   (1) K'ox sakil ch'um-te', "small white ch'um tree," is a small-fruited form. It is rather infrequent.

   (2) Muk'ta sakil ch'um-te', "large white ch'um tree," is the very common large-fruited form.

b. T'arax ch'um-te', "hairless ch'um tree" (t'an ch'um-te', t'ax ch'um-te'), is an almost completely spineless form that is commonly grown in northern Mexico and the United States as a cash crop. There are two varieties.

   (1) Sakil t'arax ch'um-te', "white hairless ch'um tree," is a more oblong form grown by *ladinos* in San Fernando and harvested in December and January. It is reputed not to produce edible roots.

   (2) Yaxal t'arax ch'um-te', "green hairless ch'um tree," is a round green spineless form, grown by a few Zinacantecs in Na Chij and Zinacantán Center. A temperate strain is widely grown, especially in Bik'it Joyijel, where it is harvested in great quantities in March.

c. Tzop ch'um-te', "fuzzy "ch'um tree" (tzav ch'um-te', tzopin ch'um-te', tzotziron ch'um-te'), is a variety with very fine, soft spines and small tubers. It is cultivated in Larraínzar and by a few Zinacantecs in highland and temperate communities. It prefers yellow soil. There are two forms.

   (1) Sakil tzop ch'um-te', "white fuzzy ch'um tree."

   (2) Yaxal tzop ch'um-te', "green fuzzy ch'um tree."

d. Yaxal ch'um-te', "green ch'um tree," is a green variety with a uniform covering of thick spines on the fruit. In this variety the fruit is green even on the interior. There are two forms.

   (1) K'ox yaxal ch'um-te', "small green ch'um tree," is a rather infrequent small-fruited form.

   (2) Muk'ta yaxal ch'um-te', large green ch'um tree," is the very common large-fruited form. It is said to be slightly sweeter than the white-fruited form.

2. Ch'um-te' ch'o, "mouse ch'um tree," refers to thin-stemmed annual or perennial vines with small white flowers and spinescent fruits 2–5 cm long.

Specifics: 2.

a. Batz'i ch'um-te' ch'o, "genuine mouse ch'um tree," is *Cyclanthera bourgeana* (9–27), though some speakers extend the term in a non-Linnaean fashion to include all those vines listed under 2b. It is a herbaceous perennial vine with small spinose fruits and superficially is very similar to *Sechium edule* (**ch'um-te'**). It is common in highland forest situations, second growth, and in disturbed ground such as yards and cornfields. Pig owners pull up the plants in the rainy season to feed their pigs. They are eaten also by sheep, horses, and cattle.

Extended range: *Gonolobus* sp.

b. **Ch'ix ch'um-te' ch'o**, "spiny mouse **ch'um** tree" (**tzop ch'um-te' ch'o**), refers to *Cucumis anguria* (1–1), *Cyclanthera langaei* (3–3), *Echinopepon horridus* (1–3), and *Sicyos microphyllus* (1–1). These are wiry, herbaceous vines with small white flowers and small spiny fruits. They occur throughout the township in disturbed and second growth habitats.

3. **Ch'um-te' pox**, "**ch'um** tree medicine" (**ch'ako' ak', xantiya ch'o**), is *Cucumis anguria* (5–11), a coarse, hispid, annual vine with yellow flowers and small (3–5 cm long) ovoid, spinescent fruits. It is common in the lowland areas, especially in disturbed areas such as roadsides and second growth.

The vine is used to lash field houses.

For a laxative, one fruit is brewed. A man's dose is a cup filled up to the first joint of the middle finger. A woman's dose is a cup filled to the first joint of the forefinger. The "hot" tea is drunk once before breakfast. An overdose is reputed to be fatal.

4. **Juxob-bail ak'**, "vine for rubbing oneself" (**ch'upak' ak', xavon ak'**), is the dishrag gourd *Luffa cylindrica* (3–3), an introduced cultivated vine with white flowers and cylindrical, green, spongy fruits up to 50 cm long, the dried central portion of which is used as a vegetable sponge. It occurs as a cultivated plant and an occasional adventive in the lowlands.

This vine is not grown by Zinacantecs. The skin of the fruit provides soap suds. The fibrous pith is used by *ladinos* as a sponge for cleaning the body.

5. **Polotz'** (**ch'upak'**) is the herbaceous vine *Cyclanthera langaei* (7–13). It is perennial with thick, starchy tubers. The flowers are white, the leaves five-parted. It has an erect spiny fruit. It is common in highland and temperate second growth and wet forest associations.

The plants were cultivated formerly. The crushed tubers are used for shampoo and occasionally to launder wool clothing. A handful of the tubers is crushed in cold water and a cupful of the infusion administered to rabid dogs twice a day for three days.

6. **Xantiya ak'**, "watermelon vine" (**mail ak', melon ak', xantiya antivo**), is *Melothria pendula* (2–5), a delicate vine with brittle, palmate leaves and small yellow flowers, which mature into miniature watermelon-like fruits 3–4 cm long. The vine is common in wet and dry temperate and lowland forests and in second growth.

The "cold" fruit is eaten at weeding time.

7. **Xavon ak'**, "soap vine" (**ch'upak' ch'o**), refers to *Cayaponia attenuata* (3–5) and *C. racemosa* (1–2), small herbaceous vines with lobed leaves and clusters of small yellow flowers. The fruits are ellipsoid, brown, fistulous, and 2–3 cm long. They are common in tropical deciduous forest and second growth in lowland areas, particularly in cornfields and in banana groves.

A handful or two of the fruits are gathered by women and pounded on rocks to produce soap for laundering and shampooing.

Extended range: *Galium aschenbornii*.

8. **Xenebal pox**, "vomiting medicine" (**ch'um-te' ak', xenobal**), refers to the wild chayote-like vines *Shizocarpum attenuatum* (1–2), *Polyclathra cucumerina* (1–4) and *Sicyos microphyllus* (1–2), thin-stemmed, wiry, herbaceous perennials with racemes of small, white flowers and small, spiny fruits. They are common in second growth and disturbed ground near cornfields throughout the township.

As a remedy for angry rebelliousness in children, the leaves are bruised and mixed in cold water. The child is given a small cupful of this "hot" infusion before breakfast, once. For tuberculosis and "wind" (**sikil kolo'al ik'**), a bunch of *P. cucumerina* is brewed and the "hot" tea drunk.

Extended range: *Gonolobus* sp.

"Mail Set"

The "**mail** set" is comprised of eight generics, members of the squash family (Cucurbitaceae). These are coarse herbaceous vines with large fleshy stems and scabrous, large, heart-shaped leaves. The flowers are yellow and up to 10 cm across.

1. **Ch'ako'** (**-tik**) is a wild form of squash *Cucurbita galeottii* (4–6) with round or pear-shaped fruits similar to miniature bottle gourds. It has a green skin with white or yellowish striping. It is locally common in second growth and roadsides of lowland areas.

This squash is said to be the result of cows eating pumpkin squash seeds, the excreted seeds producing **ch'ako'**.

The young greens may be eaten boiled. The fruits are very hard-skinned and very bitter to the taste. The gourds may be used as shot glasses for agricultural ceremonies. They are used rarely by the ensign-bearers for ceremonial gourds. Children use the gourds as toys, rolling them down steep slopes. They may be cut in half and taken home for one's children to play with.

2. **Ch'um*** (**-tik, -altik, -ch'umaltik**) is the pumpkin squash *Cucurbita moschata* (5–7), a coarse, annual vine. The fruit exhibits a vast variety of forms (most very large, up to 0.5 m in diameter). They all have a thick, hard, outer shell and thick, yellow or orange flesh and brown skin. The seeds are tan with a thin, irregular margin and are embedded in a mass of coarse strings.

Pumpkin squashes are planted when the corn is planted in the lowlands, and in the lower temperate communities. Squashes in the temperate zone never attain the size of lowland squashes.

The seeds may be mixed with the seed corn and 1–2 or (less frequently) 2–3 seeds may be dropped in the same hole as the corn. Some farmers take care to plant them in two adjacent holes, then skipping a number of holes and again planting them in two adjacent holes. A second technique that may be employed in the same field is to plant 3–4 or 5–6 seeds in mounds of compost, ash, or in leafcutter ant nests. Some claim that the ants never touch the squash plants, others maintain that once the area around the nest has been swept clean and the workers have established their trails, then the plants won't be bothered. Deer are known to eat the leaves. A productive plant will provide 15–20 squashes. Fruit is picked in November and December when the corn is harvested. Frequently the squashes will be broken open and only the seeds taken, as the squashes are difficult to transport. Their fruits and seeds are sold at market. One should not point at squash or gourd vines lest the young fruit rot.

The "cold" flowers and tender shoots are boiled and eaten by workers in the cornfields. They may be mixed with beans. The "cold" young squashes are also eaten in the cornfield in August and September, boiled and seasoned with salt, chili, coriander, and mint. The juice of a young fruit may be drunk as a purge. The "hot" ripe fruits may be roasted. A hole is dug, sticks piled in and burned, and when they have become embers, pieces of pumpkin squash are placed on top, covered with a flat rock and mud. But if too "hot" they may cause constipation. When steamed, brown sugar is added. If cooked in the lowlands, the pot is covered with pumpkin squash leaves. In the highlands, watermelon squash or corn leaves are used. As some people get sick from eating pumpkin squash sweetened with brown sugar, "cold" refined sugar may be substituted. Eating too much pumpkin squash is said to cause fever. When steamed, the flesh should have the consistency of lard. Ripe pumpkin squash, whether roasted or steamed, is not served at a meal. Cooked pumpkin squash may be placed on the household altars on All Souls' Day.

During the *Posadas* each steward must provide between 15 and 30 squashes, which may be watermelon squashes or pumpkin squashes. They are eaten by the stewards, every morning, during the *Posadas*, in front of the church of St. Lawrence so the Christ Child will be born. Each morning they present a bowlful to the civil authorities. A few pumpkin squashes are hung on the pine trees flanking the creche. They are also used for creche decoration in Apas, Atz'am, Na Chij, Paste', and Sak Lum. In temperate hamlets the squashes may be fed to pigs. In the lowlands they are fed to horses.

The seeds, classed variously as "hot" and "cold," are toasted and ground and the powder sprinkled on snails, beans, potatoes, and occasionally tomatoes and corn chowder. On Lenten Fridays and during Holy Week, this powder, seasoned with ground chili, is used to flavor white beans. They may also be toasted and eaten whole. They may be ground and drunk in cold water as a purge.

The acidity (**syail**) of the pulp of this squash may burn the hands of a person assigned the task of removing the seeds from many squashes.

Specifics: 4.

    a. **Baril ch'um**, "barrel **ch'um**" (**volajtik ch'um**), is a round or pumpkin-shaped form.

    b. **Kornéta ch'um**, "cornet **ch'um**" (**xotajtik ch'um**), is a crook-necked variety. Some claim its flesh is sweeter than the "barrel **ch'um**."

    c. **Mail ch'um**, "watermelon squash **ch'um**" (**telajtik ch'um**), is an oblong form, shaped like a watermelon squash.

    d. **Setajtik ch'um**, "squat **ch'um**," is a round form, wider than it is tall.

To these shape distinctions is added rind quality. All of the above may be soft-skinned (**xk'un** or **xk'un-pat**) or hard-skinned (**te'-pat**). Neither shape nor rind quality can be determined by examining the seed. Seeds from a single squash can produce plants with soft-skinned or hard-skinned fruits (but not mixed on a vine). The soft-skinned variety has a shiny yellowish brown, smooth skin. Many claim that the flesh is sweeter than the hard-skinned variety. It is preferred over other types of **ch'um**, because the rind is edible, although this leads to problems, as wandering cows find it attractive. The smooth-skinned, crook-necked variety has smaller fruits than the hard-skinned form. The hard-skinned form has a darker mottled brown, rough skin. The seeds should not be exposed to the dew lest they produce fruits with very thin skins. The soft-skinned, round and oblong-shaped forms may rarely have warty skin (**jol tuluk'**, turkey head). These fruits, never predominating on a vine, are said to be especially sweet-fleshed.

3. **Mail*** (**-tik**) (**mayil**) is the watermelon squash *Cucurbita ficifolia* (3–2) also called Malabar or Angora gourd. This is a large, rambling, perennial vine arising from tuberous roots. The foliage is prickly. The fruit has the shape, soft, fleshy texture, and green mottled exterior markings of the watermelon. It has black or white seeds.

Watermelon squash appears in the following creation tale:

> Man was made of mud. He was told how to grow corn, how to make tortillas.
>
> "But who will make the tortillas?" he asked.
>
> "Your wife."
>
> "Who is she?" he asked. He was shown a watermelon squash lying on the ground. The squash turned into a woman.
>
> "This is your wife. She will feed you. You live with her. I will be back in a few days. Our Lord brought a devil to show man how to sleep with his wife.
>
> Our Lord came back again. "How are things going?" he asked.
>
> "Fine, my wife is pregnant," he said. (Today when a woman becomes pregnant we say, "**Oy xa smail**." "Now she has a watermelon squash.")

Our Lord told man to plant corn. He gave man a pen and told him to become smart.

Watermelon squash is planted in the temperate and highland communities on Candelaria, 2 February, in March (St. Joseph's Day, 19 March), and at Carnival (**xlok' penton ta tajimoltik**), April, and May. The hole should be dug one month prior to planting and filled with sheep or chicken manure or compost, and ashes. Two to six seeds are planted to a hole, either in a corral, an old corral site, or in a row of corn in the cornfield. A great variety of techniques is associated with the planting of watermelon squash. The seeds should be carried on a piece of oak (**batz'i te'**) bark or on a thick potsherd so that the squashes will have thick rinds. A chunk of brown sugar should also be placed on the bark or potsherd and a bite taken out at each hole so that the squashes will be sweet. This practice is very common. To assure a plentiful crop, the planter may also carry with him a shoulder bag filled with pine cones, or 13 river pebbles. Planting should only be done when the moon is full. It may be done early in the morning, but more frequently it is postponed until after 2 or 3 P.M., or in the late afternoon when the sun is low, so that the vines will be short and have many fruits. Others wait until dusk or 8–9 o'clock when the sky is filled with stars, so their abundance may be imitated. It should not be planted near broad beans, cabbage, or flowers, for it will crowd them out.

The first sprouts should be cut off, twice, to promote vigor and abundant fruit. When the vine is flowering, coyol seeds should be chewed and spat on the plant to assure many fruit. Watermelon squashes, however, require a green thumb (**sk'abal**). When the vine runs across hard-packed ground, it cannot put down roots and must be covered with dirt. A board is placed under a watermelon squash if it is lying on the ground. Small watermelon squashes are used to decorate the creche in San Mikulax. Young watermelon squashes are harvested in August, ripe squashes in October and November. They are sold at market. Cf. **batz'i ch'aben, ch'um**.

The "cold" tips and flowers are boiled and eaten. "Cold," young squashes are boiled and seasoned with salt, chili, and coriander, or with brown sugar and fresh corn kernels. When people spend the night in the cornfield they may roast a watermelon squash. A hole is dug, a fire lit, and the squash placed on the embers. A hole is cut in the squash to insert sugar, then embers are placed on top and dirt on top of them for the night. Ripe squash if boiled or steamed with brown sugar is "hot," but with refined sugar is "cold." (Squash sweetened with brown sugar disagrees with some people.) Orange rind may be added for flavoring. When steamed, the pieces of squash are placed on the bottom of the pot, rind down, and then stood around the sides, rind out, so the flesh will not burn. Then other layers are added. The top layer is placed with the rind on top. It is covered with watermelon squash leaves or corn leaves. On top of them is placed a cloth or a clay or metal bowl turned upside down so the steam will not escape. It is best when cooking watermelon squash not to have children around lest they taste it and say it is **chi'**, "sweet," for then it will become sour. To ensure that it be sweet, the cook, when chopping up the squash should exclaim, "**mail tz'i'**," "dog watermelon squash." Ripe watermelon squash is not served at a meal. Cooked watermelon squash and pumpkin squash is placed on the household altar on All Souls' Day. For use during the *Posadas* cf. **ch'um**. It is said jokingly that one can make a nor'easter lift by eating watermelon squash. The fruits are used as horse fodder. The seeds are toasted and eaten whole. They may be ground and used to season snails, beans, potatoes, and occasionally tomatoes and **vokol ich**. They are classed variously as "hot" and "cold."

Watermelon squash leaves may be stuck in at the top of a pot of corn on the cob to keep the steam in.

To cause measles to erupt, the patient drinks the "hot" water that comes to the top of a pot of watermelon squash (**sba a'lel mail**) dyed red with the fruit of **vo'ox**. For fever sores the "cold" rind is scratched off and rubbed on the lips.

Specifics: 5.

  a. **Chij-chon mail**, "striped snake **mail**" or "gopher snake **mail**," is a light-green form speckled with white "like a turkey egg."
  b. **Sak-vayan mail**, "whitish **mail**" (**k'an-tzu mail**), is a slightly darker form.
  c. **Sakil mail**, "white **mail**", is a white form with pale green mottling. This variety is preferred as a remedy for measles.
  d. **Tz'ibaltik mail**, "striped **mail**," is a light-green form striped with white.
  e. **Yaxal mail**, "green **mail**," is a dark-green form.

There is considerable disagreement over the relation of seed color to skin color. The seeds within a fruit are of uniform color, and the fruits on a vine are of uniform color though some claim that green, speckled, and striped may occur on the same vine. Black seeds usually produce green or striped varieties, but white seeds usually produce white squashes, although crossovers occasionally occur.

4. **Melon** (**-tik, -altik**) refers to musk melons and cantaloupes.

Specifics: 2.

  a. **Batz'i melon**, "genuine melon" (**castillan ch'um***, **melon***), probably refers to the musk melon *Cucumis melo* var. *conomon* (1–2), no longer in cultivation. It is an oblong melon with smooth mottled orange-yellow skin and yellow mushy flesh. The clever exploits of Rabbit in the melon patch are familiar to all (Laughlin, 1977, T21, T49).

These insipid-tasting melons, once very common, have nearly disappeared from the local markets. They are cultivated by lowland *ladinos* in their yards, by Zinacantecs in Santa Rosa, and by a few Zinacantecs who rent bottomland along the Rio Grijalva and the Presa Angostura. Three or six to seven

130

seeds are planted in November. A hole is made with a pointed stick, which is swirled around in the sand. Six or seven seeds are planted in a circle, each seed 10 cm apart and each circle 6 m apart. When planted near the reservoir 3–4 seeds are placed in a hole, and after the plants are a few inches high, sand is brought from the riverbed and poured on the base of the plants. The vines should be separated so they do not touch. The harvest is from February to early April. They may be resold and sold at market.

Musk melons are classed variously as "cold," "medium," and "hot." They are eaten rind and all and then the rind is spit out. The seeds may be stored for their medicinal use. (Stingy people sell them to those in need.) To reduce fever, the seeds are ground and mixed with water, which is then strained. A cup of the "medium" infusion is drunk. To make a refreshing drink, refined sugar is added. This is also administered to sick chickens.

    b. **Chi'il melon**, "sweet melon," is the cantaloupe *Cucumis melo* var. *reticulatus,* a recent introduction to the markets of highland Chiapas.

This "cold" fruit may be lethal if eaten when one is angry. The seeds have the same use as above. They are resold at market.

5. Pepino, *Solanum muricatum* (1–1), is a plant introduced from Peru. It is an erect perennial or small shrub with alternate, finely pubescent or silky, oblong leaves about 5–7 cm long. The flowers are bright blue and 3–5 mm across. The fruit is purple, ovoid, and 10–15 cm long.

It is raised in Tuxtla and Larraínzar and is sold at market in San Cristóbal and Tuxtla. The "cold" fruit is rarely eaten by Zinacantecs.

6. Sakil, "white," is the cushaw *Cucurbita mixta* (2–2), a coarse, soft, hairy, annual vine cultivated for its very large (often up to 1 m long) fruits with tan skin occasionally striped with green. Its large, white seeds have prominently ridged margins.

Cushaws are planted occasionally in some of the lower temperate communities as well as in the lowlands. They are planted in the same manner as pumpkin squashes. Because these squashes are too bitter to eat when ripe they are picked when still young in late July and August, at the second weeding. The seeds may be taken in September, at bean-planting time. They are sold at market.

Marauding cows eat young cushaws. The "cold" flowers and tender shoots are boiled and eaten, alone or mixed with beans. The young fruits are boiled and seasoned with salt, chili, and mint, coriander, or mexican tea. Young cushaws are "cold." After the seeds are removed they are fed to horses. Cushaws are fed to pigs in the temperate hamlets. The seeds are toasted, ground, and eaten, but are not mixed with pumpkin squash seeds. These "cold" seeds are used to season beans, etc., but are not considered as tasty as pumpkin squash seeds. They may be eaten whole. The round forms are preferred as they have more seeds. Cf. **ch'um**.

Specifics: 4.

    a. **Kornéta sakil**, "cornet white," is a crook-necked form.

    b. **Setajtik sakil**, "squat white," is a round form, wider than tall.

    c. **Telajtik sakil**, "long white," is an oblong-shaped form. These are very bitter.

    d. **Volajtik sakil**, "round white," is a round form.

7. Tz'ol (-tik) is the summer squash *Cucurbita pepo* var. *melopepo* (1–3), also called bush scallop. Very few forms of this diverse species of *Cucurbita* are cultivated in Chiapas. The Zinacantec types are round and flat on both ends or oblong, 10–20 cm in diameter, with a thin, hard shell and thin, pale yellow flesh. The skin is green, often striped lighter. The seeds are tan-white with a prominent margin. Cf. **ch'um**.

Specifics: 2.

    a. **Batz'i tz'ol**, "genuine **tz'ol**," is the round-fruited form. It is planted at a full moon in most of the temperate and highland communities in May and June, both in corrals and in cornfields. If irrigation is available, it may also be planted in the dry season. One to six seeds are planted to a hole. If planted in rows the seeds are 60–80 cm distance in rows 1 m apart. The plants are later hilled. Some farmers provide sheep manure. Rainy season squashes are harvested from August through October. Dry season squashes, planted in March and bringing a higher price, are harvested in May. Flowers and fruits are sold at market.

The "cold" flowers and young tips are boiled and eaten alone or mixed with beans. The "cold" fruits should be eaten when young, lest they become bitter. They are boiled and seasoned with salt, chili, and mint, coriander, or Mexican tea. Two varieties are recognized.

    (1) **Sakil tz'ol**, "white **tz'ol**," having white fruits.

    (2) **Yaxal tz'ol**, "green **tz'ol**," having green fruits.

    b. **Kvarentáno tz'ol (kaxlan tz'ol, tz'ol ka')** is equivalent to zucchini cultivars, having an oblong form with smaller seeds and borne on a bushy plant that does not spread.

It is planted in most of the temperate and highland communities. If irrigation is available it may be planted throughout the year. It is planted the same way as above. Flowers and fruits are sold at market.

The "cold" flowers (but not tips) and fruits are eaten, seasoned as above.

8. Xantiya (-tik) (xanchiya) is the watermelon *Citrullus vulgaris* (4–10). Rabbit's clever exploits occur both among melons and watermelons (Laughlin, 1977, T49).

Watermelons are grown at the same time and in the same fields as musk melons, by the *ladinos* of Chiapa de Corzo and by a few Zinacantecs. Four to six seeds are planted to a hole. The harvest is from February to early April. They may be resold and are sold at market.

Watermelons are classed variously as "hot" and "cold." To eat watermelon late in the day is said to cause fever.

"Makom Set"

The "makom set" includes four generics, plants with either fruit or vegetative characteristics similar to the blackberries (*Rubus*).

1. **Makom** (**-tik, -altik**) (**makum***) refers to blackberries and strawberries.

Specifics: 5.

a. **Batz'i makom**, "genuine **makom**" (**makom mut, makom vet, pajal makom, tanal makom**), refers to *Rubus adenotrichus* (12–18) and *R. irasuensis* (2–7). These are coarse vines often forming thickets several meters across. The leaves have 3–5 leaflets and are coarsely dentate. The stems are densely armed with stout prickles. The flowers are white to pink and occur in many-flowered terminal clusters. The fruit is purple to black and very sour. The berries are 2–4 cm long. These plants are very common, especially on brushy, second growth slopes in the temperate and highland hamlets. *Ladinos* use the fruits to flavor cane liquor.

The "cold" berries are eaten by people and birds. As a remedy for dysentery, a small bunch of the fruit is crushed in the hand and mixed with cold water and sugar. A cup of the "cold" infusion is taken. This same infusion may chase a hangover away.

b. **Ch'ail makom**, "bitter **makom**," is *Rubus fagifolius* (1–4), a coarse vine often climbing to the top of the canopy in the wet highland forests, also forming thickets 2–3 m tall in second growth. The leaves are digitally divided and glossy green and impressed veined on the upper surface. The flowers are white and in large terminal clusters. The fruit is 2–3 cm long and extremely sour.

c. **Tuxum makom**, "sparsely seeded **makom** (**ik'al makom, kaxlan makom, muk'ta makom, p'utum makom, vol-jol makom**), refers to *Rubus coriifolius* (5–12) and *R. sapidus* (3–6), large vines with thick spinose stems. The leaves are 3–5 foliate. The flowers are white and in large terminal inflorescences. They are common vines in temperate and highland forests and in second growth.

The "cold," slightly sour berries are eaten by people and birds. They are sold at market. To relieve heartburn (**me' vinik**), or dysentery, the berries are mashed in cold water and sweetened with refined sugar. One cup of the "cold" infusion is drunk.

d. **Tzajal makom**, "red **makom**" (**ik'al makom**), is *Rubus humistratus* (2–3), a prostrate vine that hugs the ground in bare areas and exposed earth banks. Occasionally it climbs in low bushes. The stems root readily at the nodes and the plants often form impenetrable brambles. The stems are densely covered with prickles. The flowers are white and sparse, the fruit is black with few aggregates and very sour. It is common in second growth in the highland areas. The fruits are eaten by rabbits.

e. **Tz'unbalal makom**, "cultivated **makom**" (**muk'tik makom**), refers to cultivated *Fragaria vesca* (1–2) hybrids, the modern strawberry. Perennial herbs with trifoliate leaves, the plants produce runners that root and form new plants at the nodes; the flowers are white, arranged in several-flowered scapes. These are commonly grown by *ladinos* and are seen occasionally in markets.

2. **Makom ch'ix**, "**makom** thorn" (**makom ak'**), is *Buettneria aculeata* (5–16), a large woody vine, often forming thickets, with ribbed stems that have coarse recurved prickles. The leaves are ovate-elliptic and up to 10 cm long. The flowers are small, greenish yellow, and in axillary clusters. The fruit is a hard sphere each 2 cm in diameter and covered with stiff spines 1 cm long. It is common in second growth in temperate and lowland areas.

Extended range: *Gouania polygama*.

3. **Makom tz'i'lel**, "**makom** plant" (**k'ox makom**), is the mock strawberry *Duchesnea indica* (3–4), a small, creeping, yellow-flowered herb, vegetatively very similar to *Fragaria*, common in wet, disturbed forest situations and fencerows in the highlands. The fruit is a red, pithy, insipid aggregate similar in size and shape to a strawberry.

Mice and children eat the "cold" fruit.

4. **Xoto-chak**, "coiled bottom" (**makom xoto-chak, tan makom, tan sat makom**), is the wild raspberry *Rubus eriocarpus* (7–10). This is a slightly armed, sprawling shrub with trifoliate, strongly bicolored leaves. The stems are glaucous. The flowers are white and in axillary and terminal clusters. The fruit is red to purple, up to 2 cm long with a delicate flavor. The plants occur sporadically in thickets along streams and on steep, brushy slopes in highland areas.

The "cold" fruit is eaten by people and birds. It is sold at market in June. To relieve fever, the tips are crushed in cold water for a "cold" infusion.

Extended range: *Achimenes candida*, an herb with bicolored leaves similar to those of *Rubus eriocarpus*.

"Noch'och' Set"

The "**noch'och'** set" includes two generics, aroid vines with affinities to the members of the **pok'ok'** set of plants.

1. **Noch'och'**, "clinging," refers to *Monstera acuminata* (1–1), *M. siltepecana* (1–1), *Philodendron hederaceum* (1–1), *P. radiatum* (1–1), *P. tripartitum* (1–1), *P. warscewiczii* (1–1), *Syngonium neglectum* (1–1), *S. podophyllum* (1–1), and *S. salvadorense* (1–1). All large-leaved succulent-stemmed epiphytic vines with large fleshy fruits with red seeds, its leaves are large and extremely variable ranging from entire ovate shapes to variously lobed or divided margins. Some leaves attain a length of over 1 meter. These plants are a prominent part of any mature temperate or lowland forest.

2. **Yat kotom ak'**, "coati penis vine" (**lo'bol ak'**, **lo'bol chuch**), refers to *Monstera deliciosa* (1-4) and *Philodendron hederaceum* (3-5). These two vines are superficially quite similar to those included in **noch'och'**. The significant difference probably relates to the absence of oxalate crystals in the fruits of these making them palatable. They occur in the same habitats as **noch'och'**.

The fruit of *P. hederaceum* is eaten by people and birds.

"Pek' Me'el Set"

1. **Chenek' ak'**, "bean vine" (**chenek' ch'o ak'**, **máchita ak'**), is a non-Linnaean grouping of legume vines with large, flat, legume fruits and usually 3-parted leaves. It includes *Calopogonium coeruleum* (2-8), *Canavalia hirsutissima* (3-6), *Centrosema pubescens* (2-2), *Cologania broussonettii* (1-4), *C. glabrior* (2-3), *Nissolia fruticosa* (1-3), *Pachyrrhizus erosus* (2-2), *P. strigosus* (1-6), *Rhynchosia discolor* (2-2), and *R. minima* (1-2). These are common vines throughout the township.

Extended range: *Capparis flexuosa*.

2. **Epal nich**, "many flowers," is *Nissolia fruticosa* (1-1), a woody vine with dense racemes of tiny yellow or greenish yellow pea flowers, 4-6 mm long. Leaves are compound with five elliptic leaflets from about 4 to 7 cm long. The fruit is compressed and extended into a terminal wing, and may be sickle-shaped. This is a very common plant in second growth and tropical deciduous forest in the lowland areas.

3. **Jikamo** (**-tik**) (**jikamu**) is the cultivated tuber, jikama, *Pachyrrhizus erosus* (1-4). It is an herbaceous vine with large, trifoliate leaves and deeply lobed leaflets 5-6 cm long with spikes of blue pea flowers 1.5-2 cm long. The fruit is a softly pubescent legume. A native of central Mexico, its cultivation in Chiapas appears to be post-Conquest. Roys (1931) cited Motul (16th century ms.) describing cultivation of this plant by the Chol, who named it **chicham**.

The seeds of this perennial crop are planted by the people of Acala and Chiapa de Corzo, one to a hole in rows 20 cm apart, or, if in the cornfield, 2 m apart between the rows of corn. Planting may be in May or November. The root is sold at market from November through February.

The very starchy, sweet root is classed variously as "hot" and "cold." It is eaten raw very occasionally by Zinacantecs, but if much is eaten it is said to cause burps.

Extended range: *Calopogonium coeruleum*,, a bright blue-flowered legume vine.

4. **Jikamo ak'**, "jikamo vine" (**tz'ipak ak'**, **yuka' ak'**), is *Pachyrrhizus strigosus* (2-2) and *P. vernalis* (1-1), wild relatives of **jikamo**. The leaves of these two species are larger than those of *P. erosus* and not as deeply lobed or not lobed at all. The plants in general are very similar to *P. erosus*. The tubers are not edible. They are common in second growth in lowland areas.

5. **Kakaxon ak'**, "kakaxon vine," is *Gouania polygama* (1-1), a sprawling woody vine with alternate rounded or ovate leaves and spikes of tiny white flowers 2 mm across. Immature fruits are distinctly 3-angled and mature into 3-winged propeller-like fruits about 1 cm across. It occurs in second growth and tropical deciduous forest of the lowlands.

6. **Katu' ch'ix**, "cat thorn," refers to *Machaerium biovulatum* (1-1), *M. chiapense* (1-1), *M. cobanense* (1-1), and *M. riparium* (1-1), woody vines with wide stems up to 6 cm in diameter and alternate leaves with many leaflets. The flowers are small, up to 2 cm long, purple, violet, or white in large terminal or axillary inflorescences. The fruit is a compressed legume extended into a terminal wing, much like a samara. These are occasional plants along streams in seasonal evergreen forest of the lowlands.

7. **Leb sotz'**, "bat net" (**-tik**), refers to *Mimosa invisa* (2-8) and *Schrankia leptocarpa* (1-2). These are trailing herbs with recurved prickles on the stems. The leaves are alternate and composed of numerous small leaflets that collapse on the rachis when touched or at night (sensitive plants). The flowers are pink and in round clusters 7-15 mm across. The fruit of *Schrankia leptocarpa* is a pencil-shaped legume about 6-8 cm long bearing many straight prickles. The fruit of *Mimosa invisa* is somewhat compressed and smaller, about 1.5-2 cm long and pubescent. They are common in second growth and pine-oak forests in temperate and lowland areas.

It is eaten by horses.

Extended range: *Anoda cristata*.

8. **Majáva ak'**, "majáva vine" (**tzajal ak'**, **tzajal majáva ak'**), is the very woody vine *Dalbergia glabra* (1-2), which has prominent, woody, nodal spurs. It is a liana with once pinnately divided leaves that have ovate leaflets about 1 cm long. The flowers are small, white, and in dense, axillary clusters. The fruit is flat, thin, few-seeded and samara-like (4-7 cm long). It is very common along streams in seasonal evergreen forests in lowland areas.

The vine is used for house lashing.

9. **Ne saben**, "weasel tail" (**k'asal ak'**, **ton ak'**, **tzajal pek' me'el**, **tzajal te' ak'**, **yak' moletik**), is *Heteropteris beecheyana* (4-5), a woody vine with reddish stems and leaves and large, terminal clusters of pink flowers. The fruits have red papery wings 1.5-4 cm long. It occurs in second growth, pine-oak forest, and tropical deciduous forests in temperate and lowland areas.

The vine, stripped of its bark, is used to lash fences and the flowers are used for altar decoration. They are sold at market.

10. **Ox-'u**, "three months," is *Sageretia elegans* (6-9), a sprawling shrub with some stems twining. The leaves are small and leathery, the flowers are in terminal panicles. The fruit is red, juicy, sweet, and with a single seed. This is a common plant in second growth in temperate and lowland areas.

The name of this plant is derived from the belief that if one steps on one of its thorns it will remain embedded for three months. The trunk is used for firewood. The "cold" fruit is eaten by birds and people. In Muk'ta Jok' it is used also for the arched frame of the Christmas creche.

11. **Pek' me'el**, "woman's tumpline" (**barsin ak', máchita ak', yaxal ak'**) refers to the jack beans *Canavalia glabra* (7–8), *C. hirsutissima* (5–8), and *C. villosa* (1–2). These are coarse vines with showy purple or pink flowers and large leaves divided into three leaflets. The fruit is a large, thick-walled legume up to 15 cm long. They are common in second growth and pine-oak and tropical deciduous forests in the temperate and lowland regions. The vine often climbs into the canopy.

It is widely used as lashing for roof poles and rafters, fences, and stock corrals, but is more brittle than **pik'ok'**. It is believed that it was once used by women for their tumplines.

Extended range: *Centrosema pubescens, Galactia striata, Gouania polygama, Heteropteris beecheyana, Pachyrrhizus erosus, P. strigosus, Rhynchosia discolor, R. longeracemosa, Serjania punctata, Solanum dulcamaroides,* and *Turbina corymbosa. Rhynchosia discolor* and *R. longeracemosa* are used to lash roof poles, beams, and fence posts.

The basic and extended ranges are often referred to collectively as **chenek' ak'**, "bean vine."

12. **Yak'il vob**, "fiddle string" (**chenek' ch'o ak', yak'il vob ak'**), is *Cologania broussonetii* (2–5) a thin, wiry vine with alternate 3-parted leaves and small purple pea flowers 1.8–3 cm long. Stems, leaves, and calyces of the flowers and fruit are softly pubescent. The legumes are about 4 cm long. It is common in second growth in temperate and highland areas.

13. **Yich'ak mis**, "cat's claw" (**-tik**) (**yich'ak katu', yich'ak maxu'**), refers to *Zanthoxylum culantrillo* (1–5) and *Z. foliolosum* (3–7), sprawling shrubs, often vine-like, with dense, woody stems covered with recurved spines. The leaves are divided into many small, leathery leaflets. The flowers are small, white, and in clusters. The fruits are brown or red follicles with lustrous black seeds. They are common in thickets and wet forests in temperate and highland localities.

A bunch of stems may be tied with a 2 m long green ribbon and left on the trail where one's prospective girlfriend will pass by. If she picks it up, this indicates she will accept the boy's advances.

Extended range: *Dalbergia glabra, Machaerium biovulatum, Mimosa adenantheroides,* and *Solanum oaxacanum.*

14. **Yok' tz'i' ak'**, "dog's tongue vine," is a non-Linnaean grouping of legume vines with large flowers with protruding keels. It includes *Canavalia hirsutissima* (1–2), *Centrosema plumieri* (1–4), *C. pubescens* (1–2), and *Macroptilium atropurpureum* (2–6). This flower form, however, is very common in the Chiapas legumes and this term will probably apply to other plants as well. These vines are common in second growth of lowland, temperate, and highland situations.

Extended range: *Cologania procumbens.*

"Puyu' Set"

The "**puyu' set**" is comprised of seven generics. It centers around members of the Convolvulaceae, which are wiry vines with large, showy flowers.

1. **Amolyo** (**-tik**) (**amalyo**) is *Ipomoea microsticta* (1–3), a small vine with round leaves and purple tubular flowers, common in second growth and disturbed situations in the lowland areas, especially in cornfields.

The seeds were planted occasionally in May, but this cultivation apparently had ceased by the 1960s. The fruit is pounded on a stone and dissolved in water for women's shampoo. It is prized for softening the hair.

Extended range: *Ipomoea alba.*

2. **Bikil tz'i' ak'**, "dog intestines vine," is *Ipomoea triloba* (1–1), a common, small-flowered vine of second growth in the temperate and lowland regions. The flowers are purple and in tight clusters. The leaves are lobed. It grows in second growth sprawling over shrubs.

It is used for house lashing.

3. **Ch'uxuv ak'**, "muscle vine" (**bak ak'**), refers to *Mandevilla subsagittata* (1–3) and *M. tubiflora* (1–1). These are extensive, wiry vines with opposite, cordate leaves and bright yellow, tubular flowers 5–8 cm long. The fruit is a paired, elongated capsule 10–20 cm long. These plants are common in second growth and tropical deciduous forest situations in temperate and lowland areas.

4. **Kámpana ak'**, "bell vine," refers to two morning glory-like vines.

Specifics: 2.

   a. **Batz'i kámpana ak'**, "genuine bell vine," is *Cobaea scandens* (1–2), a lowland vine sometimes cultivated by *ladinos* for its showy, lavender, bell-shaped flowers, which are 7 cm across. The calyx lobes are broadly ovate, 3 cm long and 2.5 cm wide. It is a soft, herbaceous vine with pinnately divided leaves. The leaflets are broadly elliptic, 9–11 cm long and 4–5 cm wide.

Extended range: *Ipomoea pedicellaris.*

   b. **Sakil kámpana ak'**, "white bell vine," is *Bonamia sulphurea* (1–2), a thick, wiry vine forming mats on shrubs and small trees in tropical deciduous forest. The leaves are 3–7 cm long, 2–5 cm wide, alternate, broadly elliptic, with an apiculate apex. Both the upper and lower leaf surface is covered with a felty tomentum. The flowers are white and in small, axillary clusters.

Extended range: *Ipomoea pauciflora.*

5. **Pik'ok'** (**-tik**) also centers on morning glories.

Children play with the flowers, impaling them one above the other on twigs.

Specifics: 3.

   a. **Batz'i pik'ok'**, "genuine **pik'ok'**" (**tzajal ak', tzotziron pik'ok'**), refers to *Ipomoea signata* (1–2) and *I. tyrianthina* (4–7), large, showy, flowered vines, commonly climbing in trees or on steep banks and making a bright display when flowering. The flowers are pink, lavender, or purple, open campanulate, 4–6 cm long. This plant occurs in pine oak forest, and tropical deciduous forest in lowland and temperate regions.

The fresh vines are used for lashing roof poles, but are known to be brittle, and are not present in the dry season. They are also used as dog leashes. Children make ropes from them and lasso each other.

Extended range: *Ipomoea hederacea* and *I. triloba*.

b. **K'ox pik'ok'**, "small **pik'ok'**," refers to *Ipomoea purpurea* (3–5), sprawling vines often forming mats on bare ground or exposed earth banks. The leaves are heart-shaped or trilobate, 2–8 cm long, and the flowers are tubular, campanulate, purple and up to 5 cm long. It is very common in second growth of temperate and highland hamlets.

It is used to lash corrals.

c. **Sakil pik'ok'**, "white **pik'ok'**," is *Operculina pinnatifida* (1–4). This is a fleshy vine that forms large colonies in the lowland forests. The flowers are white and tubular campanulate. The leaves are pinnately divided. The fruit is a fleshy ovoid capsule 2 cm across.

6. **Puyu'** (-**tik**, -**altik**) refers to a different group of morning glories.

Children play with the showy flowers.

Specifics: 5.

a. **K'anal puyu'**, "yellow **puyu'**" (**k'anal pik'ok' ak'**, **yich'ak mut ak'**), refers to *Merremia umbellata* (1–4) and *Operculina pteripes* (2–7), clambering vines with strong, thin stems often climbing to the tops of trees or completely covering them. The flowers are yellow or orange and occur in terminal clusters. The plants are common in tropical deciduous forest and second growth in the lowland areas.

b. **K'ox puyu'**, "small **puyu'**" (**k'ox yaxal puyu'**, **tzotzil ak'**, **tzotzin ak'**), refers to *Ipomoea* sp. (2–5) and *Jacquemontia pentantha* (2–5). These are small wiry vines with tight clusters of blue flowers. The plants often form mats on corn plants, shrubs, and small trees in second growth in the temperate and lowland areas.

They are used for lashing roof poles and sheep corrals.

Extended range: *Gonolobus barbatus* and *Gronovia scandens*.

c. **Sakil puyu'**, "white **puyu'**" (**puyu'al chobtik**, **sakil nich puyu'**), refers to *Calonyction aculeatum* (1–1), *Ipomoea alba* (1–4), and *Merremia aegyptia* (1–2), vines similar to **k'anal puyu'** except that the leaves are lobed and the flowers white. They are common in second growth in temperate and lowland areas.

They are a pest in the cornfields and are eaten by horses.

d. **Tzajal puyu'**, "red **puyu'**" (**ik'-lo'an puyu'**, **mis tz'i' ak'**, **muk'ta puyu'**), refers to *Ipomoea pedicellaris* (3–7) and *I. suffulta* (2–3), vines very similar to **sakil puyu'** and **k'anal puyu'**. The flowers are magenta to purple. The plant is common in temperate and lowland second growth as well as pine oak and tropical deciduous forests.

Ipomoea pedicellaris is used together with ground whip-poorwill bones in a love potion. The bird is killed on a Thursday and hung in a treetop for exactly two weeks. If the bones are clean, they are taken down, burned and ground into powder, together with the morning glory. Taking the powder with him when he goes to talk to a girl, the boy should toss it at her or rub it on her neck or back when he embraces her. The following Thursday he should talk to her, because no matter how obstinate she has been, she cannot fail to fall in love and elope.

Extended range: *Valeriana scandens*.

e. **Yaxal puyu'**, "blue **puyu'**" (**ik'al nich puyu' ak'**, **k'ox pik'ok' ak'**, **puyu'al vitztik**, **yax-'ulan puyu'**), refers to *Ipomoea hederacea* (3–7), *I. lindenii* (1–3), and *I. seducta* (1–2), vines similar to **k'anal puyu'** except that the flowers are large, brilliant blue or purple, tubular campanulate 7–10 cm long. They are common in second growth and grassy slopes throughout the hamlet.

They are eaten by mules.

7. **Sakil ak'**, "white vine" (**jit'ob na**, **pojov ak'**, **poxil yayijel**), is *Ipomoea pauciflora* (2–3), a common showy vine in the tropical deciduous forests and thorn woodland of the lowland regions. It is a large, shrubby vine with thick, woody stems. In forest areas the stems climb into the crowns of the low trees, but in sparse shrub formations the stems fall back on the plant and it forms a shrub. The large white flowers are accentuated by flowering in the dry season when the plant is leafless.

It is used in lashing the beams and corner posts of field houses and also to lash fences. The "cold" sap is applied to cuts for three days.

Extended range: *Jacquemontia nodiflora*.

"T'ut' Ak' Set"

The "**t'ut' ak'** set" is comprised of five generics, members of *Smilax* or *Dioscorea*. These are wiry vines with large, ovate, glossy leaves. The fruits are a 3-winged capsule on *Dioscorea* and a fleshy, red or black berry in *Smilax*.

1. **Karos ak'**, "hoop vine" (**ch'ix ak'**, **t'ut' ak'**), refers to *Smilax bona-nox* (1–2) and *S. jalapensis* (19–13), the spiny catbriars. Wiry vines with abundant spines on the stems, the leaves are dark green, elliptic-ovates and turn black upon drying. These are common in pine oak and evergreen cloud forests of temperate and highland areas, especially along streams.

It is used by children to make hoops. The leaves are eaten by sheep.

2. **Ne inatab**, "iguana tail" (**chachi' ak'**, **kilon ak'**), refers to the glabrous lowland vines *Dioscorea convolvulacea* (1–1) and

D. floribunda (1–1). These are thin-stemmed vines arising from thick fleshy roots with corky plates. The leaves are lance-ovate up to 8 cm long. The flowers and fruit are similar to **p'uk**. They occur in seasonal growth and pine oak and tropical deciduous forest of temperate and lowland areas.

3. **P'uk** (**kilon ak', ojov ak', stz'itesob at, tz'itesob at**) refers to wild yams *Dioscorea cymosula* var. *cinerea* (1–2), *D.* cf. *dugesii* (2–6), and *D. nelsonii* (1–4). These are wiry vines arising from a giant tuber often 1 m across. The leaves are heart-shaped, the flowers are in axillary racemes, and the fruits are 3-winged and up to 3 cm long. The plants are common in tropical deciduous and seasonal evergreen forests in the lowlands.

One "cold" root may be gathered by virgin boys who wish to enlarge their penises. The root is peeled and eaten raw. As much of the tuber is chewed as the length desired for the penis. This tuber is not considered to be as effective as **yat kotom**. In famine years the "cold" root was boiled and ground with corn or mixed with potatoes. The root is also known to be a fish poison.

4. **Sik'ol ak'**, "cigarette vine" (**nok'ol sik'ol ak'**), is *Smilax domingensis* (1–1). This is a giant woody vine often covering the crowns of trees. The stems are up to 5 cm in diameter and reddish brown. The leaves are glabrous, greenish brown, elliptic and 3–5 cm long. The flowers and berries are similar to **t'ut' ak'**. It occurs in the crowns of trees in wet forest formations from evergreen cloud forest and wet pine oak forests in the highlands, to seasonal evergreen forest and montane rain forest in the temperate areas. It is used by lowland *ladinos* to decorate their household altars.

5. **T'ut' ak'***, "**t'ut'** vine," refers to catbriars.
Specifics: 2.
   a. **Batz'i t'ut' ak'**, "genuine **t'ut'** vine" (**ch'ulul ak', ik'al tz'usub, t'ut'ak ak'**), is the catbriar *Smilax subpubescens* (4–4), a coarse glabrous vine with leathery, dark-green ovate leaves and small flowers in axillary clusters. The fruits are red berries. It is common in thickets along streams in temperate and highland locations. Some speakers include the spiny forms under this term.

Three "cold" tips may be crushed and used by women when shampooing their hair, to cool their heads and stimulate hair growth. The stems are split in half and used for lashing fences. Young stems are brittle, but mature stems do not rot in the rainy season and last for two years. They are seldom used for house lashing because they become wormeaten. The leaves are eaten by sheep.
   b. **K'ox t'ut' ak'**, "small **t'ut'** vine," is the much more delicate *Smilax mollis* (6–3), a vine with alternate, ovate, palmately veined, pubescent leaves that are 6–15 cm long and 2–7 cm wide. The flowers arise in short umbels in the axils of the leaves. They are about 4 mm long. The berries are orange and round about 8 mm in diameter. It occurs in wet forests of temperate and highland hamlets.

"Tzu Set"

The "**tzu** set" is comprised of three generics, all forms of the bottle gourd *Lagenaria siceraria*. It is an herbaceous vine very similar to squash, with large, white flowers in racemes. The gourds are green to yellow when fresh and have a hard outer layer and a pulpy interior mixed with fibrous strands and black seeds.

They are planted in lower temperate communities and in the lowlands.

If the Zinacantec farmer has no gourd seeds, he commonly buys them from lowland *ladino* ranchers. Two to six seeds are planted in or next to the lowland cornfields in May and June when the corn is planted. Just as pumpkin squashes, they may be planted between clumps of corn or in fertile spots, including leafcutter ant nests. A green thumb (**sk'abal**) is required for growing gourds. They should be planted when the moon is full, lest they put out long, unproductive vines. They are harvested at the corn harvest, from November through January. Care should be taken not to expose gourd seeds to dew at night, lest they produce gourds with thin rinds.

There are two methods for preparing gourds for use. In the first, the end of the gourd is broken and the gourd is placed on a fire, if still green, to remove the outer rind. Then it is buried in the ground for two days. When it is dug up, the pulp is removed and the inner surface is scraped and rinsed. The gourd is set in the sun for 2–3 days to dry. Then, the outer surface is scraped with a knife. Following the second method, after the gourd is taken off the fire it is allowed to cool. Rather than burying the gourd, it is placed for a week in a stone corral in the river, and branches are placed on top to prevent it from rising to the surface; however, not only does this method take longer, it also produces foul-smelling gourds. Prepared gourds are sold at market.

Gourds, regardless of their shape, are classified according to the nature of their rinds. **Suy** gourds have hard, thin rinds. **Tzo' ka'**, "horse shit," gourds have soft, thick rinds that break easily. They are not mixed on a single plant.

Marauding cows eat young gourds. Cf. **ch'um**.

1. **Jay** (**-tik**) is a flat, round gourd 10–15 cm tall and 15–20 cm broad. It is planted in the lower temperate communities and in the lowlands. When planting these gourds, the farmer should sit cross-legged so that the fruit will be properly flat. Cf. **ch'um**. Some claim that there are two specifics according to size, others, that the size is individual.
Specifics: 2.
   a. **K'ox jay**, "small **jay**," is a small form.
It is used to store tortillas, to carry the snacks on a curing ceremony trip to the shrines and to scoop corn. Formerly it was widely used as a container for seed corn when planting. It is used to decorate the creche in Apas.

If a prospective parent dreams of receiving this gourd, he or she will have a girl baby.
   b. **Muk'ta jay**, "large **jay**," is a large form.
It is used as a basin for "flower water" to bathe newborn

babies and patients. Large lacquered gourds, presumably from Chiapa de Corzo, are used in the Church of St. Lawrence to store the wigs, crowns, clothing, and other adornments of the saints.

2. **Pulum vo'**, "water drawer" (**yak'il pulum vo'tik, yak'il pulum vo'altik, pulin vo', pulun vo'**), is a large, almost round gourd 30–40 cm tall and 20–30 cm broad. Some claim that they grow on the same vine as **jay**.

They are used to store tortillas and eggs. Formerly, the stewards used two of these gourds to carry meat to the tithing man of Atz'am on New Year's Day and Mid-year's.

If a prospective parent dreams of receiving this gourd, he or she will have a girl baby. Cf. **ch'um**.

3. **Tzu*** (**yak'il tzutik**) refers to bottle-shaped or oblong gourds.

When planting bottle-shaped gourds, the planter should fasten his sash or belt very tight (some say for just a moment) so that the gourd will be narrow-waisted, permitting it to be easily attached with a cord. He should also whistle so that the top of the gourd will be pleasingly shaped, as pursed lips. Thick-waisted gourds, described as barrel-shaped (**baril, barin**) or pear-shaped (**peron**), are produced by disturbing the tips of the vines.

There is considerable ambiguity in determining which gourds represent specific classes, i.e., whether their size or shape is produced by a genetic difference inherent to the seeds or the various shapes result from different ecologic exposures such as shade, sun, etc. Gourd leaves may be wilted on the fire and rubbed on itchy growths (**jak'ob ik'**) on one's legs to reduce the discomfort.

Specifics: 5.

    a. **Batz'i tzu**, "genuine **tzu**," is a large gourd holding a liter. These are used to store water and holy water. They are used by the cantors to store chicha and by the mortarmen to store gunpowder. Plastic containers have largely replaced gourds when the use is not ceremonial.

    b. **Ik'ob-bail tzu**, "person-calling **tzu**" (**k'ox tzu, lok'esob-bail tzu**), is a small, bottle-shaped gourd, borne on a short vine. Some claim that its seed is larger than that of **nene' tzu**, others, that the same seed produces both sizes of gourd.

Shamans use this gourd as a whistle to recall the soul of a person who has suffered soul-loss. This size gourd may be used to place in the coffin (**tzual anima**), providing the corpse with water on its journey.

    d. **Kornéta tzu**, "cornet **tzu**," is a crook-necked gourd. Some claim that it has a narrow seed, others, that it is a spore. These are used only as children's toys.

    d. **Muk'ta tzu**, "large **tzu**," is a very large bottle-shaped gourd holding up to five liters. They are also used to carry holy water to the cemetery. Some claim that these are merely large individuals of **batz'i tzu**.

    e. **Nene' tzu**, "baby **tzu**" (**k'ox tzu**), is a miniature

bottle-shaped gourd (8–12 cm tall), borne on a short vine.

One of these gourds may be strung on a baby's bracelet as a protection against "evil eye." As a remedy for hernia, six "hot" leaves are heated and bound to the scrotom with a rag. Three hot leaves are similarly bound to the navel. They remain for two weeks. At the end of this period the patient eats a chicken boiled with chili and black pepper.

    f. **Tzual moy**, "tobacco **tzu**" (**tzual bankilal**), is a small, oblong gourd used to carry prepared tobacco. There are two varieties.

        (1) **sme'**, "female."

        (2) **stot**, "male," a slightly smaller form with a pointed end.

Its seed has faint white stripes.

"Tz'usub Set"

The "**tz'usub** set" is a large group of 21 generics, many with thick, milky or juicy sap and coarse, soft-wooded stems.

1. **Axux ak'**, "garlic vine," is *Pachyptera hymenaea* (1–2), a large woody vine with showy, pink, lavender or purple, tubular, bilabiate flowers about 4–6 cm long. The leaves are bifoliate, the leaflets broadly elliptic or broadly ovate. The fruit is a thick oblong capsule. The flowers and foliage have a strong odor similar to garlic. It occurs in the canopy of tropical deciduous forests of the lowlands.

As a remedy for "hot" sicknesses, the root is crushed and mixed with cool water, providing a "cold" infusion. As a remedy for "cold" sicknesses, the root is brewed, and the tea drunk. As a remedy for "wind," the root may be mixed with **soro te'**.

2. **Barsin ak'**, "spotted vine" (**chan-tzelav ak', nichim anima**), refers to *Cydista diversifolia* (3–4), a large woody vine with showy, tubular, bilabiate, purple flowers, 3–4 cm long. The leaves are simple or bifoliate. The leaflets are heart-shaped or rounded with an acuminate tip. The branchlets are distinctly 4-sided. The fruit is a linear capsule about 30 cm long somewhat resembling a dry bean pod. It occurs in the canopy of tropical deciduous forest in lowland areas.

The vine is used for house and fence lashing. It is split in two for lashing thatch and roof poles, used whole for purlins, roof rods, and rafters.

Extended range: *Pithecoctenium crucigerum*.

3. **Chikin chij**, "deer ear" or "sheep ear" (**chikin chij ak', keb chij, keb vakax ak', vakax itaj**), is *Fernaldia pandurata* (3–8), a vigorous perennial, herbaceous, vines with opposite, ovate, finely soft pubescent leaves up to 10 cm long. The flowers are white, tubular salverform, up to 5 cm long, and in axillary racemes each about 15 cm long. The fruits are in paired slender follicles up to 10 cm long. The seeds have tufts of white hairs. These plants are common in scattered locations in tropical deciduous forests and persist after the forest is cleared.

At weeding time some of the plants are left undisturbed while others are pulled up, chopped and boiled, sometimes together with **mikulax itaj**, seasoned with salt, chili, and lime juice and eaten as greens. They are classed variously as "medium" and "hot." If a large portion of these greens are eaten, a stomach ache may ensue.

Extended range: *Mesechites trifida*.

4. **Kánava ak'**, "*kánava* vine" (**kámaba ak', yaxal barsin ak'**), is *Antigonon guatemalense* (2–3), a rampant vine with tough, wiry stems and thin, cordate-ovate alternate leaves up to 5 cm long. The flowers are pink with the calyces enlarging in fruit, turning the masses of vines into a profusion of color. These are very common plants in second growth, especially along roads or in fencerows throughout the lowland areas. Forty to sixty vines are used to lash roof poles for a thatched roofed house. It is also used for fence lashing.

Extended range: *Matelea prosthecidiscus*.

5. **Kranata (-tik)** (**kranate'**) is the cultivated popapple *Passiflora ligularis* (3–4), a coarse, perennial, glabrous vine with large, round leaves. It often attains considerable size, with the stems reaching high into the crowns of trees near where it has been planted. The flowers are large and showy, about 8–10 cm across. The five petals are pink or white and about 3 cm long. Above them is a purple and white fringe-like corona surrounding the central structures of the flower. The fruit is a large capsule 6–8 mm long, filled with soft, black seeds surrounded by a translucent sweet-acid flavored pulp. Both seeds and pulp are eaten. The taste is similar to pomegranate. The leaves are known to be poisonous. It is found only in cultivation in the temperate hamlets.

Popapples are grown in the temperate hamlets and in Naben Chauk. Planting techniques vary greatly. The fruit may be hung in the sun for a week and the seeds kept, or a popapple may be fed to a 2–3 year old child. After he defecates, the seeds are planted two to a hole. This procedure is said to benefit the child, causing him to grow stronger. Some plant the seeds in June–July, others on St. Andrew's Day (30 November) and **Ventex Mamal** (20 December). The seeds may be planted in a seed bed with sheep manure and transplanted to an arbor a year later. Slips, with both ends cut off, may be planted. Some maintain that if the slip is bent into a U and planted that way it will develop more branches. Others pull up young plants and transplant them, digging a hole 60 cm deep filled with sheep manure. For popapples to grow well a green thumb (**sk'abal**) is required. When slips are planted, the farmer may set down his machete next to the slip and tell it, "**Yu'un xach'i, mi mu xach'i yu'un chajmil ta j-moj!**" "Grow! If you don't grow I'll kill you once and for all!'" Some claim that the vine will fruit in a year, others say 2–3 years, still others 3–5 years. The harvest is from August through March, with the heaviest fruiting in November. In Jok' Ch'enom and Sek'emtik there is a second fruiting in May. Gophers may become serious pests by eating the roots.

The "cold" fruits are sold on the roadside and at market. Three dozen stemmed fruits are provided by the Junior Steward of St. Anthony and the Stewards of St. Sebastian on the eighth **Posada** to decorate the trees that flank the creche. They are also widely used to decorate the creches of Apas, Atz'am, Na Chij, Naben Chauk, Paste', and San Mikulax.

Extended range: *Passiflora membranacea*, a similar wild species of popapple, and *Stigmaphyllon puberum*, a large, glabrous vine with similar leaves.

6. **Kránata ak'**, "popapple vine" (**kránata chuch**), refers to *Passiflora filipes* (1–1), *P. foetida* (1–1), *P. pavonis* (1–1), and *P. subpeltata* (2–4). These are common vines in second growth and pine-oak forests in temperate and highland areas. They are similar to the cultivated popapple. The leaves are lobed and the fruit of *P. subpeltata* is not very palatable although some admit the fruit is sour and "cold."

Children play with the fruit.

Extended range: *Antigonon guatemalense, Gonolobus barbatus,* and *Matelea quirosii*.

7. **K'anal ak'**, "yellow vine" (**tzajal ak'**), is *Gaudichaudia albida* (3–7), a small, wiry-stemmed vine with elliptic, pubescent leaves. The flowers are yellow and occur in dense axillary clusters. The fruit is a red samara. The seed portion is covered with irritating hairs. It is common in second growth in temperate and lowland areas.

8. **Lo'bol ak'**, "banana vine" or "fruit vine" (**lo'bol chuch**), is *Gonolobus uniflorus* (2–2), a slender herbaceous vine, of moist canyons in montane rain, and evergreen cloud forest of the temperate and highland areas. The leaves are opposite, 5–10 cm long, thin, softly pubescent and oblong-ovate with deeply cordate bases. The basal lobes are sometimes incurved and up to 1.5 cm long. Flowers are 3–5 cm broad, green or cream. The five petals are acute and reticulate patterned and surround a five-pointed star-shaped corona in the center of the flower. The fruit is a hard woody follicle with thick ridges about 10 cm long similar to some types of banana. Seeds are blackish and flat with copious long white silky hairs. It fruits in the dry season.

The young fruit serves as children's toys and may be eaten roasted.

9. **Lo'bol kotom**, "coati's banana" or "coati's fruit" (**ch'um-te' ak', yax-'on ak'**), is *Gonolobus prasinanthus* (1–1), a slender herbaceous vine, with opposite narrow heart-shaped leaves. The flowers are green and axillary, 3–6 to a node, about 1.5–2 cm across. The fruit is a smooth woody follicle containing seeds with copious white silky hairs. It occurs in seasonal evergreen forests of the temperate and lowland regions.

10. **Mémela ak'**, "tortilla vine," is *Anemopaegma puberulum* (1–2), a woody vine with thick, glossy, ovate leaves and large, tubular yellow flowers. It has smooth fat fruits about the size of a small tortilla. It occurs in tropical deciduous forests in the lowland areas.

11. **Mikulax itaj**, "nicholas greens" (**boka itaj**), is the lowland herbaceous perennial milkweed *Matelea aspera* (3–3). It has slender vines with thin, opposite, ovate, cordate leaves,

and the flowers are green tinged with maroon and in axillary umbellate clusters. The fruit is an ellipsoid capsule covered with fleshy tuburculate spines. The seeds have tufts of white hair. These are common in lowland forests and second growth situations.

The vine is sometimes used in lashing. At weeding time in the lowland cornfields, care is taken not to dig up the plants whose tuberous roots have sprouted fresh shoots. These are cut, boiled, and eaten as greens. They are classed variously as "medium" and "hot."

Extended range: *Cynanchum rensonii, Cynanchum* sp., and *Gonolobus niger*.

12. **Pepen ak'**, "butterfly vine" (**yaxal ak'**), is *Stigmaphyllon humboldtianum* (4–3), a wiry woody vine with opposite, rounded, ovate or heart-shaped leaves to 9 cm long, cordate or broadly rounded at the base. The leaf margin may be entire or lobed, often variable in shape on the same plant. The flowers are yellow and in long pedunculate axillary umbellate clusters. The fruit is a samara, the wings about 3 cm long. It occurs in second growth and along roadsides in the lowlands.

Extended range: *Matelea quirosii*.

13. **Pojov ak'**, "milky sap vine" (**chikin t'ul ak'**), is a non-Linnaean grouping of six, and probably more, species of lowland vines, all of which have thick, white sap that exudes profusely from breaks in the stems or leaves. The plants included under this designation are *Blepharodon mucronatum* (1–1), *Mandevilla subsagittata* (2–3), *M. tubiflora* (1–2), *Matelea* sp. (1–2), and *Sarcostemma bilobum* (1–1), all of the closely related families *Asclepiadaceae* (milkweeds) and *Apocynaceae* (dogbanes) along with *Ipomoea pauciflora* (1–1) of the *Convolvulaceae* (morning glories). This non-Linnaean grouping is remarkably uniform morphologically; all with large, entire leaves attached oppositely and flowers in terminal yellow or white clusters. They are common vines in the lowland dry forests.

14. **Tz'itesob jolol**, "hair grower," is *Ampelopsis mexicana* (2–3), a woody vine arising from a fleshy rootstock. The vine is leafless most of the year. The young stems, tendrils, and flowers are reddish brown. The flowers are in terminal cymes. The young stems, including those with flowers, entwine the shrubs and trees in which they clamber often to the canopy. The fruit is a fleshy drupe up to 5 mm in diameter. They are common plants in tropical deciduous forests and because of the nature of the roots persist in second growth in the lowland areas.

This vine may be gathered by the father of an unmarried girl. The vine is soaked in cold water and the water used to wash the girl's hair so that it will grow long, and so that the boys will fall in love with her, for they think that long hair makes a good pillow. The father will also be happy to receive her suitors' cane liquor. Three vines are mashed and soaked in a pottery bowl. The girl washes her hair with the "cold" infusion in the morning for three days.

Extended range: *Cissus cacuminis, C. rhombifolia, C.*

sicyoides, and *Parthenocissus quinquefolia,* all wild grape relatives.

15. **Tz'itesob jolol ak'**, "hair grower vine," is *Sarcostemma bilobum* (1–1), a wiry vine with thin, opposite, cordate-ovate leaves up to 5 cm long. The flowers are white and in axillary umbellate clusters. The fruit is an elliptic, fleshy capsule up to 8 cm long; the seeds have tufts of white hair. A common plant in ravines, it is often very showy, climbing over shrubs in temperate hamlets and in second growth in the lowland areas.

To prevent hair from falling out and to induce its growth, the plant is crushed and soaked in water that is placed outside overnight before being used to bathe the hair.

16. **Tz'usub** (**tz'usub ak', tz'usum, tz'usum ak', tz'uxub**), refers to wild grapes and grape-like vines.

The fruits of these vines became the food of the survivors of the Flood who were turned into monkeys by Our Lord.

Specifics: 2.

a. **Batz'i tz'usub**, "genuine grape" (**tzajal tz'usub**), is *Vitis bourgeana* (6–10), the highland native grape. These are large, woody vines with stems 10 or more meters long. The leaves are thin, large, and heart-shaped. The flowers are in large clusters and the fruit is a small, sour, purple grape with a large seed.

The fruit is eaten occasionally. As a remedy for pink eye (**satil**), a young tip is cut and three drops of its "hot" sap are applied to the eye.

b. **Sakil tz'usub**, "white grape" (**ve'el vokoto** in part), for some speakers focuses on *Vitis tiliifolia* (1–4), the native grape scattered to common in temperate and lowland areas. It differs from *V. bourgeana* in that the leaves are more pubescent. For others this is a non-Linnaean grouping of grape-like vines including *Ampelopsis mexicana* (1–1), *Antigonon flavescens* (1–1), *Cissus cacuminis* (1–1), *Serjania triquetra* (2–2), and *Urvillea ulmacea* (1–1).

Antigonon flavescens is used to lash wall boards and roof poles.

17. **Tz'usub ak'**, "grape vine" (**ch'ulelal pox**), is *Didymaea alsinoides* (2–2), delicate herbaceous perennial vines with ovate leaves to 4 cm long. The flowers are small, green turning red; the fruits are black and two-lobed, about 5 mm across. The plants occur growing enmeshed in shrubs in second growth and pine-oak forests of the temperate and highland hamlets.

When the vine is mature it may be used for fence and house lashing. The fruit may be rubbed on the face of a child suffering discoloration from "embarrassment" (**apon**).

18. **Uva** (**tz'usub***) is the cultivated grape *Vitis vinifera* (2–3). This is seen only in the market, and is rarely, if ever, purchased by Zinacantecs. In the colonial Tzotzil dictionary **tz'usub** is given as the name for grape, and from the many terms referring to grape cultivation and wine-making it may be surmised that cultivated grapes were introduced into the area shortly after the Conquest.

19. **Vako' ak'**, "vako' vine" (**tzotz-ni' ak', vako ak', wapo**

ak', yat karnéro ak'), refers to *Aristolochia maxima* (2–3) and *A. sericea* (2–3), woody vines with thick corky bark on older stems. The leaves are obovate, up to 6 cm long, soft pubescent. The flowers are maroon to purple and in the shape of the classic Dutchman's pipe. The fruit is a 6–ribbed capsule up to 10 cm long, which becomes a conspicuous pendulous element in tropical deciduous and seasonal evergreen forests. They occur in lowland and temperate areas.

The woody stem of *A. sericea*, if it gives off a slight odor, is prized as a medicine for stomach "wind." It is classed then as **vinik**, "man." If it is odorless, it is termed **antzil**, "female," and has no use. Sections of the corky, thick, ribbed old wood of *A. maxima* are cut, the bark is trimmed, and a piece 40 cm long is crushed on a rock and soaked in water for an hour. The "hot" infusion is drunk before breakfast for 3–4 days.

The vine may be stored, but then the stem is cut into small sections after being debarked. If the patient takes the tea this way, however, he must abstain from cold water and "cold" foods for eight days. The tea may be taken without the intervention of a shaman, but if there is swelling or cramps, a shaman is required and the vine will be mixed with tobacco, **kururin** root, **soro te'** root, **tentzun**, and **ch'ail pox**. A large bowl of the herb tea is drunk 2–3 times. If there is no alleviation after the second dose it is thought the patient will not recover. Sections of vine may be bought by a person in need. For further medicinal uses cf. **muk'ta kachu toro te'**.

Extended range: *Prestonia mexicana*.

20. **Ve'el inatab**, "iguana food" (**t'an-'ak', t'ant'an ak'**, and **tzajal ak'** in part), refers to *Ampelocissus acapulcensis* (1–2), *Cissus cacuminis* (3–5), *C. sicyoides* (2–4), and *Parthenocissus quinquefolia* (2–3), all members of the grape family. These vines are common in dry lowland forests and in second growth. They are characterized by thick, soft stems and large leaves. The flowers are usually red and the fruit is fleshy and purple.

The plant is widely noted as a food for iguanas and birds with the fruit, flowers, leaves, and sap being utilized. As a remedy for pink eye (**satil**), the patient cuts the young tip and places three drops of the "cold" sap in the eye. Women who wish to make their hair grow mash the vine on a stone and mix it with cold water. They wash their hair applying the paste twice a day for two or three days.

Extended range: *Vitis tiliifolia*.

21. **Xinal ak'**, "stinky vine," is *Matelea prosthecidiscus* (1–2), a coarse, rank, thick-stemmed vine with large, thick opposite, cordate-ovate leaves up to 20 cm long. The stems and petioles have stiff, erect hairs. Flowers are green and in short axillary clusters. The fruit is an elliptic capsule to 12 cm long covered with fleshy tubercles 5 mm long. The seeds have tufts of long white hair. It is an uncommon plant in primary forests in lowland regions.

22. **Yak' xulem**, "buzzard's vine," is *Hiraea* aff. *fagifolia* (1–1), a woody vine with opposite narrowly elliptic leaves 11–16 cm long and yellow flowers 1–1.5 cm broad, arranged in clusters along the stem. The fruit is a samara with a globose body and large, thin, rounded wings about 2 cm wide. It occurs in undisturbed situations in tropical deciduous forests. For menstrual failure, chips of the wood are brewed to provide a "hot" tea.

23. **Yat vakax ak'**, "bull penis vine" (**chan-tzelav ak', ch'ix ak', juxob-bail ak'**), is the temperate and lowland vine *Pithecoctenium crucigerum* (5–8), a common woody vine in the dry lowland forests. It is characterized by large, elliptic, flattened, spiny fruits. The seeds are flat with broad, almost transparent wings. The leaves are bifoliate or trifoliate with broadly ovate leaflets, cordate or rounded at the base. The flowers are white or yellowish, large, 3–4 cm long and tubular.

The vine is used for lashing roof poles, fences, and fences across streams. The soft inside of the fruit is used by corn farmers to wipe off sweat and dirt.

Isolates

1. **Ich ak'**, "chili vine" (**-tik**) (**be xinich ak', ichi ak', ichil ak', muk'ta tz'usub, poxil sal-tz'i'**), refers to the virgin's bowers *Clematis dioica* (8–19) and *C. grossa* (4–10), woody vines with stems often 10 or more meters long. The flowers are white and in large, showy clusters, fruits are white plumes attached to clusters of seeds. Leaves are trifoliate with 3 ovate leaflets 8–10 cm long. It is very common in secondary formations of temperate and highland areas. The name, **be xinich ak'**, "ant path vine," may refer to the ants that are attracted to the nectar when it is in flower.

The vines are used to lash roof rods, purlins, rafters, and fences. They are considered to be stronger than **k'am-xoch'** lashing, but are hard to find. They are used to decorate the forest creche in Atz'am. As a remedy for laundry hands, women crush three flowers and bandage the hand with them 5–6 times. To remove **sal-tz'i'** blemishes, the "hot" seeds are crushed and rubbed on the affected part, though the remedy causes a sharp sting.

Extended range: *Melothria pendula* and *Mikania cordifolia*.

2. **Kururin** (**kurarina, kururin ak', kururina**) is *Cissampelos pareira* (9–17), a thin wiry vine with heart-shaped leaves ands small flowers in axillary clusters. The fruit is red, fleshy, 6–8 mm long. It is common in temperate and lowland forests. This is a variable plant and some speakers recognize this by placing some individuals of this plant in the extended range. The root, having a great variety of medicinal uses, may be stored in the house for a year. As a remedy for "wind" and stomach swelling (**ik' ta jchuttik**), the root is brewed. The "hot" tea may be drunk alone or laced with strong cane liquor. One cup is drunk before breakfast for three days. Unlaced tea may be taken for postpartum "cold" and malaria. It may also be given to mules suffering "wind." Laced tea is taken to relieve painful urination. No shaman is required for "wind" (**sikil kolo'al ik'**); a "hot" tea of the root, brewed together with rue, **tentzun**, and the root of **soro te'** may be taken. As a remedy for

snakebite or the bite of a black widow spider, four roots are crushed and brewed. A cup of the tea may be given to people or mules so afflicted. In another remedy for snakebite, four tips are brewed with six splinters of pitch pine. The victim drinks the "hot" tea immediately after being bitten, and one or two times afterward. The tea may also be made by brewing the roots in cane liquor or by crushing the fruit and brewing it. The latter prescription is also a cure for black widow and tarantula bites. For further medicinal uses cf. **muk'ta kachu toro te'**, **poxil yerva, vako' ak', xchenek' tzajal om.**

Extended range: *Sarcostemma bilobum.*

3. **K'an-ak'** "yellow vine" (**-tik**) refers to the dodders, a group of orange parasitic vines.

Specifics: 2.

   a. **Batz'i k'an-ak'**, "genuine yellow vine," refers to *Cuscuta corymbosa* var. *grandifolia* (1–4) and *C. tinctoria* (5–13). This is a slender, parasitic, bright-orange, leafless vine with clusters of white flowers. It is common in second growth as a parasite on many species of shrubs in the temperate and highland areas. In 1797 the priest of Zinacantán commented that "this vine that they call **canác** gives a flesh color for their hair ribbons" (de Leon y Goicoechea, 1797).

The entire plant is gathered by women. A netful is brewed with **batz'i chil jabnal** to dye wool yellow. The wool is then dyed blue in San Cristóbal to provide green wool for sashes and skirts.

Extended range: *Sarcostemma bilobum, Cassytha filiformis.*

   b. **K'ox k'an-ak'**, "small yellow vine," is the minute *Cuscuta yucatana* (1–1), an herbaceous hair-like wiry vine that parasitizes herbs in open grassy fields of the highland regions. The stems are leafless and straw-colored with very small white flowers about 1–2 mm across.

4. **Roxa** (**-tik, -iltik**) (**ch'ixal nichim*, nich rosa*, rosa***) refers to the cultivated members of the genus *Rosa*. In 1545 the first Dominican friars in Zinacantán received rose bushes, Rose of Castile (*Rosa gallica*) and Rose of Alexandria (*Rosa damascena*), from Fray Jordán de Piamonte in Oaxaca (Ximénes, 1929(1):423). Thomas Gage (1620) mentioned observing Rose of Alexandria in Chiapas in 1620. Neither seems to be present in Chiapas at this time.

Specifics: 5.

   a. **Batz'i tzajal roxa**, "genuine red rose" (**tz'unbalal tzajal roxa**), refers to the red-flowered individuals of the cultivated bush rose *Rosa chinensis* (10–11). Although this rose can grow in lowland areas (it is common in gardens in Tuxtla) it is found cultivated mostly in the temperate and highland areas. This is a typical ornamental plant in which all the color and shape types have been highly selected so that there is a tremendous morphological variation. Zinacantecs recognize this variation with many descriptive designations for the different forms:

   (1) **Ik''ik'-lo'an roxa,** deep red rose.
   (2) **Sak-pak'an roxa,** fat pink rose.
   (3) **Sak-vayan roxa,** pink rose.
   (4) **Sak-vayan tzajal roxa,** pink red rose.
   (5) **Sak-vilan tz'unbalal roxa,** pink cultivated rose.

Slips 40 cm long are planted in the yards generally in the rainy season, but they may also be planted in the dry season if watered.

The flowers are put in altar vases by people visiting the churches. They are used to decorate graves on All Souls' Day and when the family lights candles at the graves on the Fiesta of St. Sebastian, during Carnival and Holy Week, on St. Peter the Martyr's Day, St. John's Day, and the Fiesta of St. Lawrence.

Each ensign-bearer provides a large bowl of rose petals for the first three Lenten Fridays, and two bowls for the last three Lenten Fridays. Each steward and the cantors provide a bowl for every Lenten Friday and for Tuesday and Wednesday of Holy Week. A large basket of rose petals is provided by each steward on Maundy Thursday to "bury" a small image of Christ, and a basket of white rose petals is provided by each of the cantors and the Stewards of the Holy Cross on Good Friday. The petals are strewn on the processional path. Each steward provides half a small basket of rose petals on Holy Cross Day. In Chak Toj the flowers are used to decorate the creche. Roses are also offered in San Mikulax on Holy Cross Day. They are offered in Sak Lum on the fifth Friday of Lent, in Apas on the sixth Friday of Lent, and in Paste', and Naben Chauk on Good Friday.

As a remedy for fever sores, "cold" pink blossoms are dried on the griddle and the powder rubbed on, twice a day for two or three days. The flower may also be chewed or crushed and rubbed on the lips. It induces salivation. To reduce the "heat" of heartburn (**me' vinik**) and **majbenal**, the flower may be crushed in cold water and the "cold" infusion taken, or the flower may be scalded in boiling water and the "cold" tea drunk.

   b. **K'anal roxa**, "yellow rose" (**k'ox k'anal roxa**), is *Rosa banksiae* (1–5), a sprawling viny plant with few thorns and small yellow flowers in tight clusters. The leaves are compound with narrowly elliptic leaflets, acute at both the tip and base about 3–4 cm long. It is grown only in the highland regions.

The flowers are used for altar decoration, especially during Holy Week, and for grave decorations.

   c. **K'ox tzajal roxa**, "small red rose" (**bik'tal tzajal roxa, k'ox sak-vayan roxa, tz'unbalal bik'tal tzajal roxa**), is the viny rose *Rosa multiflora* (6–4), another cultivated, variable, ornamental rose differing from *R. chinensis* in having terminal clusters of flowers rather than solitary flowers, and somewhat smaller leaflets. Both *R. chinensis* and *R. multiflora* have stout prickles on the stems and branchlets.

It is grown in yards and along fences in temperate and

highland regions.

  d. **Makom roxa**, "blackberry rose," is *Rosa roxburghii* (1–2), an uncommonly cultivated rose with fruits that are covered with spines. The flowers are red and leaves are compound with many small, elliptic leaflets 1.5–2 cm long. It is known in only one lowland location, El Trapiche.

  e. **Sakil roxa**, "white rose" (**muk'ta sakil roxa, tz'un-balal sakil roxa**), refers to the white-flowered individuals of *Rosa chinensis* (2–4).

White roses have the same use as red roses. In addition, white rose petals are offered in Chak Toj on Good Friday, white rose petals are used in Atz'am on Our Lady of the Rosary, and white rose petals and elderberry blossoms are strewn on the path of the Christ Child on Christmas Eve in Atz'am.

After taking a store-bought laxative, water may not be drunk for one day. Instead, three flowers are brewed and a cup of the "cold" tea is drunk before breakfast and following the laxative. Or the laxative may be mixed with the tea.

5. **Te' ak'**, "woody vine" or stiff vine," is a non-Linnaean grouping that focuses on woody vines that are too brittle to be used for lashing. These are mostly members of the **pek' me'el** and **tz'usub** sets. It includes *Adenocalyma apurense* (1–1), *Anemopaegma puberulum* (1–2), *Antigonon flavescens* (1–1), *Bunchosia montana* (1–1), *Canavalia glabra* (1–1), *Combretum fruticosum* (1–4), *Didymaea alsinoides* (1–1), *Gouania polygama* (1– 2), *Hiraea reclinata* (1–4), *Passiflora sexiflora* (1–1), *Petastoma patelliferum* (1–4), *Quassia amara* (1–1), and *Serjania psilophylla* (1–1). Some speakers subdivide this term into three classes: **sakil**, "white," **tzajal**, "red," and **yaxal**, "blue-green."

The "cold" fruit of *A. apurense* is edible. It is sold in Acala, Chiapa de Corzo, and San Cristóbal.

6. **Yak' max**, "monkey's vine" *Dalechampia scandens* (1–1), is an urticating, herbaceous vine with hand-like flowers. The leaves are alternate, 3–lobed cordate at the base softly pubescent beneath. They range in size from 4.5–12 cm long. It occurs in the tropical deciduous forests and second growth of the lowlands.

7. **Yat tz'i' ak'**, "dog's penis vine" (**lo'bol chij, poxil sal-tz'i' ak', sal-tz'i' ak'**), refers to *Bomarea acutifolia* (2–2) and *B. hirtella* (7–17). These plants have a slender vine arising from a branched, edible tuber. The leaves are alternate, parallel-veined lanceolate with a long tapering apex and rounded base; the capsule is subglobose. The enclosed seeds are covered with a red pulp. The flowers are large, tubular, orange, spotted with purple and in pendent terminal clusters. The plants are common in second growth and evergreen cloud forests of the temperate and highland locations.

Zinacantecs are not aware that the root is edible. To remove **sal-tz'i'** blemishes, the "medium" berries are rubbed on the affected part.

Extended range: *Asclepias* sp., *Gentiana laevigata*, and *Smilacina scilloides*.

"Trees": "Te' Sets"

  aja-te'es
    aja-te'es   *Gaultheria odorata* (Ericaceae)
    k'ox aja-te'es   *Vaccinium confertum* (Ericaceae)
  tzis uch   *Litsea glaucescens* (Lauraceae)

  ajval te'   *Stillingia acutifolia* (Euphorbiaceae)
  bak te'   *Dodonaea viscosa* (Sapindaceae)
  majob ik'al   *Jacquinea macrocarpa* (Theophrastaceae)
  ventex mol   *Picramnia tetramera* (Simaroubaceae)

  aj
    antzil aj   *Phragmites australis* (Poaceae)
    vinik aj   *Gynerium sagittatum* (Poaceae)
    yajil ama *Arundo donax* (Poaceae)
  bix
    antzil bix *Olmeca reflexa* (Poaceae)
    ton bix   *Otatea fimbriata* (Poaceae)
  chanib   *Lasiacis hispida* (Poaceae)
              Rhipidocladum bartlettii (Poaceae)
              Rhipidocladum pittieri (Poaceae)
  ik'ob chij   *Lasiacis divaricata* (Poaceae)
  meno   *Pennisetum purpureum* (Poaceae)
  ne kotom
    k'ox ne kotom *Chusquea liebmanni* (Poaceae)
    muk'ta ne kotom *Chusquea foliosa* (Poaceae)
  otot
    k'anal otot *Bambusa vulgaris* var. *vittata* (Poaceae)
    yaxal otot *Bambusa vulgaris* var. *vulgaris* (Poaceae)

  boch   *Crescentia cujete* (Bignoniaceae)
  boch te'   *Randia aculeata* (Rubiaceae)
              Randia cineria (Rubiaceae)
  chachi'   *Parmentiera aculeata* (Bignoniaceae)
  nantzi'   *Byrsonima crassifolia* (Malpighiaceae)
  tzima'   *Crescentia alata* (Bignoniaceae)

  akit   *Guazuma ulmifolia* (Sterculiaceae)
  be xinich te' *Cordia alliodora* (Boraginaceae)
  bot
    bot   *Heliocarpus donnell-smithii* (Tiliaceae)
          Heliocarpus mexicanus (Tiliaceae)
    ch'ich' bot *Croton draco* (Euphorbiaceae)
  choch

bik'it choch *Stemmadenia eubracteata* (Apocynaceae)
         Stemmadenia obovata (Apocynaceae)
choch   *Thevetia ovata* (Apocynaceae)
         Thevetia plumeriaefolia (Apocynaceae)
ch'ilim te' *Hymenaea courbaril* (Fabaceae)
mail te'   *Pseudobombax ellipticum* (Bombacaceae)
putzkuy   *Cochlospermum vitifolium* (Cochlospermaceae)
sal-te'
  sakil sal-te' *Jatropha curcas* (Euphorbiaceae)
  tzajal sal-te' *Bursera simaruba* (Burseraceae)
saya-vun   *Morus celtidifolia* (Moraceae)
tux-nuk' te' *Luehea candida* (Tiliaceae)
xinal te'   *Gyrocarpus americanus* (Gyrocarpaceae)

chalon   *Inga vera* ssp. *spuria* (Fabaceae)
         Inga xalapensis (Fabaceae)
tz'erel   *Inga fagifolia* (Fabaceae)
         Inga jinicuil (Fabaceae)
         Inga punctata (Fabaceae)

chijil te'
  batz'i chijil te' *Sambucus mexicana* (Caprifoliaceae)
  xutax chijil te' *Sambucus canadensis* (Caprifoliaceae)
chix te'
  batz'i chix te' *Prunus serotina* (Rosaceae)
  chix te' mut *Prunus serotina* (Rosaceae)
ch'it
  jich'il anal ch'it *Diospyros nicaraguensis* (Ebanaceae)
         Wimmeria acuminata (Celastraceae)
  muk'ta tzajal ch'it *Chrysophyllum cainito* (Sapotaceae)
         Chrysophyllum mexicanum (Sapotaceae)
  sakil ch'it *Eugenia acapulcensis* (Myrtaceae)
         Eugenia amatenangensis (Myrtaceae)
         Eugenia carranzae (Myrtaceae)
         Eugenia laughlinii (Myrtaceae)
  tzajal ch'it *Ardisia escallonioides* (Myrsinaceae)
         Schoepfia vacciniiflora (Olacaceae)
  tzotzin ch'it *Eugenia yunkeri* (Myrtaceae)
  yaxal ch'it *Xylosma intermedium* (Flacourtiaceae)
ch'ix ak'   *Celtis iguanaea* (Ulmaceae)

ik'al te‘   *Bourreria huanita* (Boraginaceae)

     Ehretia latifolia (Boraginaceae)

     Hippocratia volubilis (Celastraceae)

ik'al vinik   *Garrya laurifolia* (Garryaceae)

makulixkuat   *Muntingia calabura* (Eleocarpaceae)

nampívo   *Ehretia tinifolia* (Boraginaceae)

paxamum

     batz'i paxamum   *Malpighia mexicana* (Malpighiaceae)

     muk'ta paxamum   *Symplocos limoncillo* (Symplocaceae)

     Symplocos vernicosa (Symplocaceae)

treno   *Ligustrum lucidum* (Oleaceae)

vax te‘   *Trema micrantha* (Ulmaceae)

yak' jnibak   *Daphnopsis americana* (Thymeliaceae)

yisim bolom   *Xylosma flexuosum* (Flacourtiaceae)

     Xylosma intermedium (Flacourtiaceae)

     Xylosma quichense (Flacourtiaceae)

"Chilkat Set" 157

arsyal te‘   *Baccharis trinervis* (Asteraceae)

chilkat

     batz'i chilkat   *Senecio salignus* (Asteraceae)

     k'ox chilkat   *Baccharis glutinosa* (Asteraceae)

     te'tikal chilkat   *Trixis inula* (Asteraceae)

ch'a-te‘

     bik'it ch'a-te‘   *Ageratina bustamenta* (Asteraceae)

     Ageratina ligustrina (Asteraceae)

     Ageratina mairetiana (Asteraceae)

     Ageratina pringlei (Asteraceae)

     Chromolaena collina (Asteraceae)

     Pachythamnus crassirameus (Asteraceae)

     Stevia ovata (Asteraceae)

     Stevia polycephala (Asteraceae)

     Stevia serrata (Asteraceae)

     muk'ta ch'a-te‘   *Ageratina ligustrina* (Asteraceae)

ch'a-te‘ pox   *Stevia lucida* (Asteraceae)

ch'ail pox   *Calea urticifolia* (Asteraceae)

mes te‘   *Baccharis vaccinioides* (Asteraceae)

poxil ik'   *Stevia lucida* (Asteraceae)

     Stevia polycephala (Asteraceae)

poxil tza‘nel   *Baccharis serraefolia* (Asteraceae)

"Ch'upak' Te‘ Set" 158

ch'upak' te‘

     muk'ta ch'upak' te‘   *Ricinus communis* (Euphorbiaceae)

     sakil ch'upak' te‘   *Ricinus communis* (Euphorbiaceae)

     tzajal ch'upak' te‘   *Ricinus communis* (Euphorbiaceae)

makom uch   *Datura stramonium* (Solanaceae)

tz'in-te‘   *Manihot esculenta* (Euphorbiaceae)

"Jabnal Set" 159

jabnal   *Oreopanax peltatus* (Araliaceae)

jabnal te‘   *Oreopanax xalapensis* (Araliaceae)

---

k'am-xoch'   *Chiranthodendron pentadactylon* (Sterculiaceae)

k'orok' te‘   *Cecropia peltata* (Moraceae)

mumun   *Piper auritum* (Piperaceae)

mumun te‘   *Piper amalgo* (Piperaceae)

     Piper decurrens (Piperaceae)

     Piper hispidum (Piperaceae)

     Piper jacquemontianum (Piperaceae)

     Piper marginatum (Piperaceae)

     Piper tuberculatum (Piperaceae)

"Kachímpa Te‘ Set" 159

chin te‘   *Hura polyandra* (Euphorbiaceae)

ich te‘   *Toxicodendron striatum* (Anacardiaceae)

kachímpa te‘   *Comocladia guatemalensis* (Anacardiaceae)

matal ak'   *Toxicodendron radicans* (Anacardiaceae)

"K'an-te‘ Set" 160

barsin te‘   *Guettarda macrosperma* (Rubiaceae)

     Piscidia carthagenensis (Fabaceae)

brasil   *Haematoxylon brasiletto* (Fabaceae)

chenek' te‘   *Clitoria polystachya* (Fabaceae)

     Gliricidia ehrenbergii (Fabaceae)

     Godmania aesculifolia (Bignoniaceae)

     Harpalyce formosa var. goldmanii (Fabaceae)

     Inga vera ssp. *spuria* (Fabaceae)

     Pistacia mexicana (Anacardiaceae)

     Senna hirsuta var. hirta (Fabaceae)

     Senna pallida (Fabaceae)

ch'aben te‘   *Indigofera suffruticosa* (Fabaceae)

     Indigofera thibaudiana (Fabaceae)

ch'ix-ni' te‘   *Gliricidia ehrenbergii* (Fabaceae)

jach'ub te‘   *Platanus mexicana* (Platanaceae)

kamaron te‘   *Alvaradoa amorphoides* (Simaroubaceae)

kanéla te‘

     sakil kanéla te‘   *Hauya elegans* (Onagraceae)

     tzajal kanéla te‘   *Calycophyllum candidissimum* (Rubiaceae)

kanelo   *Cinnamomum zeylanicum* (Lauraceae)

k'an-te‘   *Diphysa floribunda* (Fabaceae)

k'anal te‘   *Mahonia berriozabalensis* (Berberidaceae)

     Mahonia volcania (Berberidaceae)

milob ch'o te‘   *Gliricidia sepium* (Fabaceae)

pinto te‘   *Wimmeria pubescens* (Celastraceae)

putzul chij   *Tecoma stans* (Bignoniaceae)

yax-'ib te‘   *Senna cobanensis* (Fabaceae)

     Senna pallida (Fabaceae)

     Senna skinneri (Fabaceae)

144

yax-te'	*Senna tonduzii* (Fabaceae)
	Eysenhardtia adenostylis (Fabaceae)

"K'at'ix Set" 162

isbon	*Cornus excelsa* (Cornaceae)
k'at'ix	
k'anal k'at'ix	*Crataegus pubescens* (Rosaceae)
sijom k'at'ix	*Crataegus pubescens* (Rosaceae)
tzajal k'at'ix	*Crataegus pubescens* (Rosaceae)

"La Set" 163

chaya itaj	*Cnidoscolus aconitifolius* 'Maya' (Euphorbiaceae)
chon la	*Wigandia urens* (Hydrophyllaceae)
	Wigandia urens var. *caracasana* (Hydrophyllaceae)
la	
batz'i la	*Urtica chamaedryoides* (Urticaceae)
kilajtik la	*Gronovia scandens* (Loasaceae)
k'ox la	*Tragia nepetifolia* (Euphorbiaceae)
muk'tik la	*Urera caracasana* (Urticaceae)
sakil la	*Cnidoscolus aconitifolius* (Euphorbiaceae)
	Cnidoscolus multilobus (Euphorbiaceae)
	Cnidoscolus tubulosus (Euphorbiaceae)

"Máchita Te' Set" 164

chenek' chij te'	*Senna atomeria* (Fabaceae)
máchita te'	*Delonix regia* (Fabaceae)
nichim te'	*Caesalpinia exostema* (Fabaceae)
	Caesalpinia pulcherrima (Fabaceae)

"Mantzana Set" 164

mantzana	
batz'i matzana	*Malus pumila* (Rosaceae)
kámosa mantzana	*Malus pumila* (Rosaceae)
peróte mantzana	*Malus pumila* (Rosaceae)
tranjero mantzana	*Malus pumila* (Rosaceae)
mántzana te'	*Amelanchier denticulata* (Rosaceae)
nimpronix	*Cydonia oblonga* (Rosaceae)
nimpronix te'	*Duranta repens* (Verbenaceae)
pelex	
batz'i pelex	*Pyrus communis* (Rosaceae)
kaxlan pelex	*Pyrus pyrifolia* (Rosaceae)

"Met Set" 165

chi	
pino chi	*Agave sisalana* (Agavaceae)
te'tikal chi	*Furcraea guatemalensis* (Agavaceae)
kaxlan tok'oy	*Yucca elephantipes* (Agavaceae)
met	
chi met	*Agave kewensis* (Agavaceae)
lo'balal met	*Agave chiapensis* (Agavaceae)
muk'ta met	*Agave americana* (Agavaceae)
paxak'	
chimpo paxak'	*Bromelia hemisphaerica* (Bromeli-

	aceae)
kinya paxak'	*Bromelia pinguin* (Bromeliaceae)
muk'ta paxak'	*Ananas comosus* (Bromeliaceae)
paxak'il te'tik	*Greigia oaxacana* (Bromeliaceae)
potpot paxak'	*Bromelia plumieri* (Bromeliaceae)

"Naranja Set" 167

alaxax	*Citrus aurantium* (Rutaceae)
elamonix	*Citrus aurantifolia* (Rutaceae)
kajve	*Coffea arabica* (Rubiaceae)
kajve te'	*Casearia commersoniana* (Flacourtiaceae)
	Casearia corymbosa (Flacourtiaceae)
konkon	
konkon	*Cavendishia crassifolia* (Ericaceae)
k'anal konkon	*Galphimia glauca* (Malpighiaceae)
lima	
chu' lima	*Citrus limonia* 'Millsweet' (Rutaceae)
ch'ulul lima	*Citrus limetta* (Rutaceae)
pimil pat lima	*Citrus limonia* (Rutaceae)
limon	*Citrus limonia* 'Eureka' (Rutaceae)
mantarina	
batz'i mantarina	*Citrus reticulata* (Rutaceae)
k'ol-pat mantarina	*Citrus reticulata* (Rutaceae)
naranja	
jayal pat naranja	*Citrus sinensis* (Rutaceae)
pimil pat naranja	*Citrus sinensis* (Rutaceae)
sila	*Citrus medica* (Rutaceae)
yich'ak mut	*Fuchsia paniculata* (Onagraceae)

"Olnob Set" 169

chojchoj	*Acacia cornigera* (Fabaceae)
ch'ich' ni'	*Calliandra confusa* (Fabaceae)
	Calliandra grandiflora (Fabaceae)
	Calliandra houstoniana (Fabaceae)
kevrajacha	*Acacia pennatula* (Fabaceae)
krus ch'ix	*Pisonia aculeata* (Nyctaginaceae)
	Pisonia macranthocarpa (Nyctaginaceae)
lotz'om chij	*Mimosa albida* (Fabaceae)
molíno te'	*Poeppigia procera* (Fabaceae)
olnob	
batz'i olnob	*Leucaena leucocephala* (Fabaceae)
paka' olnob	*Leucaena collinsii* (Fabaceae)
tzajal olnob	*Leucaena diversifolia* (Fabaceae)
pit	*Enterolobium cyclocarpum* (Fabaceae)
sakil ch'ix	*Acacia farnesiana* (Fabaceae)
suk	
ik'al suk	*Lysiloma acapulcense* (Fabaceae)
	Lysiloma divaricatum (Fabaceae)
sakil suk	*Lysiloma auritum* (Fabaceae)
tamarin	*Tamarindus indica* (Fabaceae)
tzo' xulem te'	*Lonchocarpus minimiflorus* (Fabaceae)
	Lonchocarpus rugosus (Fabaceae)
vamuch te'	*Pithecellobium dulce* (Fabaceae)

voy chij te'   *Bauhinia divaricata* (Fabaceae)
                  Bauhinia pauletia (Fabaceae)
                  Bauhinia ungulata (Fabaceae)

xaxib
  batz'i xaxib   *Acacia angustissima* (Fabaceae)
  muk'ta xaxib   *Calliandra portoricensis* (Fabaceae)
                  Calliandra tetragona (Fabaceae)
xaxib ch'ix   *Mimosa pigra* (Fabaceae)
yolnob ch'o   *Aeschynomene compacta* (Fabaceae)
                  Aeschynomene purpusii (Fabaceae)
                  Chamaecrista nictitans ssp. *disadenia* var. *pilosa* (Fabaceae)
                  Desmanthus virgatus (Fabaceae)
                  Indigofera thibaudiana (Fabaceae)
                  Machaerium chiapense (Fabaceae)
                  Senna occidentalis (Fabaceae)
                  Senna pallida (Fabaceae)
                  Senna skinneri (Fabaceae)
                  Tephrosia cinerea (Fabaceae)

"On Set" 172
  aj-te'
    bik'it aj-te'   *Casimiroa edulis* (Rutaceae)
    ch'ulul aj-te' *Casimiroa edulis* (Rutaceae)
    muk'ta aj-te'   *Casimiroa edulis* (Rutaceae)
  aj-te' te'   *Tabebuia rosea* (Bingoniaceae)
  chinin   *Persea scheideana* (Lauraceae)
  itzompi   *Licania platypus* (Rosaceae)
  ja'as   *Pouteria mammosa* (Sapotaceae)
  kována te'   *Swietenia humilis* (Meliaceae)
  lumpisera   *Platymiscium dimorphandrum* (Fabaceae)

  manko
    batz'i manko   *Mangifera indica* (Anacardiaceae)
    chitom manko   *Mangifera indica* (Anacardiaceae)
    tranjero manko *Mangifera indica* (Anacardiaceae)
    xok manko   *Mangifera indica* (Anacardiaceae)
  muy   *Manilkara achras* (Sapotaceae)
  no'chi'   *Pouteria campechiana* (Sapotaceae)
  on
    batz'i on   *Persea americana* (Lauraceae)
    ch'ail on   *Persea americana* (Lauraceae)
    tzitz on   *Persea americana* (Lauraceae)
    yax-'on   *Persea americana* (Lauraceae)
  oven   *Persea donnell-smithii* (Lauraceae)
  tzitz   *Persea americana* var. *drymifolia* (Lauraceae)
  tzitz te'   *Beilschmiedia riparia* (Lauraceae)
                    Dipholis matudae (Sapotaceae)
                    Licaria peckii (Lauraceae)
                    Nectandra coriacea (Lauraceae)
                    Ocotea chiapensis (Lauraceae)
                    Styrax argentum (Styracaceae)
  uch   *Diospyros digyna* (Ebanaceae)
  yaj-te' kotom   *Elaeodendron trichotomum* (Celastraceae)

"On Te' Set" 176
  on te'
    k'ox on te'   *Comarostaphylos arbutoides* (Ericaceae)
                    Comarostaphylos discolor (Ericaceae)
    muk'ta on te'   *Arbutus xalapensis* (Ericaceae)
    nap'ap' on te' *Arbutus xalapensis* (Ericaceae)
  sakil te'   *Acer negundo* ssp. *mexicanum* (Aceraceae)

"Pitz'otz' Set" 176
  pitz'otz'   *Monnina xalapensis* (Polygalaceae)
  sat pukuj   *Solanum aligerum* (Solanaceae)
                    Solanum brachystachys (Solanaceae)
                    Solanum cervantesii (Solanaceae)
  tuil te'   *Cestrum aurantiacum* (Solanaceae)
                    Cestrum guatemalense (Solanaceae)
                    Solanum brachystachys (Solanaceae)
                    Solanum nudum (Solanaceae)
  ve'el kulajte'   *Cordia foliosa* (Boraginaceae)
                    Cordia spinescens (Boraginaceae)
                    Rauvolfia tetraphylla (Apocynaceae)

"Po'on Set" 177
  amat   *Ficus glabrata* (Moraceae)
                    Ficus glaucescens (Moraceae)
  ch'u-te'
    bik'it ch'u-te' *Cedrela oaxacensis* (Meliaceae)
    sakil ch'u-te' *Cedrela odorata* (Meliaceae)
                    C. salvadorensis (Meliaceae)
  inop   *Ceiba pentandra* (Bombacaceae)
  jovos
    batz'i jovos   *Spondias mombin* (Anacardiaceae)
    yaxal jovos   *Mastichodendron capiri* var. *tempisque* (Sapotaceae)
  kajanab te'   *Oreopanax capitatus* (Araliaceae)
  maluk   *Genipa caruto* (Rubiaceae)
  mémela te'   *Clusia rosea* (Clusiaceae)
  mojan   *Ceiba aesculifolia* (Bombacaceae)
  mutut   *Ficus cookii* (Moraceae)
                    Ficus cotinifolia (Moraceae)
  po'on
    batz'i po'on   *Spondias purpurea* (Anacardiaceae)
    te'tikal po'on *Spondias mombin* (Anacardiaceae)
                    Spondias purpurea (Anacardiaceae)
  po'on ch'ix   *Ximenia americana* (Olacaceae)
  te'el uli'   *Ficus elastica* (Moraceae)

"Pom Set" 179
  pom
    ach'el pom   *Bursera bipinnata* (Burseraceae)
    batz'i pom   *Bursera excelsa* (Burseraceae)
  pom ka'   *Bursera steyermarkii* (Burseraceae)

"Sun Set" 180
  k'ail   *Smallanthus maculatus* (Asteraceae)
                    Smallanthus oaxacanus (Asteraceae)
  sun   *Tithonia diversifolia* (Asteraceae)

	Tithonia longiradiata (Asteraceae)
	Tithonia rotundifolia (Asteraceae)
	Tithonia tubaeformis (Asteraceae)
ton k'ail	*Montanoa hexagona* (Asteraceae)
tzojoj	*Lagascea helianthifolia* (Asteraceae)

"Tilil Set" 180
bak amuch te'	*Clethra mexicana* (Clethraceae)
bakel amuch te'	*Calyptranthes chiapensis* (Myrtaceae)
ja'as te'	*Styrax argentum* (Styraceae)
karnéro te'	*Coccoloba barbadensis* (Polygonaceae)
	Coccoloba diversifolia (Polygonaceae)
	Coccoloba liebmannii (Polygonaceae)
	Coccoloba mayana (Polygonaceae)
k'ol-k'ox	*Phyllantus grandifolius* (Euphorbiaceae)
k'os	
sakil k'os	*Synardisia venosa* (Myrsinaceae)
tzajal k'os	*Parathesis chiapensis* (Myrsinaceae)
	Parathesis leptopa (Myrsinaceae)
k'oxox te'	
batz'i k'oxox te'	*Ternstroemia lineata* ssp. *chalicophylla* (Theaceae)
	Ternstroemia oocarpa (Theaceae)
ik'al k'oxox te'	*Cleyera theaeoides* (Theaceae)
poxil poslom	*Rhamnus mucronata* (Rhamnaceae)
tilil	*Rapanea juergensenii* (Myrsinaceae)
yaxal mol	*Licania arborea* (Rosaceae)

"Toj Set" 182
k'isis	*Taxodium mucronatum* (Taxodiaceae)
nukul pat	*Cupressus benthamii* var. *lindleyi* (Cupressaceae)
ok'il te'	*Juniperus comitana* (Cupressaceae)
	Juniperus gamboana (Cupressaceae)
toj	
ajan toj	*Pinus michoacana* (Pinaceae)
batz'i toj	*Pinus montezumae* var. *rudis* (Pinaceae)
chak-toj	*Pinus pseudostrobus* (Pinaceae)
ik'al toj	*Pinus oaxacana* (Pinaceae)
k'uk' toj	
sakil k'uk' toj	*Abies guatemalensis* (Pinaceae)
tzajal k'uk' toj	*Pinus ayacahuite* (Pinaceae)
tzajal toj	*Pinus oocarpa* (Pinaceae)
	Pinus teocote (Pinaceae)

"Ton Bek' Set" 184
presa	*Fraxinus uhdei* (Oleaceae)
ton bek'	*Juglans regia* (Juglandaceae)

"Top'ol Set" 185

jom akan	*Piptothrix areolaris* (Asteraceae)
k'an-'ich	
batz'i k'an-'ich	*Coreopsis mutica* var. *microcephala* (Asteraceae)
k'ox k'an-'ich	*Perymenium ghiesbreghtii* (Asteraceae)
nam te' mol	*Verbesina hypsela* (Asteraceae)
	Verbesina perymenioides (Asteraceae)
	Verbesina punctata (Asteraceae)
	Verbesina steyermarkii (Asteraceae)
	Verbesina turbascensis (Asteraceae)
top'ol	
k'anal top'ol	*Perymenium grande* var. *nelsonii* (Asteraceae)
k'ox top'ol	*Lasianthaea fruticosa* (Asteraceae)
xolom	*Vernonia leiocarpa* (Asteraceae)

"Tulan Set" 185
batz'i te'	*Quercus crassifolia* (Fagaceae)
chikin-ib	
batz'i chikin-ib	*Quercus castanea* (Fagaceae)
	Quercus crispipilis (Fagaceae)
	Quercus oleoides (Fagaceae)
jayal pat chikin-ib	*Quercus laurina* (Fagaceae)
sakil chikin-ib	*Quercus elliptica* (Fagaceae)
	Quercus sapotifolia (Fagaceae)
kachu toro te'	
muk'ta kachu toro te'	*Bucida macrostachya* (Combretaceae)
yaxal kachu toro te'	*Godmania aesculifolia* (Bignoniaceae)
kampor	*Eucalyptus camaldulensis* (Myrtaceae)
	Eucalyptus globulus (Myrtaceae)
nok	
sakil nok	*Alnus acuminata* ssp. *arguta* (Betulaceae)
tzajal nok	*Alnus jorullensis* (Betulaceae)
paj-'ul	
k'ox paj-'ul	*Rhus terebinthifolia* (Anacardiaceae)
muk'ta paj-'ul	*Rhus schiedeana* (Anacardiaceae)
tzajal paj-'ul	*Pistacia mexicana* (Anacardiaceae)
sap yok	*Quercus candicans* (Fagaceae)
tempix	*Dendropanax arboreus* (Araliaceae)
tulan	
k'an-tulan	*Quercus segoviensis* (Fagaceae)
k'evex tulan	*Quercus polymorpha* (Fagaceae)
sakil tulan	*Quercus peduncularis* (Fagaceae)
tzajal tulan	*Quercus rugosa* (Fagaceae)
tz'otz'op	*Quercus acutifolia* (Fagaceae)
tz'utuj te'	*Carpinus caroliniana* (Betulaceae)
	Ostrya virginiana var. *guatemalensis* (Betulaceae)
tz'utuj te' te'	*Ulmus mexicana* (Ulmaceae)

"Turasnu Set" 188
prixku'	

k'anal prixku'	*Prunus persica* (Rosaceae)
sakil prixku'	*Prunus persica* (Rosaceae)
sirvela	
ik''ik'-lo'an sirvela	*Prunus domestica* (Rosaceae)
k'anal sirvela	*Prunus domestica* (Rosaceae)
sakil sirvela	*Prunus domestica* (Rosaceae)
tzajal sirvela	*Prunus domestica* (Rosaceae)
turasnu	
batz'i turasnu	*Prunus persica* (Rosaceae)
karirat turasnu	*Prunus persica* (Rosaceae)
kaxlan turasnu	*Prunus armeniaca* (Rosaceae)
luranko turasnu	*Prunus persica* (Rosaceae)
merokotom turasnu	*Prunus persica* (Rosaceae)

sitit	
sakil sitit	*Vernonia deppeana* (Asteraceae)
	Vernonia oxacana (Asteraceae)
tzajal sitit	*Pluchea odorata* (Asteraceae)
suil itaj	
batz'i suil itaj	*Liabum glabrum* var. *hypoleucum* (Asteraceae)
k'ox suil itaj	*Liabum andrieuxii* (Asteraceae)
tzelo-pat	
bak tzelo-pat	*Buddleia nitida* (Loganiaceae)
batz'i tzelo-pat	*Buddleia skutchii* (Loganiaceae)
chan-tzelav tzelo-pat	*Buddleia americana* (Loganiaceae)
	Buddleia crotonoides (Loganiaceae)
	Buddleia crotonoides ssp. *amplexicaulis* (Loganiaceae)

ajo' te'	*Saurauia oreophila* (Actinidiaceae)
	Saurauia scabrida (Actinidiaceae)
atz'am te'	*Viburnum hartwegii* (Caprifoliaceae)
chivo te'	*Aloysia chiapensis* (Verbenaceae)
kastanya	*Sterculia apetala* (Sterculiaceae)
k'ux-pevul	*Solanum chrysotrichum* (Solanaceae)
	Solanum lanceolatum (Solanaceae)
	Solanum torvum (Solanaceae)
moy te'	*Solanum erianthum* (Solanaceae)
sak-nich te'	
muk'ta sak-nich te'	*Lippia cardiostegia* (Verbenaceae)
	Lippia myriocephala (Verbenaceae)
sak-nich te'	*Lippia chiapasensis* (Verbenaceae)
	Lippia substrigosa (Verbenaceae)
tzotz-ni' te'	*Viburnum jucundum* (Caprifoliaceae)

koko	*Cocos nucifera* (Arecaceae)
nap	*Acrocomia mexicana* (Arecaceae)
palma	*Sabal mexicana* (Arecaceae)
xan	
batz'i xan	*Brahea dulcis* (Arecaceae)
pik' xan	*Brahea dulcis* (Arecaceae)
	Brahea nitida (Arecaceae)

tz'oban	
batz'i tz'oban	*Phymosia rosea* (Malvaceae)
k'anal tz'oban	*Abutilon purpusii* (Malvaceae)
k'ox tz'oban	*Ayenia mexicana* (Sterculiaceae)
	Malvaviscus arboreus var. *arboreus* (Malvaceae)
yuch' max	
batz'i yuch' max	*Triumfetta grandiflora* (Tiliaceae)
	Triumfetta semitriloba (Tiliaceae)
	Triumfetta speciosa (Tiliaceae)
k'ox yuch' max	*Triumfetta dumetorum* (Tiliaceae)
tzotzin yuch' max	*Triumfetta polyandra* (Tiliaceae)
yuch' max pox	*Acaena elongata* (Rosaceae)

chil jabnal	
batz'i chil jabnal	*Miconia oligotricha* (Melastomataceae)
tzajal chil jabnal	*Leandra subseriata* (Melastomataceae)
	Miconia guatemalensis (Melastomataceae)
	Miconia mexicana (Melastomataceae)
ch'ib	
batz'i ch'ib	*Chamaedorea elatior* (Arecaceae)
muk'ta ch'ib	*Chamaedorea ernesti-augustii* (Arecaceae)
	Chamaedorea nubium (Arecaceae)
palma ch'ib	*Chamaedorea concolor* (Arecaceae)
ik'ux	
ik'al ik'ux	*Ficus carica* (Moraceae)
yaxal ik'ux	*Ficus carica* (Moraceae)
jach'ub te'	*Erythroxylon rotundifolium* (Erythroxylaceae)
jasínto te'	*Moringa oleifera* (Moringaceae)
kakav te'	*Oecopetalum mexicanum* (Icacinaceae)
kámusa te'	*Bocconia arborea* (Papaveraceae)
	Bocconia frutescens (Papaveraceae)
kilkil nichim	
sakil kilkil nichim	*Asparagus setaceus* (Liliaceae)
tzajal kilkil nichim	*Acalypha hispida* (Euphorbiaceae)
yaxyax-'ulan kilkil nichim	*Bougainvillea buttiana* (Nyctaginaceae)
	Bougainvillea glabra (Nyctaginaceae)
klávo	*Eugenia caryophyllus* (Myrtaceae)
kokov	*Theobroma bicolor* (Sterculiaceae)
kránata lo'bol	*Punica granatum* (Punicaceae)
k'ask'as te'	*Iresine angustifolia* (Amaranthaceae)
	Iresine nigra (Amaranthaceae)
k'evex	
batz'i k'evex	*Annona cherimola* (Annonaceae)
chin-jol k'evex	*Annona purpurea* (Annonaceae)

k'anal k'evex	*Annona reticulata* (Annonaceae)
papaúsa k'evex	*Annona diversifolia* (Annonaceae)
k'olo-max	*Olmediella betschleriana* (Flacourtiaceae)
k'unil te'	*Lopezia langmanniae* (Onagraceae)
linkon te'	*Acalypha macrostachya* (Euphorbiaceae)
	Acalypha mollis (Euphorbiaceae)
	Myriocarpa heterostachya (Urticaceae)
	Myriocarpa longipes (Urticaceae)
	Myriocarpa yzabalensis (Urticaceae)
lo'bol	
batz'i lo'bol	*Musa acuminata × M. bulbisiana* (Musaceae)
chan-tzelav lo'bol	*Musa acuminata × M. bulbisiana* (Musaceae)
chimpo lo'bol	*Musa acuminata × M. bulbisiana* (Musaceae)
k'ox lo'bol	*Heliconia librata* (Musaceae)
	Heliconia schiedeana (Musaceae)
mántzana lo'bol	*Musa acuminata × M. bulbisiana* (Musaceae)
mol lo'bol	*Musa textilis* (Musaceae)
natikil lo'bol	*Musa acuminata × M. bulbisiana* (Musaceae)
sakil lo'bol	*Musa acuminata × M. bulbisiana* (Musaceae)
sera lo'bol	*Musa acuminata × M. bulbisiana* (Musaceae)
tzajal lo'bol	*Musa acuminata × M. bulbisiana* (Musaceae)
lo'bol vet	*Coriaria ruscifolia* (Coriariaceae)
luchamaria	*Rheedia edulis* (Clusiaceae)
mora	*Chlorophora tinctoria* (Moraceae)
mukumu	*Euphorbia leucocephala* (Euphorbiaceae)
nankipu	*Cordia dentata* (Boraginaceae)
	Cordia dodecandra (Boraginaceae)
	Cordia sebestena (Boraginaceae)
nuk' chij	*Rubus trilobus* (Rosaceae)
papaya	
papaya	*Carica papaya* (Caricaceae)

papáya mut	*Carica cauliflora* (Caricaceae)
paraíso te'	*Melia azedarach* (Meliaceae)
patax	
k'ox patax	*Nerium oleander* (Apocynaceae)
patax nichim	
k'anal patax nichim	*Plumeria rubra* (Apocynaceae)
moraro patax nichim	*Plumeria rubra* (Apocynaceae)
sakil patax nichim	*Plumeria alba* (Apocynaceae)
tzajal patax nichim	*Plumeria rubra* (Apocynaceae)
pimenta	
batz'i pimenta	*Pimenta dioica* (Myrtaceae)
kaxlan pimenta	*Piper nigrum* (Piperaceae)
piyon te'	*Pedilanthus tithymaloides* (Euphorbiaceae)
pomos	
ik'al pomos	*Ceanothus coeruleus* (Rhamnaceae)
sakil pomos	*Gymnopodium floribundum* var. *antigonoides* (Polygonaceae)
tzajal pomos	*Holodiscus argenteus* (Rosaceae)
potov	
batz'i potov	*Psidium guineense* (Myrtaceae)
kaxlan potov	
sakil kaxlan potov	*Psidium guajava* (Myrtaceae)
tzajal kaxlan potov	*Psidium guajava* (Myrtaceae)
tzajal potov	*Syzygium jambos* (Myrtaceae)
satin	*Myrica cerifera* (Myricaceae)
sik'ol te'	*Hyperbaena mexicana* (Menispermaceae)
soro te'	*Petiveria alliacea* (Phytolaccaceae)
tok'oy	
batz'i tok'oy	*Salix bonplandiana* (Salicaceae)
kilajtik tok'oy	*Salix humboldtiana* (Salicaceae)
	Salix babylonica (Salicaceae)
k'ox tok'oy	*Salix taxifolia* (Salicaceae)
túrasnu te'	*Agonandra racemosa* (Opiliaceae)
tzajal te'	*Acalypha unibracteata* (Euphorbiaceae)
vo'ox	*Bixa orellana* (Bixaceae)
vux te'	*Curatella americana* (Dilleniaceae)
	Davilla nitida (Dilleniaceae)
x'ukun	*Erythrina chiapasana* (Fabaceae)
	Erythrina goldmanii (Fabaceae)
yisim mut bolom	*Bumelia obtusifolia* var. *buxifolia* (Sapotaceae)

"Aja-te'es Set"

The "**aja-te'es** set" includes two generics, which are highland and temperate shrubs with thick, fragrant, ovate-elliptic leaves and fleshy, purple fruits.

1. **Aja-te'es** is a generic term delimiting two specific classes that are both glossy-leaved, dense shrubs of second growth situations. They have white or pink urn-shaped flowers and small, round, fleshy, edible, many-seeded, purple berries. Specifics: 2.

    a. **Aja-te'es**, "lordly te'es" (**-tik, -altik**) (**aja-te'is, k'ox on te', muk'ta aja-te'es**), is the very common wild wintergreen *Gaultheria odorata* (6–9), a loosely branching shrub up to 2 m tall, which occurs in thickets on mountain tops or along trails in highland hamlets. The leaves are alternate, short-petiolate, broadly oblong-elliptic or oblong-ovate, rounded or subcordate at the base, 2.5–7.5 cm long. The flowers are in a terminal raceme with up to 20 pendent blossoms with a reddish rachis and bracts.

Because the forest is now distant, this shrub is transplanted in Zinacantán Center. The plant is used to adorn a patient's bed and is a basic ingredient of "flower water." As a remedy for **smajben k'ak'al**, a bunch of tips is crushed and mixed with cold water. The patient's head is bathed and the remaining water is drunk. The berries are eaten by shepherds. Most speakers consider them to be "cold."

Extended range: *Clethra suaveolens, Karwinskia hum-boldtiana, Litsea glaucescens, Viburnum elatum.*

b. **K'ox aja-te'es**, "small lordly **te'es**," is the wild blueberry *Vaccinium confertum* (2–5). This is a common plant often forming thickets on windswept high elevation ridges. It is a dense shrub 2–3 feet tall with small, alternate, leathery, acute, ovate leaves, 9–16 mm long. The flowers are about 1 cm long, white fading pink, and are in axillary clusters.

It is gathered indiscriminately with wild wintergreen for "flower water." As a remedy for **majbenal**, three tips are crushed in warm salt water. One cup is drunk. It is "cold." It is also an antidote for dog poisoning. As a remedy for chest pain (**me' vinik**) or anger (**k'ak'al o'onil**) seven or eight tips are crushed in cold water together with **batz'i vixobtakil**. A cup is drunk before breakfast. To relieve the effects of a hot sun, a handful is crushed and rubbed on one's hair while washing it. A poisoned dog may be given cold water in which the tips have been crushed, sometimes together with scarlet runner bean leaves. To make a refreshing drink the berries are crushed in cold water. For further medicinal use cf. **antzil aj**.

2. **Tzis uch**, "opossum fart" (**-tik**) (**axux tzis uch, tzis chauk***), is the bush laurel *Litsea glaucescens* (6–10), an aromatic shrub with glabrous elliptic, lanceolate, or ovate leaves to 8 cm long and purple, fleshy, drupaceous fruits. The flowers are small and greenish yellow borne in axillary clusters shorter than the leaves. It is a common element in the understory of the pine-oak forests of temperate highland hamlets.

It seems that the opossum once lacked an odor. It was asked, "Why don't you let your presence be known, how come your odor doesn't spread?"

"But how can I leave behind my odor? I haven't any odor. I just fart. That stinks," it said. Opossum was shown the laurel bush and told it was its fart.

"Listen, bathe with that. Wherever you walk you'll have an odor." So the laurel was made. Wherever the opossum walks now it has an odor. The opossum has a rank odor wherever it walks. Yes! When it is killed it has a very rank odor. It's some animal! So the laurel was made.

In Zinacantán Center and Sek'emtik where the forest is now at some distance from the habitations, these shrubs may be transplanted to the yard for convenience. The wood is used for mortar gunpowder. It is also used for firewood by corn farmers spending the night in their temperate zone fields. The sprigs are a basic ingredient of "flower water" and are used to adorn a patient's bed and the crosses during curing ceremonies. They are "cold." Whoever takes a sweat bath brews a handful of the sprigs and bathes himself with the water. A bath of bush laurel water is effective in relieving the pain of fire ant stings. A corpse is bathed with bush laurel water. The leaves are used to season roast pork. For further medicinal use cf. **antzil aj, ik'al toj**.

Extended range: *Berchemia scandens, Litsea neesiana* (though a few speakers include this in the basic range).

"Bak Te' Set"

The "**bak te'** set" has four generics, all shrubby plants with glossy leaves.

1. **Ajval te'**, "lord tree" (**-tik**), is *Stillingia acutifolia* (9–12), a small, dense shrub with milky sap, glossy, alternate lanceolate leaves 5–14 cm long, and small flowers in terminal spikes. The capsules are 3-lobed, 5–8 mm broad. They are very common in waste ground, roadsides, and second growth situations in the highlands.

The trunk is used by some people for firewood, though its sap blisters one's skin. It is also used for slingshots. Some use the branches to wrap flowers for transport. To relieve warts the "hot" sap is applied once a day for two days.

The tips are used in "steam cures." As a remedy for "wind" or **poslom**, a "hot" tea is taken, brewed from the tips of **ajval te'** together with those of **xutax chijil te', chilkat, bik'it ch'a-te', muk'ta ch'a- te', ik'al te', mes te', sakil pom tz'unun, tzajal pom tz'unun, sakil pomos**, and **tzajal pomos**. (This use is vehemently denied by one informant.) The leaves may be mashed and made into balls that are left around the house as cockroach poison. Care should be taken not to use the leaves for toilet paper!

Extended range: *Croton ciliatoglandulifer* and *Solanum aligerum*.

2. **Bak te'**, "skinny tree" (**-tik**) (**bak-julan te' bak ni' te', bak xul, xul, xul te', xulal na**), is the clammy hopseed bush *Dodonaea viscosa* (13–17), a shrub with alternate, lanceolate, sticky, lustrous leaves 5–12 cm long. The flowers are small, yellowish, in small lateral clusters. The fruits are 1.5–2.5 cm wide with three papery wings, which are broad, thin and conspicuously veined. They are common elements in the shrubby second growth formation of temperate areas.

The trunk is used for roof rods, wattle, chayote, and popapple arbors, and firewood.

Extended range: *Rhamnus capraeifolia* var. *grandifolia, Styrax argentum*. The trunk of *R. capraeifolia* var. *grandifolia* is used for hoe handles.

3. **Majob ik'al**, "wind beater" (**majob ik'al te'**), is *Jacquinea macrocarpa* (7–11), a densely branched shrub with thick, glossy, oblanceolate or oblong obovate spine-tipped leaves 3–8 cm long. The flowers are small, 8–10 mm long, and orange in few-flowered terminal racemes. The fruit is round, orange, thick-skinned, and about the size of a plum. They are common in the understory of tropical deciduous forests and occasional in second growth situations in the lowland areas.

The trunk is used for firewood. As a remedy for "wind," three or four branches are used to beat the affected part until it bleeds. Then a rag, soaked in alcohol or turpentine, is bound around it. This is a "hot" remedy.

4. **Ventex mol**, "elder's rosary" (**-tik**) (**ventex, ventex mamal, yu mamal**), is *Picramnia tetramera* (8–11), a shrub with pinnately divided leaves. The leaflets are small, thick and ovate 10–15 cm long. The flowers are small and dark red in long racemes that become pendulous in the fruit. The fruits are bright red, hard, marble-sized berries. It is common in the

150

shrubby second growth formations of highland and temperate areas.

As a remedy for "wind," a small bunch of the "hot" leaves is wilted before the fire and bound to the affected part. Children string the berries on thread to make necklaces. They also play marbles with them.

Extended range: *Bunchosia lanceolata.*

"Bix Set"

The "**bix** set" includes seven generics, all bamboos, reeds or sprawling, reed-like plants.

1. **Aj*** (-tik) refers to the large reeds that occur in moist areas and along streams in temperate and lowland areas. Tricked by Rabbit into believing that the popping of burning reeds was the skyrockets celebrating a wedding, skunk strums his guitar and has a hot time (Laughlin, 1977, T166).

Specifics: 3.
   a. **Antzil aj**, "female **aj**," is *Phragmites australis* (4–10), a tall reed often occurring in large colonies. The stems are hard and hollow, 2–4 cm in diameter and up to 3 m tall. The leaves are fibrous and up to 1 cm long and clustered near the tops of the stems.

Both slips and young plants are transplanted occasionally in many of the temperate and all of the highland communities in the rainy season, either in clumps or in rows. The short, thick stems of a clump are classified as **antzil**, or "**sme'**," "female," and multiply when transplanted, whereas the slender, tall stems are **vinik** or "**stot**," "male," and do not multiply. The former are used by women for shed rods. Both kinds of reeds are used for roof poles and wattle and may be bought for the purpose. Two dozen are provided by each of the Stewards of Our Lady of the Rosary on the eighth *Posada* for the construction of the creche. The reeds may be split and used for stewards' floral arches. They are also used for the framework of the petate bull and fireworks. For the "flower water" in which a newborn baby is bathed, the tips of **antzil aj** are brewed for a baby girl, and those of **vinik aj** are brewed for a boy. **Batz'i vixobtakil** and **sakil k'os** may be added. A more elaborate prescription would add to the reeds (1) **batz'i vixobtakil**, (2) wild blueberry, (3) bush laurel, (4) a tip of **ajan toj**, (5) lilac fuchsia, (6) geraniums, (7) six plants of **krus ech'**, (8) three ears of highland yellow corn, and (9) **ach'el pom**. These are brewed in two gourdfuls of holy water. The bath is "cold." A young child who fails to grow because his soul has been taken by an adult is bathed with water in which the young tips have been brewed together with those of bush laurel and **batz'i vixobtakil**.

Extended range: *Lasiacis procerrima, L. sorghoidea,* and *Pennisetum bambusiforme.*
   b. **Vinik aj**, "male **aj**," is *Gynerium sagittatum* (2–2), a plant very similar in morphology, habit, and habitat to *Phragmites,* but differing in having a pithy stem, serrate leaves, and a distinctive villous pubescent patch on the stems opposite the attachment of the leaves. It occurs only at lower elevations and is never cultivated.
   c. **Yajil ama**, "flute **aj**" (**vinik aj**), is *Arundo donax*

(1–1), a plant very similar in morphology, habit, and habitat to *Phragmites,* but having longer internodes and a different flower structure.

It is grown in the lower temperate communities and is used for flutes.

2. **Bix** (-tik) refers to stout, erect, solid-stemmed bamboos, 2–3 m tall, with numerous narrow leaves giving a feathery appearance. They occur in the understory of mixed oak and tropical deciduous forests in temperate areas. Zinacantecs are aware that bamboos die after flowering.

Specifics: 2.
   a. **Antzil bix**, "female **bix**," is *Olmeca reflexa* (1–2). It is characterized by hollow, green stems striped with purple, up to 5 m long, which occur in localized populations in pine-oak rain forests in the temperate cold country *parajes*. It is used by female shamans for their staffs.
   b. **Ton bix**, "hard **bix**," is *Otatea fimbriata* (2–4). It is characterized by purple, glaucous stems with a dense, hard center that attains a height of 3 m in large colonies in tropical deciduous forests mixed with oak in the temperate hamlets.

It is said that bamboo's soul went to the afterworld, where it lingered for 12 years. During this time, in the recent past, bamboo could not be found anywhere.

The trunk may be used for wattle. The trunk is cut by men and brought home to be used for loom bars and warping bar poles. Because it is "hot," women toss their loom bars outside to stop the hail. Stewards use bamboo for their banner poles. Male shamans use this bamboo for their staffs. Shamans are instructed in their initiatory dreams to take the bamboo staff to protect themselves from watchdogs wherever they must go on their curing trips. They are told to shake the staff at the dogs, but not to strike them, lest the dogs die.

The versatility and power of a shaman's staff was demonstrated one night when a curing party was en route to the next mountain shrine and a wheel of their vehicle fell off. Their progress was brought to a grinding halt. Though the metal of the frame was too bent for the wheel to be reinserted, and though there were no metal tools available, the shaman was not to be undone. Exclaiming, "I can get a replacement for this!" he crossed himself, muttered a brief prayer, and stuck his staff into the lip of the frame, laboriously forcing it open. After the wheel fell off two more times, for lack of a suitable substitute for a cotter pin, both ends of the staff were in splinters, but with the further aid of wire from a barbed-wire fence the curing party proceeded in triumph to the next six shrines! Cf. also **xchenek' tzajal om**.

3. **Chanib***, "four," refers to *Lasiacis hispida* (1–2), *Rhipidocladum bartlettii* (1–2), and *R. pittieri* (2–2), sprawling bamboos with thin, hollow canes to 8 m long and delicate, spreading foliage. They are locally abundant in ravines in the understory of tropical deciduous forests in the lower temperate and lowland areas.

The dried stems are split and used by Chamulans for basket-making.

4. **Ik'ob chij**, "sheep caller" (**bik'tal aj, tz'utuj jobel, yaj kotom, yama chij**), is *Lasiacis divaricata* (6–9), a tall, delicately branched, woody, perennial grass with a diffusely branched inflorescence terminating in small, black seeds. It is very common in the understory of pine-oak and tropical deciduous forests, especially along ravines. It is classed as **jobel**, "grass."

The trunk is cut into segments and perforated with a knife and used as a child's toy, as a sheep whistle, and a deer lure. The plants may be used in fences to make them impassible to livestock.

5. **Meno** (**meskero**) is *Pennisetum purpureum* (2–5), a coarse perennial with woody stems to 2 m tall topped by a feathery inflorescence 10–20 cm long. It is very common in marshy flats and sandy places along streams in the temperate and lowland areas. It is classed as "plant" and "grass."

It is eaten by horses.

6. **Ne kotom**, "coati tail" (**-tik**), refers to two species of *Chusquea*. These are large, spreading, and sprawling bamboos that often form dense stands or brakes in the understory of moist pine-oak and evergreen cloud forests in the highlands. The young culms have their leaves held close to the stem and resemble the bushy tail of a coati.

After the Flood, when one of the survivors claimed that he had subsisted on **yaj te' kotom** fruit, this bamboo was stuck on his rump and he was converted into a coati.

Specifics: 2.

  a. **K'ox ne kotom**, "small coati tail," is *Chusquea liebmanni* (1–2), a sprawling bamboo with canes 2–3 cm in diameter and 2–4 m long. The leaves are bunched closely along the entire length of the stems. It is very common in the understory of wet pine-oak and evergreen cloud forests. It often persists after the forest is cleared. It is classed variously as **ak'**, "vine," and **te'**, "tree."

Extended range: *Lasiacis divaricata, Olmeca reflexa, Otatea fimbriata, Paspalum* sp., and *Rhipidocladum pittieri*.

  b. **Muk'ta ne kotom**, "large coati tail," is *Chusquea foliosa* (2–6), a giant species with almost solid canes 6 cm in diameter and 8–15 m long. It is known only from a few localities near the tops of high peaks in evergreen cloud forest near Zinacantán Center.

The trunk is used for loom bars and wattle.

7. **Otot** (**-tik, -altik**) (**taro**), refers to the true bamboos *Bambusa*. These are tall, coarse plants with hollow stems, often 6–15 cm in diameter and up to 20 m tall. They are commonly cultivated by *ladinos* and occasionally persist as if naturalized in lowland areas.

The trunk is used for purlins, fieldhouse mainposts, and fence posts. It is also used by *ladinos* as the wattle for their sugar mills.

Specifics: 2.

  a. **K'anal otot**, "yellow bamboo," is *Bambusa vulgaris* var. *vittata* (2–6), a variety with yellow stems.

  b. **Yaxal otot**, "green **otot**," is *Bambusa vulgaris* var. *vulgaris* (2–2), with dark green stems.

"Boch Set"

The "**boch** set" is a group of five generics, all lowland trees, often found in savannas or poor soil situations. The trees are short, up to 5 meters tall, have leaves that are glossy above and leathery, and most have large elliptic or ovoid fruits up to 20 cm long.

1. **Boch** (**pisis boch te'**) is the cultivated calabash tree *Crescentia cujete* (2–3), characterized by its large, round gourd fruits often 25 cm in diameter borne on the stems. The leaves are short petiolate, oblanceolate, rounded at the apex, alternate at the base, 5–15 cm long. The flowers are white or greenish with dark purple veins, tubular, 4.5–7.5 cm long arising at the nodes on old wood. It is grown by *ladinos* in their yards, and by Zinacantecs in Kelem Ton. It also occurs in lowland savannas.

The trunk is used for fence posts and firewood. Bats are known to frequent its flowers. The fruit is used for half gourds for serving corn gruel and ceremonial gourds for serving coffee. It is sold at market. If a person has been struck by a car or severely beaten, causing his blood to collect in his heart, the seeds and pith are brewed and the tea drunk to "sweep away" the blood. The same tea is taken for constipation or urinary stoppage. It is "hot." The person who dreams of receiving this gourd will become a shaman.

2. **Boch te'**, "boch tree" (**ch'ix te'** in part, **krus ch'ix, k'ib te', limon ch'ix, potov te', poxil tanal eal, sboch pukuj, tzima' ch'ix**), refers to the common temperate and lowland shrub elements *Randia aculeata* (9–15) and *R. cinerea* (3–6). These are spinescent shrubs with small, gourd-like fruits borne on the stems. The stems are divaricately branched with opposite small glabrous obovate leaves or large pubescent ovate leaves. The flowers are white, terminal and sessile.

The trunk is used for fence posts and firewood.

3. **Chachi'** is the cultivated guajilote tree *Parmentiera aculeata* (3–7), similar to *Crescentia*, but with spines on the stems. The leaves are trifoliate with broadly elliptic leaflets 2.5–6.5 cm long. It has an elongated, fleshy, insipid, fibrous, sausage-shaped fruit. It is planted by *ladinos* for fencerows in lowland areas, and by Zinacantecs in their yards in the lowlands, in Masan, Minax, and Potovtik. The fruit matures in April and May.

Under a shaman's direction the fruit is boiled or roasted and the seeds eaten as a remedy for whooping cough. It is "hot." When eaten raw, the fruit is classed variously as "hot," "medium," and "cold."

4. **Nantzi'** (**chi', nanchi'**) is the nance *Byrsonima crassifolia* (4–7), a very abundant lowland savanna tree, occurring also in some temperate areas (Bik'it Nich, Ixtapa). It is a low tree with glossy, green, obovate to broadly elliptic leaves 3.5–12 cm long and round yellow, sweet fruits about the size of a cherry. The flowers are yellow fading to orange, about 1 cm broad, arranged in a terminal raceme.

The trunk is used for fence posts and firewood. The bark may be stored in the house for a year to be used as a remedy for loose teeth. It is chewed raw or is brewed and the "hot" tea held in the mouth. Nance bark tea is also a remedy for bloody dysentery.

It has been classed as both "medium" and "cold." The fruit is sold at market from June to November. It is used to flavor cane liquor or eaten fresh. It is "hot."

5. **Tzima'** (**tzima, tzima' boch**) is the wild calabash tree *Crescentia alata* (2–7), which occurs in lowland savannas and has a narrowly elliptic gourd fruit and trifoliate leaves, with oblanceolate leaflets and a winged petiole resembling the leaflets. It is a tree about 30 feet tall with a rounded or spreading crown. The branches are thick and the bark irregularly fissured. The flowers are 6–7 cm long, greenish and purple-brown with streaks of purple. The fruit is an elliptic gourd-like pod.

The trunk is used for fence posts and firewood. The fruit is used for gourds, rattles, strainers, and whistling tops.

To prepare gourds for rattles the end is pierced, the gourd is boiled, and the insides cleaned out with a stick or wire.

"Bot Set"

The **bot** set includes 11 generics, all having large, round or palmate leaves and most with very soft wood.

1. **Akit** (**-tik**) is the comomon lowland tree *Guazuma ulmifolia* (5–9). This fuzzy-leaved low tree has small, oblong, hard, spiny fruits up to 3 cm long, with a distinct chocolate odor. The leaves are alternate on short, pubescent petioles. They are obovate, acuminate at the apex, cordate and asymmetric at the base. The margins are serrate. The flowers are small, yellowish or whitish, clustered in small, axillary, branched inflorescences. These are common in fencerows and in the understory of tropical deciduous forests.

The trunk is used for hoe and billhook handles, for digging sticks, for barbed-wire fence posts, and for firewood. The bark is gathered and may be stored at home for as long as a year to be used as a remedy for diarrhea and dysentery. A handful is brewed and the tea drunk before breakfast and supper for three or four days. It is classed variously as "medium" and "hot." The fruits are eaten by children. Three or four fruits may be peeled and chewed for cough medicine. They are "hot."

Extended range: *Neopringlea viscosa, Xylosma intermedium.*

2. **Be xinich te'**, "ant path tree" (**na xinich te', te'el marimpa, xinich te'**), is the lowland tree *Cordia alliodora* (3–7), a large, hardwooded tree with terminal clusters of paniculate white flowers and swellings at the nodes of the branchlets, which house fiercely stinging ants. The foliage smells like strong garlic when dried. The leaves are alternate, elliptic, 9–15 cm long, petiolate acute to attenuate at the apex. The flowers are sessile with a tubular, conspicuously striate calyx, about 4–7 mm long. The petals are white and 6–16 mm long. This tree occurs in a variety of lowland primary and secondary forest associations but most commonly montane rain forest and seasonal evergreen forest.

The trunk is used for making marimbas, house mainposts, doors, corn bins, lamp stands, chairs, table legs, coffers, crosses, gunstocks, slingshots, gates, fence posts, hoe handles, and digging sticks.

3. **Bot** refers to two soft-wooded low elevation trees with large, thin, gray, soft pubescent, cordate leaves.

Specifics: 2.

a. **Bot** (**-tik**) (**bot ak', tz'am-te'al na**) refers to *Heliocarpus donnell-smithii* (5–11) and *H. mexicanus* (1–1), common second growth and tropical deciduous forest trees of the lowlands. They have large, alternate thin, heart-shaped leaves, palmately veined from the base, very soft wood, and bark that is fibrous and leathery. The flowers are yellow or cream-colored, small, and in terminal or axillary branched inflorescences. The fruit is sessile or petiolate, ellipsoid 6–7 mm long gray-pubescent with a fringe of long hairs around its margins. They are also planted by *ladinos* as coffee shade trees and grown in X'ukun.

The trunk is used for roof rods and purlins of houses and for rafters and roof poles of fieldhouses. The bark is used to bind thatch and to lash roof poles, wattle, and fences.

b. **Ch'ich' bot**, "blood **bot**," is *Croton draco* (1–1), a tree whose sap turns red. The leaves are alternate, heart-shaped, 12 cm long or less, with an acuminate apex, densely pubescent below. The upper leaf surfaces, stems and petioles are pubescent with a granular appearance to the hairs. The flowers are small, arranged in an elongate raceme. The fruit develops into a 3-lobed, globose, pubescent capsule 7–8 mm long. The three seeds are gray or brown, dull and roughened, about 6 mm long. It occurs in fencerows and second growth and tropical deciduous forest of the lowlands.

4. **Choch** is a generic with two specific segregates, both lowland dogbane trees with showy yellow flowers and large, bilocular fruits.

Specifics: 2.

a. **Bik'it choch**, "small **choch**" (**bik'it choch te'**), refers to *Stemmadenia eubracteata* (1–1) and *S. obovata* (5–10). These are small trees with opposite obovate leaves, 6–20 cm long, acute at the apex and attenuate at the base. The flowers are 7–8 cm long and the 2-celled ovary develops into two diverging large, thick follicles. These occur in the understory of tropical deciduous forest.

It is used for firewood.

b. **Choch** (**choch te', muk'ta choch te', pojov choch**) refers to *Thevetia ovata* (3–13) and *T. plumeriaefolia* (3–5). These may be small trees or shrubs with milky sap. The leaves are alternate, oblanceolate, rounded at the apex with the secondary veins almost perpendicular to the midvein. The flowers are yellow, tubular, expanding into five lobes 2.5–6 cm long. The fruit is broader than long, 3–5 cm broad. Common in fencerows and second growth.

The trunk is gathered by boys or by their fathers for slingshots. The trunk is also used for firewood. As a preventative or remedy for whooping cough, eight to ten fruits are strung on a necklace and worn by young children. Young children may also wear them as a protection against evil eye. They are "medium." For toothache the seed is crushed and a very small amount is held against the tooth. The pain is eased immediately, but the tooth will fall out a month later. If too much is put in the mouth the person risks losing all his teeth. It is reputed to be poisonous. It is "very hot."

Extended range: *Thevetia peruviana.*

5. **Ch'ilim te'**, "powdery tree" (**kokov te'**), is the lowland tree *Hymenaea courbaril* (3–3), which occurs along streams in seasonal evergreen and tropical deciduous forest. It is a large, hard-wooded tree with glossy leaves, pinnately divided into two sessile, inequilateral leaflets, 4–9 cm long and a thick woody legume pod about 11 cm long 4 cm wide with the seeds imbedded in a yellow edible powdery pulp. The flowers are white about 1.5–2 cm long borne in densely flowered panicles.

The pods are sold by *ladinos* at market in San Cristóbal and Tuxtla from January to May. The sweet, yellow powder that surrounds the seed is licked. It is "cold."

6. **Mail te'**, "watermelon squash tree," is *Pseudobombax ellipticum* (3–6), a lowland tree up to 15 m tall with large palmately lobed leaves, with broadly elliptic leaflets, rounded at the apex, 9–15 cm long. soft wood, and large, pendent, squash-shaped fruits, 10–15 cm long. The flowers are white or in some instances bright pink, large, and showy arising on stout branches devoid of leaves. The calyx is cup-shaped, 10–15 mm long. The petals are about 5–9 cm long, linear or oblong, pubescent. The stamens are numerous, and longer than the petals. It is common in tropical deciduous forest along streams.

Extended range: *Gyrocarpus americanus.*

7. **Putzkuy** (**-tik**) (**xam-pelípe te'**) is *Cochlospermum vitifolium* (3–4), a showy, yellow-flowered, soft-wooded tree of tropical deciduous second growth forests of lowland areas. It has large, palmately lobed leaves, with elliptic lobes. The flowers have five oblong-obovate petals, 4.5–5.5 cm long, about 4 cm wide, with an emarginate apex. The stamens are numerous, shorter than the petals with large, linear, curved anthers about 5 mm long. The fruit is about 4.5 cm long, ovoid and velvety, gray-pubescent. Branches are planted in X'ukun in the dry season to make living fences.

The trunk is placed around the base of the threshing platform to keep the corn from scattering. Farmers also fashion the trunk into log stools for their lowland fieldhouses.

8. **Sal-te'** "scaly tree" (**-tik**) refers to two lowland, scaly, red-barked trees.

Specifics: 2.

    a. **Sakil sal-te'**, "white scaly tree" (*pinyon*), is *Jatropha curcas* (3–4), a tree commonly used by *ladinos* in lowland areas as a living fence post. The wood is soft and has a thick clear sap. The leaves are alternate, heart-shaped, palmately veined, pubescent, about 7–16 cm long, on long petioles. The flowers are small, greenish yellow, or white in a dichotomously branched inflorescence, shorter than the leaves. The capsules are ellipsoid 2.5–4 cm long.

To relieve a cough the bark is brewed. The tea is "hot."

    b. **Tzajal sal-te'**, "red scaly tree" (**muk'ta sal-te'**), is the gumbolimbo *Bursera simaruba* (5–9), a striking, red-barked tree, up to 20 m tall, common in the lowland forests, and occasionally planted in some temperate locations. The wood is soft and the sap produces and aromatic resin. The leaves are pinnately divided with 5–7 pairs of elliptic leaflets, which are glabrous, asymmetric at the base, apiculate at the apex, and 5.5–11 cm long. The flowers are 3-parted, fragrant, greenish yellow in short panicles, shorter than the leaves. The fruit is a 3-valved, black, ovoid capsule, 6–10 mm long containing 1–3-angled seed. In Jok' Ch'enom, when the leaves fall in the dry season, the branches are cut off and planted in living fences.

For loose teeth, three chips of bark are chewed. They are "hot." As a remedy for "white" dysentery, four chips are brewed. A bowl of the "hot" tea is drunk before breakfast for three days. The same tea may be taken for a cough. For bloody dysentery the chips are pounded and soaked in cold water, sometimes together with **akit** bark. The infusion is "cold."

In 1797 the priest of Zinacantán reported that this tree was used to lower "burning fever" (de Leon y Goicoechea, 1797).

Extended range: *Trichilia hirta, T. martiana,* and *Zanthoxylum mayanum. Trichilia martiana* is used for fence posts and firewood.

9. **Saya-vun**, "saya paper" (**makum saya-Hun*, salya-vun, saya-Hun***), is the wild mulberry *Morus celtidifolia* (3–5). It has large, hispid, palmately veined leaves 3-lobed or entire and hard, red wood. This temperate tree, now scarce, was once a common component of montane forests and pine-oak forest. The leaves are alternate, with serrate margins 3.5–18 cm long. The flowers are inconspicuous, monecious in spikes 1–2 cm long. The fruit is juicy and red or black and superficially similar to a blackberry.

The heartwood is used for house posts. The trunk is also used for fiddle bows and ax handles. Although silkworms are mentioned in an early colonial manuscript from Zinacantán, nothing of their culture persists to today (*Diccionario en Lengua Sotzil*). This tree, whose name is included in the colonial dictionary as **saya-Hun** and **makum saya-Hun**, could have been the host, though reference is also made to an introduced form, **castillan saya-Hun**. The fruit is eaten.

Extended range: *Gaya minutiflora, Onoseris onoseroides.*

10. **Tux-nuk' te'**, "cotton tree," is the lowland tree *Luehea candida* (6–11), characterized by large, coarsely pubescent leaves 10–20 cm long, showy white and yellow flowers 4.5–5.5 cm long and a large, ribbed follicle 5–6 cm long whose shape is reminiscent of the fruit of *Abelmoschus* (Spanish cotton).

The trunk is used for the mainposts and roof rods of fieldhouses, for the sides of the corn threshing platform, for fence posts and rails, for hoe and billhook handles, digging sticks, flails, and slingshots. It is used by *ladinos* for plow handles, cotton flails, and cattle corrals. The branches are used for brush fences.

11. **Xinal te'**, "stinky tree" (**soro te', tuil te', xam-pílpe te'**), is *Gyrocarpus americanus* (5–9). This is a small or medium-sized tree or shrub with smooth whitish bark. The leaves are

large, palmately lobed, on long petioles. The flowers are small and greenish in tight clusters at the ends of a terminal branched umbel-like inflorescences, which are produced when the tree is leafless. The fruits are ellipsoid, velvety pubescent, about 2 cm long with two apical linear-spatulate wings, 5–8 cm long. It is a common component of the tropical deciduous forest in the lowlands.

The trunk is used for fence posts and firewood. For the "steam cure" in the lowlands, the leaves of this tree may be combined with tobacco, garlic, and chili. To relieve "wind" the leaves may be brewed or crushed in cold water, providing a "hot" potion. The liquid is also used to bathe the patient. For a person suffering the effects of "evil eye" or a swollen belly the tips may be used as a substitute for elderberry to "sweep away" the sickness, massaging the belly downwards.

"Chalon Set"

The "**chalon** set" consists of two generics, both legumes of the genus *Inga*. They have large, pinnately divided leaves and ribbed, elongate pods with large seeds surrounded by a pulpy white, sweet aril.

1. **Chalon** refers to *Inga vera* ssp. *spuria* (3–6), and *I. xalapensis* (1–2). These species have pubescent, pinnately divided leaves with narrowly elliptic to broadly oblong leaflets. The rachis of the leaf is prominently winged. The flowers are white, 13–25 mm long, with long exerted stamens. The pods are pubescent, somewhat terete, and strongly ribbed. They are also commonly used by *ladinos* as coffee shade trees and are common elements of the lowland and temperate forests, especially along streams.

It is planted in the lower temperate hamlets.

The trunk is used for fieldhouse mainposts, fence posts, and firewood. The "cold" fruit matures in June.

2. **Tz'erel** (**t'erel te'**, **tz'elel te'**) refers to *Inga fagifolia* (1–2), *I. jinicuil* (1–2), and *I. punctata* (1–2). These species have glabrous, elliptic leaflets 5–18 cm long, and the rachis of the leaf is not winged. The flowers are small, about 5–7 mm long, white with long exerted stamens, borne in lateral spikes. The pods are glabrous, oblong, and somewhat flattened. It occurs along streams or on shady slopes and is an element of seasonal evergreen forest in temperate and lowland regions. They are commonly used by *ladinos* as coffee shade trees, but rarely so by Zinacantecs who plant it only in Sak Lum.

The trunk is used for firewood. The fruit is eaten.

Extended range: *Senna cobanensis*.

"Chijil Te' Set"

The "**chijil te'** set" is a diverse grouping of 13 generics. These are all shrubs or small trees with small, fleshy fruits and dark green leaves.

1. **Chijil te'**, "striped tree" (**-tik**, **-altik**), refers to the elderberries *Sambucus*.

Specifics: 2.

a. **Batz'i chijil te'**, "genuine striped tree," is the low and middle elevation species *Sambucus mexicana* (9–10), a soft-wooded shrub with pithy, almost hollow stems and large, pinnately divided leaves. The leaflets are sessile, the lowest ones frequently trifoliate, narrowly ovate, oblanceolate or elliptic, 3.5–9 cm long, serrate. The small white flowers are 5–7 mm in diameter and borne in a flat-topped, branched inflorescence. The fruit is a purple, fleshy, one-seeded berry in dense terminal clusters. The seeds are sharply angled and, although the pulp is sweet, damage can result to the intestinal tract if the seeds are ingested.

It is grown in all but one of the temperate and all of the highland communities. It occurs in the wild in second growth in the temperate and some highland hamlets.

Slips may be planted for fencerows at any time of the year. The $1/2$–1 m slips have had the terminal end removed. The basal end is sometimes cut to a point. Because many of the slips die, some Zinacantecs plant them very close together; others plant them a handspan apart. They may be planted between the posts of barbed-wire fences. The trunk is used for scarlet runner bean poles and to support pole beans that have sprung up outside the corn field. Children ride elderberry "bulls" and also use the stem for popguns to shoot out wild clover root pellets. Women who are too lazy to go to the woods gather elderberry for firewood.

As a remedy for a child suffering the effects of "evil eye," the shaman sprays three tips with a salty infusion of **poxil apon** and "sweeps" the child's body with the tips. The "cold" infusion is also drunk. Alternatively, 12 tips are divided into three bunches of four tips each, or 13 tips are distributed so that the middle bunch receives five tips. The same cure may be used by an adult for depression (**ti'ol**). Elderberry tips are used in the "steam cure." A person suffering from the heat of **majbenal** takes an infusion in which three tips have been crushed with fennel in cold salt water. A simple infusion of six tips crushed in cold water is taken for stomachache and may also be given to chickens suffering from cough and blackening combs. It serves also as an antidote for dog poison. Elderberry flowers are ingredients in two "hot" teas for relieving coughs. In the first, three flowers are brewed with orange rind and marigold (**kelem vo'tus**) flowers. A small cup is drunk before breakfast for three days. In the second, one flower is brewed with six red hawthorn fruits. For further medicinal use cf. **mes te'**. The flowers are strewn on the path of the Christ Child on Christmas Eve in Atz'am. The leaves, flowers, and berries are fed to sheep in the meadows. Birds eat the berries. For further use cf. **tilil**.

b. **Xutax chijil te'**, "judas striped tree" (**tuil chijil te'**), is the high-elevation *Sambucus canadensis*. It is very similar to *S. mexicana*, but with larger leaflets, an obtuse or rounded leaf base rather than an acute or wedge-shaped base as in *S. mexicana*, and more closely serrate leaf margins. Some speakers segregate two varieties of this plant based on the stem color: **sakil**, "white," and **ik'al**, "black."

It is grown and occurs naturally on disturbed moist slopes in most of the temperate and all but two of the highland communities. This species of elderberry has many of the same uses as the preceding one, but the trunk may be used for household crosses as it is so "strong-hearted" that witches cannot enter the yard. It is not used as above to treat chickens and dogs. In treating "evil eye" this species is considered to be more effective, especially if the tips are from the dark-stemmed variety. The leaves are also used for bone breaks.

Judas' cigarette is called "**syol chijil te'**," "elderberry heart," though it is made of corn stubble.

2. **Chix te'*** (-**tik**), "**chix** tree," refers to black cherries.
Specifics: 2.

   a. **Batz'i chix te'**, "genuine **chix** tree" (**chich te'**, **kapulin**, **lo'balal chix te'**), is the form of black cherry, *Prunus serotina* (6–8), native to the mountains around Mexico City and introduced into the Chiapas highlands some time after the Conquest, where it now occurs as an element of pine-oak forest near major populations. It is a large tree to 40 feet tall with dark bark and thin, elliptic to ovate-lanceolate leaves, about 5–2 cm long, acuminate at the apex, rounded at the base, with serrulate margins. The flowers are small and white about 10 mm broad, borne in long terminal or lateral racemes. The fruit is large and sweet. Occasionally saplings are transplanted.

In 1797 this was reported by the priest of Zinacantán to be the commonest fruit tree in the people's yards (de León y Goicoechea, 1797).

The trunk is used for fence posts, hoe handles, and digging sticks. The heartwood is used for gunstocks, ax handles, the sides of guitars and fiddles, fiddle scrolls, fiddle bows, and warping bars. Because of its lightness it is chosen for the bobbins of woollen cloth looms. Although some use it for house posts, others claim that it "bites" and will not allow children raised in the house to reach maturity. If cherry wood is placed on the fire, its smoke will kill one's chickens. Cherry switches are considered to be the best for horses. As a remedy for bloody dysentery, three chips of the inner bark together with three chips of the inner bark of a peach tree are brewed. The tea is set to cool and a shot glassful is drunk before breakfast and at bedtime. This very bitter tea may be sweetened with refined sugar. It is "cold."

The tips may be used together with elderberry to "sweep away wind." They are used for the "steam cure." The leaves may be fatal to sheep, causing them to grow progressively thinner. The fruit is eaten by people and birds. It ripens from April through June and is sold at market in San Cristóbal. It is generally classed as "cold."

   b. **Chix te' mut**, "bird's **chix** tree" (**tzajal chix te'**), refers to the wild members of the same species *Prunus serotina* (4–5), which differ from the above only by the small, sour fruit.

It seems that man's mistreatment of this tree is the reason for its sour fruits (Laughlin, 1977, T36). Although the fruits are not eaten by people, the other uses are identical to those of the sweet-fruited variety.

Extended range: *Prunus barbata*.

3. **Ch'it** refers to lowland and temperate shrubs with glossy, green leaves and small, red or white, insipid fruits.
Specifics: 6.

   a. **Jich'il anal ch'it**, "narrow-leaved **ch'it**," refers to *Diospyros nicaraguensis* (1–1) and *Wimmeria acuminata* (1–1). These are medium-sized trees with very dense, hard wood 30–50 feet tall with thin green alternate elliptic leaves and small white or greenish yellow flowers. The fruit is winged in *Wimmeria* and a small fleshy drupe in *Diospyros*. They occur in tropical deciduous forest of the lowlands.

   b. **Muk'ta tzajal ch'it**, "large, red **ch'it**," refers to *Chrysophyllum cainito* (1–1) and *C. mexicanum* (1–1). These are large trees, 20–40 feet tall with alternate, elliptic, coriaceous leaves. The secondary veins are parallel and very closely spaced. The flowers are small, white or yellow, in axillary clusters. The fruit is a berry, green maturing purple-black, 5–8 cm or more long in *C. cainito* and 1–2 cm long in *C. mexicanum*. It occurs as an understory tree in tropical deciduous and seasonal evergreen forests of the lowlands.

   c. **Sakil ch'it**, "white **ch'it**" (**ch'it te'**), refers to the brush cherries *Eugenia acapulcensis* (3–3), *E. amatenangensis* (1–2), *E. carranzae* (2–7), and *E. laughlinii* (3–5). These are all dense shrubs with smooth, white bark and small, red, sweet fruits. The leaves are ovate-elliptic, 2–4 cm long, glossy green and opposite. The wood is hard, fine-grained, and white with a surface that turns red when fired. They occur in second growth and along streams in temperate and lowland regions.

The trunk is used for ax, billhook, and hoe handles, digging sticks, loom bars, fence rails, and fieldhouse mainposts.

Extended range: *Cestrum aurantiacum*.

   d. **Tzajal ch'it**, "red **ch'it**" (**bik'tal anal te'**), refers to *Ardisia escallonioides* (2–1) and *Schoepfia vacciniiflora* (3–4), shrubs superficially very similar to the *Eugenias*, but differing in having alternate leaves, red stems, and the fruits in racemes rather than clusters. The wood of these shrubs is brittle.

The range and habitat are the same as those of **sakil ch'it**.

   e. **Tzotzin ch'it**, "downy **ch'it**," is *Eugenia yunkeri* (3–5). It is a densely branched evergreen tree to 30 feet tall, with opposite, leathery, elliptic leaves, 4–6 cm long and velvety-pubescent beneath. There are axillary clusters of white flowers and purple fleshy berries to 2 cm long. It occurs as an understory element of seasonal evergreen and tropical deciduous forest of lowland and temperate areas. The trunk is used for ax handles.

   f. **Yaxal ch'it**, "green **ch'it**," is the dark, green-leaved lowland shrub *Xylosma intermedium* (2–2). The stems are armed with thorns or unarmed. The leaves are alternate ovate or ovate-elliptic. The flowers are very small and white in axillary clusters. The fruit is a

156

subglobose berry, reddish black and about 4–5 mm in diameter.

The trunk is used for hoe and ax handles, spindles, fence posts, and firewood.

4. **Ch'ix ak'**, "spiny vine" (**chi ak', chix te' ak', ch'ix te', lo'bol jti'-sip, nantzi bejuko**), is the hackberry *Celtis iguanaea* (3–5). It is a lowland vine-like shrub sprawling over trees and establishing thickets especially along small water courses. The wood is very hard and the branches have thick spines. The orange, pea-sized fruits are delightfully sweet. The leaves are alternate, very rough-pubescent, broadly elliptic to broadly obovate, 4–11 cm long, rounded to acute at the apex, rounded at the base. The veins are prominent and light-colored beneath, with three to five major palmate veins arising from the base of the leaf. Zinacantecs class this shrub as "vine."

The bark is used for house lashing. The fruits are "hot."

Extended range: *Mimosa pigra*.

5. **Ik'al te'**, "black tree" (**muk'ta ch'it, muk'ta ik'al te'**), refers to the temperate and lowland trees *Bourreria huanita* (1–2) and *Ehretia latifolia* (4–8). These are small trees with brittle wood and glossy elliptic or broadly elliptic leaves that blacken when they dry. *Ehretia latifolia* has clusters of round, white fruits that have hard-angled, stone-like seeds surrounded by insipid pulp. They are about 13 mm long. *Bourreria huanita* has larger, darker, ovoid fruits about 18 mm broad.

Ehretia latifolia is used as a coffee shade tree in Jok' Ch'enom. When these trees occur in fields planted to corn they are left undisturbed, lest wind, **ik'**, destroy the crop. The wood is used for brush fences. The fruit of *E. latifolia* is eaten by children.

Extended range: *Coccoloba mayana, Hippocratia volubilis*.

6. **Ik'al vinik**, "black man" (**ik'al te', k'ox ik'al te'**), is the temperate and highland second growth shrub *Garrya laurifolia* (8–10), a plant with brittle wood and dark-green elliptic leaves 8–12 cm long that blacken when they dry. The fruits are round, black, 8–10 mm broad and arranged on terminal racemes.

The trunk is used for roof poles, wattle, and firewood, though some say that the smoke will be fatal to one's chickens and will turn people black and kill them. Use of the wood for hoe handles, etc., is also said to have fatal consequences. For medicinal use cf. **tzelo-pat**.

Extended range: *Tournefortia densiflora*.

7. **Makulixkuat** (**chix te' ak', chix te' mut, kapulin ak'**) is the Jamaica cherry *Muntingia calabura* (6–14), a common tree in secondary growth and tropical deciduous forest of the lowlands. with solitary, white flowers borne in the axils of the leaves, 2–2.5 cm broad soft, pubescent oblong-lanceolate leaves 6–14 cm long, and a sweet, red, cherry-like fruit.

The trunk is used for wattle and firewood. The bark is used to lash fieldhouses, houses with wooden walls, and fences. The fruit is eaten by people and iguanas. It is classed variously as "hot" and "cold."

8. **Nampívo** is *Ehretia tinifolia* (1–2), a tree cultivated by *ladinos* in the lowlands, in fencerows, and as a street tree. The leaves are alternate, elliptic to obovate 4–13 cm long, rounded or acute at the apex, acute at the base. The flowers are small,

white arranged in long terminal panicles. The fruits are white, edible, fleshy, sweet drupes.

9. **Paxamum** (**paxamun**) refers to glossy-leaved trees with medium-sized, fleshy, sweet fruits.

Specifics: 2.

   a. **Batz'i paxamum**, "genuine **paxamum**," is *Malpighia mexicana* (1–2), a small tree commonly cultivated by lowland *ladinos*. It has opposite, ovate or oblong-ovate leaves that are softly pubescent beneath, 4.5–12 cm long. The flowers are small in axillary, short, branched inflorescences, much shorter than the leaves. The fruit is fleshy, ovoid, 12–18 mm broad.

The sweet, red fruit is sold on the street in Tuxtla. It is "cold."

   b. **Muk'ta paxamum**, "large **paxamum**" (**paxamum te', sakil ik'al te'**), applies to the temperate and highland trees *Symplocos limoncillo* (2–3) and *S. vernicosa* (3–4). These are glossy, dark-green leaved trees with elliptic, single-seeded fruits with a thin, purple, fleshy covering. The flowers are pink or white, 5-merous, about 8–10 mm long, borne in a few-flowered raceme. The wood is hard, red, and fine-grained. These trees occur in steep ravines with evergreen cloud and montane rain forests.

The trunk is used for hoe and billhook handles, digging sticks, and fence posts. The fruit is eaten.

Extended range: *Ardisia escallonioides, Croton guatemalensis, Rhamnus* sp., and *Viburnum elatum*.

10. **Treno** (**ik'al te', preno te', sak-nich te'**) is the cultivated highland tree *Ligustrum lucidum* (1–4), characterized by dark-green, broadly ovate to ovate oblong leaves acuminate at the apex, rounded at the base, and terminal clusters of small, white flowers. The fruit is bluish black, ovoid, 6–8 mm long. In Zinacantán its occurrence is restricted to one large tree in the courtyard of the Church of St. Lawrence. It is commonly planted elsewhere in the highlands of Chiapas. Before the kiosk was built in 1946, the musicians used to play under this tree.

11. **Vax te'**, "vax tree" (**chix te' ak', nukul pat te', tzajal ak', vax, vax ak'**), is the common temperate and lowland Mexican hackberry bush *Trema micrantha* (11–16). It is a small tree with hispid leaves and small, orange fruit. The leaves are alternate, short-petiolate, 6–15 cm long, acute to acuminate, rounded or subcordate at the base. The flowers are very small, greenish or yellowish in small dense axillary clusters.

The leathery bark is split into strips and used for lashing fieldhouses and houses with wooden walls. The leaves are thought to be poisonous to eat.

12. **Yak' jnibak**, "Ixtapanec's vine" (**nukul te'**), is *Daphnopsis americana* (3–4), a lower temperate and lowland tree to 5 m tall with glossy, lanceolate leaves 5–15 cm long and small clusters of green fruits about 1 cm long. The flowers are small, in terminal umbellate inflorescences. The bark strips into strong leather-like pieces, and is used by Ixtapanecs for house lashing. It occurs in seasonal evergreen and tropical deciduous forests and along the rocky margins of savannas near Ixtapa, and can occur in almost pure stands.

13. **Yisim bolom**, "jaguar whiskers" (**ch'ix bolom**), refers to the sparsely-branched, temperate shrubs *Xylosma flexuosum* (4–4), *X. intermedium* (1–1), and the highland shrub *X. quichense* (2–3). These plants flower on the stem. They have reduced petals and very showy, long stamens giving the appearance of a bush covered with long, reddish yellow hair. The fruit is red and single seeded.

"Chilkat Set"

The "**chilkat** set" is a grouping of eight generics referring to stiffly branched shrubs in the daisy family. They all have terminal clusters of small, variously colored flowers.

1. **Arsyal te'**, "whip tree," is *Baccharis trinervis* (1–1), a sprawling shrub with stems up to 4 m long of second growth in the temperate region especially common along ravines. It has glabrous leaves and terminal clusters of white flowers arranged in dense heads. The leaves are alternate, short-petiolate ovate to narrowly elliptic 4–8 cm long, conspicuously 3-nerved from the base. The stems grow long and straight from the sprawling clump of the main plant each year.

The stems are cut for horse whips.

2. **Chilkat** (-**tik**) refers to three willow-leaved shrubs.
Specifics: 3.
   a. **Batz'i chilkat**, "genuine **chilkat**" (**chilkan**), is the highland shrub *Senecio salignus* (8–13), a densely branched, yellow-flowered, willow-leaved plant with large, dense terminal clusters of yellow composite flowers with heads 7–10 mm broad. This is a very common shrub of second growth and fencerows of the highland hamlets. It flowers in April–May making a very showy display.

In 1797 the priest of Zinacantán mentions **chilca** as one of the trees that provided shade in the arroyos (de Leon y Goicoecha, 1797).

The trunk is used for firewood. To relieve the pain of an embedded thorn, the leaves are burned and used as an overnight poultice. A "hot" tea made from the leaves is a remedy for postpartum hemorrhaging. The leaves or flowers are put in bags of beans to kill weevils, but they are reported by many to be ineffectual. The flowers are known to cause hay fever. A small basket of **chilkat** flowers is provided by each steward for the fourth Lenten Friday and for Tuesday of Holy Week. The cantors and stewards of the Holy Cross each provide a basket for Good Friday. The flowers are strewn on the processional path. They are used also in Naben Chauk on the fourth Lenten Friday, in Apas for the sixth Lenten Friday, and in Chak Toj for Good Friday.
   b. **K'ox chilkat**, "small **chilkat**" (**chilkat**), is *Baccharis glutinosa* (2–4). For temperate-dwelling speakers this is the local **chilkat**. Shrubs or small trees with short petiolate or subsessile narrowly linear leaves with three prominent veins. They are attenuate at both the apex and the base and are about 5–12 cm long, 3–15 mm wide. The flowers are dirty white to yellowish and

in large terminal clusters. It is a common shrub along dry ravines in temperate hamlets.

The trunk is used for chayote and popapple arbors.
   c. **Te'tikal chilkat**, "wild **chilkat**," is *Trixis inula* (1–1), an erect, much-branched shrub with alternate, subsessile, elliptic leaves, 3–10 cm long. The flowers are yellow composite flowers in heads about 1.5 cm long borne in large leafy panicles. It occurs in the second growth of temperate and lowland regions.

3. **Ch'a-te'** (-**tik**), "bitter tree," refers to softwooded shrubs of the tribe *Eupatoriae* in the Compositae (daisy) family, which are common in second growth and as an understory of pine-oak and evergreen cloud forest. They all have terminal clusters of small heads of flowers, which are tipped with feathery pappus in fruit.
Specifics: 2.
   a. **Bik'it ch'a-te'**, "small bitter tree" (**ch'a-te' ka'**), refers to *Ageratina bustamenta* (1–1), *A. ligustrina* (1–4), *A. mairetiana* (2–4), *A. pringlei* (1–1), *Chromolaena collina* (1–2), *Pachythamnus crassirameus* (1–1), *Stevia ovata*, *S. polycephala* (1-3), and *S. serrata* (1–1). These are shubs from 3–15 feet tall with opposite, ovate or elliptic leaves, 3–12 cm long with acute apices. The flowers are white or pink and arranged in lateral and terminal clusters. *Ageratina ligustrina* is an extremely variable species, and some of the most divergent elements are included in this grouping. These occur in second growth and the understory of pine-oak forest of the temperate and highland hamlets.

Although these shrubs may be used as mordants, they are considered to be less effective than *Ageratina ligustrina*. A "cold" tea of *S. ovata* is drunk to reduce fever. Sheep avoid eating *S. serrata*. Its leaves are ground into a powder to stanch a cut.
   b. **Muk'ta ch'a-te'**, "large bitter tree" (**pom ch'a-te'**), is the common highland shrub *Ageratina ligustrina* (7–10). It occurs in second growth and in the understory of pine-oak and evergreen cloud forest. It is a soft-wooded shrub with lustrous, elliptic, irregularly toothed, leaves 5–10 cm long, and terminal clusters of white to pink flowers often covering the entire shrub.

A bundle of stalks and leaves is gathered by women and boiled two or three times with black earth and wool. It acts as a mordant for dyeing the wool for robes, ceremonial robes, skirts, and ceremonial huipils. Thirteen tips are used in the "steam cure."

4. **Ch'a-te' pox**, "bitter tree medicine" (**nap'ap' poxil ik'**, **poxil ik'**, **tz'akob-bail**, **tz'akob-bail pox**), is *Stevia lucida* (4–6), a highland shrub very similar to **ch'a-te'**. It has lavender flowers in heads about 12 mm long, 2 mm broad, borne in large terminal panicles and waxy-glutinous leaves, which are opposite, narrowly lanceolate to lance-ovate, 3–14 cm long. It occurs along paths and roadbanks in the understory of pine-oak forests.

As a remedy for "wind" the shaman cuts a bunch of sprigs

and beats the patient's body with them once a day for four days. They are "hot." The "hot," young leaves are used for a bone break.

5. **Ch'ail pox**, "bitter medicine" (**-tik**) (**ch'a-te' te', ch'a-te' tz'i'lel, pox jnibak, spox jnibak**), is the lowland and temperate shrub *Calea urticifolia* (5–7), characterized by narrow, scabrous leaves 4–12 cm long and terminal clusters of small yellow flowers. It is classed variously as "tree," and "plant." It occurs in second growth and waste ground.

Because of its medicinal use this plant may be stored dry for as long as a year. The parents of a child who indulges in temper tantrums may gather the tips and crush them in cold water. The child is forced to drink a cup of the infusion so that he will vomit his anger. This same infusion may be taken by adults for malaria and stomachache (**sikil ik'**). Alternatively the tips may be brewed, but after the patient drinks the "hot" tea he must not drink cold water for as many days as the shaman prescribes. The tips may be boiled and the "hot" water used to bathe a person suffering from diarrhea. To reduce swelling a "hot" tea is made from a small bunch of this plant together with similar amounts of wild basil and **k'ox yax-chel**. One cup is drunk before breakfast for as many days as necessary. For further medicinal use cf. **vako' ak'**.

Extended range: *Baccharis serraefolia, Calea ternifolia.*

6. **Mes te'**, "broom tree" (**-tik**), is the Mexican broom brush, *Baccharis vaccinioides* (8–10), a large shrub up to 6 m tall, with small, thick leaves. The flowers are white in terminal clusters of heads, and the shrubs are unisexual. These are common, often forming dense stands, in disturbed areas such as roadsides, fallow fields, or pastures throughout the highland area.

The trunk is used for bean poles and firewood. The branches are used to wrap bundles of flowers for transport. They are used occasionally for brooms. To transfer "wind" from a patient's body to another person, branches are rubbed on his body and left on a trail. The shaman may also use elderberry and pine tips, placing the **mes te'** on the bottom of the pile and the pine on the top. A horse suffering "wind" is given cane liquor to drink and its belly is struck with the branches. A sheep suffering the same malady is stretched out by two people and its belly struck similarly. A person suffering "wind" takes a "hot" tea brewed with 6–9 tips. Thirteen slivers of pine may be added to this tea. When a woman misses her period she may place seven tips upside down in a pot and brew them for a "hot" tea. The tips are used in the "steam cure." For further medicinal use cf. **chan-tzelav tzelo-pat, k'an-ak'**.

7. **Poxil ik'**, "wind medicine" (**nap'ap' tz'i'lel, tz'akob-bail, tz'akob-bail pox**), refers to *Stevia lucida* (2–5) and *S. polycephala* (3–6), delicately branched shrubs with terminal, flat-topped clusters of white composite flowers. The leaves are opposite, short petiolate, ovate to elliptic, 4–12 cm long, with serrate margins. It is common in the grassy understory of pine-oak forests in the highlands. Zinacantecs classify this plant variously as **tz'i'lel**, "plant" and **te'**, "tree." It is subdivided into two varieties. The first, **sme'**, "female," refers to *S. lucida* (cf. **ch'a-te' pox**), plants with wider leaves whose underside is sticky to the touch. The second is **stot**, "male," the

plants with narrower, whiter, smoother leaves of *S. polycephala*.

As a remedy for "wind," five tips are brewed. A large cup of the "hot" tea is drunk before breakfast for two days. Or a bunch of the tips is boiled and the "hot" water used to bathe the affected part once daily for three days. To mend a bone break the bonesetter uses three handfuls of young leaves, preferably of the "female" variety.

8. **Poxil tza'nel**, "diarrhea medicine" (**bak tz'i'lel, ch'ix pox, sakil mes te'**), is *Baccharis serraefolia* (6–8), an erect, single-stemmed plant to 2 m tall with small, leathery ovate to oblong-ovate 1.5–6 cm long leaves and terminal clusters of small, white unisexual composite flowers in an openly branched inflorescence. It is common in second growth in highland and temperate areas especially along streams.

As a remedy for diarrhea, a small handful of leaves is brewed for a "hot" tea. This same tea is given to sheep suffering diarrhea after eating peach or cherry leaves.

"Ch'upak' Te' Set"

The "**ch'upak' te'** set" includes three generics, which are brittle-stemmed shrubs with large, thin, mostly palmately lobed leaves.

1. **Ch'upak' te'**, "**ch'upak'** tree" (**-tik**) (**milob tz'i'**), is the castor bean *Ricinus communis* (12–15), a coarse herb often developing a secondarily woody habit to 3 m tall. It has large, palmately lobed leaves and small flowers. The fruit splits into three bean-like seeds. It is a common plant of waste places at all elevations. It is planted by a few people in Zinacantán Center. It is classed both as "tree," and "plant."

Three "hot" leaves are applied to a bone break and many to the aching body (**k'asemal**). The seeds were once ground and used for laundry soap. They are still used to poison dogs and other animal pests that steal young corn. The "hot" beans are mixed with corn dough and bits of glass, then stuffed into a cow intestine and hung up in the cornfield.

Extended range: *Datura stramonium,* another coarse herb with poisonous properties.

Specifics: 3.

   a. **Muk'ta ch'upak' te'**, "large **ch'upak'** tree," refers to the very large plants regardless of color.
   b. **Sakil ch'upak' te'**, "white **ch'upak'** tree," refers to white-stemmed and flowered plants.
   c. **Tzajal ch'upak' te'**, "red **ch'upak'** tree," refers to plants with red stems and flowers.

2. **Makom uch**, "oppossum **makom**," is jimson weed *Datura stramonium* (1–3), a plant that grows in rubbish heaps and in fencerows throughout the township. It is classed as **tz'i'lel**, "plant." It is a coarse weedy herb 1 m or less tall with large ovate to elliptic leaves, which are sinuate to shallowly lobed 8–30 cm long. The flowers are large, white-tinged violet, trumpet-shaped to 27 cm long. The fruit is ovoid, 2.5–3.5 cm long, and armed with numerous spines.

3. **Tz'in-te'**, "**tz'in** tree (**yuka, yuka te', yuka'**), is *Manihot esculenta* (3–6), cultivated by lowland *ladinos*. Large plants

arising from thick tuberous roots. The leaves are large, palmately lobed into 3–7 divisions, which are narrowly linear or oblanceolate, 8–15 cm long. The petioles are long, green at the base, red towards the leaf blade. The flowers are about 1 cm long in terminal panicles. The term **yuka te'** refers to the wild form. *Ladinos* boil the tuber with sugar to make candy.

Yucca has been introduced recently to some of the lower temperate communities, where it is grown by a few people. It is planted by cuttings in the rainy season. It produces edible roots in one year. There seldom is a large enough crop to sell.

The tuber, sold at market by *ladinos,* is rarely eaten by Zinacantecs. They class it variously as "hot" and "cold."

Extended range: *Cleome spinosa, Euphorbia pulcherrima,* and *Manihot aesculifolia.*

"Jabnal Set"

The "**jabnal** set" includes six generics, all trees or shrubs with soft wood and large, peltate or ovate leaves.

1. **Jabnal**, "leaf" (**-tik**) (**kelem jabnal, yich'ak mut**), is *Oreopanax peltatus* (6–7), a small to medium-sized tree with peltate palmately lobed leaves, which are rusty pubescent below, 10–26 cm long and small flowers arranged in round, pubescent clusters 5–15 mm in diameter in terminal racemes. This tree was formerly a prominent element of evergreen cloud forests in the highlands.

These trees, now increasingly scarce, and occasionally cultivated, provide the leaves most often used to wrap bean tamales for weddings and other ceremonial occasions. They are preferred to **k'am-xoch'** leaves as they are larger and smoother. The leaves from both trees are removed before eating the tamale. The cantor needs 400–500 leaves for Carnival Saturday. Those in charge of the ceremonies for Holy Cross Day and the groom's family also need leaves for tamales.

Extended range: *Senna nicaraguensis, Urera caracasana.*

2. **Jabnal te'**, "leaf tree" (**sakil yich'ak mut, yich'ak mut**), is *Oreopanax xalapensis* (4–5), a small to medium-sized tree with digitately compound leaves. The leaflets are narrowly elliptic to obovate, 10–25 cm long, acuminate at the apex, attenuate at the base. The flowers are in small round clusters, 5–15 mm in diameter arranged in an elongate terminal raceme. It is a common element of montane rain forest and wet oak forests in the temperate and highland regions.

3. **K'am-xoch'**, "loop xoch'" (**-tik**), is the highland tree *Chiranthodendron pentadactylon* (6–5). These are large, buttressed trees to 30 m tall with massive trunks to 2 m in diameter, scattered on a few high ridges, mostly individuals left from primary forests of Zinacantán. The leaves are large and velvety, and lobed in the shape of a hand. The flowers are apetalous with a large, broadly expanded, red stamineal column, also in the shape of a hand.

The trunk is used for firewood. The bark from its suckers is preferred for house lashing, but the cliff-growing trees are difficult to access. The leaves are used to wrap bean tamales (**chenek'ul vaj**) and corn tamales (**pisil vaj**). Cf. **jabnal.**

Extended range: *Bakeridesia* sp., *Senecio* sp.

4. **K'orok' te'**, "k'orok' tree" (**be xinich te', k'oro te'**), is the common lowland second growth tree *Cecropia peltata* (4–8), which has hollow stems occupied by colonies of stinging ants. It attains a height of 15–25 m and is common along streams. The leaves are very large and palmately lobed. The flowers are minute and massed in pendulous finger-like clusters.

The trunk, split and stripped of bark, is used for threshing platforms. To lengthen one's penis, a bowl of **pozol** should be placed at the foot of this tree at a distance corresponding to the length desired. When the shadow of the tree reaches the bowl, the **pozol** is drunk and the tree should be hugged. When one's penis has grown to the desired length the tree should be felled lest the penis continue to grow. Any suckers that sprout from the stump later should also be cut.

5. **Mumun** (**-tik, -altik**) (**mum**) is *Piper auritum* (4–9), a soft-stemmed shrub common in moist places in primary and secondary forests of the temperate and lowland areas. It has large cordate leaves as much as 60 cm long and 35 cm wide. The basal lobes are rounded, one of them 1.5–3 cm longer than the other. The rat-tail inflorescence is 20–25 cm long and is opposite the leaves.

Young plants are transplanted occasionally in the rainy season in the lowlands and in most of the temperate and highland communities. They may be planted by slip, but this is considered undependable.

When the Virgin Mary was hiding in the banana grove with the Christ Child she laid her baby on a carpet of **mumun** and **ch'aben** leaves.

The young stems may be peeled and eaten raw. The pungent leaves are boiled and eaten as greens. More commonly they are used to season beans and snails and to provide an edible wrapping for bean tamales. They are classed variously as "hot" and "cold." They are sold at market. The plants, however, should not be cut indiscriminately or their caterpillars (**xchanul**) will eat them up.

6. **Mumun te'**, "mumun tree," refers to the wild, non-edible species of *Piper*: *P. amalgo* (1–1), *P. decurrens* (1–1), *P. hispidum* (1–1), *P. jacquemontianum* (1–1), *P. marginatum* (1–1), *P. tuberculatum* (1–1), all shrubs with rat-tail inflorescences. The leaves are variable, but all are alternate and petiolate and sheathing the stem. These are common shrubs in second growth and along streams in seasonal evergreen forest in the temperate and lowland areas.

As a remedy for constipation or urinary stoppage (**makel**) the leaves are brewed to provide a "hot" tea.

"Kachímpa Te' Set"

The "**kachímpa te'** set" is comprised of four generics.

1. **Chin te'**, "eczema tree" (**luchleb vet, xinal te'**), is *Hura polyandra* (1–1), a large, deciduous tree with corky-ribbed bark, glabrous, broadly ovate leaves, cordate at the base with prominent, parallel secondary veins, 9–20 cm long, a viscous, irritating sap, and round-ribbed, hollow, woody, apple-sized fruits. The female flowers are large, about 6 cm long, solitary in

the upper leaf axils. The male flowers are small, arranged in small spikes along a thick rachis, 5–8 cm long. It occurs in mature tropical deciduous forest along streams in the lowlands.

When this tree is chopped, its "rays" and its sap cause blisters.

2. **Ich te'**, "chili tree," is a poison sumac, *Toxicodendron striatum* (1–1). This tree is reputed to be so toxic that its "rays" may cause death by merely passing near it. The leaves are pinnately divided into lance-oblong, ovate, or elliptic leaflets, 5–13 cm long. The flowers are small white and in large axillary panicles. The fruit is oval, white with black striations, about 7 mm in diameter. Touching the leaves or sap will cause a blistering rash. It is a prominent member of seasonal evergreen and montane rain forests occuring in Zinacantán only along streams in temperate hamlets.

3. **Kachímpa te'**, "kachímpa tree" (**ch'in te'**, **kachúmpa te'**), is *Comocladia guatemalensis* (3–5), a soft, rusty, pubescent, small tree to 10 m tall with red sap and wood that may be very irritating to the skin. The leaves are large and pinnately compound. The leaflets are oblong-oval, rusty pubescent, and 9.5 cm long or less. The flowers are minute, red, and in large, terminal panicles and produce black, date-sized fruits. It is very common in tropical deciduous forest and is used by *ladinos* in fencerows. Some people recognize two varieties: **sak**, "white," and **tzoj**, "red," referring to the color of the heartwood. The latter is ascribed a "very strong heart" (**toj tzotz yo'on**) responsible for causing more severe itching.

Like poison ivy and poison sumac, this tree has "rays" (**xojobal**) that blister some people who merely walk by it, perhaps because they are fearful. Several individuals remarked that the "rays" of these plants are visible at night. To prevent any ill effects when chopping the tree you should first call it by name several times or cross yourself and address this arboreal woman endearingly, "**Chin, kunen, te'**," "Little girl, my baby, tree!" The itching may be relieved by bathing the affected parts with salt water. The trunk is used for house mainposts.

4. **Matal ak'**, "magdalen vine" (**xmatal ak'**), is poison ivy *Toxicodendron radicans* (1–2), a woody vine with toxic oils causing skin rashes. The leaves are glossy, alternate, and tri-foliate. The leaflets are mostly ovate from 4–12 cm long with acute to acuminate apices. Like poison oak or poison ivy of the north, the leaves turn bright red in the fall. The flowers are small, green, white, or yellowish in axillary panicles. Fruits are white berries borne in axillary clusters up to 8 cm across. It occurs clambering up large trees in the montane and evergreen cloud forests, as well as pine-oak forests of the temperate and highland regions. It is classed as a "vine."

The ill effects resulting from contact with this vine, from passing in its shadow or from exposure to its "rays" (**xojobal**), may be avoided by a variety of techniques. The person may return to the vine and tell it to exchange names with his. Another method is to dance in front of it. Or when you see this vine you should say, "**Matal, ta jk'elot**," "Magdalen, I am looking at you." Or you should say, "Magdalen, I am visiting you, I am talking to you. Come, come let's talk to each other."

Or, "**Me'el Matal mu k'u xacha'leon, lakil xa!**" "Mother Magdalen, don't do anything to me, I saw you!" Because if you don't see the vine it is surely saying to itself, "**Chkak'be pox, chkak'be chamel**," "I'll give him medicine, I'll give him sickness." A not so subtle procedure is to whip it with a tumpline or a rope.

To relieve the itching, the affected part should be bathed with lime water in which oak bark has been boiled together with the tips of **k'ox paj-'ul**.

"K'an-te' Set"

The "**k'an-te' set**" is a loose grouping of 16 generics. They are all lowland trees with smooth, flaky bark, peeling in large, thin strips. All flower profusely with bright showy clusters and most have fine-grained hardwood.

1. **Barsin te'**, "spotted tree" (**barbaskóva te'**), refers to *Guettarda macrosperma* (1–1), and *Piscidia carthagenensis* (1–1). These are trees 30–60 feet tall with leaf blades that are broadly ovate or broadly obovate, apiculate, or acute at the apex. *Guettarda macrosperma* has entire opposite leaves and *P. carthagenensis* has pinnately divided leaves. The leaflets are opposite each other on the rachis and are similar in size and shape to those of *G. macrocarpa*. These occur in tropical deciduous forest (*Piscidia*) and seasonal evergreen and montane rain forest (*Guettarda*).

The root is pounded on a rock and used to poison fish. It is also steeped in water and the liquid applied to a dog's belly to remove fleas and lice, but this must be done with care, for the root is so "hot" (**k'ok', ya**) that if the liquid gets in the dog's eyes it will cause blindness. The trunk is used for hoe handles, digging sticks, and threshing platforms.

2. **Brasil** (**-tik**) (**chak-te'***, **frasil**, **prasil**) is the common lowland tree, bloodwood *Haematoxylon brasiletto* (3–7), a small tree with a convoluted trunk, very hard, red wood, peely bark, pinnately compound leaves with obovate leaflets, emarginate at the apex, 10–20 mm long and clusters of bright, yellow flowers about 1 cm long. It often flowers when leafless. The pods are thin and flat, 3–5 cm long. The wood is an important dye source. It occurs as a common element in thorn scrub and tropical deciduous forest.

The trunk is used for fence posts. The heartwood is used for corn shuckers. Chamulans soak the heartwood in water to dye the margins of net bags red and yellow. The heartwood may be steeped and the "hot" solution drunk as a cough medicine.

Extended range: *Phyllanthus mcvaughii, Pithecellobium dulce,* and *Wimmeria pubescens.*

3. **Chenek' te'**, "bean tree," is a non-Linnaean grouping of shrubs and trees with pea flowers or pea-like pods. It includes *Clitoria polystachya* (1–4), *Gliricidia ehrenbergii* (1–2), *Godmania aesculifolia* (1–3), *Harpalyce formosa* var. *goldmanii* (1–1), *Inga vera* ssp. *spuria* (3–5), *Pistacia mexicana* (1–2), *Senna hirsuta* var. *hirta* (1–3), and *S. pallida* (2–4).

The trunks of some are used for firewood.

4. **Ch'aben te'**, "ch'aben tree" (**k'ox yax-'ib**), refers to *Indigofera suffruticosa* (1–2), and *I. thibaudiana* (3–4),

densely branched shrubs with long, dense terminal racemes of small orange or maroon flowers. The leaves are pinnate with elliptic to oval leaflets. The pods are linear, 1.5–3 cm long, narrow, 2 mm thick and densely crowded and reflexed on the peduncle. They are common in second growth and fallow fields throughout the township. Their use in providing indigo dye is not known today.

Extended range: *Sesbania emerus* and *Spartium junceum.*

5. **Ch'ix-ni' te'**, "spiny-tipped tree," is *Gliricidia ehrenbergii* (1–2). This is a shrub or small tree with pinnately divided leaves. The leaflets are pubescent below, elliptic to oblong-elliptic, 1–5 cm long. The flowers are magenta to lavender-pink, 12–15 mm long in densely flowered axillary racemes. The pods are oblong about 4 cm long. It is common in second growth and rocky exposed slopes of the temperate and highland regions.

6. **Jach'ub te'**, "comb tree" (**sakil jach'ub te'**), is the sycamore *Platanus mexicana* (2–3), a large tree locally abundant along temperate and lowland streams. It has straight trunks, peely bark, large, palmately lobed leaves 9–23 cm long, 6–19 cm wide and minute flowers in pendulous ball-shaped inflorescences 2.5–3 cm in diameter.

The trunk is used for roof purlins and rafters of fieldhouses, bridge planks, ax handles, fence posts, and firewood. The wood is used for combs.

7. **Kamaron te'**, "shrimp tree" (**tzajal jach'ub te'**), is the common lowland tree of second growth forests *Alvaradoa amorphoides* (3–9). It is a small tree with pinnately compound leaves, up to 15 cm long with small leaflets and pendent, catkin-like inflorescences that enlarge in fruit to 8 cm long and turn pink, resembling a shrimp.

The trunk is used for fieldhouse mainposts, fence posts, and firewood. The heartwood is used for combs that are sold in San Cristóbal.

Extended range: *Lonchocarpus rugosus* and *Senna foetidissima* var. *grandiflora.*

8. **Kanéla te'**, "cinnamon tree" (**-tik**) (**kována te'**), is the generic for two lowland trees with red and white peely bark. Specifics: 2.

   a. **Sakil kanéla te'**, "white cinnamon tree," is the sparsely distributed, temperate and lowland tree *Hauya elegans* (4–9), a medium-sized tree with tan, peely bark, alternate ovate, pubescent leaves 6–11 cm long, and large, showy, white, tubular flowers to 10 cm long. The capsule is woody, cylindrical, about 6 cm long, splitting longitudinally downward from the apex to release the winged seeds. It occurs in tropical deciduous forest and dry oak forests of temperate and lowland areas often along steep ravines.

   It is used for rafters, roof rods, and purlins of houses and for mainposts, roof rods, and ridge poles of fieldhouses, hoe handles, digging sticks, fence posts, fence rails, and firewood.

   Extended range: *Psychotria* sp.

   b. **Tzajal kanéla te'**, "red cinnamon tree," is the common, lowland tree of streamsides *Calycophyllum*

candidissimum (4–12), a large, hardwood tree with peely red bark and glabrous, opposite ovate leaves about 4–12 cm long. The small white flowers are subtended by a showy white bract 5–8 cm long, which is broadly ovate to rotund and narrowed abruptly into a thin petiole. The inflorescence is terminal and dichotomously branched. The fruits are pubescent, oblong, about 6–10 cm long. It occurs in seasonal evergreen forest.

The trunk is used for rafters, roof rods, and purlins of houses and for fieldhouse mainposts, cross beams, roof poles, and firewood.

Extended range: *Wimmeria pubescens.*

9. **Kanelo** is cinnamon *Cinnamomum zeylanicum,* a spice rarely cultivated in Mexico and at present only known from the coast of Chiapas near Tapachula. Imported bark is sold in markets. The peely bark must remind Zinacantecs of the other members of this set.

It is used to flavor corn gruel, rice, and pork. It is "cold." *Ladinos* make a refreshing red drink from it.

10. **K'an-te'**, "yellow tree," is *Diphysa floribunda* (4–4), a temperate and lowland tree with large, finely divided, pinnately compound leaves with oblong leaflets, 8–22 mm long and bright yellow pea flowers about 1 cm long, arranged in racemes. The pods are oblong about 4–7 cm long and inflated. It occurs in second growth and tropical deciduous forests.

The trunk is prized for house mainposts. It is also used for bobbins for cotton-cloth looms, ax, hoe, and billhook handles, digging sticks, and firewood.

Extended range: *Dalea versicolor, Mahonia berriozabalensis, M. volcania, Phyllanthus mcvaughii,* and *Tecoma stans.*

11. **K'anal te'**, "yellow tree," is *Mahonia berriozabalensis* (1–4) and *M. volcania* (1–2). These are glabrous-leaved shrubs or small trees with pinnately divided alternate leaves. The leaflets are elliptic to oblong ovate and may have entire or spiny margins. The flowers are small and yellow in axillary racemes and develop into an ellipsoid, dark-blue drupe about 7–11 mm long. The wood is bright yellow. These occur on rock outcrops in primary forest of the temperate and lowland areas.

The root is pounded and used as fish poison.

12. **Milob ch'o te'**, "rat killer tree" (**mataraton, ratonero**), is the common lowland tree *Gliricidia sepium* (1–4). It is a medium-sized tree with smooth, peely bark and pinnately compound leaves with elliptic or ovate elliptic leaflets, 3–6 cm long. It flowers when leafless and presents a showy display of purple blossoms, 2–2.5 cm long. It is often planted by *ladinos* for living fencerows, and occurs in second growth and tropical deciduous forest throughout the lowlands.

The seeds, leaves, and bark may be ground with corn for rat poison.

Extended range: *Indigofera thibaudiana.*

13. **Pinto te'**, "spotted tree" (**palopínto, potosoára**), is the common lowland tree *Wimmeria pubescens* (4–5), a densely branched, hard-wooded tree with peely red and gray bark and small, obovate clustered leaves 1–2 cm long. The flowers are

162

small, arranged in axillary inflorescences and the fruit is 3-winged and red, turning the entire tree red when the fruit is mature. It is a common element of tropical deciduous forests.

The trunk is used for fieldhouse mainposts, hoe and billhook handles, digging sticks, flails, fence posts, and firewood.

14. **Putzul chij**, "sheep's **putzul** or deer's **putzul**" (-**tik**), is the common lowland, yellow trumpet bush *Tecoma stans* (9–18), a small tree with pinnately divided leaves and large, showy, tubular, yellow flowers 3.5–5 cm long. The leaflets are elliptic to narrowly ovate with serrate margins, 4.5–12 cm long. The pods are linear, narrow, pendent, commonly 25 cm long, about 8 mm broad. It occurs in fencerows, along roadcuts in second growth, and occasionally in primary tropical deciduous forests and pine-oak forest of lowland and temperate regions.

The trunk is used for house walls, hoe, billhook, and pick handles, digging sticks, fence posts, and firewood. As a remedy for skin disease (**chin**), a small bunch of leaves is dried on the griddle and ground into a "cold" powder, which is applied to the affected part. The itching caused by poison ivy may be alleviated by bathing the blisters with a solution made by boiling these leaves.

Extended range: *Senna foetidissima* var. *grandiflora, S. pallida* var. *brachyrrachis,* and *S. polyantha.*

15. **Yax-'ib te'**, "green armadillo tree" (**lan te', na vonon te', putzul t'en, santa roxa te', santa roxail te', tzis chitom te', xinal te'**), refers to the sennas *Senna cobanensis* (2–4), *S. pallida* (1–2), *S. skinneri* (1–4), and *S. tonduzii* (5–7). These are small trees with large, pinnately compound leaves and large clusters of bright, yellow-orange flowers. The foliage in some is foetid. They occur for the most part in second growth and fencerows of temperate and lowland areas.

The trunk of all but the first species is used for house mainposts, roof purlins, steambaths, corn bins, gates, benches, beds, crosses, gunstocks, slingshots, hoe handles, fence posts and firewood. *Ladinos* decorate their graves and churches with the flowers.

Extended range: *Gliricidia ehrenbergii, Machaerium chiapense,* and *Turpinia occidentalis.*

16. **Yax-te'**, "green tree," is the common temperate and lowland tree, kidney wood *Eysenhardtia adenostylis* (4–6). This tree is superficially similar to **k'an-te'**, but differs in having smaller leaflets, which are black dotted below and 10–15 cm long racemes of small white pea flowers about 8 mm long. The wood was an important dye source for 17th and 18th century Europe. It occurs in second growth and tropical deciduous forest of the lowlands.

The trunk is prized for house mainposts. It is also used for lintels, doors, corn bins, steambaths, beds, benches, chairs, hooks, lamp stands, bobbins for cotton cloth looms, fiddle bows, ax, billhook, and hoe handles, digging sticks, flails, fence posts, and firewood. To prevent the spread of sickness among chickens, the bark or the wood is soaked in their drinking water.

Extended range: *Diphysa floribunda, Euphorbia pseudofulva, Gliricidia ehrenbergii,* and *Indigofera thibaudiana.*

"K'at'ix Set"

The "**k'at'ix set**" includes two generics, both divaricately branching shrubs to trees with white wood. They occur along streams in temperate and highland areas.

1. **Isbon** (-**tik**, -**altik**) is the common creek dogwood *Cornus excelsa* (6–11) that occurs along streams in temperate and highland situations. It has fine-grained, white wood and the stems can grow quite straight. The leaves are elliptic, 5–10 cm long, and have the nerves strongly impressed. The flowers are white, 3.5–4.5 mm long, and in terminal clusters. The fruit is blue, fleshy drupe, 5–6 mm in diameter.

The trunk has a great variety of secular and ceremonial uses, including hoe and billhook handles, digging sticks, machete hooks, hooks, stirring rods, warping bar poles, crossbeams and wattle, fence posts, sheep corral rails, tethering posts, dog hobbles, bean poles, shepherds' switches, slingshots, snares, tamale platforms, drumsticks, drum collars, and firewood. Dogwood poles were used as frames for the floral arches at the church entrances, but have been replaced by metal reinforcing rods. They are still used as frames for the floral arches of the stewards and the grand alcalde. Two dozen rods are cut by the Stewards of Our Lady of the Rosary of which 18 of the best are chosen on the ninth *Posada* to make the frame of the straw bull. Twelve rods are brought by the godfathers of the Christ Children on the ninth *Posada* to make the creche in the Church of St. Sebastian. Dogwood poles are also used to make the creche frame in Atz'am, Chak Toj, Sak Lum, San Mikulax. Dressed poles are carried as walking sticks by the prefects every Sunday and at every fiesta; by the publicans and stewards-royal on New Year's Day and at the Fiesta of St. Sebastian; by the constables on 23–25 December, and at the Fiesta of St. Sebastian. Dogwood is used for the tethering post of the straw bull and for the bows and arrows of the **sak-joletik** and **ka'benaletik** at the Fiesta of Ka'benaletik St. Sebastian. The branches are used for brush fences.

In 1797 the priest of Zinacantán reported: "Black earth, which they get at the edge of town, gives the black color to the wool. It is fixed with leaves of a plant called **hisbon** which is also here" (de Leon y Goicoechea, 1797). This function is now served by **ch'a-te'**, but it may be that its former use is confirmed by its name, for -**bon** means dye or paint.

2. **K'at'ix** (-**tik**) (**ch'ix**) is the hawthorn *Crataegus pubescens* (15–15), a densely branched, spinescent tree common near creeks and sinks in pine-oak forest of the highland area. The leaves are short-petiolate, oblanceolate or obovate, 4–7 cm long. The flowers are white with petals about 1 cm long, in lax terminal clusters. The fruits can be large or small, red or yellow, and individuals of all types occur mixed throughout the highlands.

In 1797 the priest of Zinacantán cited **manzanillo** as having "very strong and incorruptible" wood (de Leon y Goicoechea, 1797).

Specifics: 3.

    a. **K'anal k'at'ix**, "yellow hawthorn," the yellow fruited form.

    b. **Sijom k'at'ix** is the small-fruited form regardless of color, though most are red.

    c. **Tzajal k'at'ix**, "red hawthorn," the red fruited form.

It is grown in a few of the temperate and all but one of the highland communities.

Hawthorn saplings are pulled up in the rainy season and transplanted two meters apart either for fencerows or within the yard. If the latter, apple or pear slips are grafted onto them from December to March. The grafting of apples is reported to be more successful than that of pears. Planting may also be done by slip, but is less successful.

The roots of any red-fruited hawthorn have medicinal importance when the husband of a postpartum woman "cannot endure" the necessary period of chastity (which should last more than two weeks and preferably a month or even two months after childbirth). By sleeping with his wife she is apt to become infested with worms which may be fatal unless she is given a tea of hawthorn roots to which has been added freshly squeezed sugarcane juice. The "hot" tea kills the worms. By drinking this tea the woman imitates the hawthorn that causes its fruit to drop in great numbers and pile up on the ground. In the same way the woman discharges the worms.

The trunk is used for house mainposts, corn bin posts, fence and corral posts, bed posts, bed and corn bin planks, billhook, hoe, rake, and ax handles, digging sticks, slingshots, the dudes' horses, and firewood. Women use the spines for tenterhooks. The spines are also used to extract snails from their shells.

The branches are used for brush fences. The leaves are eaten by sheep.

The fruits, which ripen in November and December, are eaten by people, sheep, and pigs. When eaten raw they are "cold," and if many are eaten will cause hiccups; when boiled with brown sugar they are "hot." *Ladinos* make hawthorn apple jam. The fruit is sold at market in San Cristóbal and Tuxtla. Large hawthorn apples are gathered by the assistants of the Stewards of Our Lady of the Rosary to decorate the creche and the Church of St. Sebastian. They also provide the large hawthorn apples that are strung on henequen fiber for the dudes' necklaces. Four or six **almudes**, half yellow and half red, are provided on the eighth *Posada* for such purposes. Ten armspans of strung hawthorn apples are required from each of the Stewards of Our Lady of the Rosary to decorate the creche. Three armspans apiece are needed for the Church of St. Sebastian. These fruits are widely used for creche decoration in Apas, Atz'am, Chak Toj, Na Chij, Naben Chauk, Paste', Sak Lum and San Mikulax.

"La Set"

1. **Chaya itaj**, "**chaya** greens" (**-tik**), is *Cnidoscolus aconitifolius* c.v. 'Maya' (1–3). Slips of this edible shrub are planted in most of the temperate hamlets. Unlike **sakil la** it is classed uniformly as "tree." This cultivated form of *C. aconitifolius* lacks the characteristic stinging hairs found on wild plants. It is a shrub or small tree with palmately lobed leaves on long, slender petioles. The flowers are white and arranged in a terminal dichotomously branched inflorescence. The capsules are 3-celled and about 8 mm long.

2. **Chon la**, "snake **la**" (**k'an-'ich la, la ka', la te', muk'ta la, tzajal la**), refers to *Wigandia urens* (4–7) and *W. urens* var. *caracasana* (4–6), large shrubs (to 3 m tall) with huge leaves with soft, slightly irritating hairs. The flowers are bright blue and in elongate, terminal panicles. It is very common in second growth roadsides, and rocky outcrops in temperate and highland areas.

Bush nettle was a snake with a mortal bite, so Our Lord transformed it into a plant.

As a remedy for "wind," three or four "hot" leaves are used to beat the affected part.

3. **La** (**-tik**) refers to herbs and soft-wooded shrubs with stinging hairs on the leaves and stems.

Specifics: 7.

    a. **Batz'i la**, "genuine **la**" (**kilkil la**), is the nettle *Urtica chamaedryoides* (1–4), a small woody herb that is an occasional pest in cornfields in highland areas. It grows in yards and along fences. It is a simple or branched herb with stinging hairs. The leaves are opposite, elliptic to ovate, dentate, 1.5–6 cm long. The flowers are tiny, white, in axillary clusters, shorter than the petioles.

As a remedy for "wind," a small handful of the "hot" leaves is used to beat the affected part so that the "wind" will depart with the blood that is shed.

    b. **Kilajtik la**, "pendulous **la**" (**k'ox la, la ak', xelajtik la**), is *Gronovia scandens* (4–8), an herbaceous vine with stinging hairs and pale yellow, tubular flowers about 7–10 mm long. The inflorescence is opposite the leaves, slender, and branched. The leaves are alternate, long petiolate, cordate, and deeply 5-lobed, 3–8 cm long. It is common in the understory of tropical deciduous forest and the second growth formations of lowland areas. It is an occasional pest in the cornfields. It is classed variously as **ak'**, "vine," and **tz'i'lel**, "plant."

    c. **K'ox la**, "small **la**" (**bik'tal la, poxil sep'**), refers to *Tragia nepetifolia* (2–3), a small perennial, erect plant with slender branches and stinging hairs concentrated on the fruits. The leaves are small, alternate, triangular, triangular linear, or ovate with serrate margins, 1–5 cm long. The flowers are very small, in short spikes opposite the leaves. The capsules are 3-lobed, 6–7 mm

164

broad, and pubescent with stiff white hairs. It occurs in second growth, rocky outcrops, and waste ground in temperate and lowland areas.

To relieve aches caused by "wind," the affected part is struck with the nettle. As a remedy for mange, the plant is crushed and mixed with cane liquor and, if the patient is a man, woman's urine, and, if a woman, a man's urine. The medicine is applied to the affected parts. It is classed as a "plant."

    d. **Muk'tik la**, "large **la**," is *Urera caracasana* (1–1), a shrub or small tree 10–25 feet tall with abundant stinging hairs, caustic sap, and broadly ovate, pubescent leaves, which are often 30 cm long. The flowers are very small in axillary clusters. The fruit is about 2–3 mm in diameter, fleshy, orange-red, and is borne in large clusters on the old wood, at times covering the branches of the shrub beneath the leaves. It occurs along streams in tropical deciduous forest in the lowlands.

    e. **Sakil la**, "white **la**" (**la ka'**, **muk'ta la**), refers to *Cnidoscolus aconitifolius* (7–14), *C. multilobus* (1–1), and *C. tubulosus* (2–3), soft-wooded shrubs with fiercely stinging hairs and caustic, white, latex-like sap. The flowers are white and in terminal clusters. These shrubs are common in second growth and disturbed ground along roadsides in lowland and temperate areas. They are classed variously as "tree" and "plant."

To relieve aches caused by "wind," the affected part is struck with this nettle. The "hot" sap may applied to boils (**chakal**) so they will burst.

"Máchita Te' Set"

The "**máchita te' set**" is a group of three generics, all caesalpinoid orange-flowered trees or shrubs, with long, flat pods.

1. **Chenek' chij te'**, "sheep bean tree" or "deer bean tree" (**máchita te'**), is *Senna atomeria* (1–2), a common lowland tree with long, narrow, sickle-shaped pods 16–35 cm long and large, yellow flowers borne in few-flowered axillary racemes. The leaves are pinnate with 1–5 pairs of broadly oblong to suborbicular leaflets 2–10 cm long. It occurs in second growth and tropical deciduous forest.

Extended range: *Tephrosia lanata*.

2. **Máchita te'**, "machete tree," is *Delonix regia* (3–5), a tree cultivated in the lowlands by *ladinos* and especially popular as a street tree in Tuxtla and Chiapa. It has finely divided, compound leaves 30–50 cm long, with oblong leaflets 4–10 mm long and large, bright-orange flowers. The fruit is a flat pod (40–50 cm long), which hangs pendulously from the tree.

The trunk is used for firewood.

Extended range: *Bauhinia pauletia* and *Senna atomeria*.

3. **Nichim te'**, "flower tree" (**k'ox máchita te'**, **yaxal ch'ix**),

refers to *Caesalpinia exostemma* (1–4) and *C. pulcherrima* (3–4), spiny shrubs with large, terminal panicles of bright-orange flowers with five spreading, imbricate petals and long exerted stamens. The leaves are coarsely decompound with leaflets 1.5–2 cm long. These are common in waste ground and in second growth situations of the lowlands.

The flowers are cut and sold by *ladinos* and Zinacantecs.

"Mantzana Set"

The "**mantzana** set" is a group of five generics, all having pomaceous fruits.

1. **Mantzana** (**-tik**, **-altik**) (**castillan potov***) is the apple *Malus pumila* (6–4). Zinacantecs recognize four specifics, but with the materials at hand it is impossible to apply modern varietal names to these plants. The situation is complicated further by the recent influx of apples shipped to the San Cristóbal market from central and northern Mexico.

Because the apple that Adam stole from Our Lord's orchard stuck in his throat, men have adam's apples today (Laughlin, 1977, T54). According to another tradition, a *ladina* mistress went out of her house, leaving her maid to guard the apples, but she ate three apples. When the mistress returned she accused her maid of the deed. Her maid insisted that no one touched the apples. "But you can see the sign on your mouth. You ate three apples." Her maid continued to deny it, but the *ladina,* who is Our Holy Lady, knows. She tells her maid that she will suffer for it. Her maid becomes pregnant and has a difficult five-day delivery. Because of her, women have pain giving birth.

In early colonial times the apple was known under the name of **castillan potov**, castilian guava.

In 1797 the priest of Zinacantán commented that the apple was the sixth most common tree to be found in the yards. "[It] is truly the best that this Province boasts. Aside from the great number of trees, the fruit is exceptionally large, weighing up to 6, 7, 8 ounces and they pick many of this size" (de Leon y Goicoechea, 1797).

Apples are planted in a few of the temperate and all of the highland communities by seed, seedling, slip, or graft. Grafting and the planting of slips is done from December through February. Slips are planted with compost and sheep manure, compost and ashes, or fertilizer and lime. They are watered in the dry season and transplanted in the rainy season.

Apples are classed as "cold." They are eaten raw or may be boiled together with peaches and refined sugar until they form the consistency of corn gruel. They may be soaked in cane liquor to give it a fruity flavor. Apples are frequent grave offerings on All Souls' Day. Cf. **ixim**.

Specifics: 4.

    a. **Batz'i mantzana**, "genuine apple" (**mántzana ulo'**, **pajal mantzana**), is a small, sour apple, once the dominant variety, but now, because of grafting and the introduction of new varieties, very scarce. These apples are sold at market by Chamulans in August.

b. **Kámosa mantzana**, "suede apple," is a yellow apple grown by Chamulans and by a few highland Zinacantecs in their yards. The harvest is in September and October. It was a favorite apple for All Souls' Day offerings.

In 1748 the priest of Zinacantán listed *camuesas* or pippins among the local fruit trees (Monrroy y Calcadilla, 1748). This may be the golden pippin, "the most highly prized dessert apple in the 16th and 17th centuries" (Harrison, Masefield, and Wallis, 1973:48).

c. **Peróte mantzana**, "peróte apple," is a tough, sour, green highland apple that has nearly disappeared. It fruits from August to October.

d. **Tranjero mantzana**, "foreign apple" (**kaxlan mantzana, tanjero mantzana**), refers to three varieties: the first, **sakil**, "white," or **k'anal**, "yellow," is yellow delicious, the second, **tzajal**, "red," is red delicious, and the third, **tz'ibal**, "striped," is gravenstein.

These varieties have been introduced into temperate and highland hamlets in increasing numbers in recent years by government assistance. They fruit in August. They may be resold and are sold at market.

2. **Mántzana te'**, "**mántzana** tree" (**mántzana ka'**), refers to the highland shrubs *Amelanchier denticulata* (3–8) and *A. nervosa* (2–4). These are low shrubs with small, thick, ovate, bicolored leaves 3–4.5 cm long and small, red or pink, apple-like fruits up to 2 cm in diameter. The flowers are white with five petals and many stamens arranged in a terminal few-flowered raceme. They are common elements in highland second growth situations especially on rocky exposed slopes.

The trunk is used for hoe handles, digging sticks, and firewood. The fruit is eaten by birds.

Extended range: *Viburnum acutifolium* ssp. *blandum*.

3. **Nimpronix** (-**tik**, -**altik**) (**membrillo***, **rimponix**) is the quince *Cydonia oblonga* (2–3). It is a small tree, thickly branched with ovate leaves, which are woolly beneath. The flowers are pink with five petals and numerous stamens. The fruit is similar to an apple or a pear. A few Zinacantecs in many of the highland communities plant quince saplings in their yards and in gullies during the rainy season. They should not, however, be planted by young people. The trees fruit in 5–6 years.

The trunk is used for Sir Spook's walking stick and for the walking sticks of the other Carnival spooks. Stewards use the trunks for tamale platforms when tamales (**pisil vaj**) are steamed and then distributed at the change of office. Stewards-royal use the trunks similarly every other Saturday for the visit of the tithing man. To curb a child's rebelliousness, a switching of the hands with a quince switch is considered particularly effective. Quinces are sold at market in San Cristóbal and Chiapa de Corzo in August. They are eaten raw or roasted and are also used to flavor cane liquor. They are "cold." Quince confection is made by *ladinos*. At the Fiesta of St. Sebastian the grand and petty Spanish lords buy this confection and distribute it to the other entertainers.

4. **Nimpronix te'**, "**nimpronix** tree," is *Duranta repens* (1–1), shrubs from about 8–10 feet tall with long pendent branches. The leaves are small, alternate, obovate to elliptic, glabrous, 2.5–7.5 cm long. The flowers are white, 8–15 mm across, with a short tube expanding into five lobes. They are arranged in terminal and axillary racemes. The fruit is yellow, globose, 7–12 mm in diameter, fleshy, and edible, with a single seed, and enclosed by the calyx. It occurs in second growth of temperate and lowland regions.

5. **Pelex** (-**tik**, -**altik**) (**peras***) is the pear *Pyrus communis* (4–6), and *P. pyrifolia* (1–1).

Pears are planted in the same way as apples, but if a young person does the planting, for his own protection, he should snip off the top of the tree once it is established.

The trunk is used for firewood. Pears are generally classed as "cold." They are eaten raw or are boiled with refined sugar until they form the consistency of corn gruel. Cf. **ixim**.

Specifics: 2.

a. **Batz'i pelex**, "genuine pear," is a sweet, small-fruited form very like the cultivar "madeleine," which has been known in cultivation since 1628.

In 1797 the priest of Zinacantán reported that this was the fifth commonest yard tree. "Though small, it is tasty and provides in abundance" (de Leon y Goicoechea, 1797).

This variety, which does not fruit for 8–10 years, has nearly disappeared. It is sold at market in June and July. It is grown in a few of the highland communities.

b. **Kaxlan pelex**, "castilian pear" (**muk'ta pelex, pera, peron**), *Pyrus pyrifolia,* the oriental pear, is a very large-fruited form that fruits in 4–5 years. It is grown in a few of the temperate and many of the highland communities. It may be resold and is sold at market from late August to early November. It may be a grave offering on All Souls' Day.

"Met Set"

The "**met**" set includes four generics, all succulent plants with rosetted, fibrous leaves.

1. **Chi*** (-**tik**) is the generic term for the narrow-leaved agave-like plants.

Specifics: 2.

a. **Pino chi**, "fine **chi**" (**batz'i chi, tz'unbalal chi**), is the cultivated *Agave sisalana* (2–4). The sword-shaped leaves are about 1–2 m long and about 10 cm wide with entire margins. The flowers are yellow, 4.5–6 cm long, with the ovary and petals being about equal. The stamens are long with anthers about 2.5 cm long. It is grown by *ladinos* in low and temperate regions including the *ejido* land of Bik'it Nab, Muk'ta Nab, and X'ukun.

The fiber was bought formerly for the weaving of nets and shoulder bags and for the sewing of hats. It is now sewn on the hats of the **sak-joletik** for the Fiesta of St. Sebastian to give them their white-haired appearance. Fiber tumplines are replacing leather ones.

b. **Te'tikal chi**, "wild **chi**" (**chi met**), is *Furcraea guatemalensis* (5–9), a stalked, rosetted plant common in second growth temperate situations and in the understory of dry oak forest. It has narrow spine-margined leaves, 10–15 cm wide, and a stalk of pendulous, white flowers, 1–2 m long. The flowers are about 6 cm long, with ovary and petals about equal. The stamens are short, included in the corolla. The anthers are V-shaped and about 2 mm long.

The fiber is used for house lashing, nets, and ropes. The leaf is burnt first and stripped.

The fiber is tied around corn kernels in deadfalls for rats.

2. **Kaxlan tok'oy**, "castilian willow" (**chi met, chi vet, tok'oy, tok'oy chi, tok'oy te'**), is the bulb stem yucca *Yucca elephantipes* (6–10), a tree to 10 m tall with rosettes of stiff narrow dagger-like leaves on the ends of the stems. The flowers are white, campanulate, about 3–4.5 cm long, arranged in large terminal panicles. The fruit is oblong ovoid with a white or yellowish flesh and black seeds. It occurs as a scattered element of the lowland and temperate dry forests and is often planted near Chamulan and Tenejapan crosses. *Ladinos* plant it in fencerows.

As a remedy for earache and deafness, a leaf is roasted under the ashes and the juice squeezed into the ear.

Extended range: *Beaucarnea goldmanii.*

3. **Met** (**-tik, -altik**) refers to the broad-leaved agaves. These were created by Our Lord when He spat on his finger and rubbed it on the rocks. During the famine of 1918, maguey stalks were peeled, ground raw on the *metate,* and mixed with the corn dough to make tortillas. The inflorescence stalk may be split and used to make traps to catch doves live.

Specifics: 3.

a. **Chi met** (**k'ox j'alnom met, lo'balal met**) is *Agave kewensis* (3–4), similarly occurring on rock outcrops and cliff faces in the temperate and highland areas. It differs from *A. chiapensis* in having bright yellow flowers that are arranged in large clusters on a branched inflorescence.

The "cold" inflorescence stalk is roasted and eaten. It is said that the redder stalks are bitter, but others claim that the flavor is all in the "hand" of the person who cuts the stalk. When someone goes to get it, he should not refer to it as **komenal met**, "maguey inflorescence, but rather, **vale'** "sugarcane" or **svale'al tontik**, "rock sugarcane," lest it be ticklish when it is eaten.

b. **Lo'balal met**, "edible **met**" (**batz'i met, bik'it met, komenal met**), is *Agave chiapensis* (5–8), a plant with thick, spine-margined leaves in a clumped rosette up to one meter across. The flowers are produced on an elongated stalk 1.5–2 m tall. They are about 6–7 cm long, yellow or green tinged with reddish brown, with stamens twice as long as the corolla. The anthers are 2 cm long. Each flower is subtended by an ovate or triangular bract, long acuminate at the apex and arranged in a long narrow unbranched inflorescence. It occurs on rock outcrops and cliff faces in the temperate and highland areas.

Chamulans roast the core. They dig a hole, pile wood on the bottom, make a layer of stones on the top, and then put in the core that has been well-wrapped with leaves so no dirt will enter. The wood is lit. When a good fire is burning, earth is piled on top. The core is roasted for three days and three nights. Chamulans bring the roasted core to Zinacantán Center on major fiestas. The individual leaf bases are broken from the core and sold. They are generally classed as "hot." The "cold" young inflorescence stalk may be roasted and eaten. The inflorescence stalk is also split and used for corral posts.

The plants are used to decorate the creche in Chak Toj.

As a cure for warts, a dry pod should be shaken next to the warts, then when you are in your house and see lightning flashes you should sit with your back to the open door and, as the lightning flashes, you should quickly rub your warts with three corn cobs, one after another, then toss them over your shoulder far outside. Finally, you should run around three clumps of closely spaced **ch'ix jobel** three times with your eyes shut tight. After a couple of weeks your warts will disappear.

c. **Muk'ta met**, "large **met**" (**muk'ta j'alnom met, yax-met**), is *Agave americana* (3–8). The rosettes are up to 2 m across and the stalk is up to 3 m tall. The leaves are spine-margined, and up to 30 cm wide and often striped white and green. The flowers are yellow, 8.5–9 cm long, the ovary longer than the petals. The stamens are long-exerted with yellow-green anthers 2.5–3 cm long. They are arranged in an openly branched inflorescence. It is cultivated and used for fencerows throughout the highlands.

Young plants are transplanted a handspan apart for fence-rows at any time of the year.

The "cold" inflorescence stalk is roasted and eaten like sugarcane. The stalk may also be split and used as posts to enclose vegetable patches. Children use the leaves as sleds to slide down banks. The leaves were used as candle holders on major fiestas. The spines were cut off and square holes cut in a row down the center of each leaf. The leaves were placed at the foot of the altar. The Stewards of St. Sebastian provided two dozen leaves for the Fiesta of St. Sebastian. The Stewards of the Holy Cross provided four dozen leaves for the fourth Lenten Friday and for Holy Week. The Stewards of the Holy Cross still use six leaves apiece for their household altars on the fourth Lenten Friday and during Holy Week. The publican provides 15 for the church in Apas on the sixth Lenten Friday, and one dozen are used in Naben Chauk on the fourth Lenten Friday.

4. **Paxak'** (**-tik, -iltik**) refers to the pineapple and its wild, terrestrial relatives, all classed as **tz'i'lel**, "plant." All are rosetted, fibrous-leaved plants.

Specifics: 5.

a. **Chimpo paxak'** (**jol itajil paxak'**, **paxak' ch'o**) is the wild *Bromelia hemisphaerica* (2–5), a large rosette with narrow, spiny leaves 1 m long. The flowers and fruits are on a stout stalk. The flowers are tubular, narrow, about 4.5 cm long with a wooly tubular calyx in a large, woolly head-like inflorescence, 8–10 cm long, 4–6 cm wide. The inflorescence is closely subtended by a woolly leaf-like oblong bract with an abruptly long acuminate tip. The fruits are large, black, glabrous fusiform, about 6 cm long. Lowland *ladinos* plant it in fencerows. It occurs in the rocky understory of tropical deciduous forests.

The fruit, classed variously as "hot" and "cold," is eaten by squirrels, rats, and people, but eating it raw will cause one's mouth to bleed.

Extended range: *Hechtia glomerata.*

b. **Kinya paxak'**, "banana **paxak'**" (**yat chitom paxak'**), is *Bromelia pinguin* (3–5), a plant similar to *B. hemisphaerica,* but with a longer, more open inflorescence. The flowers are about 6 cm long. The fruit is a yellow and pink, fusiform berry. It occurs in second growth and waste ground in the lowlands.

The fruit is eaten by squirrels, rats, magpie jays, and people, but, if eaten in quantity, especially when raw, will cause bleeding of the gums. Classed as "hot," the fruit is eaten raw, roasted, or boiled. It is sold at market occasionally.

c. **Muk'ta paxak'**, "large **paxak'**" (**batz'i paxak'**, **jolom paxak'***), is the pineapple *Ananas comosus* (1–2). It is not cultivated locally, but may be resold by Zinacantecs and is sold at market in San Cristóbal from June to January.

The fruit is eaten raw and is used to flavor the *chicha* that is provided by the entertainers at the Fiesta of St. Sebastian and by the cantors at Carnival. It is classed variously as "hot," "medium," and "cold."

d. **Paxak'il te'tik**, "forest **paxak'**," is *Greigia oaxacana* (1-2), a rosetted plant with small inflorescences buried in the leaf axils. The leaves are linear with very short, small spines along the margins. The flowers are about 3.5–4.5 cm long, tightly clustered in a bracteate head-like inflorescence. The bracts are glabrous, triangular-ovate, 2.5–4.5 cm long, and strongly imbricate. In Zinacantán this bromeliad occurs only in the understory of evergreen cloud forest on Muk'ta Vitz.

e. **Potpot paxak'**, "clustered **paxak'**" (**potom paxak'**, **setom paxak'**, **setomal paxak'**), is *Bromelia plumieri* (3–6), a large, rosetted plant common in the understory of tropical deciduous forests. Margins of the leaves are clothed with curved spines and the base is covered with dense scale-like hairs. The inflorescence is sessile in the rosette and colored bright pink to red. The flowers are tubular, lavender, very hairy at the base, 9–11 cm long. The bracts are red. The fruits are covered with brown, irritating hairs, which must be rubbed off with leaves before they can be eaten.

The fruit is classed variously as "hot" and "cold."

"Naranja Set"

The "**naranja** set" is a loose grouping of 11 generics, including the citrus fruits, coffee, and three wild plants. Coffee and the latter plants all have glossy, green, citrus-like leaves and fragrant white flowers produced in a showy profusion.

1. **Alaxax** is the sour orange *Citrus aurantium* (1–2). It is a rough-skinned, globose fruit about 7–8 cm in diameter. It is acid with 10–12 segments and a hollow, red core.

A very few Zinacantecs in Bik'it Joyijel, X'ukun, and in most of the highland communities grow sour oranges in their yards. Young plants are transplanted in the rainy season. Compost and sheep manure may be used.

An **almud** basket or a burlap bagful of young tips are gathered or purchased by wedding petitioners. These, together with geranium blossoms, are made into wedding bouquets that are distributed to each of the wedding guests during the dance and tied to the harp and guitar. Some guests make the leaves whistle. Three or four leaves may be brewed as a substitute for coffee. The tea is "hot." The juice may be used to season cabbage and kale.

2. **Elamonix** (**-tik**, **-altik**) (**elomonix**, **limon**, **limones***) is the lime *Citrus aurantifolia* (1–4). The fruit is yellowish green, thin-skinned, round-oblong, and about $1\frac{1}{2}$ inches in diameter. The pulp is abundant and very acid.

Limes are planted in the lowlands and in many of the temperate communities. In Santa Rosa one seed is planted to a hole filled with black earth 3 m apart. A circle of stones is made around the tree, and compost is piled on the earth inside so that the heat of the sun will not be felt. It fruits in 3–6 years.

To reduce fever the leaves may be brewed in sweetened water, and the "cold" tea drunk at bedtime. The fruit is sold at market from June to mid-March. It is "cold." Lime juice and sugar are added to water for limeade. Lime juice is used together with chili, mint, coriander, and salt to flavor beef broth. It is also used to flavor fish, shrimps, snails, radishes, cabbage, kale, amaranth, **ch'aben**, and wild nightshade. To cure a hangover, radishes and cabbage, seasoned with lime juice, is eaten. For skin irritation (**jak'ob ik'**) the juice is mixed with white salt and applied. To ease chest pains (**me' vinik**) or bloody dysentery a glass of the sweetened juice is drunk. White salt may be substituted for refined sugar. Lime juice and white salt is given to a dog as an antidote for poisoning. This is also a remedy for chicken disease. Or they may be given lime juice in which prickly pear pads have been chopped up and in which a tomato has been crushed. All these remedies are "cold." Bartenders may serve sliced limes and radishes as hors d'oevres, cf. **kokov.**

3. **Kajve** (**-tik**) (**kajvel**, **kape**) is the cultivated coffee *Coffea arabica* (4–6). It is a small tree with white sweet-smelling

flowers in clusters in the axils of the glossy, opposite, elliptic leaves. The flowers are about 2.5 cm long with a short tube expanding into five white petals. The berries are first green, turning red when ripe, and containing two seeds or coffee beans.

Zinacantecs plant coffee in some of the temperate communities and in *ejido* land below Apas. One berry may be planted to a hole and the seedling transplanted in two years, or plants that have sprouted from fallen berries are pulled up when they are 1 m tall and transplanted $1^1/_2$ m apart. It fruits in 3–4 years. The coffee groves are weeded twice a year: in June (St. John's Day) and again in November (All Saint's Day). The berries are picked three times, from mid-February to Holy Week. After picking, the berries are ground on a *metate* or in a mill to loosen the skin. They are soaked in water for 2–3 days until the water foams. Then they are rinsed and spread in the sun for 4–5 days to dry.

The trunk is used for ax, hoe, billhook, and pick handles, for slingshots, fiddle bows, and firewood. The coffee beans are sold to fellow Zinacantecs or at market. They are roasted on the griddle and ground, either on a *metate* or in a grinder. All but the poorest Zinacantecs drink sweetened coffee. It is "hot." Bitter coffee is taken for malaria. Ground coffee is sprinkled on wounds to induce clotting, cf. **kokov**.

4. **Kajve te'**, "coffee tree" (**lo'bol k'ux kumum, ventex mamal**), refers to the temperate and lowland shrubs *Casearia commersoniana* (1–2) and *C. corymbosa* (4–7). These are densely branched, deciduous shrubs with alternate elliptic leaves and clusters of angular, ovoid, orange fruits. The flowers are small, about 8 mm broad, and clustered in the axils of the leaves. The plants in fruit resemble coffee plants. The fruits are eaten by birds. They occur in second growth and in the understory of tropical deciduous forest.

Extended range: *Citharexylum donnell-smithii, Eugenia amatenangensis,* and *Viburnum elatum.* The trunk of the latter is used for fence posts and firewood.

5. **Konkon** refers to one highland and one lowland shrub, both with very showy flowers from November to January. They are classed as "plant."
Specifics: 2.
    a. **Konkon** is *Cavendishia crassifolia* (3–4), a thick-leaved shrub with white and pink flowers in terminal racemes. The leaves are leathery, glossy, alternate, elliptic with an abruptly acuminate top and impressed veins. The flowers are tubular-urn shaped, about 15 mm long with five lobes. The fruit is round and about 6–8 mm in diameter and fleshy with many minute seeds. It is common in exposed situations in evergreen cloud forests of the high mountain ridges.
The flowers are gathered for sale by Chamulans and *ladinos.* They are put in altar vases. Zinacantecs may substitute sprays of this shrub for orange tree sprays normally used in wedding bouquets.
    b. **K'anal konkon**, "yellow **konkon**" (**k'anal yich'ak**

mut, muil te', snichim jsoktom, va'al nich), is *Galphimia glauca* (4–8), a glossy-leaved shrub with dense, terminal clusters of bright yellow flowers, which become papery and turn orange in fruit. The leaves are opposite, elliptic to ovate, 2.2–6.0 cm long, lighter below than above. The flowers have petals about 7–12 mm long and develop into glabrous, smooth capsules about 3.5–4.5 mm long. This is a very common plant in second growth on rocky slopes of the temperate regions. It occasionally occurs in oak forest.

Ladinos, especially of Chiapa de Corzo, the people of Muk'ta Jok', and Zinacantecs from the temperate hamlets gather the flowers for sale in the lowlands to adorn altars.
Extended range: *Celastrus vulcanicola* and *Viburnum hartwegii.*

6. **Lima** (**-tik, -iltik**) (**limas***) refers to sweet limes and sweet lemons.
Specifics: 3.
    a. **Chu' lima**, "breast **lima**" (**lima jmalalena**), is the sweet lemon *Citrus limonia* cv. 'Millsweet' (2–4). The fruit is depressed at the top around the prominent nipple. It is grown in Magdalenas and Oxchuc. It is also cultivated in the lowlands and in a few of the temperate and highland communities.
On the eighth *Posada* the Stewards of the Sacrament and the Senior Steward of St. Dominic provide three dozen stemmed fruits (one dozen apiece) to adorn the Christmas trees that flank the creche. They are also used to decorate the creche in Apas, Na Chij, Naben Chauk, Sak Lum, and Sek'emtik. Thirty fruits are placed in the net of fruit given by the fiancé to his fiancée. A smaller number is included in the net of fruit presented by the elders to each of the scribes on the fiestas of St. Sebastian and St. Lawrence. The fruit is "cold." For medicinal use cf. **inojo**.
    b. **Ch'ulul lima**, "smooth **lima**" (**chitom lima, jax-chu' lima, lima chinchina, naranja lima**), is the sweet lime *Citrus limetta* (3–4). The fruit is similar to the common lime *C. aurantifolia*. It is about the size of a lemon with thin yellow rind and abundant, sweet, insipid juice. It is planted in the lowlands, in Tenejapa, and in some of the temperate communities.
The fruit is used to decorate the creche in Atz'am.
The fruit is sold at market from September through December. It is "cold."
    c. **Pimil pat lima**, "thick-skinned **lima**" (**bik'it tubajtik lima, chu' lima**), is an unnamed cultivar of the sweet lemon *Citrus limonia* (1–2). This is less commonly cultivated and has the same range as **chu' lima**. Some fruits have a small nipple, whereas others growing on the same tree have none.
The seeds are planted in June, one to a hole. When the seedlings are 60 cm to $1^1/_2$ m tall they are transplanted. The tree fruits in 5–6 years.
The fruit is given as grave offerings on All Souls' Day.

The trunk is used for firewood. The fruit is sold in market in November and December. It is "cold."

7. **Limon** (**muk'ta elamonix**) is the lemon *Citrus limonia* cv. 'Eureka' (1–2). This true lemon, generally scarce in Chiapas, is cultivated in Magdalenas and Santa Marta. It is an oval, somewhat mammilate fruit with an acid pulp. The skin is yellow, conspicuously gland-dotted, thick and rough. It is sold at market.

8. **Mantarina** is the tangerine *Citrus reticulata* (2–6).
Specifics: 2.

  a. **Batz'i mantarina**, "genuine **mantarina**" (**mántzana naranja**), is the small tangerine sold at market from October through March. The fruits are usually sold attached to their stems, bearing one or two leaves. They are smaller than oranges, and the skin is a deeper orange or a reddish color. It is loose and separates easily from the fruit. The pulp is sweet and juicy. They are generally classed as "hot." They decorate the creche in Apas, Chak Toj, Paste', and San Mikulax.

  b. **K'ol-pat mantarina**, "rattling rind **mantarina**" (**k'ol-pat naranja**), is the large tangerine with a thick, warty skin, which is sold at market when still green. They are sold from November through April. They are generally classed as "hot."

9. **Naranja** (**-tik**) (**naranjas***) is the cultivated orange *Citrus sinensis* (2–4).
Specifics: 2.

  a. **Jayal pat naranja**, "thin-skinned orange" (**ch'ulul pat naranja**), is the Valencia type that is planted in the rainy season by the Tenejapanecs. It may be resold and is available in the market every month of the year except June. Twenty fruits of this or the thick-skinned variety are placed in the net of fruit given by the fiancé to his fiancée. A smaller number are included in the net of fruit presented by the elders to each of the scribes on the fiestas of St. Sebastian and St. Lawrence. The fruit is "hot." These oranges are essential grave or household altar offerings on All Souls' Day, and for the Christmas creche in most communities.

  b. **Pimil pat naranja**, "thick-skinned **naranja**," is the navel type but with seeds. Although these oranges are rarely cultivated in the highlands because they do not fruit there for many years, they are cultivated in the lowlands and most of the temperate communities. Seeds or seedlings are planted in the rainy season. They fruit in 4–5 years.

In the temperate hamlets women used the spines formerly for tenterhooks. As a substitute for coffee, poor people prepare a "hot" tea of orange leaves or rind. For cough medicine a tea of orange rind, marigold blossoms (**kelem vo'tus**), and elderberry blossoms (**batz'i chijil te'**) is brewed. The rind is also used to flavor cane liquor and watermelon squash. Three-dozen stemmed thick-skinned oranges (one dozen apiece) are provided by the Senior Steward of St. Anthony and the Stewards of the Holy Cross on the eighth *Posada* to decorate the pine trees flanking the creche. Thick-skinned oranges, sweeter than the thin-skinned variety, may be resold and are sold at market in December. They are sold in Zinacantán Center at Christmas and New Year's. They are "hot." Cf. **jayal pat naranja**.

10. **Sila** (**silo**) is the citron *Citrus medica* (1–4). The fruit is large and elongate, resembling a the shape of a pear. It has a rough, thick, spongy, greenish yellow to golden-yellow rind, and a small sour pulp, which is very acid. It is grown by lowland *ladinos*, by the people of Chenalhó, and in some of the temperate communities.

The rind is used by *ladinos* for lemonade. The fruit, classed variously as "medium" and "cold," is very rarely eaten by Zinacantecs. The Stewards of the Holy Cross formerly provided a few fruits on the eighth *Posada* to decorate the pine trees flanking the creche. The fruits are still used to decorate the creche in Atz'am and Sak Lum. For stomach ache a tea is made of the leaves.

11. **Yich'ak mut**, "bird claw," is the lilac fuchsia *Fuchsia paniculata* (3–5). It is a glabrous-leaved shrub with large, terminal panicles of lilac flowers. The leaves are alternate, elliptic and narrowly elliptic or narrowly obovate, 6–15 cm long. The flowers are about 10–12 mm long, tubular, with spreading lobes and exerted stamens. The fruit is a round, purple, fleshy berry. It is common in moist ravines in the evergreen cloud forests of the highland area.

The tips are used in the "flower water" to bathe newborn babies. Cf. **antzil aj**.

"Olnob Set"

The "**olnob** set" is comprised of 17 generics, legume trees and shrubs with finely divided leaves.

1. **Chojchoj** (**-tik**, **-altik**) (**xulub vakax ch'ix**) is the bull's horn acacia *Acacia cornigera* (5–10), a shrub or small tree with large, swollen, nodal spines in the shape of a bull's horns, in which stinging ants make their nest. The yellow flowers are in a dense raceme. The fruit is a swollen, apiculate pod. It is very common in the understory of the tropical deciduous forest and in lowland second growth situations.

Zinacantecs note that this tree likes to live separately. The ants' intense foraging under this tree has given rise to the belief that the tree is a woman who has swept diligently. The wood is reputed to be so "hot" (**k'ok'**) that if used for hoe handles the corn will not grow. The branches are used for brush fences.

2. **Ch'ich' ni'**, "bloody nose" (**-tik**) (**ch'ich' ni' te'**, **tzajal xaxib**), refers to *Calliandra confusa* (1–1), *C. grandiflora* (5–12), and *C. houstoniana* (7–12), shrubs with large, red flowers in terminal racemes. The color is produced by the long, filamentous stamens. The leaflets are linear, 4–7 mm long. The pods are flat, pubescent, and up to 10 cm long. They are common elements in shrubby second growth formations at all elevations.

The trunk is used for fence posts and firewood, but some

170

believe that putting it in the fire will cause nosebleeds. It is used in Chak Toj for the framework of the crèche. The branches are used for brush fences and are fed to sheep and horses. The "cold" flower is passed two or three times near the nose to stop nosebleeds.

Extended range: *Calliandra caeciliae.*

3. **Kevrajacha (-tik) (ch'ix te', kebrajacha, kervajacha, kervejacha, sakil ch'ix te')** refers to *Acacia pennatula* (10–16), a dense, low tree of grassy savannas of temperate areas. The trunks have large branches with projecting, often branched spines. The flowers are small and yellow, and the pod is thick and flattened and 4–6 cm long.

The trunk is used for roof rods, fence rails and posts, and firewood. Saplings may be used for hoe handles. The tender shoots and pods are eaten by horses. The spine is used to extract snails from their shells.

4. **Krus ch'ix,** "cross spine" **(sakil ch'ix)**, refers to *Pisonia aculeata* (1-1) and *P. macranthocarpa* (1-5), stiff, divaricately branched trees with thick spines opposed on the stem like a cross. The leaves are opposite, entire, thin, large, and broadly elliptic to broadly ovate, up to 12 cm long in *P. aculeata* or smaller and elliptic to oblanceolate to about 8 cm long as in *P. macranthocarpa*. The flowers are small and greenish in axillary clusters. The fruit is club-shaped or oblong about 1–7 cm long, 5-angled with stiff stipitate black glands on the angles. The trees occur in tropical deciduous forest of lowland areas and are especially common along ravines.

5. **Lotz'om chij,** "deer cramp" or "sheep cramp" **(chame-'at ch'ix, lot'om ch'il, lotz'om chij ch'ix, lotz'om chij tz'i'lel)**, is *Mimosa albida* (12–18), a very common, sprawling subshrub with divided, sensitive leaves, with broad ovate leaflets up to 7 cm long, prickly, wiry stems and terminal, spherical clusters of pink flowers. The divided leaves are likened to deer hoofs. It is common in disturbed situations and second growth in temperate and lowland areas. It is classed variously as **te'**, "tree," **tz'i'lel**, "plant," and **ak'**, "vine."

It is eaten by sheep.

Extended range: *Mimosa adenantheroides.*

6. **Molíno te',** "mill tree" **(molinyo, mololinyo)**, is *Poeppigia procera* (2-3), a large tree that becomes covered in yellow flowers at the end of the rainy season (October). They are arranged in small, many-flowered, dense, terminal panicles and have five imbricate petals, 8–10 mm long. The leaflets are oblong, 1–2 cm long, and glabrous. The fruit is a short, glabrous flat pod, 4–9 cm long. The tree is a common element in tropical deciduous forest.

The trunk is used for fieldhouses, fence posts, gates, and beds.

7. **Olnob (-tik, -altik) (onob)** refers to *Leucaena,* lowland trees with clusters of flat pods bearing edible beans.

"There is good evidence that 2000 years ago Mayans used leucaena for this same purpose (nitrogen fixation and soil-building), at least in the Yucatan Peninsula" (National Academy of Sciences, 1977:71).

The edible seed contains mimosin, a toxic amino acid, which, when eaten in quantity, has been reported to cause hair loss among humans in Central America and Indonesia. Sheep growers have experimented with this attribute of leucaena, providing their sheep with an exclusive diet of the forage for 10 days as a substitute for shearing—"a stroke of the hand is all that is needed to separate wool from skin" (ibid., 39).

Specifics: 3.

a. **Batz'i olnob,** "genuine **olnob**" **(sakil olnob)**, is *Leucaena leucocephala* (3-6), a tree with large round clusters of white flowers up to 2 cm in diameter. The divided leaves have narrow leaflets about 6–16 mm long, and the fruit is a long flat, glabrous pod 15–20 cm long. It is cultivated and occurs wild in the lowlands in second growth forests and tropical deciduous forest. Many lowland *ladinos* plant the beans in their yards.

In Santa Rosa, Kelem Ton, and the lower temperate communities the beans are planted with a digging stick just before the first rains, 1–2 to a hole, 2–3 armspan's distance. Seedlings may also be transplanted in the rainy season. They are cultivated as well in the temperate hamlets and in Muk'ta Jok', fruiting in three years.

The trunk is used for house mainposts, rafters, roof rods, roof purlins, fiddle bows, fence posts, bobbins, and firewood. The heartwood is used for corn shuckers. The "cold" tips are eaten raw. The "cold" beans are sold at market in their pods from September through December. They are also eaten raw. Zinacantecs claim that some individuals suffer hair loss, not by excessive consumption of these beans, but rather by eating them after having eaten beef, iguana, chicken, eggs, fish, snails, or **ch'aben** earlier in the day. Those who are affected lose all their hair in a week or two week's time. Some maintain that the beans of any **olnob** may have this effect, others restrict it to **paka' olnob**.

Extended range: *Piptadenia flava.*

b. **Paka' olnob** is *Leucaena collinsii* (3-7), a tree with large, round clusters of white flowers, about 2 cm in diameter, narrow leaflets, about 4–8 mm long, and long pods (15–25 cm long). They occur in second growth forests and tropical deciduous forests of lowland areas. Individuals are often left untouched when fields are cleared for corn. It is cultivated occasionally, as in Minax. Zinacantecs recognize two varieties, **sak**, "white," and **tzoj**, "red," according to the color of the pods.

The trunk is used for house mainposts, rafters, roof rods, purlins, fence posts, ax and pick handles, and digging sticks. The heartwood is used for corn shuckers and drumsticks. If the corn farmer runs out of food he may chew the bark with tortillas. The tips and buds, predominately classed as "cold," are eaten by some at weeding time. The branches are eaten by horses. The pods, maturing in January and February, are sold at market. The beans, generally classed as "hot," are eaten raw with tortillas. They are said to kill worms.

   c. **Tzajal olnob**, "red **olnob**," refers to *Leucaena diversifolia* (5–11), trees with small leaflets, 4–7 mm long, small pods, 5–10 cm, and small clusters of white or pink flowers. It is a low tree common in second growth temperate and lowland forests.

The trunk is used for house mainposts, rafters, roof rods, roof purlins, fence posts, fiddle bows, hoe, pick, and billhook handles, and firewood. The heartwood is considered to be the strongest wood for ax handles. It is also used for corn shuckers. The tips and beans (which mature from December to early January) are classed variously as "cold" and "hot." The beans become bitter when fully ripe. They are sold at the fiesta of St. Sebastian by people from Atz'am. They are sold at market in San Cristóbal by Elan Vo' merchants.

8. **Pit** is the guanacaste *Enterolobium cyclocarpum* (3–7). These are immense trees with swollen trunks and a large spreading canopy. The flowers are small, white, in round clusters 1–1.5 cm in diameter. The fruit is a flat round pod contorted into the shape of an ear, 4–6 cm across. It is common in the tropical deciduous forest. Large trees are often left when fields are cleared for planting. Cows are said to spread the seeds in their patties. *Ladinos* use the trunks for dugouts.

The trunk was once used for drums.

The trunk is also used for fence posts, corral posts, and firewood. As an antidote for black widow spider bite, a "hot" tea of the bark may be taken. The "hot" sap is drunk for whooping cough. The fluff that surrounds the seeds was formerly used for soap. The seeds, generally classed as "hot," are roasted and eaten. For further medicinal use cf. **tz'oban**.

Extended range: *Jacaranda acutifolia*.

9. **Sakil ch'ix**, "white spine" (-**tik**) (**sakil kevrajacha**), is *Acacia farnesiana* (5–10), a densely branched shrub or small tree with clusters of small, yellow flowers and short, thick pods. The branches have long, stiff, white spines at the nodes. It is common in temperate savannas and in lowland second growth.

The root is brewed for a "hot" tea for tuberculosis. The trunk is used for firewood, and the branches for brush fences.

Extended range: *Diphysa spinosa*.

10. **Suk** (-**tik**) refers to the shaggy-barked legumes *Lysiloma*. The two specific classes are distinguished by the color of their bark.

Specifics: 2.

   a. **Ik'al suk**, "black **suk**" (**tzajal suk**), refers to *Lysiloma acapulcense* (3–5) and *L. divaricatum* (2–4), medium-sized trees with flat pods hanging from the branchlets. The flowers are white and in racemes of buttons. The leaflets are linear, very small, 2–9 mm long, pubescent or glabrous. These trees are common elements in tropical deciduous forests.

The trunk is used for fieldhouse mainposts, fence posts, benches, and firewood, but is very hard to cut.

The branches are used for brush fences.

   b. **Sakil suk**, "white **suk**," is *Lysiloma auritum* (5–6), a tree very similar to those included in **ik'al suk**, but with the leaflets glabrous and flowers in globose clusters. The pods are 5–7 cm wide, up to 20 cm long, covered with a dark maroon-red skin, and borne in clusters. These are also common in tropical deciduous forests of lower temperate and lowland areas.

The trunk is used for fieldhouse mainposts, rafters, roof purlins, ax handles, and fence posts. *Ladinos* use it for cattle corrals, floor boards and oxcarts. The branches are used for brush fences.

11. **Tamarin** (**tamarin te'**) is the tamarind *Tamarindus indica* (3–8), a cultivated tree in lowland areas. It is a large tree up to 25 m tall with a widely spreading crown. The leaflets are oblong, 12–25 mm long. The pale yellow flowers are about 9–11 mm long and borne in few to several-flowered racemes that are shorter than the leaves. The pod is thick, brown, and scaly, 5–15 cm long, 2 cm wide. The seeds are brown, shiny, and 1 cm broad. *Ladinos* plant the seeds in their yards in the rainy season. They soak the fruit in sweetened water for a refreshing beverage. The fruit is sold at market from December to April.

The "cold" tamarind drink is also taken to allay fever. The fruit may be brewed to provide a "medium" tea for dysentery.

Extended range: *Mimosa nelsonii*.

12. **Tzo' xulem te'**, "buzzard shit tree" (**matabey**), refers to *Lonchocarpus minimiflorus* (1–2) and *L. rugosus* (2–3), medium-sized trees with pinnately divided leaves, large oblong elliptic leaflets, 2–5 cm long, pubescent below, and with prominent veins, clusters of purple pea flowers, and short, flat pods. They are scattered in the tropical deciduous forest, especially streamside situations and in lower pine-oak forests. The trunk is used by *ladinos* for ox yokes.

This is a coffee shade tree. The trunk is used for fence posts and firewood.

Extended range: *Senna atomaria* and *Harpalyce formosa* var. *goldmanii*.

13. **Vamuch te'** (**vamoch**) is guamuchil, *Pithecellobium dulce* (3–7), a medium-sized tree with pinnately divided leaves and broad, ovate leaflets. The flowers are white and in dense racemes. The fruit is a thick pod in which the seeds have a fleshy, sweet, aril. It is common in tropical deciduous forests and thorn scrub, where it is sometimes cultivated by the *ladinos* in the lowlands.

The trunk is used for **metate** platforms, planks, chairs, tables, chests, beds, benches, gunstocks, slingshots, crosses, gates, doors, and corn bins. The "hot" resin is brewed as a tea for whooping cough. The fruit is eaten by orioles and humans.

Extended range: *Acacia pringlei*.

14. **Voy chij te'**, "sheep hoof tree" or "deer hoof tree" (-**tik**) (**voy ch'ix te'**), refers to *Bauhinia divaricata* (5–18), *B. pauletia* (3–3), and *B. ungulata* (2–6). These are shrubs or small trees with leaves divided into two leaflets resembling the hoof of a sheep or deer. The flowers are white or pink and

showy. The fruit is a flat pod. They are scattered to common in second growth and tropical deciduous forest in the lowlands.

The trunk is used for fieldhouse roof poles, ax, hoe, and pick handles, digging sticks, fence posts, and firewood.

Extended range: *Calliandra emarginata, Senna nicaraguensis,* and *Pithecellobium dulce.*

15. **Xaxib** (-**tik**, -**altik**) refers to thinly branched shrubs or small trees, with divided leaves and feathery, white or red flowers.

Specifics: 2.

  a. **Batz'i xaxib**, "genuine **xaxib**" (**k'a'esob nukul, k'ox xaxib, timbre, timpre**), is *Acacia angustissima* (18–21), a variable plant that is a shrub or small tree with buttons of small, white flowers arranged in lax terminal panicles. The leaflets are linear, 4–7 mm long. The stems are occasionally spinescent. The fruit is a thin flat pod. It occurs in dry, second growth situations at all elevations.

In 1797 the priest of Zinacantán recorded that "for tanning they use **timbre**, whose bark gives body and strength to their sugarcane drinks. And it is to this same tree that the little worm fastens and fattens that provides the oil for Chiapanec lacquer" (de Leon y Goicoechea, 1797).

The trunk is used for tamale platforms, bean poles, corn and flower stakes, digging sticks, and firewood. The bark of this tree was especially prized as a tanning agent. In San Sigro, after the children climbed the trees and stripped the bark down to the ground, causing the trees to die, the *ejido* representative prohibited the practice. The bark was sold by the *arroba* to the people of Acala and Chiapa de Corzo, who ground the bark, placing it under and over the hides which were allowed to soak in troughs of water for 4–6 days (though some report for two weeks). Some say the hides are soaked with lime water, others, that the hides are covered with ashes after soaking.

The branches are used for brush fences, and are eaten by horses, cattle, and sheep.

The fruit is deemed poisonous and may be lethal to unsuspecting children.

  b. **Muk'ta xaxib**, "large **xaxib**" (**k'a'esob nukul, xaxib te'**), are *Calliandra portoricensis* (5–7) and *C. tetragona* (3–5), thinly branched shrubs or small trees with large, terminal clusters of white flowers with numerous stamens, 1.5–2 cm long, the leaflets are oblong-linear, 8–16 mm long. The stems are angled with recurved spines. This plant occurs in second growth in temperate and lowland areas.

The trunk is used for digging sticks and fence posts.

The bark was sold to be used as a tanning agent. The leaves are thought to be poisonous.

16. **Xaxib ch'ix**, "**xaxib** spine," is *Mimosa pigra* (1–1). It is a stiff erect shrub with pubescent leaflets. The stem is armed with stout recurved prickles and the rachis of the leaves with stiff straight spines. The flowers are pink in dense, round heads. The pods are about 3–8 cm long and densely pubescent with rather stiff brown hairs. It occurs along sandy stream banks and in waste ground near standing water in the lowlands.

17. **Yolnob ch'o**, "rat's **olnob**" (**olnob te', vax tz'i'lel, xaxib te', yolnob chij, yolnob ka', yolnob vakax, yolnob vet**), is a non-Linnaean term applied to *Aeschynomene compacta* (1–1), *A. purpusii* (1–1), *Chamaecrista nictitans* ssp. *disadena* var. *pilosa* (1–2), *Desmanthus virgatus* (2–1), *Indigofera thibaudiana* (2–2), *Machaerium chiapense* (1–2), *Senna occidentalis* (2–6), *S. pallida* (1–1), *S. skinneri* (1–2), and *Tephrosia cinerea* (1–1). These are temperate and lowland shrubs or perennial herbs with pinnately divided leaves and flat pods. They occur predominately in waste ground or second growth formations. They are classed variously as "tree" and "plant."

The branches are used for brush fences. They are eaten by sheep and horses.

"On Set"

The "**on** set" is a loose association of 16 generics, all trees with glossy elliptic leaves and large globose fruits.

1. **Aj-te'**, "reed tree" (-**tik**), is the white sapote *Casimiroa edulis* (2–5), a tree up to 20 m tall. The leaves are palmate with five elliptic leaflets and lateral panicles of greenish yellow or whitish flowers about 8 mm broad. The fruit is green or yellowish, resembling an apple, 6–10 cm broad. This tree occurs wild in temperate and highland areas, where it is protected. It also is used as a shade tree in the coffee groves. It is planted in most of the temperate and all but one of the highland communities. In San Sigro the fruit does not ripen until April.

The trunk was used formerly to make log stools. It is used for fence posts and bridges. The fruit is not esteemed by Zinacantecs, who scornfully classify it as "fit for Chamulans," who eat it together with tortillas. It is sold in Chamula and San Cristóbal in August and September. It is "cold." The seed may be stored and utilized as a remedy for boils (**chakal**). It is ground and the powder applied to the boil. This remedy is "cold." The seed may be put in the fire to split and then is applied hot to the boil, then replaced by another, etc. This "hot" remedy has a more involved variant: a part of the seed is ground, mixed with tallow and urine and applied. If the boil does not shrink, three seeds are crushed, mixed with tallow, and brewed in strong cane liquor. This is applied in a compress so the boil will burst. The sore is later bathed with **k'ox pak' chak** tea. For further medicinal use cf. **k'anal sat mes.** To rid one's yard of gophers the seed may be inserted or burned in the gopher's burrow so that its teeth will fall out.

White sapotes are subdivided into three classes, all occurring in the same environment and having identical uses. The fruits of each have white or yellow (sweeter) flesh. Cf. **ixim.**

Specifics: 3.

  a. **Bik'it aj-te'**, "small reed tree," has smooth leaves and smooth, round, hawthorn-sized fruit. This is the sweetest variety. Whereas the other two varieties fruit in August, this ripens in September.

b. **Ch'ulul aj-te'**, "smooth reed tree," is a white sapote with smooth leaves and round, smooth-skinned fruits, the size of a small orange. The flavor is considered superior to that of the large-fruited variety.

c. **Muk'ta aj-te'**, "large reed tree," is a form with rough, thick leaves and large, irregularly shaped fruits that have a rough skin and furrows. The flavor of individual fruits varies as much as that of avocados.

2. **Aj-te' te'**, "reed tree tree," is the common lowland tree *Tabebuia rosea* (2–5). It has large, digitally compound leaves and large clusters of tubular, purple flowers that cover the tree in the dry season when it is leafless. The leaflets are broadly elliptic to ovate, 8–16 cm long. The flowers are 5–8 cm long with a small tubular, lobed calyx, 1.5–2 cm long. The fruit is an elongate, narrow pod up to 20 cm long with papery winged seeds.

The leaves are used for bone breaks.

3. **Chinin** (**koyoy**): this lowland tree is a large, leathery-skinned, yellow, stringy-meated form of *Persea scheideana*. It grows in San Lucas and Bik'it Nich and fruits in May through mid-August. It is "cold." This variety, prized by *ladinos,* is seldom bought by Zinacantecs who claim that it causes burps. It may be buried in pine needles to ripen and be resold.

4. **Itzompi** (**jisan-tzotz, matz'an-tzotz**) is the lowland tree son sapote *Licania platypus* (1–6). It is a tree up to 20 m tall with large oblong leaves, 15–35 cm long, rounded at the base, acute at the apex. The flowers are small, about 6 mm broad, white in gray-pubescent panicles. The fruit is large and heavy, ovoid, 8–20 cm long, 5–14 cm broad, dark brown. The flesh is deep yellow, juicy, and sweet. There is one seed about 3–8 cm long, 2.5–4.5 cm broad, covered with dense fibrous hairs. Slips are transplanted by *ladinos* in the rainy season. It occurs along streams in seasonal evergreen forest.

The fruit is sold in Zinacantán Center during the Fiesta of St. Lawrence. It is generally considered to be "hot." The pit may be stored to serve in a variety of medicinal teas. For a baby suffering stomach ache the pit is chopped up and brewed together with brown sugar or preferably honey. The tea is "hot." The pit may also be brewed to provide a "hot" tea for dysentery or infant hernia. To calm whooping cough a decoction of son sapote pits and walking stick insects is drunk. For other medicinal uses cf. **j'ak'-'uch, tan pox**.

5. **Ja'as** (**-tik**) is the mamey sapote *Pouteria mammosa* (2–7). A large tree to 30 m tall with a large trunk and shaggy to smooth reddish brown bark. The leaves are obovate, 7–30 cm long, acute at the apex, alternate at the base. The flowers are about 10 mm long, sessile and densely clustered on older branches below the leaves. The fruit is 10–15 cm long, ellipsoid or globose, brown. The flesh is pink or yellowish, sweet with one large, glossy brown seed with a large, pale scar on one side. It is commonly cultivated by lowland *ladinos* and occurs in the wild along streams in seasonal evergreen forest.

The trunk is used for fence posts and firewood. Dropping many sapotes down, Rabbit wedged poor Coyote's jaws open so he could flee (Laughlin 1977, T166). The fruit is harvested by Zinacantecs in Kelem Ton. The fruit may be resold and is sold at market from January to July. To speed ripening it may be buried in pine needles. It is classed both as "hot" and "cold." The pit may be boiled, the skin removed and then cut in pieces, dried in the sun, toasted on the griddle, and ground into powder, which is added as seasoning to corn gruel (**pamal ul**). To soften their hair, women may rub it with the pit when shampooing. As a remedy for cramps the pit may be ground and brewed to provide a "hot" tea, or the pit may be toasted and rubbed on the afflicted area.

Extended range: *Eriobotrya japonica*.

6. **Kována te'**, "**kována** tree" (**kováno te', marímpa te'**), is the lowland tree *Swietenia humilis* (4–4). It is a small tree with dense foliage, pinnately compound leaves with elliptic, long acuminate leaflets, 6–15 cm long, and large, woody, erect ellipsoid fruits, 20–30 cm long. The flowers are about 1 cm broad in open axillary panicles, shorter than the leaves.

The trunk is used for marimbas, fence posts, fieldhouse roof and wall poles, and firewood.

7. **Lumpisera** (**lumpijera**) is the lowland tree *Platymiscium dimorphandrum* (1–2). It is a small tree with pinnately divided leaves with elliptic to ovate leaflets, 5–15 cm long, and racemes of white flowers, about 1 cm long. It occurs in tropical deciduous forest and seasonal evergreen forest. It is a very common element of tropical deciduous forest.

The trunk is used for fieldhouse roof poles, fence posts, and firewood.

8. **Manko** (**-tik, -altik**) is the mango *Mangifera indica*. It is cultivated in suitable locations throughout the lowland area.

When Xut, the Christchild, was hiding in the banana grove with the Virgin Mary she offered him one of her fruits, a banana.

"I don't want to eat it very much. You see, I have a fruit. I'll bring it for you. We'll see what the fruit is like. But that would be better," said Xut.

"Ah, what is the fruit like?" asked [Our Holy Mother].

"See, it's good," said Xut.

"See what I'm eating," he said. Our Holy Father [Xut] ate. He ate mangoes. He just ate mangoes. "But this will multiply. It will grow anywhere. It won't disobey. But see, I'm eating it. I'll plant its pit. I'll make it multiply. You'll see! It will grow everywhere. It won't disobey. But see, I'm eating it. I'll plant its pit. I'll make it multiply. You'll see! It will grow everywhere," said [Xut].

"Ah, is it good?" [asked Our Holy Mother].

"It's good, try eating it!" said Our Holy Father. He ate a lot, he finished it. "But my fruit is very sweet. Your fruit is less so. But it's eaten differently. My fruit is better," said Xut.

"Ah!" said [Our Holy Mother].

"Well, let it multiply then. If it grows have everyone eat it. They'll learn since I'm eating it too. They'll eat it too," said [Xut].

"Ah!" said [Our Holy Mother].

"They'll learn since I'm eating the fruit. They'll learn, but [the banana] doesn't grow everywhere. It has its own place where it grows. The other one doesn't disobey. It grows wherever you plant it." said her son.

"Ah!" said [Our Holy Mother].

"The other [fruit] everyone will eat, said [Xut].

Then Xut explains to his mother how parakeets will come and peck out the middle of the fruit and eat it.

"It's the one that eats lots of fruit and young corn to today—the parakeet. Yes! That's why it is shot. They kill it. They kill it. Yes!"

"So the mango multiplied. Xut ate it. That's how the mango was born. Yes!"

Specifics: 4.

a. **Batz'i manko**, "genuine mango," is the small-fruited form, with very fibrous seeds, cultivated by lowland *ladinos* and by Zinacantecs in Kelem Ton and Santa Rosa.

The trees fruit in March, April, and May, but by June the fruit is wormy. To speed ripening the fruits may be buried in pine needles. They are resold by Zinacantecs. They are "hot." Mangoes are sold at market in Zinacantán Center on the fourth Friday of Lent and during Holy Week. Each steward presents 10 mangoes to their musicians and to the sacristans on Corpus Christi.

b. **Chitom manko**, "pig mango" (**baroso manko**), is a fibrous form with larger, yellower, sweeter fruit, which grows adventive in the lowlands along streams. It fruits at the same time as the **batz'i manko**. It is "hot."

c. **Tranjero manko**, "foreign mango," is the large-fruited form with few fibers. It grows in groves in lowland towns. The fruit is sold at market from late April to early August. Zinacantecs resell the fruit in Tuxtla. It is "hot."

d. **Xok manko**, "mottled mango," is a small-fruited form with short fibers and a large seed. The black mottling of the skin increases as the season progresses.

Both pits and saplings are planted in many of the temperate communities in the rainy season, but they should not be planted by young people. They are used by Zinacantecs as coffee shade trees. They fruit in 6 to 10 years. Mangoes seldom fruit in Atz'am, but they are common in the temperate hamlets of Jok' Ch'enom, Masan, Potovtik, and occur also in Muk'ta Jok' and the towns of Burrero, Ixtapa, and Soyalò. The fruits ripen in late June and continue into August.

The trunk is used for firewood. The "cold" bark is boiled and the tea drunk for dysentery. A wooden mango is kept by the Senior Steward of Our Lady of the Rosary in his coffer. It is removed and washed on St. Rose Day. The fruit is sold at market. It is "hot."

9. **Muy** is the chico sapote *Manilkara achras* (2-7), a large tree up to 30 m tall with a very thick trunk. The leaves are coriaceous, elliptic to oblong, 5–12 cm long, 3.5–5.5 cm wide, the nerves are almost obscure. The flowers are solitary in the leaf axils, about 14 mm long. The fruit is variable in size and shape, usually ovoid or globose, 3–9 cm in diameter. The skin is rusty brown with a pebbled surface. The meat is white with the texture of a pear. It occurs wild along streams throughout the lowland area and is cultivated by *ladinos*.

The trunk is used for fence posts and firewood. The commercial use of its sap for chicle is not known by Zinacantecs. Zinacantecs harvest the trees occurring in Kelem Ton. The fruit is sold by *ladinos* at market from October to April. It is "hot."

10. **No'chi'** (**k'anas te'**, **nochi**, **tzo' olol**, **tzo' unen**) is the yellow sapote *Pouteria campechiana* (2-2). A tree to 20 m tall with a broad spreading crown and irregularly furrowed brown trunk, the leaves are elliptic, alternate, 9–20 cm long, acute at the apex and base. The flowers are small and axillary. The fruit is ellipsoid, about 5–10 cm in diameter and up to 20 cm long, yellow, green or brown. The flesh is yellow and sweet, with 1–4 seeds. It is cultivated in the lowlands by *ladinos,* and by a few Zinacantecs in Santa Rosa. The pit is planted in June. It occurs naturally along streams in seasonal evergreen forest.

The fruit is sold in San Cristóbal from July to January. It is classed variously as "hot" and "cold."

11. **On*** (**lo'balal on***) refers to the Mexican and Guatemalan races of the avocado *Persea americana*.

Specifics: 4.

a. **Batz'i on**, "genuine avocado" (**pimil pat on**), refers to the thick, hard, warty-skinned forms of the Guatemalan race of the avocado *Persea americana*. These are large or medium-sized trees with alternate, oval to elliptic leaves, 10–30 cm long, acute or acuminate at the apex. The inflorescence of small greenish flowers is paniculate and gray pubescent. It is known only in cultivation. It is grown in the yards of Pat Osil and most temperate communities and in the coffee groves. Some believe that avocados must not be planted by young people, though the young planter may protect himself by burying several pits together and, when they sprout, pulling up all but one. Both pits and saplings are planted, generally in the rainy season. Compost or sheep manure may be applied. When the seedlings are 1 1/2 m tall they may be transplanted in rows. The tree is reported to fruit after 5–15 years. Fruiting is encouraged by slashing the trunk or "feeding" it with meat. On St. Andrew's Day or Holy Saturday, the owner of the tree, accompanied by a friend, visits the uncooperative tree to "give it a tumpline." He takes his machete or his ax and scolds the tree, slashing it three times, saying, "I'm going to cut you down!" Then, his friend offers him a shot of cane liquor—"Take pity on it, here is a little cane liquor, don't cut down my avocado!" "But I'm going to cut it down, it doesn't fruit," replies the owner. "Don't cut it down, we'll see if it doesn't fruit next year," urges his friend. The two drink the cane liquor together and the following year the avocado, out of gratitude, provides a bounty of fruit. Slashed avocado trees may be seen in Zinacantán as witnesses to this technique that is practiced also in Veracruz (Coe and Diehl, 1980).

A non-fruiting avocado tree may also be convinced to fruit by giving it its "meal, hanging a pig head, horse or cow bones, or fresh sheep meat in its branches. It is said that if a cow or pig is slaughtered beneath an avocado tree it is good to hang some of the meat in the tree so it will fruit better. To prevent the pregnant wife of the owner of an avocado tree from spoiling the fruit she should take three bites out of three fruits.

The trunk is used for log stools and firewood. The fruit is harvested from December to March and is sold at market in San Cristóbal. The avocado is the only fruit that is eaten raw with salt and tortillas as part of a meal. It is "cold." As a remedy for bloody dysentery the pit is chopped up and brewed. The tea is "cold." As a remedy for boils (**chakal**) the pits are placed on the fire to split and then pressed against the boil until they cool, when another is applied. It is "hot."

b. **Ch'ail on**, "bitter avocado," is a smaller, not so tasty form of the Guatemalan race with little flesh. It grows wild in temperate habitats such as Atz'am and Ibestik in steep ravines in montane rain forest.

c. **Tzitz on** is a maroon, thin-skinned avocado with bright green, sweet meat of the Mexican race of *Persea americana*. The fruit has two forms: 6–7 cm long and ovoid or 8–12 cm long with a narrow, crooked neck. It is cultivated by Zinacantecs in Pat Osil and most of the temperate communities, especially Atz'am. Fruit is produced in 8 to 10 years. The fruit matures from October through November.

d. **Yax-'on**, "green avocado" (**ch'ulul on, pajajtik on, va'ajtik on**), applies to the larger-fruited forms of the Mexican race of *Persea americana* and thin-skinned interracial hybrids cultivated by lowland *ladinos* and by Zinacantecs of Kelem Ton, and Santa Rosa, and in Masan and Minax. These have thin skins and sweet, green flesh. Zinacantecs recognize red- and green-skinned varieties. They are planted similarly to the hard-skinned forms. The fruit matures in late June through August. It is resold by Zinacantecs, who may bury it in pine needles for ripening.

12. **Oven** (**oven on, oven te', yoven chuch**) is *Persea donnell-smithii* (1–2), a tree common in the evergreen cloud forest of the high mountain ridges. It is similar to *Persea americana* except that the leaves are densely pubescent and the fruit is small.

When the survivors of the Flood were asked what they ate, one held up an **oven** fruit in his hand and said that it was delicious. "Won't you try it?" he asked the boss. "No, I don't want it. Take it away! That's what you'll live on. I'll give you a tail, I'll give you fur, get going!" And that is how the squirrel was created.

The trunk is used for gunstocks. Zinacantecs report that the acid-tasting fruit is eaten by Chamulans. It is "cold."
Extended range: *Ilex brandegeana*.

13. **Tzitz** (**ik'al tzitz**) refers to the small, thin, shiny, purple-skinned forms of the Mexican race of *Persea americana* var. *drymifolia*. The ovoid fruits, 5–8 cm long, have bright green meat. The odor of the strongly-scented leaves and fruit is similar to that of the herb *Tagetes lucida,* which is also called **tzitz**, a clear homonym. The phonetic value of this name is extended to explain the creation of the tree by a yellow-eyed junco, **tzitzil-'ul:**

"How do you live?" the junco was asked.
"As for me, I have eggs," it said.
"What are your eggs like?" (someone) asked. "Look!" it said. Its eggs were glossy black.
"What are your eggs called, then?"
"They're called **tzitzal lo'bol** (**tzitzal** fruit)," it said.
"Ah," he said. "**Tzitzal** fruit—is it edible?"
"It is."
"But how does it grow?"
"Look, I bury it in the ground. You'll see, I bury it in the ground where I scratch," it said. It dug a hole for it, the junco dug up the ground.
"You'll see, in four or five days," it said. [That meant] in four or five years. "In four or five days," it said.
"Ah, I guess we'll see," he said. Already the bird's egg had big sprouts. It was the **tzitz** avocado that came up, the **tzitz** avocado that came up. It was the glossy black little **tzitz** as we call it. It was [the junco's] egg that was transformed like that long ago.

This form occurs wild and is planted in many of the temperate and most of the highland communities in the same way as **batz'i on**. It fruits in 5 to 9 years. The leaves are used as a substitute for *Tagetes lucida* to season corn gruel. The fruits are sold at market in May and early June and again in late October and early November. They are classed variously as "cold" and "hot."

14. **Tzitz te'**, "tzitz tree," refers to the wild trees *Beilschmiedia riparia* (1–1), *Dipholis matudae* (1–1), *Licaria peckii* (1–4), *Nectandra coriacea* (3–7), *Ocotea chiapensis* (1–1), and *Styrax argentum* (1–1). These small to medium-sized trees, occur in temperate forests and have pungent leaves and small avocado-like fruits.

The stems were once used for bodkins. The trunk of *L. peckii* is used for threshing platform posts and for the drums of the elders' and ensign-bearers' musicians. Birds eat the fruit. The trunk of *S. argentum* is used for wattle, roof poles, and gate rails.

176

15. **Uch** (**-tik**, **-altik**) is the black sapote *Diospyros digyna* (1–6), tall trees to 35 m, with alternate, leaves on short petioles, narrowly elliptic to 30 cm long. The fruits are large and globose, 4–7 cm broad, chive green or yellowish green. The flesh is black and seeds are 1.5–2 cm long, smooth to somewhat compressed. The flowers are white and fragrant in small axillary clusters. The name of this tree is a homonym of the name for opossum. Once the flesh of its fruit was grayish white, the color of opossum fur (as it still is when unripe). The ancestors called it opossum's fruit, but the a chicken flew up, crunched its seeds, and shat in the fruit, so its flesh turned black. Sometimes now the people call it "chicken shit **uch**." This tree is cultivated by *ladinos* in temperate and lowland areas and occurs naturally in seasonal evergreen forest along steep ravines. Individual trees often persist long after habitation in areas that have been abandoned. Such trees are harvested by the new Zinacantec settlers of Kelem Ton.

The trunk is used for fence posts and for firewood. The fruit is sold at market by *ladinos* from October to April. Zinacantecs may bury the fruits in pine needles to speed ripening before reselling. If many fruit are eaten a stomach ache will follow. The pit is reputed to be poisonous. The fruit is classed variously as "cold," "medium," and "hot."

Extended range: *Diospyros nicaraguensis*.

16. **Yaj-te' kotom**, "coati's reed tree" (**sakil k'oxox te'**), is the lowland tree *Elaeodendron trichotomum* (2–6). It is a medium-sized tree with opposite, leathery, ovate leaves, 8–13 cm long and a hard, walnut-shaped fruit, 1–2.5 cm long. The flowers are in small, few-flowered axillary clusters. The tree is scattered in lowland areas.

After the Flood one of the survivors is asked what he ate. When he points out this fruit that fills his canoe he is told that because all the corn has rotted he can subsist on it, but he is condemned to live in caves. Provided with a striped face and a bushy tail, to this day coatis eat the fruit.

"On Te' Set"

The "**on te' set**" is composed of two generics referring to highland trees and shrubs with shiny, red bark and soft, brittle wood.

1. **On te'**, "avocado tree" (**-tik**, **-altik**), refers to the manzanitas and madrones. These are plants with red, peely bark, small, red or black, flesh-covered, single-seeded fruits, and white urn-shaped flowers in terminal clusters.
Specifics: 3.
   a. **K'ox on te'**, "small avocado tree," refers to the shrubby manzanitas *Comarostaphylos arbutoides* (1–2) and *C. discolor* (6–9). These shrubs have dark red, peely bark, glossy, green, elliptic to obovate leaves, 3.5–11 cm long, with serrulate or crenulate margins and terminal racemes of white, urn-shaped flowers, 6–7 mm long. The single-seeded fuits are covered with black papillate flesh. They are a common element in

second growth formations and on rock outcrops in highland areas.
The tips may be used in the "steam cure."
   b. **Muk'ta on te'**, "large avocado tree," is the madrone *Arbutus xalapensis* (2–3), a medium-sized tree with smooth, orange-red, peely bark and glossy, elliptic leaves, 8–14 cm long, very similar to leaves of avocado. The flowers are urn-shaped, white or pinkish, 6–8 mm long, in a many-flowered terminal panicle. It is a common element in the pine-oak forests of temperate and highland areas.
Madrone wood and the wood of the bush laurel are considered to be best for mortar gunpowder. The trunk is used for bean poles and for firewood. It smokes very little. If the madrone has many blooms this is a sign that mangoes, which fruit at the same time as the madrone, will bear many fruits. The flowers are scattered on the processional path of the Christ Child in Atz'am. The berry is eaten by robins, band-tailed pigeons, and people. It is "cold."
   c. **Nap'ap' on te'**, "sticky avocado tree" (**xuch'al on te'**), also refers to *Arbutus xalapensis* (3–6), but is restricted to those members of the population with sticky glandular pubescence that have on occasion been segregated by botanists as a separate species *A. glandulosa*.
Three tips are used to mend a broken bone. They are "hot."
2. **Sakil te'**, "white tree," is the box elder *Acer negundo* ssp. *mexicanum* (4–7), a soft-wooded tree that is common along highland streams. It has large, soft, pubescent, pinnately compound leaves, with ovate, acuminate, serrate leaflets, 5–16 cm long, and red catkin-like clusters of flowers that resemble bunches of hair on the leafless stems. The fruit is a samara, about 2.5–3 cm long.

Slips are planted in Zinacantán Center for fencerows. The trunk is used for house mainposts, but is scarce. The trunk is split and used for sheep corrals and fences for vegetable and flower gardens. Some say that if it is burned for firewood the smoke will kill one's chickens. The branches may be used to wrap flowers for transport.

"Pitz'otz' Set"

The "**pitz'otz' set**" includes four generics, soft-wooded shrubs with small flowers in terminal inflorescences and elliptic leaves. All are classed variously as "plant" and "tree," demonstrating the ambiguous application of "tree" to non-woody shrubs.

1. **Pitz'otz'** (**-tik**) (**lo'bol mut**, **ve'el chij**) is *Monnina xalapensis* (13–17), a glabrous-leaved shrub with terminal racemes of blue and yellow flowers. The leaves are alternate, narrowly elliptic to oblanceolate, short petiolate, 3.5–7 cm long. The flowers are similar to pea flowers, about 6 mm long. The fruits are fleshy, purple drupes with a single seed. These shrubs are common in the understory of the open pine-oak

forests of highland and temperate areas.

Sheep eat the leaves. Birds eat the berries. To cure laundry hands (**esel k'obol**), women crush the "hot" leaves or ripe berries on their palms for three or four days. The berries may also be crushed on the fingernails to cure **unen k'obol**, an infection under the fingernails that causes them to fall out.

Extended range: *Cuphea cyanea, Fuchsia encliandra* ssp. *tetradactyla, F. thymifolia* ssp. *minimiflora*, and *Ludwigia octovalvis*.

2. **Sat pukuj**, "devil's eye" (**-tik**) (**sakil ik'al te'**), refers to *Solanum aligerum* (9–13), *S. brachystachys* (1–1), and *S. cervantesii* (2–3). These are glabrous-leaved shrubs with terminal or axillary cymes of nodding, white flowers and small, green or red, tomato-like fruits. They are common in the understory of evergreen cloud forests and wet canyons in pine-oak forests of temperate and highland areas.

Thirteen tips form a basic ingredient of the "steam cure." Birds eat the berries.

3. **Tuil te'**, "stinky tree" (**bik'tal xinal te', ik'al te', xavon te'**), refers to the temperate and highland shrubs *Cestrum aurantiacum* (5–10), *C. guatemalense* (3–5), *Solanum brachystachys* (4–4), and *S. nudum* (1–1). These are shrubs with glossy, dark green, foetid leaves and fleshy, round, white (*Cestrum*) or black (*Solanum*) fruits.

The trunk is used in the construction of brush fences and for fence posts and firewood. The berries of *Cestrum* are mashed and used for laundry soap.

Extended range: *Cestrum nocturnum, Ligustrum ovalifolium, Solanum cervantesii*, and *Tournefortia densiflora*.

4. **Ve'el kulajte'**, white-winged dove food" (**ajval te'** in part, **barsin te', ik'al sat tz'i'lel, sak-paran te'** in part, **ve'el chuch, ve'el mut, yich koyote, yich xulem**), refers to *Cordia foliosa* (2–6), *C. spinescens* (4–10), and *Rauvolfia tetraphylla* (5–6), shrubs with scabrous or glabrous, elliptic leaves and terminal inflorescences. The fruits are small, fleshy drupes. They occur in the understory of tropical deciduous forest and in lowland second growth formations.

The trunk is used for firewood. White-winged doves and red-billed pigeons eat the fruit.

"Po'on Set"

The **po'on** set includes 12 generics, mostly broad-leaved evergreen lowland trees, many with edible fruits, large trunks, and large, thin, compound leaves.

1. **Amat** refers to the wild fig trees *Ficus glabrata* (3–7) and *F. glaucescens* (2–7), large, buttressed trees with thick, fibrous bark and white, milky sap. The leaves are alternate, large, thick, entire and ovate, 8–23 cm long. They occur along streams in the seasonal evergreen forests of the lowlands.

The edible fruit is classed variously as "hot" and "cold." It is also eaten by birds and river snails. Jaguars are said to toss these fruit at people to frighten them away. Some believe that the tree's soul will kill the person who chops it down, others

use the trunk for benches, shelves, lamp stands, gates, fence posts, and firewood. The buttress is used for **metate** platforms.

2. **Ch'u te'***, "God tree" (**-tik**) (**santo te', tuil te'**), refers to the tropical cedars.

Specifics: 2.

    a. **Bik'it ch'u-te'**, "small God tree," is *Cedrela oaxacensis* (2–3), a medium-sized tree common in the tropical deciduous forest. It is very similar to *C. odorata*, but differs in being a much smaller tree and having very large, woody obovoid fruits, about 12 cm long and 4 cm thick.

For use cf. **sakil ch'u te'**.

    b. **Sakil ch'u-te'**, "white God tree," refers to the common wild and cultivated *Cedrela odorata* (4–5) and *C. salvadorensis* (1–1), large trees with red, aromatic wood, large pinnately compound leaves with ovate or oblong ovate leaflets, 5 to about 23 cm long. The flowers are small in large, terminal panicles. The fruit is small, oblong, woody and hangs in clusters. When mature it splits open from the apex into five segments releasing the winged seeds. *Ladinos* living in temperate areas plant them in fencerows. They also occur along streams, in seasonal evergreen forest (*C. odorata*), and on steep slopes in montane rain forest of temperate hamlets.

Because of the unceasing aroma exuded by its wood, this tree is thought to have divine qualities. In 1977, when the Church of St. Lawrence was gutted by fire and the patron saint consumed by flames, the bishop donated a plaster image of St. Lawrence as a replacement. It was not long before the town decided that their patron saint must be made of Spanish cedar. A search was made throughout the township until a tree suitable for carving was discovered. That tree, in the form of St. Lawrence, now stands above the altar. The trunk is also used for crosses, drums, fiddles, fiddle bows, coffers, benches, shelves, lamp stands, chairs, tables, doors, gunstocks, and grain measures cf. **nukul pat**.

3. **Inop** (**-tik**) (**pánsuro te'**) is *Ceiba pentandra* (3–3), the legendary tree of life of the classic Maya. They have immense, swollen trunks, which branch after 40–50 m. The trees, when leafless, bear flowers in clusters. The flowers are white or pink with petals 3–3.5 cm long and densely silky-hairy outside. The leaves are digitately compound, with 5–7 oblanceolate or oblong leaflets, 8–20 cm long. The fruits are similar to *C. aesculifolia* (**mojan**). In this region they occur along streams in the seasonal evergreen forests of the lowlands and are planted in market places and town squares.

Young trees, having straight trunks, are classed as "male," (**vinik** or **stot**), whereas the old trees, with swollen trunks, are "female," (**sme'**). Ceibas are considered to be "sources of water" (**me' vo'**) and accordingly should not be felled. He who does so will swell with water and die. Although some claim that the same fate awaits the person who hugs a ceiba, others assert that a man who wishes to become fat should hug a "female"

178

ceiba, briefly wrap his sash around its trunk, or walk around it three times. To fatten a pig some ceiba bark should be mixed with its corn, or it should be provided with a leash made from the same bark.

4. **Jovos** refers to two lowland trees with elliptic, single-seeded, fleshy fruits borne on the stems below the terminal leaf clusters.

Specifics: 2.

　a. **Batz'i jovos**, "genuine **jovos**" (**chitom po'on, k'anal po'on, ovos, po'on chitom, po'on te', simaron po'on, te'tikal po'on, yat chitom po'on**), is the wild hog plum *Spondias mombin* (9-11), medium-sized trees with pinnately divided leaves and plum-sized, oblong fruits borne on the stems. These are yellow or orange and sweet. The fruits that have large pits and little flesh are termed **jovos**, while those that are very juicy are termed **po'on**. The trees are common in the tropical deciduous forests of the lowlands and are planted in fencerows by *ladinos*.

At the time of the Flood the racoon ate **mutut** fruit and wild hog plums and was given stripes and a tail.

Lowland *ladinos* graft mango slips onto the trunk. The trunk is used for benches. The stems are debarked and used as stoppers for water gourds and powder horns. The fruit is eaten by birds and by people. It is sold at market in April, May, and October. Hog plums are eaten raw or used to flavor cane liquor. They are classed variously as "hot" and "cold."

Extended range: *Trichilia hirta* and *Zanthoxylum mayanum*.

　b. **Yaxal jovos**, "green **jovos**," is the wild sapote *Mastichodendron capiri* var. *tempisque* (1-2), a medium-sized or large tree scattered along small streams in seasonal evergreen forest in the temperate and lowland areas. The leaves are glossy, entire, elliptic, 6–12 cm long, on long petioles, 5–9 cm long with a conspicuous white margin. The flowers are cream-colored, 7–8 mm long, arranged in dense clusters on the stems below the leaves. The green fruit, the same size and shape as that of *Spondias mombin,* is sweet, with a milky sap. It is "hot."

5. **Kajanab te'**, "shelf tree" (**bik'it k'os, matapálo, sakil mutut, yaxal bot te'**), is the highland tree *Oreopanax capitatus* (5–10), a soft-wooded tree often epiphytic of the evergreen cloud forest with leaves and stems very similar to **mutut**. The flowers are small and clustered into heads that are arranged in panicles or racemes, about 9 cm long. The fruits are about 5 mm in diameter, globose. Because of its medicinal use slips are planted in Pat Osil.

It is used for firewood, and the "hot" leaves are wilted (causing great cracking and popping sounds) and applied to bone breaks and aching bodies (**k'asemal**).

6. **Maluk** (**malok**) is *Genipa caruto* (3–7), a medium-sized tree with large, opposite, entire, obovate to oblong leaves, 1.5–3.5 cm long, and tubular white flowers, 2–4.5 cm long. It has apple-sized, soft, fleshy fruits that are borne in the dry

season, when the tree is leafless. It is scattered in the lowland areas in second growth and tropical deciduous forest.

The trunk is used for fence posts. The edible fruit is generally classed as "cold."

7. **Mémela te'**, "perforated tortilla tree" (**pik'in te'**), is *Clusia rosea* (6–9), a small to medium-sized tree with very thick, glabrous, obovate leaves, 10–20 cm long. The flowers are large, fleshy, and red and white. The fruit is a thick, fleshy capsule with red, arilate seeds. The bark is smooth. The sap is thick and clear. This is a common tree in dry, steep canyons and cliff faces in temperate regions mostly with pine-oak forest but occasionally in tropical deciduous forest or seasonal evergreen forest.

The mother of a girl who does not want to make tortillas gathers three leaves and places them on the griddle. When piping hot, she places them in her daughter's hands and presses her hands together. It is considered to be an effective punishment.

Extended range: *Oreopanax obtusifolius*.

8. **Mojan** (**ajan te', mujan, nanta'**) is the common lowland tree *Ceiba aesculifolia* (6–9) with large, spinescent trunks, digitately compound leaves, with 5–8 elliptic or obovate leaflets, 5–15 cm long, and large, white flowers, 10–16 cm long. The fruits are woody and elliptic, 12–18 cm long, smooth and brown. The seeds are globose and imbedded in the wool inside the capsule. It occurs as a dominant in tropical deciduous forest.

The trunk is used for benches, fence posts, and firewood. Deer eat the flowers and fruit. The "hot" seeds, resembling corn kernels, are eaten raw.

9. **Mutut** (**-tik**) is the common wild fig *Ficus cookii* (11-17) and *F. cotinifolia* (1-2). These are glossy, ovate-leaved trees with smooth trunks and thick, milky sap. The leaves are about 6–15 cm long. The fruits are sessile or short pedunculate, globose, about 1 cm in diameter, subtended by a bilobate involucre. They are a common element in temperate and lowland forests. Lowland *ladinos* plant them in fencerows.

The fruits are eaten by birds. To induce clotting, the bark is cut and the "medium" sap is collected on a leaf and poured on a cut. Some use the trunk for fence posts and firewood, but it is widely believed that to fell this wild fig will cause the rain to stop because it is the "source of water" (**me' vo'**). Old trees, credited with a soul, will receive the corn field offering if they are standing near a corn field. Cf. **batz'i jovos**.

10. **Po'on*** (**-tik, -altik**) refers to cultivated and some wild hog plums.

Specifics: 2.

　a. **Batz'i po'on**, "genuine **po'on**," is the cultivated shrub *Spondias purpurea* (2–4), a densely branched, short tree with red, very sweet, plum-like fruits. The leaves are pinnately divided into 5–12 pairs of subsessile leaflets. The flowers are borne in large panicles when the tree is leafless. They are bright red or red-purple with petals about 3 mm long.

Lowland *ladinos* and Zinacantecs in Kelem Ton and Santa Rosa and in a few of the temperate hamlets cultivate these trees. After the tree fruits, and just before the first rains, branches are lopped off, cut into 1 m sections and planted in holes 3 m apart filled with black earth. It takes 4–5 years to produce many fruit.

The "cold" tips are chewed for chest pain (**me'-vinik**). The fruit may be resold and is sold at market in April and early May. It is eaten raw or used to flavor cane liquor. It is classed variously as "hot," and "cold."

Extended range: *Trichilia hirta*. The trunk is used for fence posts and firewood.

b. **Te'tikal po'on**, "wild po'on," refers to both *Spondias mombin* (1–2) and *S. purpurea* when they occur in fencerows. The fruit of the former is not as sweet as that of the cultivated hog plum and the latter is a purplish fruited variety. Both are medium-sized trees.

11. **Po'on ch'ix**, "po'on spine," is *Ximenia americana* (4–7), a densely branched, spinescent shrub or small tree with entire, elliptic leaves, 3–7 cm long, and acrid, plum-like fruits. The flowers are small, tightly clustered in the leaf axils, and white with fringed petals. It occurs in a variety of habitats from dry pine-oak forests of temperate hamlets to savannas and tropical deciduous forest in the lowlands.

The fruit is eaten by birds and by some people.

Extended range: *Zanthoxylum* sp.

12. **Te'el uli'**, "rubber tree" (**pojov te', uli' te'**), is the rubber tree *Ficus elastica* (3–5). It is cultivated by lowland *ladinos*. Rubber gum was once smeared on cloth to make raincapes, although the source of gum was probably *Castilleja elastica*.

"Pom Set"

1. "The **pom** (-**tik**) set" is a set of two generic terms referring to *Burseras*. These are all thick-trunked trees or shrubs with resinous sap that can be made into incense. After slashing, the trunk becomes very red. The resin of the different kinds of *Bursera* may be mixed together and may also be mixed with **pit** resin. The "hot" resin is used to plug cavities. It is applied once a day for three days. The whitest resin is used to resin fiddle strings. Both resin and chips are sold by the people of Muk'ta Jok'.

Long ago when people saw the incense tree they did not know what it was. They thought it was a useless tree that hardly grew. Our Lord told them, "It will grow tall. It will have fruit." He cut a strip of bark off. "Come, look in three days!" he said.

They came back to look and then they saw the resin. Our Lord took it. "This is the tree's smoke," he said. "It is very fragrant. Use it with flowers in your curing ceremonies!" he said. Our Lord gave them a censer and an ember. "This is how you cense the patient, this is how you cense the clothes." he said.

Then he told them, "There are two kinds, genuine incense and mud incense, but mud incense is not as good."

In ritual speech, incense is referred to as **j-p'ej yo jpom, j-p'ej yo jch'ail**, my lowly chunk of incense, my humble cloud of smoke (the person marker may vary).

Specifics: 2.

a. **Ach'el pom**, "mud **pom**" (**tzo' ka' pom**), is *Bursera bipinnata* (8–13), shrubs or trees to 10 m tall. The leaves are fern-like, pinnate two or more times into small ovate leaflets. The inflorescence is small and few-flowered. The fruits are green or red, ovate, about 6–7 mm long.

It is planted in a few of the temperate communities.

The trunk is used for firewood and incense, but the incense is less fragrant than that of **batz'i pom**. For swelling, 13 splinters are brewed with gunpowder, but **batz'i pom** is considered more effective. For a loose tooth, 13 splinters are brewed together with 13 splinters of **tzajal tulan**. One cup of the "hot" tea is also drunk before breakfast. The fruit is eaten by white-winged doves. For further medicinal use cf. **antzil aj**.

b. **Batz'i pom**, "genuine **pom**" (**muk'ta pom, pom ryox**), is *Bursera excelsa* (7–12). The leaves of this tree are pubescent, alternate and pinnately divided into ovate or oblong ovate, coarsely crenate leaflets, 2.5–5 cm long. The rachis is sometimes winged. The flowers are small in axillary panicles, shorter than the leaves. The fruit is glabrous, subglobose, about 1 cm long. Lowland *ladinos* plant slips in fencerows in April.

Fencerows of this tree are also planted in many of the temperate communities.

The trunk is used for incense. The wood is cut into slivers 15 cm long and then chopped into chips. An ensign-bearer entering office presents six chips to the corresponding musician. The cantors and judge ordinary give three apiece to the musicians and to father spook. An elder, when entering office should have six burlap bagfuls of incense. The elder's wife burns the incense three times daily. Stewards and stewards-royal need eight bagfuls. One basket is required by the official in charge of each Holy Cross Day ceremony. One basket is needed for a curing ceremony. Three or six "hot" splinters are a basic ingredient of "flower water." For swelling, 13 splinters are brewed with gunpowder. One cup of the "hot" tea is drunk before breakfast. The fruit is eaten by white-winged doves.

Extended range: *Zanthoxylum mayanum*.

2. **Pom ka'**, "horse **pom**" (**sotz' te'**), is *Bursera steyermarkii* (3–3). These are broad shrubs, 2–3 m tall. The leaves are large, pubescent pinnately divided into three ovate to elliptic leaflets, 4–6.5 cm long, or unifoliate. The panicle is few-flowered and produces fruit very close to the stem. The capsules are about 8 mm long. The shrub occurs on limestone outcrops in tropical deciduous forest in the lowlands.

As a remedy for heartburn (**k'ak'-nuk'**), a tea of bark and wood chips, brewed with brown salt, is taken. A "hot" tea of six or 13 splinters is taken for "wind." The leaves are used for the "steam cure."

"Sun Set"

The "**sun** set" is a group of four generics, all large-headed, soft-wooded shrubs, with daisy-like flowers.

1. **K'ail** (**-tik**) (**k'ayil**) refers to *Smallanthus maculatus* (10–11) and *S. oaxacanus* (2–2), soft-wooded shrubs with large, pinnately lobed, scabrous leaves, large yellow heads of flowers, and fleshy achenes. They are very common in wet, open places, waste ground, and second growth situations in the highland and temperate areas.

The root is brewed to make a "hot" tea for "wind." The leaves may be brewed for a "hot" tea for postpartum hemorrhaging. The plant is used as fodder for sheep and horses. On Christmas Eve in Atz'am, the cave where the Christ Child is born is decorated with the flowers. They are also strewn, together with the flowers of **sak-nich te'** and rose petals, on the processional path to the church.

Extended range: *Ageratina chiapense, Matudina corvii,* and *Montanoa* sp.

2. **Sun** (**-tik**) refers to *Tithonia diversifolia* (4–6), *T. longiradiata* (2–4), *T. rotundifolia* (1–2), and *T. tubaeformis* (4–6). These are weedy shrubs with large, pubescent leaves and large, yellow, terminal, sun flowers. They are common in second growth shrubby waste ground formations of all elevations. They are classed variously as "tree" and "plant."

The trunk is used for fieldhouse walls. To relieve aches and swelling in the limbs the "hot" leaves are warmed, made into a ball, and rubbed on the affected area. As a remedy for tuberculosis three leaves are brewed and the "hot" tea is drunk once daily for three days.

3. **Ton k'ail**, "hard k'ail" (**-tik**) (**muk'tik k'ail, sak-nich te'**), is *Montanoa hexagona* (4–8), a large shrub or small tree with white, rayed, daisy-like flowers in terminal clusters maturing into inflated papery balls in fruit. The leaves are large, soft, pubescent, and palmately lobed. These are common in rocky, exposed sites in the highland area.

The trunk is used for the roof rods of hip-roofed houses, but the trees are often very difficult of access.

Extended range: *Montanoa speciosa, M. tomentosa* ssp. *xanthiifolia.* The latter is cultivated by *ladinos* and the flowers used to decorate altars.

4. **Tzojoj** (**joj, sakil sun, soj**) is *Lagascea helianthifolia* (6–6), a sparsely branched shrub with terminal rayless clusters of white flowers. The leaves are large, clasping, opposite, and very rough-pubescent. It is a common element in the understory of open pine-oak forests and second growth of temperate regions. It is classed variously as "tree" and "plant."

"Tilil Set"

The "**tilil** set" includes 10 generics. All are forest trees or shrubs with large, entire, glossy leaves and small round fruits.

1. **Bak amuch te'**, "toad bone tree" (**toj-cho' te'**), is the temperate and highland tree *Clethra mexicana* (1–1), a medium-sized tree, often a dominant in wet oak forests and evergreen cloud forests, with large, obovate, coarsely serrate leaves, 9–15 cm long and pubescent below, and small, white flowers in dense, terminal, arching racemes. The fruits are small, dry, many-seeded capsules.

The trunk is used for rafters and sheep corral rails.

2. **Bakel amuch te'**, "toad bone tree," is *Calyptranthes chiapensis* (1–1). This shrub or small tree has subsessile opposite leaves, with cordate bases and acute to attenuate apices. They are glabrous oblong-ovate, ovate or lanceolate, 10–21 cm long. The small, pinkish flowers are borne in a terminal or axillary branched inflorescence. The fruit is round, black, 7–12 mm in diameter, with a small collar-like projection at the apex. It occurs along streams in the tropical deciduous forest of lowland areas.

Extended range: *Colubrina elliptica, Parathesis chiapensis, P. leptopa,* and *Rhamnus mucronata.*

3. **Ja'as te'**, "mamey sapote tree," is *Styrax argentum* (1–2), a large tree up to 25 m tall. It is a common element of seasonal evergreen and tropical deciduous forests of the lowlands. The leaves are alternate, gray-pubescent beneath, variable in shape, lanceolate, oblong or obovate, 7–16 cm long. The flowers are white fading pink, 9–15 mm long, in terminal or axillary racemes or panicles. The calyx is cup-shaped, pubescent, and 4–5 mm long. The fruit is subglobose to ellipsoid, 0.7–2 cm long, with an apiculate tip and a wrinkled, pubescent outer skin.

The trunk is used for wattle, roof poles, and firewood. The berry is eaten.

4. **Karnéro te'**, "sheep tree" (**sakil karnéro te', sne ba**), refers to the sea grapes *Coccoloba barbadensis* (2–5), *C. diversifolia* (1–1), *C. liebmannii* (1–1), and *C. mayana* (3–7). These are trees, 10–30 m tall, with thick, glossy leaves and small, hard, round fruits in long, lateral racemes. They occur in a variety of primary forest associations including tropical deciduous, seasonal evergreen, and montane rain forests in the temperate and lowland areas.

The trunk is used for hoe and billhook handles, digging sticks, fence posts, and firewood.

Extended range: *Ehretia tinifolia* and *Licania arborea.*

5. **K'ol-k'ox**, "child's rattle" (**-tik**) (**k'ol-k'ox moletik**), is *Phyllanthus grandifolius* (10–10), a glossy, thick-leaved shrub with large, round, inflated, red fruits the size of small apples. The leaves are short-petiolate, broadly ovate or broadly elliptic, 4.5–12 cm long, 2.5–7 cm broad. The flowers are small, pink, and in pendent axillary clusters. It is common in second growth formations in temperate areas.

The trunk is used for firewood. The tips are eaten, boiled, as greens. Children play with the fruit. The seeds may be toasted and eaten.

Extended range: *Bunchosia lanceolata, Garcia nutans, Malpighia glabra,* and *Viburnum acutifolium* ssp. *lautum.*

6. **K'os** (**-tik**) is a generic term for two members of the Myrsinaceae with large, glossy, ellipic leaves and clusters of red, fleshy single-seeded fruits.

Specifics: 2.

a. **Sakil k'os**, "white k'os," is *Synardisia venosa* (3–6), a small to medium-sized tree with large, oblanceolate glabrous leaves, 15–25 cm long, and pink flowers on large terminal panicles. The fruits are small, up to 1 cm in diameter, round, and single-seeded with a fleshy, red to purple covering. It is a common element in montane rain forest, seasonal evergreen forest, and wet canyons in pine-oak forests of the temperate areas.

In everyday speech the descriptive term **sakil**, "white," is not used, as **k'os** most usually refers to this plant.

Slips or young plants are transplanted in the rainy season by a few individuals in the highland hamlets. Some believe that if the planter is young he should have a ceremony in his house, followed by a visit to Kalvaryo. When the tree has grown, the tips should be cut and used in a second, similar ceremony and visit. It is widely believed that this tree requires a "green thumb" (**sk'abal**) to propagate in one's yard, and there are those who claim that the tips of a cultivated tree are ritually less powerful than the tips from a wild tree.

One tip is a basic ingredient of "flower water." The tips are also used to adorn a patient's bed. Eighteen tips are required for a major curing ceremony, and nine for a minor one (three for each cross). They are classed as "medium" or "cold." For further medicinal use cf. **antzil aj, ik'al toj**.

Extended range: *Oreopanax capitatus, Senecio uspantanensis.*

    b. **Tzajal k'os**, "red k'os" (**bakel amuch te', k'ox k'os, muk'ta k'oxox te', piménta te', pimyénta te'**), refers to the common temperate and lowland shrubs *Parathesis chiapensis* (4–7) and *P. leptopa* (1–2). These are glossy-leaved shrubs with clusters of fleshy red or purple, small, round, single-seeded fruits. The leaves are alternate, oblanceolate, obovate or elliptic, acute or acuminate at the apex, attenuate at the base, 6–22 cm long. The flowers are in terminal or axillary panicles. They are pink or white with petals 7–8 mm long. They occur along streams and on moist slopes usually as an element of montane rain or seasonal evergreen forests.

The trunk is used for house posts and fence posts. The leaves are used to mend broken bones.

Extended range: *Colubrina erecta* and *Rhamnus mucronata.*

7. **K'oxox te'**, "toasted tortilla tree," refers to three common highland and temperate trees that have opposite, elliptic, glossy leaves and nodding, fragrant, axillary, white flowers.

Specifics: 2.

    a. **Batz'i k'oxox te'**, "genuine toasted tortilla tree" (**naranja te', tzajal k'oxox te'**), is the very abundant temperate and highland tree *Ternstroemia lineata* ssp. *chalicophila* (7–9), and *T. oocarpa* (2–4), densely-branched, small trees that are often dominant in the understory of evergreen cloud forests or wet oak forests. The leaves are glossy, leathery, oblong-obovate, 7–13 cm long. The flowers are solitary in the leaf axils with five pinkish white petals about 7–10 cm long. The fruit is round and the seeds have bright, red

arils. The wood turns a reddish yellow when cut.

The trunk is used for fence posts and firewood. Just before jumping on a deer's back the Charcoal Cruncher's head was seen feasting on the fruit of this tree (Laughlin, 1980:303). In recent years when the use of pine has been forbidden by the state, the constables have provided a bundle of branches of this tree to decorate the processional path on the fourth Lenten Friday, Wednesday of Holy Week, and Good Friday. It is used in Sak Lum on the fifth Lenten Friday. Two bundles of this tree, of wax myrtle and of **tilil**, are provided by the Junior Stewards of the Holy Cross, and St. Dominic on the Fiesta of the Immaculate Conception, and the same by the Junior Stewards of Our Lady of the Rosary, St. Anthony, and St. Sebastian on the Fiesta of Our Lady of Guadalupe to decorate the old wing of the Church of St. Lawrence. It is used for the processional path in Atz'am on Christmas Eve.

Extended range: *Diospyros nicaraguensis, Drimys granadensis, Ilex vomitoria,* and *Myrcianthes fragrans.*

    b. **Ik'al k'oxox te'**, "black toasted tortilla tree" (**ch'ulul anal k'oxox te', muk'ta k'oxox te'**), is *Cleyera theaeoides* (2–2), a large shrub or small tree with glabrous, alternate, obovate, short-petiolate leaves, 2–15 cm long. The flowers are white or greenish yellow, solitary in the leaf axils with five petals about 5–8 mm long. The fruit is globose about 8 mm in diameter. This is a very common tree of the understory of evergreen cloud and wet oak forest.

The trunk is used for rafters, roof rods, purlins, fence posts, and firewood.

8. **Poxil poslom**, "poslom medicine" (**piménta te', sat vet**), is *Rhamnus mucronata* (1–1). This is a shrub up to 15 feet tall with alternate, narrowly elliptic to narrowly ovate leaves, 3–10 cm long. The flowers are small, greenish, solitary or fasciculate in the leaf axils. The fruit is purple black, subglobose, with 3-cells, about 6–8 mm in diameter. It is a common plant in the understory of the pine-oak forests in the highland and temperate regions.

As a remedy for **poslom** the leaves are brewed together with those of a number of other plants. The tea is "hot."

9. **Tilil** (**-tik**) is the common highland shrub *Rapanea juergensenii* (4–7). It is a dense shrub with alternate obovate, glabrous, leaves, 6–12 cm long. The flowers are small and borne in dense clusters on the old stems. The fruits are small, round, single-seeded berries, 5–6 mm in diameter. It occurs as a dominant in the understory of the evergreen cloud forests. A few Zinacatecs are now transplanting this shrub to their yards.

Recently, when the state government has forbidden the cutting of pine, branches of this shrub have been substituted for cross decoration, especially so in Na Chij where the church stands alongside the Inter-American Highway. One tip is a basic ingredient of "flower water." They are used to adorn a patient's bed. For further medicinal use cf. **ik'al toj**. Prior to 1985 and the paving of the churchyard, a bundle was required to mark the processional path on the fourth Friday of Lent,

182

Wednesday of Holy Week, and Good Friday. These were provided by the constables. These are used similarly in Naben Chauk on the fourth Lenten Friday and in Chak Toj and Naben Chauk on Good Friday. On Holy Saturday, at 5 P.M., those who are in the Church of St. Lawrence beat themselves with these branches together with wax myrtle and elderberry as they shout, "**Kuxan bek'et, kuxan bek'et, tzjam ti' tak'in,**" "Revive flesh, revive flesh, the door to the bell is opening," as the churchbell once again rings. On Holy Cross Day three branches are provided by the Stewards of the Holy Cross to decorate each of 11 crosses. On Independence Day the schoolhouse pillars are decorated with two small bundles provided by men, appointed by the magistrate, who have failed to do their communal labor. The constables provide two small bundles to decorate the courthouse pillars on New Year's. Cf. **batz'i k'oxox te'.** Branches may be used to decorate the graveyard crosses on All Souls' Day.

Extended range: *Cleyera theaeoides, Microtropis contracta, Ternstroemia lineata* ssp. *chalicophila,* and *T. oocarpa.*

10. **Yaxal mol,** "green old man" (**ik'al k'oxox te'**), is the lowland tree *Licania arborea* (4–7). These trees are scattered in lowland areas as a riparian element of tropical deciduous and seasonal evergreen forests and have thick, dark green, broadly oval, 4–11 cm long, and small, hard, round fruits. The flowers are small, white in tight clusters in large terminal or axillary panicles. The fruit is ovoid, 2–3 cm long, and contains one seed. Probably because of the hardness of their wood they are often left undisturbed after clearing of the land. They resemble giant, green sentinels.

The trunk is used for fieldhouse rafters, fence posts, and firewood.

"Toj Set"

The "**toj** set" is a group of four generics that includes all the coniferous trees that occur in the township.

1. **K'isis*** (**saus, savus**) is the bald cypress *Taxodium mucronatum* (4–6), a giant-trunked, often buttressed tree that is common along fast-moving streams in lower temperate and lowland areas. The leaves are thin, soft, deciduous, and 6–12 mm long. The cones are subglobose, brown, 1.5–2.5 cm in diameter. *Ladinos* use the trunk for chests, coffins, doors, boards, tables, and chairs.

2. **Nukul pat***, "leather bark" (**-tik**), is the cypress *Cupressus benthamii* var. *lindleyi* (5–6), a tall tree very commonly cultivated by *ladinos* as a street tree and in yards in the highlands. There are very few natural stands known from rocky ravines in dry highland situations. The leaves are aromatic and scale-like, imbricate and 4-ranked. The cones are globose, 12–15 mm in diameter, with 6–8 peltate cone scales terminated by an elongate pointed projection.

In 1797 the priest of Zinacantán cited *ciprés,* **pinabete** (**tzajal k'uk' toj**), and *"un cedro blanquesino"* (**ch'u te'**) as providing house planks (de Leon y Goicoechea, 1797).

Formerly the belief that cypresses could not be planted by young people limited the cultivation of these trees, but now extensive government reforestation programs are under way in all the highland hamlets. To prevent the planter from dying, the tops were snipped off the young trees.

The trunk is used for house mainposts, rafters, doors, jail doors (formerly), lintels, balcony railings, courthouse posts (formerly), chests, coffers, coffins, chairs, tables, benches, **metate** platforms, shelves, lecterns, harp handles, and bell stocks. It is also used for gates, fence posts, corn bin posts, sheep corral posts, graveyard crosses, crosses at the entrances to the churches, telephone and electricity posts (formerly), staves of the stewards-royal and the publicans. When used for firewood it may speed recovery from sickness.

The branches are used to enclose the walls of the creche. They are sold in Tuxtla for decoration. Chamulans sell them in San Cristóbal. Zinacantecs may resell them in Tuxtla. Cf. **ixim.**

3. **Ok'il te'***, "coyote tree" (**-tik**) (**sipres**), refers to the junipers *Juniperus comitana* (1–1) and *J. gamboana* (1–1), a tree often occurring in dense, pure stands in flat areas with poor soil in the highlands. They are aromatic with small scale-like leaves in whorls of four and with a fleshy berry-like fruit with a strong resinous odor.

A few Zinacantecs plant junipers in their yards and in fencerows in the rainy season but, as with cypress, measures were taken to prevent the planter from dying.

The trunk is used for house mainposts, rafters, roof rods, purlins, chairs, tables, gates, doors, warping bars, corn bins, steambaths, and crosses. It is used for boards and is split to make fence posts. Some claim that juniper should not be used for house posts because it "bites" and the children will fall sick and die. *Ladinos* use the wood occasionally for incense. Chamulans sell the branches to *ladinos* in San Cristóbal who use them for altar and grave decorations. Zinacantecs may resell them in Tuxtla. Zinacantecs may also use them for grave decoration on All Souls' Day. The juniper is used for the creche framework in Atz'am, Chak Toj, San Mikulax, and Sek'emtik. For the shamans' three annual ceremonies it is used to decorate the cross and doors of the Chapel of Our Lord of Esquipulas. Cf. **ixim.** They are widely used to decorate hamlet creches.

4. **Toj*** (**-tik, -altik**) is the generic for pines.

The vain effort of the Zinacantecs to have a dancing pine tree divert an army of invading soldiers is described frequently. It was credited by one to have occurred in the Mexican Revolution (Laughlin, 1977, T17, T56). The native classification of the pines is very complicated, with three separate systems, based on bark, needles, and fruit, superimposed on the specifics. Individual trees may be classified according to the following characteristics:

bark color	**ik'al pat,** "black bark," or **tzajal pat,** "red bark"
bark thickness	**jayal pat,** "thin-barked," or **pimil pat,** "thick-barked"
foliage density	**jich'il anal,** "narrow-leaved," or **pimil**

	anal and yijil anal, "thick-leaved"
cone size	muk'ta ajan, "large ear of corn," or
	kelem ajan, "boy ear of corn"

Red, thin bark and thin foliage is associated together, as is black, thick bark and dense foliage. The wood of the former is preferred for being denser, with fewer knots that are scattered randomly, not in tiers, and so stronger, permitting the use of more slender trunks. The latter is preferred for ceremonial decoration. Large-coned trees are restricted to *Pinus michoacana* and *P. oaxacana* and have specific ceremonial uses. They have long needles, five in a bunch.

The trunk is used for house mainposts, wall poles of wooden houses, rafters, A-frame bars, roof rods, lintels, doors, shelves, planks (for attics, corn bins and beds), benches, chairs, log stools, tables, chests, coffers, coffins, lamp stands, hooks, *metate* platforms, warping bars, gates, crosses, *almud* measures, adobe molds, spoons, fence posts, and firewood. Pine tops are used in the flower changes of all chapels except in Chak Toj. The usual pattern is three for the cross in front of the church, two for the church doorway, three for the cross in front of the official's house, and two flanking his alter. In Na Chij, because of the proximity of the highway and a former governmental ban on the use of pine, the chuch and cross is decorated with **tilil**. In Sek'emtik 22 pines are provided to adorn the church and six crosses. One "thin-leaved" pine tree is provided by the senior stewards and another by the junior stewards to flank the cross on the night of Maundy Thursday. In Sak Lum six trees are provided on the fifth Lenten Friday and in Naben Chauk two are used to flank the cross on Good Friday. One pine tree is provided by the grand Spanish lord and one by the petty Spanish lord on the Fiesta of St. Sebastian for the jousting frame. Eighteen poles are provided by each of the Stewards of Our Lady of the Rosary on the eighth *Posada* to form the frame of the creche. These are selected by the Stewards of the Holy Cross. Four boughs are taken by the stewards to Atz'am on the Fiesta of Our Lady of the Rosary. They are also used to flank the creche in Apas, Atz'am, Na Chij, Paste', Sak Lum, and Sek'emtik.

In ritual speech, candles are referred to as **j-sil yo jtoj, j-sil yo jkantela**, a splinter of my lowly torch, a shaving of my humble candle (the person marker may vary).

The poverty of Zinacantán relative to San Cristóbal today is traced to the departure of the Indian king when the *ladinos* strew pine needles at his feet, while the Zinacantecs scattered coins (Laughlin, 1977, T11).

As an antidote for a black widow spider bite, 13 splinters are boiled, providing a "hot" tea.

To mend a bone break, pine resin may be used together with castor bean leaves or a plaster. Three tips of "ear of corn" or "thick-leaved" pine are a basic ingredient of "flower water." They are classed variously as "medium" and "hot." Twenty-four boughs are required for a curing ceremony, two to flank the entrance to the patient's bed. One tip may be used to beat a horse suffering "wind." Three tips of "thick-leaved" pine are needed for the wand used by a shaman to beat the earth when recalling a lost soul. Pine boughs are used to decorate all the crosses visited during a curing ceremony, on Holy Cross Day, and during the annual renewal ceremonies three tips are placed at the back of the enclosure for the sacrificial chicken. At each major fiesta the house cross is decorated with three pine tips. The grave cross is so decorated at the funeral and on All Souls' Day. When a new house is inaugurated, three tips decorated with geraniums are planted diagonally in each corner of the house before the soup offering. For each flower change the senior steward provides two boughs of "thin-leaved pine" to decorate the house altar and 19 boughs of "thick-leaved pine" to decorate the house altar and 19 boughs of "thick-leaved pine" to decorate the crosses.

Pine needles have a wide variety of uses, both secular and sacred. To speed the ripening of fruits that are to be resold, such as avocadoes, mangoes, black sapotes, mamey sapotes, the fruits are buried in pine needles. Dry pine needles are mixed with the mud used for daub and adobe walls. They are spread over the wood that is to be made into charcoal. When pine needles are handy they may be scooped up from in front of the household altar and used to scrub the dirty dishes after a meal. They may be slipped between firewood and a person's back to prevent chafing. Children at play may braid the needles into long strings. A single needle is used to tie three candles together when they are offered at the shrines or the house cross. At a major curing ceremony, after the shaman bathes and bleeds the sacrificial chicken, he places it, still alive, on a plate or half gourd covered with pine needles. He may also cover the chicken with pine needles before wrapping it in a cloth to take to Kalvaryo. Fresh pine needles are strewn on the floors of patients' and religious officials' houses, formerly on the major church floors, on a fresh grave, and on all household altars and graves on All Souls' Day. The senior steward in charge of a flower change provides one net for his house. Each of the stewards in charge formerly provided one bagful for the church, whereas the others provided two small baskets. Both Stewards of the Holy Cross formerly provided a bag for Maundy Thursday, but now they share a small bag between them. They also furnish two bunches for Holy Cross Day to decorate each of 11 crosses. All stewards provide a bag for the creche on New Year's Day. Each of the Stewards of the Sacrament, the Holy Cross, and St. Dominic provide a bag of pine needles on the Fiesta of the Immaculate Conception. Each of the Stewards of Our Lady of the Rosary, formerly St. Anthony and St. Sebastian, provide a bagful for the Fiesta of Our Lady of Guadalupe. Pine needles are still used to decorate the Chapel of Our Lord of Esquipulas every other week. They are also used to carpet the churches in Apas, Atz'am, Chak Toj, Kelem Ton, Muk'ta Jok', Sek'emtik. Some say the Charcoal Cruncher feasted on pine seeds before landing on the deer's back (Laughlin, 1977, T60).

For further uses of pine cf. **ixim, muk'ta kachu toro te', kururin, mantzanilya, mes te', tilil,** and **batz'i turasnu.**

184

Specifics: 6.

  a. **Ajan toj**, "ear of corn pine," is *Pinus michoacana* (2–3), another large pine with very large cones, 25–30 cm long, that occurs on knolls and rock outcrops in the mixed pine-oak forests of temperate and highland areas. It has five needles in a bunch, 30–35 cm long.

The tips of this pine are preferred for "flower water."
For use cf. **antzil aj, ik'al toj**.

  b. **Batz'i toj**, "genuine pine," is *Pinus montezumae* var. *rudis* (1–2), a 5-needled, yellow pine common in mixed pine-oak forests of temperate and highland hamlets. The needles are about 14–21 cm long. The cone is ovoid, about 8.5–15 cm long.

  c. **Chak-toj**, "red pine," is *Pinus pseudostrobus* (3–3), a common yellow pine in highland and upper temperate hamlets. It occurs in mixed forests with other pines, oaks, and madrones.

  d. **Ik'al toj**, "black pine," is *Pinus oaxacana* (6–5), a large pine with big cones and coarse needles, 30 cm long. It occurs in the mixed pine-oak forests with *P. pseudostrobus*.

Our Lord made three bunches of "flowers": **ajan toj, ik'al toj**, laurel, **krus ech'**, and **tilil** or **k'os**, saying, "These are your flowers for curing."

Three tips are a basic ingredient of "flower water," though only one is used for bathing newborn babies. Three tips are also used in a curing ceremony to shield the candles at each of the three churches, at each of the mountain shrines, and before the house cross.

  e. **K'uk' toj***, "feather pine," refers to firs and white pines.

    (1) **Sakil k'uk' toj**, "white feather pine" (**cha'-lamal yanal toj, romero**), is the fir *Abies guatemalensis* (2–3), at present a very rare tree occurring only in San Cristóbal and in one steep-walled canyon in Zinacantán. It is a large tree with leaves appearing 2-ranked, 1–4.5 cm long, dark, lustrous, green above, silvery beneath. The cones are 8.5–11.5 cm long, 4.5–5 cm in diameter, erect with broadly rounded, closely imbricated cone scales, which fall from the axis at maturity.

    (2) **Tzajal k'uk' toj**, "red feather pine," is the white pine *Pinus ayacahuite* (3–4), a very tall pine of steep rocky slopes in the highlands. It has large, thin-scaled cones, 20–30 cm long, and five needles in a bunch, 8–15 cm long.

In everyday speech the descriptive **tzajal**, "red, is dropped as **k'uk' toj** generally refers to this species.

The wood is used for musical instruments, warping bars, crosses, and doors, and by *ladinos* for shingles. For the seventh *Posada* the Stewards of Our Lady of the Rosary provide two trees to flank the creche. One tree is also provided by the other senior stewards, and the fourth by the other junior stewards. These trees are also used to decorate the creche in Apas and Naben Chauk, cf. **nukul pat**.

  f. **Tzajal toj**, "red pine," refers to *Pinus oocarpa* (4–3) and *P. teocote* (1–1).

These are particularly resinous pines whose roots and trunk are made into torches. They have three or five needles in a bunch about 17–30 cm long, and cones 5.5–9 cm long. Chamulans sell fat pine slivers at market. Formerly, Zinacantecs bartered fat pine in the Chamula market for potatoes, cabbages, tomatoes, and corn on the cob. An ensign-bearer entering office presents six slivers to the corresponding musician. The cantors and judge ordinary give three splinters to each of the musicians and to father spook. For a loose tooth a "hot" tea is brewed of 13 splinters of this pine and 13 splinters of **tzajal tulan**. Cf. also **xchenek' tzajal om**.

"Ton Bek' Set"

The "**ton bek' set**" is a grouping of two cultivated trees. **Ton bek'** and **presa** have similar pinnately divided leaves.

1. **Presa**, "planted tree" (**fresno, tz'unbalal te'**), is the common street tree *Fraxinus uhdei* (3–4). It is a large tree to 30 m tall with pinnate leaves. The leaflets are ovate or narrowly ovate, 5.5–15 cm long. The flowers and fruits are borne in axillary panicles. The fruit is a samara with a narrow linear wing 3–3.5 cm long. This was introduced into Zinacantán in the 1940s when the state government claimed that the people had started a forest fire, provided them with plants, and told them to plant these trees the whole length of the Pan American highway that transverses the township. The reluctant Zinacantecs were assured that the trees would provide walnuts! A few persist in the upper temperate hamlets.

2. **Ton bek'***, "hard seed" or "rock seed" (**nuez***), is the walnut *Juglans regia* (5–7), a large, hard-wood tree rarely cultivated in the highlands. The leaves are pinnate with 5–9 leaflets that are ovate, glabrous, and have entire margins. The fruit is subglobose, 4–5 cm in diameter. There are a few very rare species of wild walnuts for which this name might once have applied. The cultivated walnut is most common in Larraínzar.

In 1797 the priest of Zinacantán rated the walnut as the fourth most abundant tree planted in the yards. "The root of the walnut is used successfully for the black die in painting. Charcoal from its branches is used for drawing. Its fruit is one of the most marketable in the Indies. Except here they scarcely occur for many leagues. They pick them in season. And although they could be sold at the end of the dog-days or in September, they are not sold for a year, when they are better. There is a wild walnut that has a very small nut" (de Leon y Goicoechea, 1797). We made a concerted effort to locate *Alfaroa* and *Oreomunea*, the wild walnuts, in or near Zinacantán. At present the nearest populations are in the townships of Jitotol and Berriozabal.

A very few Zinacantecs in Zinacantán Center plant walnut

slips in their yards in the rainy season.

A "hot" tea of walnut leaves is taken for menstrual failure. The nuts are sold at a high price by *ladinos* at market in August. They are "cold." The meat of a walnut should not be shared lest lightning strike.

"Top'ol Set"

The "top'ol set" includes five generics, all shrubby composites with broad pubescent leaves and white or yellow flowers arranged in terminal clusters of heads.

1. **Jom akan**, "hollow stem" (**bak te'**, **pom akan**), is *Piptothrix areolaris* (3–4), a common shrub in the understory of the dry pine-oak forests of highland and temperate regions. It has soft, pubescent opposite, ovate leaves, 6–13 cm long, and white flowers about 7 mm long in conical, terminal clusters.

It is associated with unproductive land.

The trunk is used for firewood. It is eaten by sheep.

Extended range: *Euphorbia heterophylla*.

2. **K'an-'ich**, "yellow chili" (**-tik**), refers to sprawling, thin-branched shrubs with small, yellow flowers.

Specifics: 2.

  a. **Batz'i k'an-'ich**, "genuine yellow chili," is *Coreopsis mutica* var. *microcephala* (7–13), a sprawling, soft-wooded shrub with bright yellow daisy flowers with rays about 1.5 cm long. They are arranged in terminal branched inflorescences. The leaves are opposite, petiolate, elliptic to narrowly ovate, glabrous, 5–13 cm long. It is a common element of second growth formations of the highland area.

The presence of this shrub is said to signal fertile soil, good for planting corn. The trunk is used for shuttles and firewood.

Extended range: *Bunchosia montana*, *Piptothrix areolaris*, *Salmea scandens*, *Senecio chenopodioides*, *Verbesina crocata*, and *V. neriifolia*.

  b. **K'ox k'an-'ich**, "small yellow chili" (**chak'ak' tz'i'lel**, **poxil chin**), is *Perymenium ghiesbreghtii* (2–4), a small shrub with many small, yellow daisy flowers about 10–15 mm broad. The leaves are opposite narrowly elliptic to lanceolate, serrulate, strongly veined below, 3–12 cm long, rough to the touch above and below. It occurs in the understory of pine-oak forests and in second growth in highland and temperate hamlets. It is classed as a "plant."

As a remedy for skin disease (**chin**), three or four stalks are ground, mixed with lime juice and soot, and the "hot" infusion applied to the affected part.

3. **Nam-te' mol**, "elder's walking stick" (**k'anal potzan te'**, **sak-paran te'** in part), refers to *Verbesina hypsela* (3–9), *V. perymenioides* (1–1), *V. punctata* (1–2), *V. steyermarkii* (1–4), and *V. turbascensis* (4–7). These are soft-stemmed shrubs with large, pinnately lobed leaves and terminal clusters of white or yellow flowers, common in second growth throughout the township.

The trunk of *V. hypsela* is used for house walls and wattle. It is eaten by sheep, horses and cattle.

Extended range: *Verbesina crocata*.

4. **Top'ol** (**-tik**) refers to two yellow-flowered shrubs. Specifics: 2.

  a. **K'anal top'ol**, "yellow **top'ol**" (**muk'ta top'ol**, **petet**, **petet te'**, **te'el petet**, **tok'ol**, **top'ol te'**), is *Perymenium grande* var. *nelsonii* (8–11), a large shrub or small tree with terminal groupings of large, yellow, daisy-like inflorescences. The ray flowers are 8–13 mm long. The wood is hard. The leaves are toothed opposite, broadly ovate, rounded to subcordate at the base and coarsely pubescent, 6–14 cm long. The plant is very common in the shrubby second growth formations of temperate regions and along ravines in pine-oak and tropical deciduous forests.

The heartwood is used for spindles. The weaver selects the particular tree, which is dressed by her husband. The trunk is used for house mainposts, wattle, corn bin posts, fence and corral posts, and firewood. The branches are used for brush fences.

  b. **K'ox top'ol**, "small **top'ol**" (**tan-mukan tz'i'lel**), is *Lasianthaea fruticosa* (4–5), a shrub with terminal and axillary groups of yellow daisy flowers about 1–2 cm broad and coarsely pubescent opposite, lanceolate to ovate leaves, 3–20 cm long. It is a common plant in the shrubby second growth formations of highland and temperate areas. This shrub is classed variously as "plant" and "tree."

It is associated with unproductive land.

The trunk is used for fence posts and firewood.

5. **Xolom** (**-tik**) is *Vernonia leiocarpa* (4–6), a soft-wooded shrub with alternate velvety, gray, pubescent ovate to lanceolate leaves, 7–14 cm long, and terminal clusters of leafy inflorescences. The flowers are small, 4–5 mm high, and lavender to white. When in fruit the seeds are topped with hairs covered in fuzz. This is a very common element in the shrubby second growth formations of the temperate regions.

It is associated with unproductive land.

The trunk is used for firewood.

Extended range: *Perymenium grande* var. *nelsonii*.

"Tulan Set"

The "tulan set" is a diverse grouping of 12 generics including all of the oaks, four trees with catkin-like inflorescences, and three other trees having leaves similar to one or another of the oaks.

1. **Batz'i te'**, "genuine tree" (**boch jay te'**), is the black oak *Quercus crassifolia* (7–6), which has thick, large, ovate leaves with spine-tipped dentations, which are velvety rusty pubescent on the undersurface. It is a dominant in the highland pine-oak forests.

The trunk is used for roof rods, tamale platforms, and scarlet runner bean poles. It may be used for warping bars, but tends to crack. The trunk may also be used for corral posts, but, because it has no heartwood, rots quickly. The ease with which the wood of this oak may be split makes it the most highly esteemed for firewood, though it does not provide so hot a coal as other oaks. The leaf may be used to scoop up water to drink. The branches are used for brush fences. Mules eat the leaves. An entering ensign-bearer presents two bundles of 40 logs apiece to the corresponding musician. The cantor and judge ordinary give one bundle apiece to each musician and to Sir Spook.

2. **Chikin-ib***, "armadillo ear" (**-tik**), refers to the small, narrow-leaved oak species.

Specifics: 3.

  a. **Batz'i chikin-ib**, "genuine armadillo ear" (**ik'al chi-kin- ib, ik'al pat chikin-ib, pimil anal chikin-ib, pimil pat chikin- ib**), refers to *Quercus castanea* (2–4), *Q. crispipilis* (6–9), and *Q. oleoides* (1–2). These have elliptic leaves 3–6 cm long, with dense pubescence on the undersurface. *Quercus crispipilis* is a common element of the dry pine-oak forests of the highland and temperate areas. *Quercus oleoides* occurs in lowland savannas.

The trunk is split and used for barrel staves and corral posts. The trunk is used for ax and pick handles. The hamlet of Naben Chauk formerly had the responsibility of providing planks for the repair of bridges in Zinacantán Center. The trunk is used for firewood. The wood is reputed to make the best charcoal because it does not crumble. The branches are used in brush fences.

  b. **Jayal pat chikin-ib**, "thin-barked armadillo ear" (**jich'il anal chikin-ib**), is *Quercus laurina* (5–8). This tree has very small (2–4 cm) lanceolate-elliptic leaves that are entirely glabrous and irregularly toothed. The tree is common in the highland pine-oak forests and evergreen cloud forests.

For use cf. **batz'i chikin-ib**.

  c. **Sakil chikin-ib**, "white armadillo ear" (**ch'ulul anal chikin-ib, muk'ta chikin-ib**), refers to the temperate *Quercus elliptica* (5–6) and *Q. sapotifolia* (2–4). These have leaves a little larger than the other types of **chikin-ib** (4–8 cm long). They may be densely pubescent (*ellipticas*) or totally glabrous (*sapotifolias*) on the undersurface of the leaves. They occur in pine savannas in the temperate regions.

It is used for firewood.

3. **Kachu toro te'**, "bull horn tree," refers to two lowland trees with large, thin leaves prominently clustered on the ends of the branches.

Specifics: 2.

  a. **Muk'ta kachu toro te'**, "large bull horn tree" (**tulan te', tzajal kachu toro te'**), is *Bucida macrostachya* (5–13), a large tree of the tropical deciduous forests. It has small flowers and fruits in catkin-like racemes

borne on the tips of the branches amongst the clusters of leaves. The leaves are glabrous or pubescent, obovate or elliptic, 12–25 cm long. The inflorescence is pubescent as are the small ovoid, sessile fruits. It often occurs in almost pure stands along small streams.

The red heartwood is used by *ladinos* for house mainposts and cattle corral posts. *Ladinos* and Zinacantecs use it for fence posts, but the wood is extremely difficult to cut. The bark was once sold in San Cristóbal for lashing.

For a stomach ache remedy, chips of the wood are brewed together with the heartwood of **batz'i tulan**, the root of **kururin** or the trunk of **vako' ak'**, and splinters of **tzajal toj**. A shot of strong cane liquor is added to the "hot" tea and a glassful is drunk before breakfast. No shaman is needed, but the patient should not drink cold water nor wash with cold water during the day. This remedy should only be taken if the symptoms are mild, otherwise it would be fatal.

  b. **Yaxal kachu toro te'**, "green bull horn tree" (**máchita te', sakil kachu toro te', xulub vakax**), is *Godmania aesculifolia* (4–7), a tree with palmately divided leaves, small, maroon, short tubular flowers, and long (20–30 cm), narrow, ribbed pendulous pods. It is a common element in the tropical deciduous forest.

The trunk is used for fence posts and firewood.

4. **Kampor** (**-tik**) refers to the gums *Eucalyptus camaldulensis* (1–2) and *E. globulus* (1–2), tall, straight, smooth, peely-barked, cultivated trees at scattered localities throughout the state. The leaves are alternate, narrow, lanceolate, sometimes curved, 7–21 cm long. The flowers are solitary and large or small and in clusters. They have no petals but numerous colorful stamens, exerted from a rigid cup-like base. It was planted extensively by *ladinos,* and now is common near ranchos and small towns throughout temperate and lowland areas (*E. camaldulensis; E. globulus* only is cultivated in highland areas near San Cristóbal and Zinacantán.) The leaves and fruit are used by *ladinos* in sweat baths. They also brew a handful of leaves for "hot" tea when suffering from the common cold. During childbirth a woman may drink cane liquor seasoned with camphor. Her stomach may be rubbed with camphor ointment.

As a remedy for "wind," a "very hot" tea of the leaves or fruit is taken. To relieve a tired and aching body, a eucalyptus bath may be taken at bedtime. The fruits may be strung on a necklace and worn as a preventative for whooping cough. For fright the leaves and fruit may be placed in a bag and hung around the neck at bedtime. For further medicinal uses cf. **mantzanilya.**

5. **Nok** (**-tik**) (**xnok**) is the alder. Alders have ovate-elliptic leaves, and flowers in catkins. The female inflorescence produces a cone-like fruit. The bark is gray and smooth, the inner bark is bright red-orange.

Specifics: 2.

  a. **Sakil nok**, "white alder," is *Alnus acuminata* ssp. *arguta* (2–2), a tree similar to **tzajal nok** but lacking the red hairs on the undersurface of the leaves. It occurs on the moist, high ridges in evergreen cloud forest. It has the same uses as **tzajal nok**, though it grows too far from the Church of St. Sebastian to be selected for the jaguar tree.

   b. **Tzajal nok**, "red alder" (**ik'al nok**), is the common alder *Alnus jorullensis* (2–6), which occurs along streams and in wet places throughout the highland and upper temperate regions. It is characterized by red-orange pubescence on the lower surface of the leaves. Zinacantecs remark on its rapid growth.

The trunk is used for roof purlins, roof rods, rafters, wattle, and steambath rafters. Now that nails have largely replaced vines in house construction, the ease with which nails can be driven into the soft wood has made it more popular. Care must be taken, though, not to leave the dressed logs exposed to the elements before construction, lest they weaken and break (as occurred at one house inauguration ceremony). The trunk is also used for firewood.

For the Fiesta of St. Sebastian the jaguar and spook entertainers must provide an alder for the jaguar tree. The abundance of branches, permitting easy climbing, is given as a reason for selecting the alder. Before the tree is felled, they beg its pardon so that it will not splinter when it falls. The ends of the branches are lopped off, leaving the basal parts for climbing. The heavy trunk is borne on poles by some 20 assistants to the churchyard where they scrape off the outer bark so that the tree takes on a bright orange appearance. The jaguar players boil a handful of the bark to dye their costumes. Chamulans use the bark to dye hides yellow when making leather chin straps and sashes. The inner bark is pounded and placed above and below the hides, in a large pot, and covered with cold water. It is left to stand for 10 days. Then the tree is cut down and the stump left until the next year.

A "cold" tea of three alder flowers or cones is taken once to induce an abortion.

6. **Paj-'ul**, "sour corn gruel," refers to sumac shrubs with large, pinnately decompound leaves. The wood is dark red when dry. The flowers are small and arranged in long panicles. They have single-seeded fruits with a thin pulp and a thick, sticky surface with a sour lemon flavor.

Specifics: 3.

   a. **K'ox paj-'ul**, "small sour corn gruel" (**paj-'ul ak'**, **poxil eal**), is *Rhus terebinthifolia* (13–15), a laxly branched, sprawling shrub common in the understory of open pine-oak forests. The leaflets are small and thin, elliptic to lanceolate, 2–6 cm long. The flowers are small, white, in terminal panicles. The fruit is round, red, and about 6 mm in diameter, pubescent and glandular. It is classed variously as "vine" and "tree."

The wood is used for drum collars.

As a remedy for fever sores a few of the berries are chewed. For further medicinal use cf. **matal ak'**.

   b. **Muk'ta paj-'ul**, "large sour corn gruel," is *Rhus schiedeana* (12–15), a dense shrub common in the shrubby second growth formations of dry highland and temperate slopes. The leaves are pinnate. The leaflets are thick and glossy above, elliptic to ovate, 3–8 cm long. The flowers are white, about 7 mm broad, in axillary panicles shorter than the leaves. The fruit is red, round, about 8 mm or less in diameter, and pubescent.

The trunk is used for house mainposts, gate posts, fence posts, pack rope cleats, digging sticks, hoe and billhook handles, and mortarmen's mallets. The wood is so durable that in one instance the same house posts were used by three generations. As a remedy for fever sores the "cold" leaves may be chewed.

The "cold" fruit is eaten by birds and by people when they are feeling hot. The fruit may be mixed with water and sugar added to provide a refreshing drink.

   c. **Tzajal paj-'ul**, "red sour corn gruel," is *Pistacia mexicana* (1–1), a shrub or small tree to 5 m tall with reddish pinnate leaves, with many elliptic leaflets, 1–2 cm long. The flowers are very small, reddish, and in lateral panicles. The fruit is small, rounded, 3–4 mm long, and very pungent when crushed. It is a very common element of dry pine-oak and tropical deciduous forests of temperate and lowland hamlets.

7. **Sap yok**, "sap its trunk" (**-tik**), is *Quercus candicans* (4–6), a totally unique oak with large, thin, obovate leaves that are strongly bicolored, dark green above, white tomentose beneath. It occurs in the highland pine-oak forest and in the evergreen cloud forest, but because of deforestation has become very scarce.

The trunk is used for chayote and popapple arbors and for fence posts. It splits easily for firewood.

The leaves are used to wrap tamales (**pisil vaj**). They are needed for this purpose every Saturday by the stewards royal and by the stewards for their office change.

8. **Tempix** (**tempich**) refers to the temperate and lowland wet forest tree *Dendropanax arboreus* (1–4). The wood is soft and white. It has leathery, lustrous, glabrous leaves, 8–15 cm long, simple or compound. The flowers are in umbels. The fruit is a fleshy, round, purple berry. It occurs as an epiphytic tree or free standing on steep rocky slopes in dense montane rain forest and occasionally in seasonal evergreen forest.

The trunk is used for fieldhouse mainposts, fence posts, cattle corrals, and firewood. The *ladinos* of Chiapa de Corzo and Acala use the boughs for altar decorations.

Extended range: *Trichilia hirta*.

9. **Tulan*** (**-tik**) is a complicated generic that refers to all of the broad-leaved white oaks.

It is said that jays planted all the oaks with acorns, but no one knows where they got the acorns.

In recent years the state government has encouraged Zinacantecs to aid in reforestation by planting acorns with a digging stick.

188

The branches of all oak trees are used for brush fences. Branches are provided on the Fiesta of St. Sebastian by the stewards royal to make their hut, by the grand alcalde for the banquet arbor, and by the grand Spanish lord for the jousting runway.

Children should not play with the acorns of any oak lest they become mute.

Specifics: 4.

a. **K'an-tulan**, "yellow **tulan**" (**ik'al tulan, k'anal tulan, sakil k'evex tulan**), refers to *Quercus segoviensis* (12–10). These oaks have thinner leaves with sparser pubescence on the undersurface than those delimited by **sakil** and **tzajal tulan**. The size and shape of the leaves are the same and the configuration of the trees are the same. This oak occurs in pine-oak associations in temperate and even some lowland situations.

In 1797 the priest of Zinacantán mentions **cantulan** as one of the trees that provided "very strong and incorruptible wood" (de Leon y Goicoechea, 1797).

The trunk is used for house mainposts, fence posts, and for firewood.

Extended range: *Quercus peduncularis* and *Q. rugosa*.

b. **K'evex tulan**, "cherimoya **tulan**," refers to *Q. polymorpha* (4–4), oaks with large (10–15 cm long), ovate-elliptic, dull, pea green leaves. This oak occurs in dry, steep, canyons in the temperate areas.

The trunk is used for house mainposts, for fence posts, and for firewood. It is favored for mainposts as nearly the whole trunk is heartwood.

Extended range: *Quercus peduncularis* and *Q. segoviensis*.

c. **Sakil tulan**, "white **tulan**" (**batz'i tulan** of temperate hamlets), is the common temperate and highland oak *Q. peduncularis* (10–12), a spreading tree with thick trunks and flat, obovate, coarsely toothed leaves up to 25 cm long, which are loosely white pubescent beneath.

The trunk is used for house mainposts and for firewood.

Extended range: *Quercus rugosa, Q. segoviensis*.

d. **Tzajal tulan**, "red **tulan**" (**batz'i tulan** of highland hamlets, **jayal pat tulan, muk'ta tulan**), refers to *Q. rugosa* (14–6). These oaks have large (15–20 cm long), thick, cupped, ovate leaves with dense, glandular pubescence on the undersurface and impressed veins above. The trees are large with massive trunks and occur in mixed forests of pine and oak throughout the drier portions of the highlands. Highland Zinacantecs say that the color distinction, **tzajal**, "red," and **sakil**, "white," refer to the heartwood; others distinguish **tzajal tulan** by noting the red leaves at the growing tips of young trees, and the thick bark of old trees. **Tzajal tulan** is known to "get angry," "scold," and spark badly.

The acorns are eaten by deer, goats, squirrels, jays, and bandtailed pigeons.

The trunk is a favorite for house mainposts. It is also used for roof rods, purlins, corral posts, fence posts, telephone poles, vertical wattle poles, household altars, steambaths, corn bin planks, bridge planks, stiles, gates, bedposts, tamale platforms, stirring rods, pot stands, hooks, axe handles, mortarmen's mallets, and firewood. The crooked grain of this wood, however, often makes it very difficult to split for firewood. A "hot" tea of the bark is taken as a remedy for loose teeth, swelling, and malaria.

The tips are used for the "steam cure." Together with pine tips and marigolds they are used by shamans for beating out "wind." The shaman uses three tips when recalling a lost soul. For further medicinal uses cf. **ixim, muk'ta kachu toro te', matal ak', tzajal toj**. The leaf may be used to scoop up water to drink.

Extended range: *Quercus peduncularis*.

10. **Tz'otz'op** (-**tik**) is *Quercus acutifolia* (4–6), an oak with large, glabrous, elliptic leaves (10–15) cm long), with spine-tipped dentate margins. It occurs in extensive stands with pine in temperate and lowland poor soil areas.

It is used for fence posts. It is easy to split for firewood.

11. **Tz'utuj te'**, "corn tassel tree," refers to American hornbeam *Carpinus caroliniana* (2–3) and the hop hornbeam *Ostrya virginiana* var. *guatemalensis* (6–8), a small or medium-sized tree common in canyon and north slope situations of temperate and highland areas in association with pine-oak forests and evergreen cloud forests. The flowers are in catkins and the fruit is pendulous, each seed covered with a papery bract. They resemble young corn tassels. The leaves are elliptic and serrate.

The trunk is used for crossbeams, rafters, roof purlins, roof rods, and mainposts. The trunk is also used for hoe handles, digging sticks, and firewood.

Extended range: *Cornus disciflora*.

12. **Tz'utuj te' te'**, "corn tassel tree tree," is the elm *Ulmus mexicana* (1–1). It is an immense, buttressed tree up to 50 m tall, with gray, somewhat scaly bark very similar to those of *Ostrya* and *Carpinus*. The leaves are deciduous, oblong-ovate, serrate, 6–9 cm long. The flowers are small and yellow. The fruits are about 5 mm long with a fringe of long white hairs around the margin.

This is a canopy tree of montane rain forests in steep canyons in the temperate regions, but it no longer occurs in Zinacantán.

"Turasnu Set"

The "turasnu set" includes three generics referring to peaches, apricots and plums.

1. **Prixku'** is the freestone peach *Prunus persica,* having soft flesh that separates freely from the stone. It is grown in Jok' Ch'enom, Petz Toj, Sak Lum, and all of the highland communities. It has the same medicinal uses as **turasnu**.

Specifics: 2.

a. **K'anal prixku'**, "yellow peach," is the yellow-fleshed form. The fruits are sold at market in late July and August. They are classed variously as "hot" and "cold." For use cf. **batz'i turasnu**.

b. **Sakil prixku'**, "white peach," is the white-fleshed form. The fruit ripens in late July and August. It is classed as "cold." For use cf. **batz'i turasnu**.

2. **Sirvela** (-**tik**) is the plum *Prunus domestica* (4–4). It is grown in all of the highland communities. Plum pits are planted and seedlings are transplanted in the rainy season and occasionally in the dry season (if watered). Slips may be grafted on peach trees in December through March. If transplanted, plums fruit in four years, but if grafted, in two years. The "cold" fruit is sold at market in May and June.

Specifics: 4.

a. **Ik''ik'-lo'an sirvela**, "purple plum," is a purple-fruited plum grown by a few Zinacantecs.

b. **K'anal sirvela**, "yellow plum," is a yellow-fruited plum grown by a few Zinacantecs.

c. **Sakil sirvela**, "white plum," is a greenish white plum grown by many Zinacantecs.

d. **Tzajal sirvela**, "red plum," is a red-fruited plum grown by many Zinacantecs. A small, **bik'it** form and a large, **muk'ta** form are recognized.

3. **Turasnu** (-**tik**, -**altik**) (**durasnos***, **turasno**, **turesno**, **turesnu**, **turisnu**) refers to cling peaches and apricots.

In 1797 the priest of Zinacantán rated the peach tree as the second commonest yard tree. "There are large and small peaches, white and yellow. They are so abundant that at the very least they pick 2 million fruits annually in the town " (de Leon y Goicoechea, 1797).

Specifics: 5.

a. **Batz'i turasnu**, "genuine **turasnu**" (**batz'i sakil turasnu**), is a small peach (*Prunus persica*) with firm (when ripe) white or greenish flesh. It is grown in a few temperate and all highland communities. This peach, formerly ubiquitous in highland hamlet yards, is being replaced through grafting by newer varieties. Although it also occurs in temperate hamlets it produces few fruits in that environment. Pits are planted, one to a hole, and young plants are transplanted, primarily in the rainy season. St. Rose Day (August 29) is considered particularly auspicious. They may also be planted in the dry season, if watered for the first week. Their fruits are said to be sweeter. Sometimes seed beds are prepared for them. Zinacantecs who provide their seedlings with compost and/or sheep manure claim that they will fruit in one year rather than taking the usual three years. Trees that do not fruit well may be slashed or "fed" horse or cow bones. Peach trees that are planted outside one's yard are often stripped by marauding kids of all their peaches before they have ripened. This will cause the tree to produce inedible fruits that exude sap. Bats are known to feed on

peaches. To cause an enemy's peach tree to die a stick of pine is buried at its foot.

Living trees serve as supports for scarlet runner beans and pole beans. The trunk is used for bean poles, fence posts, and firewood. Peach switches are most commonly used to punish disobedient children and runaway sheep. The branches are used for brush fences. The sap may be eaten. As a remedy for worms, a handful of leaves and a few chips of bark are brewed with a handful of brown sugar. A cup of this "medium" or "hot" tea is drunk before breakfast for one or two days. When a year- or year-and-a-half-old baby cries constantly and hits its mother frequently, it may be forced to down a cup of cold water in which a handful of tips have been crushed. The bitter brew causes the child to spit up its anger. This cure is classed variously as "hot" and "cold." Peach leaves may be applied to a bone break. As a remedy for suppurating fingernails (**unen k'obol**) or toenails (**spojoval koktik**) a leaf may be rubbed on the underside with a tallow candle and passed before the fire before being bound around the affected part.

Young, unripe peaches may be roasted on the fire. Ripe peaches are eaten raw or are boiled with apples and refined sugar until forming the consistency of corn gruel. Peaches may be soaked in cane liquor to give it a fruity flavor. They are generally classed as "cold." Peaches may be resold and are sold at market in August. They may be transported for sale to Tuxtla, Arriaga, Tonalá, Villa Flores, and Juchitán.

b. **Karirat turasnu**, "charity **turasnu**" (**karera**, **karida**, **santoal turasnu**), is a type of small peach with hard white flesh that turns red where it clings to the pit. The fruit ripens in September and October, but often rots before becoming fully ripe. It is grown by few Zinacantecs in Jok' Ch'enom and in all but one highland community. For use cf. **batz'i turasnu**.

c. **Kaxlan turasnu**, "castilian **turasnu**," is the apricot *Prunus armeniaca* (1–2). It is grown by a very few Zinacantecs in some of the highland communities. Apricots are planted in the same way as peaches. They fruit three or four years after planting. They are sold at market in San Cristóbal and Tuxtla in May and early June. They are classed variously as "hot," "medium," and "cold. Cf. **ixim**.

d. **Luranko turasnu**, "durango **turasnu**" (**duranko**, **luranko**, **turanku**), is a type of peach with soft, white, flesh turning red where it clings to the pit. Many consider it to be the sweetest and best variety. It is grown in all highland communities. It is classed variously as "hot," "medium," and "cold." It is harvested in August. For use cf. **batz'i turasnu**.

e. **Merokotom turasnu**, "melocoton turasnu" (**kotom**), is a small, deep yellow-orange type of peach with soft flesh. Both small, **bik'it**, and large, **muk'ta** varieties are recognized, the latter most recently introduced by grafting. It is cultivated in Jok' Ch'enom, Petz Toj, and all highland communities. These are not grown by many Zinacantecs, but the fruits bring a better price than the other peaches. The harvest is in August and September. They are generally classed as "cold." For use cf. **batz'i turasnu.**

Extended range: *Chiococca alba.*

"Tzelo-pat Set"

The "tzelo-pat set" is a grouping of three generics. These are highland and temperate shrubs and small trees with soft, gray, pubescent, opposite, ovate leaves.

1. **Sitit (tik)** refers to the shrubby composites in the genera *Vernonia* and *Pluchea.* These have large, woolly leaves and terminal clusters of inflorescences with pink or lavender flowers.

Specifics: 2.

    a. **Sakil sitit,** "white **sitit,**" refers to *Vernonia deppeana* (7–11) and *V. oaxacana* (1–5). These are brittle-wooded shrubs often 4–6 m tall with pale lavender flowers in terminal, openly branched inflorescences. The leaves are alternate, elliptic, ovate, or oblong ovate, pubescent beneath, 4–15 cm long. They are common in the shrubby second growth formations of the temperate areas.

They are used as shade trees in the coffee groves and as firewood. The tips are used to sweep away "wind."

    b. **Tzajal sitit,** "red **sitit,**" is *Pluchea odorata* (3–5), a dense, soft-wooded shrub 4–6 feet tall with pink, cottony flowers 8–12 mm broad. The leaves are alternate, 7–15 cm long, elliptic to oblong-ovate. It is common in moist, disturbed ground, such as road banks and ditches throughout the *municipio.*

The trunk is used for firewood.

2. **Suil itaj,** "suil greens" (-tik) (**suyul itaj**), refers to *Liabum,* shrubby, yellow-flowered composites with strongly bicolored leaves.

Specifics: 2.

    a. **Batz'i suil itaj,** "genuine **suil** greens," is *Liabum glabrum* var. *hypoleucum* (5–9), a shrub or occasionally a tree to 6 m tall that flowers with a terminal panicle of golden yellow flowers, 10–13 mm broad, in the dry season when it is leafless. The leaves are broadly triangular ovate and strongly bicolored. It leafs during the wet season (June–September) and is a common element of the shrubby second growth formations of temperate and lowland areas. It often occurs in large expanses. When the Virgin Mary was hiding in the banana grove with her baby, she used these leaves to wipe the Christ Child's bottom.

When the shrub is found in the cornfield, the tuber is dug up and planted in the yard in Carlos A. Vidal, Chikinibal Vo', Muk'ta Jok', and Ya'al Tz'i'. It is an important green in the lower temperate communities. The tips and young leaves are boiled together with beans, though highland Zinacantecs claim

they are leathery and do not cook properly. They are classed predominantly as "cold," but also as "hot."

Extended range: *Desmanthodium perfoliatum, Liabum discolor, Senecio schaffneri,* and *S. thomasii.*

    b. **K'ox suil itaj,** "small **suil** greens," is *Liabum andrieuxi* (1–2), a shrub similar to *L. glabrum,* but with large, single orange-flowered heads, 5–6 cm broad, that appear while the plant is in leaf. It occurs in the same habitat as *L. glabrum.* It is not edible.

3. **Tzelo-pat,** "plated bark" (-**tik**) (**tzele-pat**), refers to Buddleias, shrubs or trees with opposite, gray leaves and small terminal pale yellow flowers.

Specifics: 3.

    a. **Bak tzelo-pat,** "skinny plated bark" (**jich'il anal tzelo-pat**), is *Buddleia nitida* (7–10). These are densely branched shrubs or trees with bicolored leaves, alternate, elliptic to oblong lanceolate, 5–7 cm long, deep green above, brownish pubescent below. The flowers are yellow, about 5 mm broad, in small clusters erect on the branches of a terminal panicle. It occurs in second growth in wetter highland slopes.

The trunk is used for roof rods, purlins, corn bin, stile, and gate rails, corn stubble rakes, digging sticks, hoe handles, and firewood.

    b. **Batz'i tzelo-pat,** "genuine plated bark" (**ik'al tzelo-pat, j'ak'-tzeluel**), is the tree Buddleia *Buddleia skutchii* (5–8), having alternate strongly bicolored, large, elliptic leaves, 8–15 cm long, and small flowers in small clusters on the branches of a large terminal panicle, 15–20 cm high. It is a small to medium-sized tree that is a common element of the pine-oak forests and in exposed situations in the evergreeen cloud forest of highland hamlets.

The trunk is used for house mainposts, rafters, roof rods, purlins, posts of wooden-walled houses, and fence posts. It is also used for corn bin, stile, and gate rails, for corn stubble rakes, hoe handles, and digging sticks. Though some use this wood for firewood it is widely believed that a person warming himself before such a fire will suffer cramps (**tzeluel**). The branches are used to wrap flowers for transport.

Extended range: *Vernonia leiocarpa.*

    c. **Chan-tzelav tzelo-pat,** "four-ridged plated bark" (**k'ox tzelo-pat, sakil tzelo-pat, tzan tzelo-pat**), refers to the shrubby Buddleias *Buddleia americana* (4–7), *B. crotonoides* (12–10), and *B. crotonoides* ssp. *amplexicaulis* (1–1). These have leaves 5–20 cm long, with gray pubescence on both surfaces and pale yellow flowers in dense clusters along an interrupted spike, 3–5 cm long. The stems are prominently 4-angled. They are common in second growth shrub formations of both highland and temperate situations.

The tips may be used together with elderberry to sweep away "wind." They are also used in combination with a wide variety of plants in the "steam cure," for "wind" (**sikil kolo'al ik'**), to reduce swelling (**poslom**), and after bloodletting. Recipe 1: (1) 13 tips of **ajval te'**, (2) 13 tips of **ch'a-te'**, (3) six tips of **yaxal pom tz'unun**, (4) a large handful of **sat pukuj**, (5) a handful of **ajal toj**, and (6) a handful of **chan-tzelav tzelo-pat**. It is "hot." Recipe 2: (1) **xutax chijil te'**, (2) **chix te' mut**, (3) **nap'ap' on te'**, (4) **tzajal pom tz'unun**, (5) **yaxal pom tz'unun**, (6) **satin**, (7) **chan-tzelav tzelo-pat**, and (8) **tz'utz'un tz'unun**. Recipe 3: (1) **ajval te'**, (2) **on te'**, (3) **satin**, (4) **chan-tzelav tzelo-pat**, and (5) **xinal te'**. Recipe 4: (1) **batz'i chix te'**, (2) **chix te' mut**, (3) **ik'al vinik**, (4) **mes te'**, (5) **on te'**, (6) **satin**, (7) **toj**, (8) **tulan**, and (9) **chan-tzelav tzelo-pat**. In this final recipe, 13 tips of each are brewed for a tea. The same plants are used for the steam cure, but not counted.

"Tzotz-ni' Te' Set"

The "**tzotz-ni' te' set**" includes eight generics, shrubs or trees with large, coarsely pubescent leaves.

1. **Ajo' te'**, "ajo' tree" (**ajo'**, **ajoj**, **ajoj te'**, **jabnal te'**, **te' la**, **tzajal tzotz-ni' te'**, **tzotzin te'**), refers to *Saurauia oreophila* (1–1) and *S. scabrida* (6–6). These are very soft-wooded, small trees with large, scabrous, pubescent, elliptic leaves. The flowers are white and in axillary inflorescences. The fruit is a clear, sweet, fleshy berry. These trees are a common element of second growth forests in the wet temperate regions. *Saurauia oreophila* differs in having smaller leaves, and shorter inflorescences with fewer flowers.

The trunk is used for wall poles and fence rails. The fruit, occasionally eaten, is classed variously as "medium" and "cold."

2. **Atz'am te'**, "salt tree" (**ch'ulul te'**), is *Viburnum hartwegii* (3–3). These are shrubs 8–20 feet tall with opposite, ovate to elliptic, glabrous leaves, 6–15 cm long, and terminal cymes of small white, 5-lobed flowers. The fruits are ovoid, purplish black and about 8 mm long. It occurs as a common element of second growth in temperate regions.

The trunk is used for roof rods, purlins, wattle, hoe handles, and digging sticks. Sheep eat the leaves.

3. **Chivo te'**, "goat tree," is *Aloysia chiapensis* (1–1). This is a yellow-flowered shrub from 3 to 8 feet tall. The leaves are opposite, the upper surface rough, the lower surface pubescent. They are narrowly ovate or lanceolate with crenulate or serrulate margins, 1.5–13 cm long, and prominent netted venation beneath. The very small flowers are borne in bracteate, short, axillary spikes, about 1–3 cm long. It occurs in second growth and on dry barren slopes in temperate and lowland areas.

A "hot" tea of the leaves is taken for diarrhea and stomach ache.

4. **Kastanya** (**kastansya**) is the lowland tree *Sterculia apetala* (2–4), a large, buttressed tree often cultivated around *ladino* houses and found occasionally in adjacent forests in the lowland areas. The leaves are large, palmately lobed and scurfy pubescent. The flowers are yellow and maroon, 5-lobed, 2.5–3 cm wide, in open many flowered panicles equaling or shorter than the petioles. The fruit produces a pubescent pod about 10 cm long with edible seeds that are oval, lustrous, and about 2 cm long.

Zinacantecs do not use the trunk, but have heard that it is very hard. Seeds, which are roasted, are classed variously as "hot" and "cold."

5. **K'ux-pevul**, "painful **pevul**" (**-tik**), refers to *Solanum chrysotrichum* (10–16), *S. lanceolatum* (1–5), and *S. torvum* (1–5). These are spiny shrubs with soft, densely pubescent, elliptic leaves, blue or white rotate flowers, and green to black tomato-like fruits. The stems and ribs of the leaves have coarse spines. They are common in second growth and waste ground at all elevations.

A tea of the leaves and stems is taken for lung and liver disorders. As a remedy for urinary pain (**makel**), three leaves are brewed. The "hot" tea is drunk before breakfast for three days. To strengthen the blood, the leaves are brewed at the end of the day and the "hot" tea drunk the next morning. To cure wounds, boils, or pack sores, 12 leaves are brewed, dried, and ground into powder. The sores are bathed with the water, then the "hot" powder is applied several times. The leaves are eaten by horses.

As a remedy for toothache, a bit of the "hot" fruit is crushed in one's hand and applied to the molar. The fruits may be boiled and the warm water used to bathe the sore nipples of nursing mothers. They may also be rubbed raw on the nipples to wean a baby.

Extended range: *Cirsium subcoriaceum, Lippia chiapasensis,* and *Solanum candidum.*

6. **Moy te'**, "tobacco tree" (**jik'ik' te'**, **k'ux-pevul te'**, **moy ka'**), refers to *Solanum erianthum* (7–13). These are shrubs with large, ovate, scurfy gray, pubescent leaves. The flowers are rotate, white, and in terminal cymes. The fruit is green and tomato-like. They are common in the tropical deciduous forests and second growth forest of the lowlands.

As a remedy for bloody dysentery, the leaves are crushed in cold water, providing a "cold" infusion. For "white" dysentery a tea of these leaves is taken.

7. **Sak-nich te'**, "white-flowered tree" (**-tik**), refers to Lippias, soft wooded shrubs with aromatic, opposite leaves and flowers borne in head-like clusters.

Specifics: 2.

a. **Muk'ta sak-nich te'**, "large white-flowered tree," refers to *Lippia cardiostegia* (1–3) and *L. myriocephala* (2–3). These are shrubs or small trees with opposite, soft pubescent, narrowly elliptic to ovate leaves, with crenate or serrate margins. The flowers are white and very small arranged in small globose or cylindrical, bracteate inflorescences. The peduncles are several in the axils of the leaves, longer than the inflorescences and usually shorter than the leaves.

These trees occur in second growth in temperate and lowland regions.

The trunk is used for ridge poles, roof rods, wattle, chayote and popapple arbors, hoe handles, and digging sticks.

b. **Sak-nich te'**, "white-flowered tree," refers to *Lippia chiapasensis* (5–5), and *L. substrigosa* (3–5). These are shrubs or small trees with very stiff pubescent, elliptic, rugose leaves and small, white and yellow flowers in bracteate, pendulous heads in the leaf axils. They are common elements in the understory of pine-oak forests and in the shrubby second growth formations of highland and temperate areas.

The trunk is used for roof rods and wattle.

Extended range: *Lippia bracteosa, Solanum lanceolatum,* and *Viburnum hartwegii.*

8. **Tzotz-ni' te'**, "downy-tipped tree" (-**tik**), is *Viburnum jucundum* (5–10), a shrub or small tree with large, ovate, opposite densely white, pubescent leaves, 6–19 cm long, and small white flowers in large, flat, terminal cymes up to 15 cm across. These are common in wet pine-oak forests and evergreen cloud forests of the highland areas.

The trunk is used for stirring rods, wattle, fence posts, and firewood.

Extended range: *Viburnum hartwegii* and *V. jucundum* × *V. acutifolium* ssp. *lautum.*

"Xan Set"

The **xan** set is a grouping of four generics, all large-trunked palms.

1. **Koko** (**kok**) is the coconut *Cocos nucifera* (2–5), cultivated in Chiapa de Corzo and a few other lowland towns. The trees are large and unarmed with pinnately divided leaves. The flowers are sessile, valvate, 11–12 mm long.

Few Zinacantecs eat coconut. It is classed predominately as "cold."

2. **Nap*** (-**tik**) is the coyol *Acrocomia mexicana* (3–7), a large, crowned tree up to 10 m tall and as much across, with pinnately dissected leaves up to 4 m long. They have the rachis and bases of the leaf divisions bearing flat, black spines. The inflorescence, up to 1 m long, is borne suspended by a broad spathe. The flowers are spicate, about 6 mm long. The fruit is ovate, about 1.5 cm long. The trees are scattered in sandy places in temperate and lowland localities. *Ladinos* cultivate these palms in their yards, planting one nut to a hole in the rainy season. They adorn their altars with the flowers. They boil the fruit with sugar for candy.

When coyols occur in fields that are to be cleared for milpas, just the fronds may be lopped off, leaving the trunk to put forth new fronds after the field has been burned.

The "cold" heart is preferred for its sweetness. During the famine it was ground and mixed with corn dough for tortillas. The sap is collected by cutting a depression in the fallen trunk. The depression is a foot long and 4 inches wide and deep.

Leaves are placed on the top with a rock to hold them down. The sap is drunk through a straw covered with a cloth to strain out the bugs. It is drunk in the morning and in the afternoon. The sides are scraped out clean each day and the bugs removed. The rhinocerus beetles (**chanul nap**) that are attracted to it are eaten raw. The trunk will produce sap for a month. The sap may be allowed to stand for a week until it ferments and becomes a powerful liquor (*taverna*). Coyol sap may be mixed with onion, chili, and salt to produce a sauce that is drunk with the meal in the fieldhouses at the time of clearing and burning. The spines are used to prick the bellies of ticks that have fastened on to one's skin. The fruit that ripens in May and June is sucked as a candy, and the nut is broken and eaten. It is "medium." To induce a fruit tree to bear, the chewings of coyol nuts should be spat on it.

3. **Palma** (-**tik**) (**muk'ta xan**) is the sabal palm *Sabal mexicana* (1–1), a tall tree with elongate, flabellately multifid, fan-shaped leaves, 1–2 m long. The pendulous branched inflorescence is up to 1 m long. The flowers are about 5 mm long and spikate. The fruits are irregularly rounded and very numerous, 15–20 mm broad. These trees often form dense stands in sandy alluvial flats in the Grijalva valley. *Ladinos* use the trunks for fence posts and bridges and the fronds for thatch.

The fronds may be used for thatch in temperate hamlets.

Zinacantec men split and folded the ribs of the leaves as reinforcement for their hats. The leaves are still used for the hat of religious officials of other Tzotzil and Tzeltal towns. They were used for the high-peaked hats once worn by Chamulans. The "cold" heart, together with that of the coyol, are preferred for their sweetness. Children play with the nuts.

4. **Xan*** refers to the fan palms *Brahea*.
Specifics: 2.

a. **Batz'i xan**, "genuine fan palm" (**ch'ix xan**), is *Brahea dulcis* (1–2), a small tree, up to 8 m tall, of scattered localities in steep canyons and cliff faces in temperate and lowland areas. It has minute flowers imbedded in the dense tomentum of the branchlets of the inflorescences. The inflorescencs are pendent and up to 1.5 m long. The leaves are up to 1 m long, plicate and palmate, green on the undersurface. The margins of the petiole are spinose-dentate.

The leaves are used by Zinacantecs to weave hats, by convicts to make brooms, and by the people of Soyaló to weave mats. Though woven plastic hats have nearly replaced the traditional palm hats, the preparation of the latter is still common knowledge. The young leaves were boiled and spread in the sun to bleach. They were laid on the roof overnight for 1–3 nights so that the action of the dew would give more permanence to the bleaching.

When a man dies, the black palm band in his hat is removed and burnt lest it become a snake.

Three hundred fronds each are provided by the Junior Steward of St. Dominic and by the Junior Steward of the Sacrament for distribution on Palm Sunday. Formerly 500, then

450, and now 250 fronds are provided by each of the Stewards of the Holy Cross and St. Anthony for distribution on St. Peter the Martyr's Day. In Na Chij fronds are distributed on the Fiesta of St. Anthony. They are distributed on St. Peter the Martyr's Day in Apas, Atz'am, Bik'it Joyijel, Elan Vo', Na Chij, Naben Chauk, and Paste'.

On St. Peter the Martyr's Day some palm fronds are attached on top of the church bells, replacing the previous years'. They serve as protection from lightning. From one of the leaves distributed on that day the men may weave a narrow strip, terminating in a cross. This is hung from the crown of their hats, with the ribbons. It, too, serves as protection from lightning. A similar strip may be tied to the corn stalks nearest each of the four corners of the cornfield, as a protection against wind damage. Small palm crosses may be placed in a grave. The fronds were used formerly for rain capes that also served as blankets on trips. They are used in sweatbaths to fan the steam. The "cold" palm heart is eaten.

b. **Pik' xan**, "toothless palm" (**-tik**) (**xanil ixim**), is *Brahea nitida* (2–4), a small tree of similar habit and habitats to *B. dulcis*. It differs in having leaves waxy glaucous below, and no spines along the margins of the petiole.

The sheath was used as a wad for guns. The fronds were once used for thatch by some people of Elan Vo', Naben Chauk, Paste', and the temperate hamlets. Poor people may cover their corn bins with these fronds instead of with burlap or plastic bags. The fronds are used in sweatbaths to strike oneself. They may also be used to fan the fire to singe chickens. They are tied up to make whisk brooms to clean the griddle. Men from Elan Vo' appointed by the magistrate provide a load of fronds to decorate the kiosk on major fiestas when a band has been hired, to decorate the pine trees on the processional path on the fourth Lenten Friday, and also to decorate the school and the courthouse on Independence Day. Two fan palms are provided on the eighth *Posada* by the Junior Stewards of Saint Dominic and the Sacrament to flank the creche door. Formerly, two bundles were provided to decorate the Church of St. Lawrence on major fiestas. Fan palms are used for religious decoration in Na Chij on the Fiesta of Our Lord of Esquipulas and on Palm Sunday, in Chak Toj on St. Joseph's Day and the Fiesta of the Virgin of Guadalupe, in Elan Vo' on the Fiesta of St. Sebastian, in Paste' on St. Peter's Day and on the Fiesta of Our Lady of the Rosary, in Naben Chauk on the fourth Lenten Friday, in Atz'am on the Fiesta of Our Lady of the Rosary, and in Sak Lum on the fifth Lenten Friday. The "cold" heart is eaten raw, roasted or boiled in periods of famine.

"Yuch' Max Set"

The "yuch' max set" has three generics, all wiry-stemmed shrubs with dense, fuzzy leaves and bur-like fruits.

1. **Tz'oban** refers to *Abutilon, Malvaviscus,* and *Phymosia,* all soft, pubescent-leaved shrubs with hibiscus-like flowers and leathery bark.

Specifics: 3.

a. **Batz'i tz'oban**, "genuine **tz'oban**," is *Phymosia rosea* (2–5), a large (to 4 m), purple-flowered shrub with woolly, palmately lobed leaves, 5–20 cm long. The flowers are large, 5–7 cm long, white or red with a central column of fused stamens. They are arranged on woolly pedicels and peduncles in terminal groups usually of two or three flowers. It occurs in fencerows, along roads, and in yards. It is planted occasionally by Zinacantecs, but is also naturalized in highland areas.

The flowers are sold in Tuxtla. As a remedy for whooping cough, three flowers are brewed with **pit** seeds. The "hot" tea is drunk once or twice. One small basket of the flowers was formerly provided by the Stewards of Our Lady of the Rosary to be strung on a necklace that is placed in a bowl and carried by the first prefect to the houses of the junior stewards on St. Rose Day. (Now the stewards use five bunches of red carnations and five bunches of white carnations as this shrub is no longer so common.) The woman who tends the incense wears it for a moment after it has been revered.

b. **K'anal tz'oban**, "yellow **tz'oban**," is *Abutilon purpusii* (1–1), a large shrub with large, bright yellow flowers, 3–3.5 cm long, and big, round, or heart-shaped, soft pubescent leaves, 10–20 cm long. The fruit is made up of 8–10 fused carpels, about 3 cm in diameter. It occurs in second growth in temperate and lowland areas.

c. **K'ox tz'oban**, "small **tz'oban**" (**tz'oban ak', tz'oban te'**), is *Malvaviscus arboreus* var. *arboreus* (7–13), a many-branched shrub with densely woolly alternate broadly ovate leaves, sometimes, 3-lobed, and palmately veined. The flowers are solitary in the upper leaf axils, red, with petals 3–5.5 cm long and a stamen-tube exerted from the corolla. It is a very common element in second growth on exposed slopes in temperate and lowland areas. *Ladinos* use the flowers for altar decorations. It is classed variously as "vine," "plant," and "tree."

As cough medicine, a flower is brewed with sugar. A cup of the "cold" tea is drunk twice a day. As a remedy for whooping cough, 13 flowers are brewed and the "medium" tea is drunk before meals for three days. The flowers may be brewed together with spanish moss. Cf. **xanxanil ton**.

Extended range: *Ayenia mexicana, Mirabilis jalapa.* The latter may also be brewed to provide a "hot" tea for whooping cough.

2. **Yuch' max**, "monkey's louse" (**-tik**), refers to members of the genus *Triumfetta*. These have ovate, coarsely toothed leaves, 4–10 cm long, yellow or orange flowers in terminal or axillary inflorescenses and small, hard, round fruits covered with stiff bristles. They are common in the understory of pine-oak and tropical forest and in second growth in temperate and lowland regions.

When the survivors of the Flood misspoke and were transformed into monkeys, they were condemned to scratch their lice. This plant is associated with that primordial event.

Specifics: 3.

    a. **Batz'i yuch' max**, "genuine monkey's louse" (**yak' ch'o**), refers to *Triumfetta grandiflora* (2–4), *T. semitriloba* (6–9) and *T. speciosa* (1–2), large shrubs with bright yellow or orange flowers, which are arranged in axillary, branched inflorescences. They have five distinct sepals and petals, though they appear tubular in bud. The stamens are many and exerted. The leaves are broadly ovate to narrowly ovate rounded and palmately veined from the base, softly pubescent or rough to the touch above and below. They have very leathery bark. They occur in second growth on sunny, exposed slopes in temperate areas.

The bark is used for house and fence lashing, and by children to make traps.

Extended range: *Malvaviscus arboreus* var. *mexicanus,* having the same uses as above.

    b. **K'ox yuch' max**, "small monkey's louse," is *Triumfetta dumetorum* (3–7), a wiry-branched shrub with a profusion of small axillary yellow flowers that develop in small spinose burs. The leaves are pubescent, ovate to elliptic, 2–9 cm long. It is very common in second growth, exposed slopes of highland and temperate areas. It is classed variously as "tree" and "plant."

Extended range: *Ayenia micrantha, A. mexicana, Bidens bicolor,* and *Kearnemalvastrum lacteum.*

    c. **Tzotzin yuch' max**, "downy monkey's louse," is *Triumfetta polyandra* (1–2), a low shrub with large, short petiolate, palmately veined oval to oblong, woolly leaves, 7–15 cm long, and large yellow flowers in terminal inflorescences with yellow petals, 2.5–3.5 cm long. The spinescent burs are 2–4 cm in diameter and densely pubescent. It occurs on grassy slopes in pine forest of temperate areas.

3. **Yuch' max pox**, "monkey's louse medicine" (**votzvotz pox**), is *Acaena elongata* (4–6), a low, densely branched shrub with dissected leaves, 2–4 cm long, and racemes of small flowers developing into ellipsoid burs 6–8 mm long with stiff spines. It is a common, often dominant element in wind-swept, shrubby association on the tops of high ridges and peaks. It is classed as "plant."

As a remedy for "wind," diarrhea, and bloody dysentery a small bunch is brewed. One cup of the "hot" tea is drunk before breakfast and lunch for one day.

Isolates

1. **Chil jabnal**, *"chil leaf"* (**-tik**), refers to members of the genus *Miconia*.

Specifics: 2.

    a. **Batz'i chil jabnal**, "genuine **chil** leaf" (**sakil chil jabnal**), is *Miconia oligotricha* (2–6), a densely branched, soft-wooded shrub with glabrous, 3-nerved, elliptic leaves. The flowers are small, white, and in terminal panicles. The fruit is a small, juicy berry. They are common in the evergreen cloud forest and in wet situations of pine-oak forests of highland areas.

Chamulans gather the branches and sell them to Zinacantec women to dye wool. The leaves are boiled with dodder to produce a yellow dye. After the wool is dyed, it is taken to San Cristóbal where it is immersed in blue dye to provide green wool for sashes.

    b. **Tzajal chil jabnal**, "red **chil** leaf" (**chilkat te'**, **jabnal**), refers to *Leandra subseriata* (3–5), *Miconia guatemalensis* (7–11), and *M. mexicana* (1–4), small, soft-wooded shrubs with reddish, pubescent, ovate, three-nerved leaves. The flowers are small, white and pink, and in terminal panicles. These are common elements of the shrubby, second growth formations of the temperate regions.

The leaves are boiled with fuchsia dye to produce the red dye for sashes.

Extended range: *Heterocentron subtriplinervium.*

2. **Ch'ib** (**-tik**) refers to small forest palms of the genus *Chamaedorea*.

Specifics: 3.

    a. **Batz'i ch'ib**, "genuine **ch'ib**," is the bamboo palm, *Chamaedorea elatior* (4–4), an extremely variable plant with a slender, dense, hard stem to 3 m tall and long leaves divided into narrow segments. The flowers are on an erect-branched inflorescence that develops round, black fruits along the rachis. It occurs in the dense, moist understory of evergreen cloud forest in the highlands and in montane rain forests of the temperate area ravines below Apas and near Masan.

The assistants of the stewards in charge of replacing the floral adornment of the church entrances formerly gathered 600 sprays for each of the two churches in Zinacantán Center, and 60 sprays for the altar of the two steward's in charge. Five hundred and seventy are gathered for the creche by the Junior Steward of Our Lady of the Rosary (but the expenses shared by all stewards). These are provided on the eighth *Posada*. Four dozen more are provided on the ninth *Posada* by the Junior Stewards of the Sacrament and St. Sebastian (the costs also shared by all stewards). Bamboo palm is used to decorate the creche in Na Chij. The assistants of the elders gather 100 for the grand alcalde's altar, every two weeks; 330 sprays are provided by the publicans every two weeks for the decoration of the Chapel of Esquipulas. Thirty of these are given to the elders. The waterhole crosses are decorated with these stems on Holy Cross Day. The stems may be used to adorn the graveyard crosses on All Saints' and All Souls' Days. Two hundred sprays are taken by the stewards to Atz'am on the Fiesta of Our Lady of the Rosary. Because of the increasing scarcity of this plant, **muk'ta ch'ib** has largely replaced it for church and altar decoration. Bamboo palm is used in the flower changes in all chapels except those of Chak Toj and Kelem Ton. For further use cf. **krus ech'**.

Now all stewards combine to provide 40 dozen sprays for each church and 3¹/₂ dozen for every steward's altar, making a total of 1440 sprays.

b. **Muk'ta ch'ib**, "large ch'ib" (**chayna nichim** and **palma ch'ib** in part), refers to *Chamaedorea ernesti-augustii* (1–2) and *C. nubium* (1–2), plants with a delicate stem to 2 m tall and leaves divided into two or a few broad segments. The flowers are on a few-branched inflorescence and produce marble-sized, black fruits. They occur in deep montane rain forest and moist slopes in seasonal evergreen forests in temperate to lowland areas.

For use cf. **batz'i ch'ib**. *Chamaedorea ernesti-augustii* is gathered in the Malpaso area or bought at the market in Tuxtla.

c. **Palma ch'ib**, "palm ch'ib" (**jetav ch'ib**), is *Chamaedorea concolor* (1–2), a plant with a thin, hard stem to 2 m tall and leaves divided into many broad segments. The flowers and fruits are similar to **batz'i ch'ib**. It occurs in the dense understory of montane rain forest in temperate and lowland areas.

3. **Ik'ux** (higos*) is the fig *Ficus carica* (4–5), very commonly cultivated by *ladinos* in temperate and some highland areas. They are small trees about 30 feet tall or less with palmately 3–5 lobed leaves on long petioles. Figs are classed variously as "hot," and "cold."

According to the priest of Zinacantán in 1797, figs were the third most common yard trees. "The figs grow much taller here than in all the other places of the kingdon, although usually they are not the best kind" (de Leon y Goicoechea, 1797).

Ladinos sell figs at market in August. They brandy the figs in cane liquor and make fig candy.

Specifics: 2.

a. **Ik'al ik'ux**, "black fig," is a black-fruited variety.

b. **Yaxal ik'ux**, "green fig," is a green-fruited variety. A very few Zinacantecs in Na Chij, Naben Chauk, Petz Toj, Sak Lum, X'ukun, and Zinacantán Center plant the slips in their yards in the rainy season.

4. **Jach'ub te'**, "comb tree" is *Erythroxylon rotundifolium* (1–1). These are shrubs or small trees with small, glabrous, broadly ovate leaves, 1–2.5 cm long, which are alternate on the short branches. The flowers are white, very small, 1–4 in the axils of the leaves. The fruit is oblong, red, 4–6 mm long. This is an understory tree in the tropical deciduous forest of the lowlands.

5. **Jasínto te'**, "jasínto tree," is *Moringa oleifera* (1–2), a tree cultivated by *ladinos* for fencerows in the lowlands. It has pinnately divided leaves, with obovate leaflets, 1–2 cm long, large inflorescences of pink flowers, 2.5 cm broad, and large pods with triangular seeds that yield an oil of commercial use in perfume and machinery oil. The people of Chiapa de Corzo

decorate their graves on All Souls' Day with the flowers of this tree.

6. **Kakav te'**, "kakav tree," is *Oecopetalum mexicanum* (2–3), an unusual tree, often a dominant of the montane rain forests of the northern escarpment of the central highlands. It produces a large nut reminiscent of a walnut, but with a uniform meat. The leaves are large, coriaceous, elliptic to broadly oblong, 9–24 cm long. The flowers are white with five petals and arranged in axillary clusters. Occasionally it is cultivated by Chamulans, but most of the seeds sold come from wild trees. The bitter nuts are boiled and sold at market in San Cristóbal in October and November, but are rarely eaten by Zinacantecs.

7. **Kámusa te'**, "hat strap tree" (**poxil javal okol**), refers to *Bocconia arborea* (2–4) and *B. frutescens* (1–1), soft-wooded shrubs with large, pinnately lobed leaves, which are pubescent below. The wood and inner bark are bright orange and the sap forms an orange latex. The flowers are small, in large pendent panicles. The fruits are ellipsoid, 7–10 mm long. The seeds are black with red arils. It is common in shrubby second growth formations of temperate areas. Chamulans soak hides in cold water together with the branches of this shrub to dye the hides yellow for use as hat straps and sashes.

The "hot" sap of young shoots may be applied to cracked feet every two or three days. The tips of *B. frutescens* may be used with elderberry to "sweep away wind."

8. **Kilkil nichim**, "pendent flower," is a non-Linnaean grouping of plants cultivated for their drooping habit.

Specifics: 3.

a. **Sakil kilkil nichim**, "white pendent flower," is *Asparagus setaceus* (1–4), which is commonly grown by *ladinos* in hanging baskets in the highlands. It is a pendent woody, wiry stemmed plant with lacy fern-like leaves, dissected into numerous green, spine-like leaflets. Slips or seedlings are planted in the rainy season. *Ladinos* decorate their altars with the stems on Pentecost. This is classed as a "vine."

b. **Tzajal kilkil nichim**, "red pendent flower" (**ne kotom nichim, sim tuluk' nichim**), is *Acalypha hispida* (1–6), a cultivated shrub with long (to 5 cm), red, fuzzy, pendent, rat-tail inflorescences. The leaves are alternate, long, petiolate and broadly ovate, 11–18 cm long. It is grown by *ladinos* in lowland yards. They use the flowers for altar decoration.

c. **Yaxyax-'ulan kilkil nichim**, "purple pendent flower," refers to *Bougainvillea buttiana* (1–2) and *B. glabra* (1–4), cultivated vines with long, sprawling, pendent sprays of white or purple-bracteate flowers. The leaves are alternate, ovate or elliptic, 3–7 cm long. *Ladinos* at all elevations plant the slips or seedlings in the rainy season. The flowers are used for altar decoration. They are classed variously as "vine" and "tree."

9. **Klávo**, clove, *Eugenia caryophyllus,* is only seen by Zinacantecs in the market. It is used occasionally to season

chicken and turkey. It is "hot."

10. **Kokov*** is cacao, *Theobroma bicolor*. Cacao seed may be toasted, ground and added to **pamal ul**.

There is scarcely a hint of the former importance of cacao, when, during pre-conquest and early colonial times, chocolate beans served as currency. Zinacantán paid heavy tributes in cacao to the Spanish Empire. During the 17th century, recipes abounded for the preparation of chocolate seasoned with cinnamon, almonds, hazel nuts, orange water, petals of the rose of Alexandria, musk, etc. With the aid of *achiote* it was transformed from muddy brown to brick red. "But the meaner sort of people, as Blackmores and Indians, commonly put nothing into it but *Cacao*, and *Achiotte, Maiz,* and a few *Chiles*, with a little Anniseed" (Gage, 1648:108).

Indians celebrated their fiestas by drinking cold chocolate, whereas the ladies of San Cristóbal insisted on having their chocolate served hot at Mass! The bishop's protests went unheeded. In desperation he nailed letters of excommunication on the cathedral door. To this the ladies responded by attending mass elsewhere, and "sleighted his excommunication, drinking (chocolate) in iniquity in the Church, as the fish doth water" (ibid., p. 103). Shortly thereafter, a young lady tendered the bishop a cup of foaming chocolate whose particular recipe guaranteed his unlamented death. "And it became afterwards a Proverbe in that Country, Beware of the Chocolatte of Chiapa," (ibid.).

As a burlesque reminder of the festive importance of chocolate, on Carnival Tuesday Sir Spook serves the elders and the ensign-bearers **chukul'at**. It consists of finely ground coffee, brown sugar, cane liquor, one onion, and two limes!

When a young man asks for a girl's hand in marriage he places a bag of chocolate on the bottom of the basket presented to her parents. Chocolate is drunk rarely now in Zinacantán, either alone, or mixed with coffee. It is "cold."

11. **Kránata lo'bol**, "**kránata** fruit" (**castillan makum***, **granada***, **granadiya**), is the pomegranate *Punica granatum* (2-2), a dense, stiffly branched shrub, which produces bright orange flowers and large, round, red, sour, aggregate fruits, 5-10 cm in diameter. The leaves are opposite, oblong, 2-6 cm long. The flowers are terminal, with petals 1.5-2.5 cm long. It is cultivated occasionally by *ladinos* in temperate and highland regions and is most often seen in markets, but is rarely eaten by Zinacantecs.

12. **K'ask'as te'**, "brittle tree," refers to *Iresine angustifolia* (1-2) and *I. nigra* (1-2), shrubs with swollen leaf nodes, which make the stems extremely brittle. The leaves are large, thin, and elliptic-ovate, about 12 cm long or less, with a reddish tinge. The flowers are small, white, and in terminal panicles, 10-25 cm tall. The shrubs are common in the understory of tropical deciduous forests.

They are cut and used as fodder for sheep and horses.

13. **K'evex (-tik)** refers to the custard apples *Annona*. Specifics: 4.

a. **Batz'i k'evex** (**te'tikal k'evex**) is the common, cultivated and wild tree *Annona cherimola* (9-10), a small to medium-sized tree with large, velvety, elliptic leaves, 8-15 cm long, and large, round, sweet fruits with white pulp and black seeds. The flowers are opposite the leaves, solitary or two at a node. They are pubescent, about 1.5-2.5 cm long, and greenish inside. It is grown in all but two of the temperate communities, and in a few of the highland communities, where it seldom fruits. It also occurs as a wild element of tropical deciduous forest.

The seeds are planted in the rainy season.

The trunk is used for fence posts and firewood. The fruit, predominately classed as "cold," is sold at market in October and early November. Eating this fruit after taking an aspirin (**mejoral**) is said to have fatal effects. To rid horses and dogs of fleas or lice, the seed is ground and mixed in cold water, but when bathing the animal care must be taken not to let any water get in its eyes lest it be blinded.

b. **Chin-jol k'evex**, "bumpy head k'evex" (**chinkul k'evex**, **chinkuya**), is the lowland tree *Annona purpurea* (3-8), common in second growth dry forests. It is characterized by a globose fruit, 10-12 cm in diameter, covered with short, thick, spiny projections. The leaves are large, pubescent, broadly obovate, 12-30 cm long. The fruit, classed variously as "hot" and "cold," is harvested by the people of San Lucas in September and October. It is sold at market.

The pit, reputed to be poisonous, is occasionally used to kill head lice. It is ground and mixed with shampoo, but, if it has contact with the eyes, it will cause blindness.

c. **K'anal k'evex**, "yellow k'evex" (**sakil k'evex**), is the wild lowland tree *Annona reticulata* (1-2), a tree very similar to *A. cherimola*, but the fruit has a harder skin and is somewhat insipid.

The fruit is harvested by Zinacantecs in Kelem Ton. It is classed variously as "hot," and "cold."

d. **Papaúsa k'evex**, (**papausa**, **papayusa**), is *Annona diversifolia* (1-2), a cultivated tree with very large, oblong fruits, 13-15 cm long, with fleshy projections on the surface. The leaves are glabrous, obovate, 8-14 cm long. It is grown by lowland *ladinos* in their yards and along the river's edge.

It is grown in Masan, Minax, and Santa Rosa.

Slips or seeds are planted in Santa Rosa, one to a hole, in black earth, 3 mm apart, in the rainy season. The fruit is sold at market from mid-August to September. It is predominately classed as "cold."

14. **K'olo-max**, "monkey rattle" (**-tik**) (**k'olo-max te'**), is *Olmediella betschleriana* (1-5), a large tree of the evergreen cloud forest. The leaves are alternate leathery, glossy, and often coarsely dentate and spine tipped, 8-23 cm long. The flowers are minute. The fruit is large, round, and gourd-like. The bark is smooth and white.

15. **K'unil te'**, "soft tree" (**k'unil ok te'**), is *Lopezia*

langmanniae (1–2), a soft-wooded shrub with velvety, pubescent, oblong-elliptic to oblanceolate leaves, 18 cm long or less, and bright red, tubular flowers, 15–17 mm long. The capsules are ovate, 6–8 mm long, on long pedicels, 3.5 cm long or less. It is common in second growth in temperate hamlets.

16. **Linkon te'** is a non-Linnaean grouping of shrubs or small trees with long, stringy flowers in wet forests of temperate and upland areas. It includes *Acalypha macrostachya* (1–1), *A. mollis* (1–1), *Myriocarpa heterostachya* (1–1), *M. longipes* (1–1), and *M. yzabalensis* (1–1).

The trunk is used for house posts, digging sticks, and hoe handles.

17. **Lo'bol**, "fruit" (**-tik, -altik**), refers to plantains and bananas. They represent clones that are reproduced only by cuttings. Many of the nine varieties are cultivated elsewhere in lowland Mexico and known to Zinacantecs only through the market. All but **k'ox lo'bol** and **mol lo'bol** are hybrid clones of *Musa acuminata* × *M. balbisiana*.

Because Christ planted banana palms they must not be cut down. Others say that they sprung up and provided the Virgin Mary with shelter when she was fleeing the devils.

When Our Holy Mother was chased by devils, she slipped into a banana grove.

> [The banana] became the Virgin's food since she hid under the banana palms.
> When she was being chased by devils and hid, sitting in the weeds, now they weren't weeds anymore. They turned into a banana grove, just cultivated bananas.
> When she escaped from the devils and wasn't caught she left a name [for the banana]. Its name was **kinya**. After she gave it a name, the Virgin ate it.

Young plants are transplanted in the rainy season, or, if the ground is humid, at any time of year. Young plants should be weeded and hilled. Compost is sometimes provided. Gophers may become serious pests by eating the roots. The trees fruit in 2–3 years. The local varieties are used as shade trees in the coffee groves. The leaves are used as umbrellas and to wrap food when going to work. They are sold to *ladinos* who wrap tamales, **posol**, and meat in banana leaves. In the lowlands tortillas are patted on banana leaves. During the famine of 1918 young bananas were boiled and mixed with corn dough to make tortillas. People of the temperate hamlets flavor **vokol ich** with bananas. Banana peels should not be eaten lest someone in one's family die. Chamulans joke about using banana peels when far from their women (cf. **manko**).

Specifics: 10.

a. **Batz'i lo'bol**, "genuine fruit" (**ik'al lo'bol, túxta kinya**), is the lowland plantain.

The fruit may be resold and is sold at market from August to mid-March. Plantains eaten raw, when very ripe, and black-skinned, or roasted are classed predominately as "hot," but also are "medium" and "cold." They are an essential ingredient of the net of fruit given by the fiancé to his fiancée and of the net presented by the elders to each of the scribes on the fiestas of St. Sebstian and St. Lawrence. They are also essential gifts to the dead on All Souls' Day.

b. **Chan-tzelav lo'bol**, "four-ridged fruit" (**chan-tzelav kinya, kinya lo'bol, lo'bol chitom, ve'el chitom**), is a banana cultivated in Santa Rosa and Kelem Ton, and in most of the temperate communities.

Two trees are provided by the Stewards of Our Lady of the Rosary on the eighth *Posada* to flank the entrance to the creche. They are also used for creche decoration in Apas, Atz'am, and Sek'emtik. They adorn the church in Sak Lum on the fifth Lenten Friday. The fruit, generally classed as "cold," is available year round. It is also fed to pigs.

c. **Chimpo lo'bol**, "chimpo fruit" (**chimpo kinya, yaxal kinya**), is a low-growing banana cultivated in most of temperate hamlets and Kelem Ton. The "cold" fruit is available year round.

d. **K'ox lo'bol**, "small fruit," refers to *Heliconia librata* (1–2) and *H. schiedeana* (1–2), New World relatives of the banana with few, large banana leaves and bright orange or red, erect, terminal inflorescences. The flowers are subtended by large, boat-shaped, coriaceous, spreading bracts, 3.5–30 cm long. They are classed as "plant." They occur in wet situations of montane rain forest and seasonal evergreen forest of temperate Zinacantán.

e. **Mántzana lo'bol**, "apple fruit" (**mántzana kinya**), is a highly prized miniature variety cultivated in Magdalenas, Santa Marta, Santa Rosa, and most of the temperate communities. The "cold" fruit is available year round.

f. **Mol lo'bol**, "big fruit," is manila hemp *Musa textilis* (3-3), a large non-fruiting banana that is cultivated by a very few people in Ibestik, San Sigro, X'ukun, and some of the highland communities.

The sheaths were once cut into strips and used for string to tie flowers in bunches.

g. **Natikil lo'bol**, "long fruit" (**natikil kinya**), is a banana found only at market. The generally "cold" fruit is available year round.

h. **Sakil lo'bol**, "white fruit" (**sakil kinya**), is a banana cultivated in most of the temperate communities. The "cold" fruit is sold at market in January.

i. **Sera lo'bol**, "wax fruit" (**sera kinya**), is a banana found only at the market. The "cold" fruit is available in April and May.

j. **Tzajal lo'bol**, "red fruit" (**tzajal kinya**), is a banana cultivated in Kelem Ton and in all but one of the temperate communities. The fruit, predominately classed as "hot," is available year round.

18. **Lo'bol vet**, "fox fruit" (**lo'bol sat vet, sekaro, sekarovel**), is *Coriaria ruscifolia* (7–11), a sprawling shrub with finely divided, fern-like leaves up to 1.5 m long. The leaflets are ovate, 7–17 mm long. The flowers are small, in

pendulous racemes, the fruit is a fleshy, purple berry. It is very common on exposed slopes in evergreen cloud forests and second growth situations that replace this formation.

The trunk is used for firewood. To make their hair grow longer, women pound six young tips and rub them on their hair. The "cold" berries are eaten, but if 4–5 seeds are swallowed the results may be fatal. The berries are also eaten by gray foxes, steller's jays, and rufous-collared robins. Young girls' dirty white skirts may be dumped in a pot of raw berries and dyed. The berries are also used to write political slogans on trails.

In 1797 the priest of Zinacantán reported, "I will add a dye that I just discovered in the fruit or wild grape of a plant named **lobuluec** that gives a fast, dark purple" (de Leon y Goicoechea, 1797).

19. **Luchamaria** is *Rheedia edulis* (1–1), a tree of the seasonal evergreen forests adjacent to the Rio Grijalva. These are large trees with thick, glabrous leaves, 8–10 cm long, and large, round, fleshy fruits, about 2 cm long. The flowers are small and white with four petals, 5–7 mm long, and lateral clusters at defoliated nodes. The trees are sometimes cultivated by *ladinos*. The fruit is edible.

20. **Mora (jol tuk' te', k'anal te', mora te')** is *Chlorophora tinctoria* (4–12), a tree with large, scabrous leaves, 4.5–9 cm long, and small, catkin-like flowers. The fruit is an aggregate, like a mulberry, about 1 cm in diameter. The tree is scattered in canyon situations in the lowlands. Ladinos use the trunk for draw poles for their oxcarts.

The trunk is used for fieldhouse mainposts, doors, lintels, rafters, shelves, chests, coffers, chairs, tables, benches, *metate* platforms, bobbins, ax and billhook handles, slingshots, gunstocks, crosses, gates, fence posts, and rails. The fruit is eaten.

21. **Mukumu (anima nichim, nichim chij, nichim ninyo, sakil nichim, santo nichim, snichim jsoktom)**, is *Euphorbia leucocephala* (8–12), a soft-wooded shrub with milky sap and thin, lanceolate to elliptic leaves, 2.5–5.5 cm long. The flowers are small, subtended by white oblanceolate bracts 10–12 mm long and in showy terminal clusters. It is very common in second growth shrubby formation of temperate and lowland areas. It is classed variously as "plant" and "tree."

The flowers are sold in Tuxtla for the fourth Friday of Lent. They are also used by *ladinos,* especially in Chiapa de Corzo, for All Souls' Day wreaths.

Extended range: *Chamaesyce hirta, C. hypericifolia, Euphorbia graminea,* and *E. macropus.*

22. **Nankipu (nankeo, nankipo, nankipu te', nankipu', nankito, nanta')** refers to *Cordia dentata* (4–9), *C. dodecandra* (2–6), and *C. sebestena* (1–2), small trees with hard wood, ovate, scabrous, pubescent leaves, and clusters of bright orange or white flowers. The fruit is a large drupe enclosed in a fleshy calyx. These are common trees both cultivated and in natural situations in tropical deciduous forest in lowland areas. *Ladinos* plant the nut in fencerows in the rainy season and use the trunk for house mainposts.

The trunk is used for benches, slingshots, hoe, pick, and billhook handles, digging sticks, gunstocks, fence rails, and posts. The fruit is eaten as cough medicine. The nut of *C. dodecandra* is "hot."

23. **Nuk' chij,** "sheep neck" or "deer neck," is *Rubus trilobus* (7–10), a thin-stemmed shrub with palmate, lobed, soft, pubescent leaves, large, single, white flowers, and a few-seeded, aggregate, sweet, fleshy fruit. It is common in exposed situations of the evergreen cloud forest and wet second growth formations in the highlands.

Women gather the trunks for loom bars and shuttles. For loom bars, the ends are cut even and the bark is stripped. For shuttles, the bark is stripped and the ends are flattened and forked. The trunk is also used for shepherds' switches. In Apas the trunk is used for the frame of the creche. The fruit is edible, but dyes the lips purple. It is generally classed as "cold," but also as "medium," and "hot."

24. **Papaya (-tik)** refers to two members of *Carica.*
Specifics: 2.

    a. **Papaya** is *Carica papaya* (2–3), a thick-trunked, soft-wooded tree with the flowers and fruits borne on the trunk. The leaves are large, palmately lobed, mostly 30–60 cm wide. The creamy white flowers are of two kinds. The male flowers have an elongate slender tube lobed at the apex, 2.5–3 cm long. The female flowers have distinct petals and are slightly larger. All are borne on axillary inflorescences. It is cultivated by lowland *ladinos* in their yards.

Although some say that Rabbit dirtied melons and watermelons, others say his target was papayas (Laughlin, 1977, T166). The resemblance of the seeds to rabbit pellets may not be coincidental!

Zinacantecs plant the seeds with a digging stick in the rainy season, one to a hole, in black earth in Kelem Ton, Masan, Minax, and Santa Rosa. The tree fruits in a year. Papayas are eaten by people and birds. They are sold at market from January to mid-March. They are classed variously as "hot" and "cold."

    b. **Papáya mut,** "bird papaya" (**k'ox papaya, te'tikil papaya**), is *Carica cauliflora* (3–6), a tree about 10–15 ft tall with large, palmately veined, ovate leaves. They are long petiolate and deeply lobed. The flowers are white, tubular, 2–3 cm long, and are arranged in short axillary racemes. The fruit is a large fleshy berry, up to 6 cm in diameter, with numerous seeds. It occurs along roadsides and in second growth in wet situations in the lowlands.

The "cold" fruit is eaten occasionally.

25. **Paraíso te',** "paradise tree," is the chinaberry or umbrella tree *Melia azedarach* (1–4), a cultivated tree at scattered locations mostly in the lowlands. It has large, finely divided, drooping leaves with serrate, ovate to lanceolate leaflets, 2–6 cm long, and large, spreading clusters of lavender flowers with spreading petals about 1 cm long. The fruits are small, hard, yellow, and sculptured, about 13–15 mm in diameter. In other

areas they are often used medicinally and for beads.

26. **Patax** refers to frangipanni and oleander, which are trees or shrubs with bright-colored rotate or salverform flowers.

Specifics: 2.

a. **K'ox patax,** "small **patax**" (**nichim te'**), is *Nerium oleander* (2–3). These are shrubs to about 20 feet tall with oblong lanceolate or linear leaves about 25 cm long or less. The flowers are showy, yellow, white, pink, or magenta, about 2.5–4 cm across, in large terminal branched inflorescences. Lowland *ladinos* plant oleanders in their yards, using the flowers for altar decoration.

b. **Patax nichim,** "**patax** flower" (**pataxéte nichim, xela nichim**), refers to *Plumeria alba* (1–5) and *P. rubra* (6–7). The fragrant white flowers are borne in large terminal inflorescences. The narrow tube expands into five obovate petals about 2.5–6 cm long. The leaves are oblong-elliptic, 12–50 cm long, alternate on the thick branches of the large shrubs or small trees. *Ladinos* cultivate frangipanni in their yards. The people of Chiapa de Corzo and Chamula thread the flowers on strings for altar decorations during Holy Week and for grave decorations on All Souls' Day. Only the white form occurs as an element of mature vegetation in tropical deciduous forests. Slips are planted in the rainy season by a few people in Jok' Ch'enom and Muk'ta Jok', and the flowers are sold in Tuxtla.

(1) **K'anal patax nichim,** "yellow **patax** flower," is the yellow-flowered variety of *P. rubra.*

(2) **Moraro patax nichim,** "purple patax flower," is the purple-flowered variety of *P. rubra.*

(3) **Sakil patax nichim,** "white **patax** flower," is *P. alba.*

(4) **Tzajal patax nichim,** "red **patax** flower," is the red-flowered variety of *P. rubra.*

27. **Pimenta** (**castillan ich***, **especies***, **pimilta, piminta**) refers to black pepper and allspice that are only seen in the market by Zinacantecs.

Specifics: 2.

a. **Batz'i pimenta,** "genuine **pimenta**" (**pimentail ul**), is allspice, *Pimenta dioica*. It is used to season corn gruel (**sakil ul**). It is "hot."

b. **Kaxlan pimenta,** "castilian **pimenta**," is black pepper *Piper nigrum*. This "hot" spice is used to season chicken and corn gruel (**pamal ul**). For medicinal use cf. **sakramentual nichim.**

28. **Piyon te',** "piyon tree," is *Pedilanthus tithymaloides* (1–1). This is an erect branched shrub with alternate, almost sessile leaves, which are thick and fleshy, elliptic to broadly oblong, 3.5–13 cm long. The flowers are red, tubular, 11–13 mm long. The capsule is about 7 mm long and 3-lobed. The sap is applied to cuts to stanch bleeding. Its leaves are reputed to be poisonous. It occurs in the understory of tropical deciduous forest in the lowlands. **Piyon** may be a variant form of **pinyon,** the name applied to *Jatropha curcas,* a close botanical relative of *Pedilanthus.*

29. **Pomos** (**-tik, -altik**) refers to three shrubs with showy clusters of terminal flowers.

Specifics: 3.

a. **Ik'al pomos,** "black **pomos**" (**muk'ta pomos, yaxal pomos**), is *Ceanothus coeruleus* (8–11). These are large blue-flowered shrubs with strongly bicolored, alternate, elliptic to oblong, ovate leaves, 3–8 cm long. They are prominantly veined and brown pubescent beneath, dark green and glabrous above. The blue flowers are small, 2.5 mm long, and are arranged in small, dense, terminal panicles. The fruit is subglobose, somewhat 3-lobed, about 5 mm across. It occurs in second growth in the highland hamlets.

The trunk is used for wattle, hoe handles, digging sticks, loom bars, bean poles, and stirring rods. The trunk is also used for firewood, but the bark sends off many sparks. The branches are used for brush fences. They are also planted in a circle around flower plants to protect them from wind and rain.

b. **Sakil pomos,** "white **pomos**," is *Gymnopodium floribundum* var. *antigonoides* (2–5). These are shrubs or small trees with crooked branches and small elliptic leaves, 2–3.5 cm long, which are subsessile and fasciculate. The flowers are white, about 7–8 mm across, in long lateral racemes. The fruit is enclosed in a dry, three-sided, perianth about 1 cm long. It occurs on dry slopes in second growth on lowland slopes.

c. **Tzajal pomos,** "red **pomos**" (**-tik**) (**k'ox pomos**), is *Holodiscus argenteus* (5–7), a shrub or small tree with dense terminal panicles, 5–15 cm long, of small white flowers. The leaves are bicolored, dark green and glabrous above, white pubescent below. They are alternate on the red branches, narrowly ovate to lanceolate or oblanceolate, coarsely serrate, 3–7 cm long. It occurs as a prominent element in second growth in the highlands.

Zinacantecs distinguish this shrub from **sakil pomos** by its reddish brown bark. The trunk is cut by women to make loom bars and stirring rods. Loom bars were formerly made exclusively of bamboo (*Otatea fimbriata*), but the near disappearance of this bamboo in the township has promoted the substitution of this wood. The trunk is also used for wattle, bean poles, fence posts, and firewood. This wood also sparks.

Extended range: *Spiraea cantoniensis*, which grows in yards and whose flowers are used as altar decorations.

30. **Potov** refers to guavas and related plants.

Specifics: 3.

a. **Batz'i potov,** "genuine **potov**" (**k'ox potov, pajal potov**), is *Psidium guineense* (6–10). These are shrubs or trees with softly pubescent broadly elliptic leaves, about 6–10 cm long, with short petioles. The flowers are solitary or three in the leaf axils. The petals are white, 10–14 mm long, extending from the cup-like pubescent base of the calyx. The stamens are numerous and exerted from the flowers. The fruit is round, 1–2 cm in diameter, yellowish green or yellow. It occurs in savannas in lower temperate hamlets.

It is grown in Kelem Ton and in most temperate communities.

Some claim that the leaves are poisonous, but others use them medicinally. As a remedy for dysentery, the "hot" leaves and bark may be brewed. One cup of the tea is drunk before breakfast and, if necessary, before lunch and supper for two or three days. It is classed variously as "medium" and "cold." The tip is mashed and applied to fever sores. The fruit is sold at market in October. It is classed variously as "hot" and "cold." It was once bartered by the people of Atz'am for cabbages and tomatoes.

Extended range: *Eugenia yunckeri*.

b. **Kaxlan potov**, "castilian **potov**" (**muk'ta potov**, **tz'unub potov**), is guava, *Psidium guajava* (6–9). It is cultivated in Magdalenas and Santa Marta, and sold at market in October and November. It is very similar to *P. guineense*. *Psidium guajava* usually has one flower per inflorescence. *Psidium guineense* often has three. Buds are usually larger and more pointed and peduncles shorter in *P. guajava*. The two species hybridize in nature and are sometimes difficult to distinguish. It occurs with **batz'i potov**.

It is grown in some temperate communities.

(1) **Sakil kaxlan potov**, "white castilian **potov**" (**k'anal kaxlan potov**), is a variety of guava with light-colored flesh.

(2) **Tzajal kaxlan potov**, "red castilian **potov**," is a red-fleshed guava. This variety is cultivated more frequently, especially in Masan.

The trunk is used for firewood. The raw fruit is "cold." It may be boiled with refined sugar until it forms the consistency of corn gruel. Then it is classed as "hot."

c. **Tzajal potov**, "red **potov**," is *Syzygium jambos* (1–1). This is a glabrous shrub or small tree with large alternate narrowly elliptic to lanceolate leaves, 12–20 cm long. They are short petiolate and have entire margins. The flowers are white, large and showy, 7–8 cm across, with numerous conspicuous long stamens. They are arranged in a terminal raceme. The fruit is depressed-globose, 6 cm or less in diameter, 3–4 cm long, pale yellow, enclosing 1 seed, which is about 2.5 cm in diameter. It is a temperate and lowland cultivated tree.

31. **Satin** (-**tik**) is wax myrtle *Myrica cerifera* (6–8). These are sparsely to densely branched shrubs with alternate, glabrous, oblanceolate, fragrant leaves, 5–10 cm long. They are characterized by the short, dense lateral racemes of globose, waxy, papillate fruits, which are about 4 mm in diameter. It is a highland shrub, common in second growth.

A "hot" tea of the roots is taken as a remedy for menstrual failure. The trunk is used for bean poles. The branches are used to wrap flowers for transport. The branches, provided by constables until 1984 when the churchyard was paved, were tied to stakes on either side of the processional path in Zinacantán Center on the fourth Friday of Lent, Wednesday of Holy Week, and Good Friday. They are used in Chak Toj and Naben Chauk for the fourth Friday of Lent and in Naben Chauk on Good Friday as well. They are used similarly for visits from government officials and to decorate the school on Independence Day. Cf. **batz'i k'oxox te'**.

It is also used to decorate the graves on All Souls' Day. In Atz'am it is used for the processional path on Christmas Eve. A horse suffering "wind" is beaten with the branches. The tips are used in the "steam cure." The branches are used to wrap flowers for transport. The use of the berries for making candles is not known. For further use cf. **muk'ta pom tz'unun** and **tilil**.

32. **Sik'ol te'**, "cigarette tree" (**nok'ol sik'ol te'**), is *Hyperbaena mexicana* (1–1). These are shrubs to trees, 50 feet [~15 m] tall, with short thick trunks. The leaves are large, coriaceous, glabrous, often glossy, oblong 10–22 cm long. The fruits are ovoid, 1-seeded and fleshy much like a plum, about 3 cm long. This is an occasional element in the tropical deciduous forest of the lowlands.

33. **Soro te'**, "skunk tree" (**soro pox**), is *Petiveria alliacea* (3–9). These are stiff woody plants with alternate, elliptic to obovate, glabrous, rank leaves, 5–15 cm long. The flowers are small, white or pink with four spreading linear sepals, about 5 mm long. They are arranged in very long narrow racemes, 10–35 cm long. This plant occurs in waste ground and second growth in the temperate and lowland regions.

The root is prized for its medicinal qualities and may be stored for later use. If the root is straight it is called "man," (**vinik**), and if it bifurcates it is "woman" (**antz**). The former is considered to be more powerful. The root may be brewed for toothache. As a remedy for "stomach wind" and for women's sickness (**pumel**), a 1″ section of two or three roots may be used. The roots are brewed or are mashed and steeped in cold water. A cup is drunk before breakfast for 2–3 days. It is "hot." If the tea is taken the patient must be quarantined for six days. No shaman is required. Some consider these foul-smelling roots more powerful than **vako' ak'**. The leaves are rubbed on aching legs to remove the "wind." For further medicinal use cf. **kururin, vako' ak'**.

34. **Tok'oy*** (-**tik**, -**altik**) refers to willows.

In 1797 the priest of Zinacantán reported that "there are two kinds of willow, one true, one false. They are mixed together in the yards and fields. One has longer leaves that are less green. The other has a bigger flower" (de León y Goicoechea, 1797). This probably refers to **kaxlan tok'oy** (*Yucca elephantipes*) now conceptually related to agaves (**met**). The willow was used for quinsy (tonsilitis) and provided shade in the arroyos (de Leon y Goicoechea, 1797).

Specifics: 3.

a. **Batz'i tok'oy**, "genuine willow" (**sakil tok'oy, va'ajtik tok'oy**), is *Salix bonplandiana* (2–4), an erect tree common along streams in highland and temperate areas. The bark is brown and irregularly fissured. The branches are drooping. The leaves are narrowly lanceolate, 5–15 cm long, 1.5–2.5 cm wide. The male and female flowers are small and borne in separate erect spikes. It is often cultivated and used for living fences in the Atz'am valley and in many highland communities.

Slips may be planted in the rainy season, but they grow better if planted in the dry season when their leaves have dropped. Both ends of the branch are cut off to form the slip. It may be planted in dry land for fencerows, but the ground should not be tamped tight. This tree is considered to be the origin of water (**me' vo'**) and accordingly is planted by waterholes so they will not dry up. Some claim that it should not be planted by young people. A young person who has planted a willow should lop off the ends of the branches and the top of the tree in the dry season, so "killing" the tree. In the rainy season it will sprout again.

The trunk is used to make gunpowder. It is burned in an outdoor fire. The firebrands are pulled out, wetted down and allowed to cool for two to three days. The charcoal is ground by women on a *metate* in the yard. During the grinding a half-pint of cane liquor is served. The charcoal powder is poured into a gourd and shaken to make it finer. Then it is poured on a plastic sheet and left in the sun for two days to dry. One **almud** of gunpowder is made by mixing three 5 liter measures of charcoal with 1 kilo of sulphur and 4 kilos of saltpeter. The gunpowder is used by mortarmen for the change of office of elders, stewards, stewards-royal, ensign-bearers, and for Holy Cross ceremonies. Four loads are needed. The shoots are gathered and fed to sheep. The leaves are used by girls as stoppers for their water jugs.

To ease muscular pains in one's legs the patient bathes with water in which "hot" willow branches have been boiled.

b. **Kilajtik tok'oy**, "pendulous willow," is the less common *Salix babylonica* (1–2) and *S. humboldtiana* (1–2). Both are very similar to *S. bonplandiana,* but differ in having branches that droop often for several meters. The leaves are narrower, 3–10 cm wide. *Salix babylonica* is also cultivated in fencerows in the same highland communities as above. *Salix humboldtiana* occurs along streams at low elevations. It has the same non-medicinal uses as **batz'i tok'oy**.

c. **K'ox tok'oy**, "small willow (**tok'oy te'**), is the lowland, shrubby *Salix taxifolia* (2–5). It is common along lowland streams. It is classed variously as "plant" and "tree." The leaves of this willow are linear and small, 1–1.5 cm long, almost sessile, and are silvery pubescent on both surfaces. The spikes are dense and oblong. The fruits are pubescent.

Extended range: *Baccharis salicifolia.*

35. **Túrasnu te'**, "peach tree," is *Agonandra racemosa* (1–1), a glabrous tree with slender branches and small lanceolate to ovate leaves, 4–8 cm long, very like those of peaches. The flowers are very small in axillary racemes, which may be longer or shorter than the leaves. The fruit is fleshy and 1-seeded, globose, about 1 cm in diameter. It occurs as an element of tropical deciduous forests in the lowlands.

The trunk is used for ax and hoe handles and digging sticks.

36. **Tzajal te'**, "red tree," is *Acalypha unibracteata* (6–11), a shrub with coppery foliage and small catkin flowers in the axils of the leaves. The leaves are thin, short-petiolate, ovate, 2–5 cm long, with acuminate apices. It is a very common plant in second growth in temperate and lowland areas.

The red heartwood may be used for loom bars.

37. **Vo'ox** (**-tik, -altik**) is achiote, *Bixa orellana* (2–7). These are shrubs or trees to 30 feet [~9 m] tall. The leaves are large, broadly ovate, palmately veined, broadly rounded at the base, acute at the apex, 9–15 cm long. The flowers are white or pink with petals about 2.5 cm long, in small panicles. The fruits are ovoid capsules, 2.5–4–5 cm long, densely covered with flexible spines. The seeds are covered with a reddish orange pulp. It is planted by lowland *ladinos* and the people of Masan and X'ukun in the rainy season. The young plant must not be handled. The fruits, which are harvested in January, are spread out on a mat to dry in the sun. They are sold at market. *Ladinos* use the pulp to dye cooked turkey red.

The "cold" pulp is used to color a chicken, but indigestion will result if cold water is drunk after eating it. It is also used to color pork and beef. It is the dye for **tzajal vokol ich** that is served at the veneration of the coffers of the Stewards of the Holy Sacrament, St. Dominic, and Our Lady of the Rosary. To cause measles to erupt, it is soaked in warm water or lime water, providing a "medium" infusion. Cf. also **ixim, mail**. The pulp is also used to dye wool red for sashes.

38. **Vux te'**, "rubbing tree" (**kokov te'**), refers to *Curatella americana* (2–2) and *Davilla nitida* (2–6). These are shrubs or small trees with rough leaves that are alternate, broadly ovate, oblong to broadly elliptic with conspicuous parallel secondary veins. The flowers are bright yellow or white with 5–6 imbricate petals that are arranged in lateral or axillary panicles.

These trees are dominant in poor soil savannahs of the lowlands.

The trunk is used for firewood. The leaves are used to rub hoe and ax handles smooth.

39. **X'ukun** (**-tik, -altik**) refers to *Erythrina chiapasana* (4–7) and *E. goldmanii* (2–6). These are soft-wooded trees with pinnately trifoliate leaves. The leaflets are large and broad. The large pea flowers are showy and arranged in spikes. Flowers are pink, pale red, or red and about 5–8 cm long. The pods are constricted between the seeds, resembling a chain of beads. The seeds are bright red. They occur in second growth in temperate hamlets (*E. chiapasana*) and as an element of tropical deciduous forest (*E. goldmanii*).

It is grown in all but one of the temperate and highland communities.

Some maintain that slips can be planted for fencerows only in the dry season, others claim that they may be planted throughout the year. The branches are cut at both ends to provide slips. Some plant them immediately, others, claiming they will rot, pile them first on the ground for two weeks, allowing them to sprout. The slips are an armspan long, planted 5–7 handspans apart.

The trunk is used for stools, fence posts, for the dudes' masks, and for spoons. The flowers, which bloom in May, are sold at market. They may be boiled alone or together with beans. They are "cold." The "cold" buds may also be toasted.

40. **Yisim mut bolom**, "jaguar bird whiskers," is *Bumelia obtusifolia* var. *buxifolia*. This is a large shrub armed with nodal spines. The leaves are opposite, oblong, obovate or broadly ovate, 2–8 cm long. The flowers are small, white or yellow, in small clusters in the axils of the leaves. The fruits are subglobose on short pedicels about 1 cm long. It occurs along streams in tropical deciduous forest in the lowlands.

"Plants": "Tz'i'lel Sets"

alavanux
  ch'ix alavanux   *Raphanus sativus* (Brassicaceae)
  kaxlan alavanux   *Raphanus sativus* (Brassicaceae)
  muk'ta alavanux   *Raphanus sativus* (Brassicaceae)
  natikil alavanux   *Raphanus sativus* (Brassicaceae)
  sakil alavanux   *Raphanus sativus* (Brassicaceae)
metabel   *Beta vulgaris* (Chenopodiaceae)
mustisya
  k'ox mustisya   *Brassica juncea* (Brassicaceae)
  muk'ta mustisya   *Brassica nigra* (Brassicaceae)
napux
  batz'i napux   *Brassica campestris* (Brassicaceae)
  jolinom napux   *Brassica rapa* (Brassicaceae)
  kaxlan napux   *Brassica campestris* (Brassicaceae)
sanorya   *Daucus carota* var. *sativa* (Apiaceae)

bero   *Rorippa nasturtium-aquaticum* (Brassicaceae)
    Rorippa × sterilis (Brassicaceae)
bertulaka
  batz'i bertulaka   *Portulaca oleracea* (Portucaceae)
  k'ox bertulaka   *Bacopa monnieri* (Scrophulariaceae)
  muk'ta bertulaka   *Boldoa purpurascens* (Nyctaginaceae)
  yaxal bertulaka   *Talinum paniculatum* (Portulaceae)
bilil itaj   *Talinum triangulare* (Portulaceae)
nex
  kilajtik nex   *Boerhaavia diffusa* (Nyctaginaceae)
  va'ajtik nex   *Boerhaavia erecta* (Nyctaginaceae)

boraja
  batz'i boraja   *Borago officinalis* (Boraginaceae)
  k'ox boraja   *Cynoglossum amabile* (Boraginaceae)
poxil obal   *Salvia lavanduloides* (Lamiaceae)

chichol
  putzul chichol
    batz'i putzul chichol   *Physalis philadelphica* (Solanaceae)
    muk'ta putzul chichol   *Physalis ixocarpa* (Solanaceae)
  tzajal chichol
    k'ox tzajal chichol   *Lycopersicon esculentum* var. *cerasiforme* (Solanaceae)
    muk'tik tzajal chichol   *Lycopersicon esculentum* var. *commune* (Solanaceae)
    telajtik tzajal chichol   *Lycopersicon esculentum* var. *commune* (Solanaceae)
chichol ak'   *Gaya minutiflora* (Malvaveae)
    Herissantia crispa (Malvaveae)
chichol ch'o   *Jaltomata procumbens* (Solanaceae)
chichol te'   *Lycianthes lenta* (Solanaceae)
    Lycianthes quichensis (Solanaceae)
espináka   *Tetragonia expansa* (Aizoaceae)
koko'on   *Chenopodium ambrosioides* (Chenopodiaceae)
koko'on chij   *Iresine celosia* (Amaranthaceae)
ob
  sakil ob   *Phytolacca icosandra* (Phytolaccaceae)
  tzajal ob   *Phytolacca rugosa* (Phytolaccaceae)
pa' itaj   *Cleome magnifica* (Capparaceae)
pich'   *Lepidium virginicum* var. *pubescens* (Brassicaceae)
sikil ton   *Parietaria debilis* (Urticaceae)
tz'ul itaj
  batz'i tz'ul itaj
    sakil tz'ul itaj   *Amaranthus hybridus* (Amaranthaceae)
    Amaranthus scariosus (Amaranthaceae)
    tzajal tz'ul itaj   *Amaranthus hybridus* (Amaranthaceae)
    Amaranthus scariosus (Amaranthaceae)
  ch'ixal tz'ul itaj   *Amaranthus spinosus* (Amaranthaceae)
  tan tz'ul itaj   *Chenopodium murale* (Chenopodiaceae)
    Chenopodium nuttalliae (Chenopodiaceae)
uskun-te'   *Galinsoga quadriradiata* (Asteraceae)

chenek' chij   *Lupinus elegans* (Fabaceae)
    Lupinus sp. (Fabaceae)
ch'aben
  batz'i ch'aben   *Crotalaria mucronata* (Fabaceae)
  tontikil ch'aben   *Crotalaria incana* (Fabaceae)
    Crotalaria pumila (Fabaceae)
    Crotalaria quercetorum (Fabaceae)
  ch'aben ka'   *Crotalaria acapulcensis* (Fabaceae)
mesob jol bakal   *Marina scopa* (Fabaceae)

natz' amuch — *Lisianthius nigrescens* var. *chiapensis* (Gentianaceae)

poxil mako' — *Haplophyton cinereum* (Apocynceae)

poxil vayichil — *Crotalaria sagittalis* (Fabaceae)

tzukum tz'i'lel — *Acalypha arvensis* (Euphorbiaceae)

Acalypha botteriana (Euphorbiaceae)

Acalypha setosa (Euphorbiaceae)

Acalypha sp. (Euphorbiaceae)

Barleria micans (Acanthaceae)

Dalea foliolosa (Fabaceae)

Dalea leporina (Fabaceae)

Dalea lutea var. *gigantea* (Fabaceae)

Dalea tomentosa var. *psoraleoides* (Fabaceae)

Dalea versicolor (Fabaceae)

Hyptis suaveolens (Lamiaceae)

ch'il vet

  ch'ix ch'il vet — *Lantana camera* (Verbenaceae)

  sakil ch'il vet — *Lantana hispida* (Verbenaceae)

ten-jol pox — *Lantana achyranthifolia* (Verbenaceae)

chikaryo

  batz'i chikaryo — *Sonchus oleraceus* (Asteraceae)

  ch'ix chikaryo — *Sonchus asper* (Asteraceae)

chikaryo tz'i'lel — *Conyza chilensis* (Asteraceae)

ch'ix

  lo'balal ch'ix — *Cirsium horridulum* (Asteraceae)

  tomal ch'ix — *Cirsium mexicanum* (Asteraceae)

Cirsium nigriceps (Asteraceae)

Cirsium subcoriaceum (Asteraceae)

ch'oliv

  batz'i ch'oliv — *Dahlia imperialis* (Asteraceae)

  k'ox ch'oliv — *Dahlia australis* var. *chiapensis* (Asteraceae)

  tzajal ch'oliv — *Dahlia coccinea* (Asteraceae)

dalya

  ik'-lo'an pino dalya — *Dahlia pinnata* (Asteraceae)

  ik'-lo'an pinto pino dalya — *Dahlia pinnata* (Asteraceae)

  ik'-lo'an potz pino dalya — *Dahlia pinnata* (Asteraceae)

  k'an-set'an pino dalya — *Dahlia pinnata* (Asteraceae)

  k'an-set'an potz pino dalya — *Dahlia pinnata* (Asteraceae)

  k'anal pino dalya — *Dahlia pinnata* (Asteraceae)

  k'anal potz pino dalya — *Dahlia pinnata* (Asteraceae)

  k'ox sakil pino dalya — *Dahlia pinnata* (Asteraceae)

  moraro dalya — *Dahlia pinnata* (Asteraceae)

  rosaro pino dalya — *Dahlia pinnata* (Asteraceae)

  sak-vayan pino dalya — *Dahlia pinnata* (Asteraceae)

  sakil pino dalya — *Dahlia pinnata* (Asteraceae)

  sakil potz pino dalya — *Dahlia pinnata* (Asteraceae)

  tzajal pino dalya — *Dahlia pinnata* (Asteraceae)

kampray — *Cosmos bipinnatus* (Asteraceae)

matas

  k'anal matas — *Bidens aurea* (Asteraceae)

Bidens bicolor (Asteraceae)

Bidens humilis (Asteraceae)

Bidens ostruthioides (Asteraceae)

Bidens triplinervia (Asteraceae)

  sakil matas — *Bidens pilosa* (Asteraceae)

saju'

  batz'i saju' — *Simsia amplexicaulis* (Asteraceae)

  ch'ix saju' — *Simsia grandiflora* (Asteraceae)

asasena

  batz'i asasena — *Lilium candidum* (Liliaceae)

  k'anal asasena — *Hemerocallis fulva* (Liliaceae)

  sakil asasena — *Hippeastrum solandriflorum* (Liliaceae)

  tzajal asasena — *Hippeastrum bifidum* (Liliaceae)

Hippeastrum vittatum (Liliaceae)

Sprekelia formosissima (Liliaceae)

  yaxal asasena — *Agapanthus africanus* (Liliaceae)

asaséna tz'i'lel — *Hymenocallis riparia* (Liliaceae)

asaséna vola — *Kniphofia uvaria* (Liliaceae)

ch'uch'

  k'ox chuch' — *Calathea soconuscum* (Marantaceae)

Maranta arundinacea (Marantaceae)

  tzajal ch'uch' — *Canna edulis* (Cannaceae)

kartucho — *Zantedeschia aethiopica* (Araceae)

liryo — *Amaryllis belladonna* (Liliaceae)

nichim ninyo — *Hippeastrum vittatum* (Liliaceae)

snichim koyta — *Crinum amabile* (Liliaceae)

vojton tz'i'lel — *Costus sanguineus* (Zingiberaceae)

alajebal pox — *Satureja mexicana* (Lamiaceae)

ch'ulelal nichim

  batz'i ch'ulelal nichim — *Salvia mexicana* (Lamiaceae)

  tzajal ch'ulelal nichim — *Fuchsia microphylla* ssp. *quercetorum* (Onagraceae)

poxil sal-tz'i' — *Erigeron karwinskianus* (Asteraceae)

poxil t'ajel — *Symphoricarpos microphyllus* (Caprifoliaceae)

bioleta — *Vinca major* (Apocynaceae)

Viola nannei (Violaceae)

Viola odorata (Violaceae)

chuchu' — *Solanum mammosum* (Solanaceae)

ich

  bak ich — *Capsicum annuum* (Solanaceae)

  jlok'ol-chak ich — *Capsicum annuum* (Solanaceae)

k'anal ich	*Capsicum pubescens* (Solanaceae)
mórte ich	*Capsicum annuum* (Solanaceae)
natikil ich	*Capsicum annuum* (Solanaceae)
pujkan ich	*Capsicum pubescens* (Solanaceae)
sakil ich	*Capsicum annuum* (Solanaceae)
tzo' mut ich	*Capsicum annuum* var. *aviculare* (Solanaceae)
volajtik ich	*Capsicum annuum* (Solanaceae)
yich kurik	*Capsicum annuum* (Solanaceae)
unen mu	
sakil unen mu	*Solanum americanum* (Solanaceae)
tzajal unen mu	*Solanum americanum* (Solanaceae)
unen mu tz'i'lel	*Rivina humilis* (Phytolaccaceae)
ye aja-chon	*Solanum angustifolium* (Solanaceae)
yich joj	*Lycianthes ciliolata* (Solanaceae)

is-ak'	
batz'i is-ak'	
sakil batz'i is-ak'	*Solanum tuberosum* (Solanaceae)
tzajal baz'i is-ak'	*Solanum tuberosum* (Solanaceae)
tranjero is-ak'	
sakil tranjero is-ak'	*Solanum tuberosum* (Solanaceae)
tzajal tranjero is-ak'	*Solanum tuberosum* (Solanaceae)
tzajal is-ak'	*Ipomoea batata* (Convolvulaceae)
is-ak' tz'i'lel	*Solanum morelliforme* (Solanaceae)

batz'i itaj	*Brassica oleracea* var. *acephala* (Brassicaceae)
jol itaj	*Brassica oleracea* var. *capitata* (Brassicaceae)
muk'ta jol itaj	*Brassica oleracea* var. *capitata* (Brassicaceae)
yo'on vakax itaj	
k'ox yo'on vakax itaj	*Brassica oleracea* var. *capitata* (Brassicaceae)
muk'ta yo'on vakax itaj	*Brassica oleracea* var. *capitata* (Brassicaceae)
koliflor	*Brassica oleracea* var. *botrytis* (Brassicaceae)
kolinábo	*Brassica oleracea* var. *gongyloides* (Brassicaceae)
tzukum jol itaj	
sakil tzukum jol itaj	*Brassica oleracea* var. *acephala* (Brassicaceae)
tzajal tzukum jol itaj	*Brassica oleracea* var. *acephala* (Brassicaceae)

aros	*Oryza sativa* (Poaceae)
avéna	*Avena fatua* (Poaceae)
	Avena sativa (Poaceae)
ixim	
bik'it sak	*Zea mays* (Poaceae)

chix te'	*Zea mays* (Poaceae)
ik'al ixim	*Zea mays* (Poaceae)
k'anal chix te'	*Zea mays* (Poaceae)
muk'ta k'on	*Zea mays* (Poaceae)
muk'ta sak	*Zea mays* (Poaceae)
pinto ixim	
ik'al pinto ixim	*Zea mays* (Poaceae)
sakil pinto ixim	*Zea mays* (Poaceae)
sakramentual ixim	*Zea mays* (Poaceae)
ye tz'i'	*Zea mays* (Poaceae)
vitztikal bik'it k'on	*Zea mays* (Poaceae)
vitztikal bik'it sak	*Zea mays* (Poaceae)
vitztikal muk'ta k'on	*Zea mays* (Poaceae)
vitztikal muk'ta sak	*Zea mays* (Poaceae)
bik'it sak	*Zea mays* (Poaceae)
enáno	*Zea mays* (Poaceae)
ik'al ixim	*Zea mays* (Poaceae)
ivriro	
bik'it ivriro	*Zea mays* (Poaceae)
k'anal ivriro	*Zea mays* (Poaceae)
muk'ta ivriro	*Zea mays* (Poaceae)
krema	*Zea mays* (Poaceae)
kvarentáno	*Zea mays* (Poaceae)
napalu	
k'anal napalu	*Zea mays* (Poaceae)
k'ox k'anal napalu	*Zea mays* (Poaceae)
sakil napalu	*Zea mays* (Poaceae)
tzajal napalu	*Zea mays* (Poaceae)
pacha	*Zea mays* (Poaceae)
pinto ixim	*Zea mays* (Poaceae)
rokame	*Zea mays* (Poaceae)
teralényo	*Zea mays* (Poaceae)
tuspényo	*Zea mays* (Poaceae)
triko	*Triticum aestivum* (Poaceae)
tukum j'ik'al	*Sorghum bicolor* (Poaceae)
vale'	
sakil vale'	*Saccharum officinarum* (Poaceae)
tzajal vale'	*Saccharum officinarum* (Poaceae)
vale' j'ik'al	*Saccharum officinarum* (Poaceae)
ximo'	
batz'i ximo'	*Tripsacum laxum* (Poaceae)
bik'it ximo'	*Tripsacum maizar* (Poaceae)
	Tripsacum manisuroides (Poaceae)

akuxa tz'i'lel	
k'ox akuxa tz'i'lel	*Erodium cicutarium* (Geraniaceae)
	Erodium moschatum (Geraniaceae)
muk'ta akuxa tz'i'lel	*Geranium goldmanii* (Geraniaceae)
sakil akuxa tz'i'lel	*Geranium seemannii* (Geraniaceae)
chintuli' jobel	*Plantago linearis* (Plantaginaceae)
k'ojom	*Ranunculus petiolaris* (Ranunculaceae)
poxil chuvaj	*Polygala chiapensis* (Polygalaceae)

Polygala costaricensis (Polygalaceae)

poxil pat ka'   Psychotria erythrocarpa (Rubiaceae)

poxil sep'   Pinaropappus spathulatus var. chiapensis (Asteraceae)

poxil yerva   Elytraria imbricata (Acanthaceae)

yok' tz'i'   Plantago australis ssp. hirtella (Plantaginaceae)

Plantago major (Plantaginaceae)

"Moy Set" 241

kámpana nichim

batz'i kámpana nichim   Datura candida (Solanaceae)

bik'tal kámpana nichim   Escobedia guatemalensis (Scrophulariaceae)

cha'-koj kámpana nichim   Datura candida (Solanaceae)

sakil kámpana nichim   Bouvardia longiflora (Rubiaceae)

tzajal kámpana nichim   Hibiscus rosa-sinensis (Malvaceae)

kámpana tz'i'lel

k'anal kámpana tz'i'lel   Ludwigia octovalvis (Onagraceae)

Ludwigia peruviana (Onagraceae)

tzajal kámpana tz'i'lel   Lonicera pilosa (Caprifoliaceae)

yaxal kámpana tz'i'lel   Achimenes cettoana (Gesneriaaceae)

Achimenes grandiflora (Gesneriaceae)

Achimenes longiflora (Gesneriaceae)

Ruellia hookeriana (Acanthaceae)

Ruellia nudiflora (Acanthaceae)

malva   Mirabilis jalapa (Nyctaginaceae)

moy   Nicotiana tabacum (Solanaceae)

poxil aja-chon   Martynia annua (Martyniaceae)

"Nok'ol Sik'ol Set" 243

nok'ol sik'ol

nok'ol sik'ol   Phoradendron annulatum (Viscaceae)

Phoradendron falcatum (Viscaceae)

Phoradendron nervosum (Viscaceae)

Phoradendron quadrangulare (Viscaceae)

Phoradendron robustissimum (Viscaceae)

Struthanthus deppeanus (Loranthaceae)

Struthanthus tacanensis (Loranthaceae)

nok'ol sik'ol j'ik'al   Psittacanthus calyculatus (Loranthaceae)

yikatz toj   Arceuthobium globosum (Viscaceae)

"Pak' Chak Set" 244

pak' chak

k'ox pak' chak   Malva nicaeensis (Malvaceae)

Malva parviflora (Malvaceae)

muk'ta pak' chak   Kearnemalvastrum lacteum (Malvaceae)

pem-k'ulub

batz'i pem-k'ulub   Verbena carolina (Verbenaceae)

Verbena litoralis (Verbenaceae)

sakil pem-k'ulub   Borreria laevis (Rubiaceae)

Crusea calocephala (Rubiaceae)

Crusea parviflora (Rubiaceae)

poxil jolol   Anoda cristata (Malvaceae)

sat mes

k'anal sat mes   Sida barclayi (Malvaceae)

Sida rhombifolia (Malvaceae)

sakil sat mes   Corchorus siliquosus (Tiliaceae)

Melochia tomentosa (Tiliaceae)

Sida acuta (Malvaceae)

Turnera ulmifolia (Turneraceae)

Waltheria americana (Sterculiaceae)

xtalaj tz'i'lel   Pavonia schiedeana (Malvaceae)

"Petok Set" 245

chikin ton

batz'i chikin ton   Epiphyllum crenatum var. kimnachii (Cactaceae)

bik'it chikin ton   Mammillaria eriacantha (Cactaceae)

muk'ta chikin ton   Hylocereus undatus (Cactaceae)

chorísyo ch'ix   Opuntia pubescens (Cactaceae)

ch'ixal amuch   Acanthocereus horridus (Cactaceae)

ne bolom   Selenicereus grandiflorus (Cactaceae)

petok

batz'i petok   Opuntia ficus-indica (Cactaceae)

ik'-lo'an petok   Opuntia ficus-indica (Cactaceae)

te'tikil petok   Opuntia sp. (Cactaceae)

tzajal petok   Nopalea cochenillifera (Cactaceae)

yoyal vinajel   Cephalocereus maxonii (Cactaceae)

Stenocereus eichlamii (Cactaceae)

"Pimil Anal Set" 246

pimil anal

batz'i pimil anal   Sedum praealtum (Crassulaceae)

k'ox pimil anal   Sedum guatemalense (Crassulaceae)

tontikil pimil anal   Pilea microphylla (Urticaceae)

poxil chin   Echeveria acutifolia (Crassulaceae)

Echeveria mucronata (Crassulaceae)

Echeveria sessiliflora (Crassulaceae)

Villadia albiflora (Crassulaceae)

poxil eal — *Pinguicula moranensis* (Lentibulariaceae)

poxil yat chij — *Echeveria bella* (Crassulaceae)

sentavo tz'i'lel — *Peperomia campylotropa* (Piperaceae)

vixobtakil

  batz'i vixobtakil — *Peperomia galioides* (Piperaceae)

  muk'ta vixobtakil — *Peperomia humilis* (Piperaceae)

    Peperomia liebmannii (Piperaceae)

  setajtik vixobtakil — *Peperomia deppeana* (Piperaceae)

    Peperomia quadrifolia (Piperaceae)

vixobtakil chon — *Peperomia heterodoxa* (Piperaceae)

alpajo — *Medicago sativa* (Fabaceae)

chak'ak' — *Spilanthes americana* (Asteraceae)

chikin ch'o — *Dichondra argentea* (Convolvulaceae)

ch'aben tz'i'lel — *Indigofera miniata* (Fabaceae)

  Indigofera mucronata (Fabaceae)

  Melilotus alba (Fabaceae)

  Melilotus indica (Fabaceae)

mail tz'i'lel — *Houstonia serpyllacea* (Rubiaceae)

pitzak'

  batz'i pitzak' — *Trifolium amabile* (Fabaceae)

  muk'ta pitzak' — *Trifolium repens* (Fabaceae)

  tzajal pitzak' — *Medicago polymorpha* (Fabaceae)

    Melilotus indica (Fabaceae)

poxil chuvaj — *Anagallis arvensis* (Primulaceae)

poxil me'-vinik — *Oxalis frutescens* ssp. *angustifolia* (Oxalidaceae)

tzotz-ni' tz'i'lel — *Hieracium abscissum* (Asteraceae)

  Hieracium stuposum (Asteraceae)

vala-pojov

  batz'i vala-pojov — *Oxalis galeottii* (Oxalidaceae)

    Oxalis latifolia (Oxalidaceae)

  k'ox vala-pojov — *Oxalis albicans* (Oxalidaceae)

    Oxalis corniculata (Oxalidaceae)

    Oxalis frutescens ssp. *angustifolia* (Oxalidaceae)

  muk'ta vala-pojov — *Begonia biserrata* (Begoniaceae)

    Begonia fischeri var. *tovarensis* (Begoniaceae)

    Begonia oaxacana (Begoniaceae)

jol olol — *Dalembertia triangularis* (Euphorbiaceae)

on te' pox

  bik'it on te' pox — *Asclepias contrayerba* (Asclepiadaceae)

    Asclepias oenotherioides (Asclepiadaceae)

  muk'ta on te' pox — *Asclepias similis* (Asclepiadaceae)

pojov tz'i'lel

  batz'i pojov tz'i'lel — *Chamaesyce densiflora* (Asclepiadaceae)

    Chamaesyce hirta (Asclepiadaceae)

    Chamaesyce hypericifolia (Asclepiadaceae)

    Chamaesyce hyssopifolia (Asclepiadaceae)

    Euphorbia dentata (Asclepiadaceae)

    Euphorbia francoana (Asclepiadaceae)

    Euphorbia graminea (Asclepiadaceae)

    Euphorbia heterophylla (Asclepiadaceae)

    Euphorbia macropus (Euphorbiaceae)

  tzajal pojov tz'i'lel — *Asclepias curassavica* (Asclepiadaceae)

poxil chin — *Phyllanthus mcvaughii* (Euphorbiaceae)

poxil chu'ul — *Euphorbia anychioides* (Euphorbiaceae)

poxil ti'ben lukum — *Chamaesyce hyssopifolia* (Euphorbiceae)

pamal jabnal — *Anthurium schlechtendalii* (Araceae)

pi

  sakil pi — *Xanthosoma violaceum* (Araceae)

  tzajal pi — *Xanthosoma violaceum* (Araceae)

  pok'ok' — *Xanthosoma robustum* (Araceae)

ba ikatzil — *Fuchsia splendens* (Onagraceae)

j'ak'-'uch — *Castilleja arvensis* (Scrophulariaceae)

latzbil tonal pox — *Salvia lasiantha* (Lamiaceae)

nap'ap' tz'i'lel — *Ageratum houstonianum* (Asteraceae)

  Bastardia viscosa (Malvaceae)

  Conyza chilensis (Asteraceae)

  Cuphea cyanea (Lythraceae)

  Cuphea leptopoda (Lythraceae)

  Desmodium amplifolium (Fabaceae)

  Galium sp. (Rubiaceae)

  Galium uncinulatum (Rubiaceae)

  Gnaphalium sp. (Rubiaceae)

  Mentzelia aspera (Rubiaceae)

  Priva lappulacea (Rubiaceae)

  Salvia misella (Rubiaceae)

  Siegesbeckia jorullensis (Asteraceae)

  Stevia polycephala (Asteraceae)

208

batz'i nap'ap' tz'i'lel	*Siegesbeckia jorullensis* (Asteraceae)
bik'it nap'ap' tz'i'lel	*Galium orizabense* (Rubiaceae)
	Galium uncinulatum (Rubiaceae)
k'anal nap'ap' tz'i'lel	*Mentzelia aspera* (Loasaceae)
k'ox nap'ap' tz'i'lel	*Salvia misella* (Lamiaceae)
yaxal nap'ap' tz'i'lel	*Priva lappulacea* (Verbenaceae)
nochleb buluk' sat	*Salvia tiliifolia* (Lamiaceae)

pom tz'unun
k'anal pom tz'unun	*Cuphea cyanea* (Lythraceae)
muk'ta pom tz'unun	*Hemichaena rugosa* (Scrophulariaceae)
puj-'akan pom tz'unun	*Priva aspera* (Verbenaceae)
sakil pom tz'unun	*Hyptis mutabilis* (Lamiaceae)
	Hyptis tomentosa (Lamiaceae)
	Hyptis urticoides (Lamiaceae)
tzajal pom tz'unun	*Kohleria elegans* (Gesneriaceae)
	Salvia chiapensis (Lamiaceae)
	Salvia cinnabarina (Lamiaceae)
	Salvia coccinea (Lamiaceae)
	Salvia excelsa (Lamiaceae)
	Salvia holwayi (Lamiaceae)
	Salvia karwinskii (Lamiaceae)
yax-'ulan pom tz'unun	*Salvia urica* (Lamiaceae)
yaxal pom tz'unun	*Salvia polystachya* (Lamiaceae)
	Salvia purpurea (Lamiaceae)
	Salvia reptans (Lamiaceae)
	Salvia rubiginosa (Lamiaceae)
poxil k'ok'	*Loeselia mexicana* (Polemoniaceae)
poxil majbenal	*Cuphea pinetorum* (Lythraceae)
primon	*Centropogon grandidentatus* (Campanulaceae)
	Lobelia laxiflora (Campanulaceae)
sten uch	*Stachys coccinea* (Lamiaceae)
tentzun	*Ruellia inundata* (Acanthaceae)
tzajal kampana	*Lamourouxia viscosa* (Scrophulariaceae)
yalem bek'et	*Castilleja integrifolia* (Scrophulariaceae)
yich'ak ch'o	*Hamelia patens* (Rubiaceae)

orisyon tz'i'lel	*Oenothera kunthiana* (Onagraceae)
	Oenothera pubescens (Onagraceae)
poxil apon	*Oenothera rosea* (Onagraceae)

ana-jobel	*Muhlenbergia macroura* (Poaceae)
ch'ix jobel	*Festuca amplissima* (Poaceae)
	Muhlenbergia breviligula (Poaceae)
	Muhlenbergia cf. *emersleyi* (Poaceae)
	Muhlenbergia robusta (Poaceae)
	Muhlenbergia stricta (Poaceae)

| jobelal xalma | *Andropogon bicornis* (Poaceae) |
| | *Andropogon glomeratus* (Poaceae) |

limon jobel
batz'i limon jobel	*Cymbopogon citratus* (Poaceae)
k'ox limon jobel	*Scleria bourgeaui* (Cyperaceae)
	Scleria hirtella (Cyperaceae)
	Scleria pterota (Cyperaceae)
ne chuch	*Piptochaetium virescens* (Poaceae)
	Stipa ichu (Poaceae)

sakaton
batz'i sakaton	*Panicum bulbosum* (Poaceae)
	Panicum maximum (Poaceae)
tzajal sakaton	*Sorghum halepense* (Poaceae)

bot'-jol tz'i'lel	*Gomphrena decumbens* (Amaranthaceae)
mixto	*Salvia microphylla* (Lamiaceae)
oregano	*Origanum vulgare* (Lamiaceae)
tan pox	*Helianthemum glomeratum* (Cistaceae)
tomyo	*Thymus vulgaris* (Lamiaceae)
tz'i' nichim	*Matthiola incana* (Brassicaceae)

axux
batz'i axux	*Allium sativum* (Liliaceae)
yaxux ka'	*Allium scorodoprasum* (Liliaceae)
ch'upak'	*Agave brachystachys* (Liliaceae)
ch'upak' joj	*Anthericum eleutherandrum* (Liliaceae)
	Anthericum vestitum (Liliaceae)
	Echeandia macrocarpa (Liliaceae)
	Echeandia macrophylla var. *longifolia* (Liliaceae)
	Echeandia parviflora (Liliaceae)

pech'e-'ok jobel
batz'i pech'e-'ok	*Orthosanthus chimboracensis* var. *centro-americanus* (Iridaceae)
k'anal pech'e-'ok jobel	*Sisyrinchium angustissimum* (Iridaceae)
	Sisyrinchium convolutum (Iridaceae)
	Sisyrinchium scabrum (Iridaceae)
	Sisyrinchium tinctorium (Iridaceae)
sakil pech'e-'ok jobel	*Schoenocaulon officinale* (Liliaceae)
tub chil	*Agave brachystachys* (Agavaceae)

tuix
batz'i tuix	*Allium cepa* (Liliaceae)
j'alnom tuix	*Allium ascalonicum* (Liliaceae)
sakil tuix	*Allium cepa* (Liliaceae)
te'tikil tuix	*Allium kunthii* (Liliaceae)
tuix jobel	*Nothoscordum bivalve* (Liliaceae)
tuix tz'i'lel	*Calochortus ghiesbreghtii* (Liliaceae)
ve'el k'ovix	*Hypoxis decumbens* (Liliaceae)

altamixa — *Ambrosia cumanensis* (Asteraceae)

espáyder

  k'anal espáyder — *Dendranthema morifolium* (Asteraceae)

  moraro espáyder — *Dendranthema morifolium* (Asteraceae)

  sakil espáyder — *Dendranthema morifolium* (Asteraceae)

jjaral-me'tik — *Tanacetum parthenium* (Asteraceae)

kartolina

  k'anal kartolina — *Dendranthema morifolium* (Asteraceae)

  moraro kartolina — *Dendranthema morifolium* (Asteraceae)

  sakil kartolina — *Dendranthema morifolium* (Asteraceae)

klavel

  ik''ik-lo'an klavel — *Dianthus caryophyllus* (Caryophyllaceae)

  korona klavel — *Dianthus caryophyllus* (Caryophyllaceae)

  rosaro klavel — *Dianthus caryophyllus* (Caryophyllaceae)

  sak-vayan klavel — *Dianthus caryophyllus* (Caryophyllaceae)

  sakil klavel — *Dianthus caryophyllus* (Caryophyllaceae)

  tzajal klavel — *Dianthus caryophyllus* (Caryophyllaceae)

klavelina — *Dianthus caryophyllus* (Caryophyllaceae)

kopita — *Iberis simplex* (Brassicaceae)

krisantema

  k'anal krisantema — *Chrysanthemum coronarium* (Asteraceae)

  rosaro krisantema — *Chrysanthemum coronarium* (Asteraceae)

  sakil krisantema — *Chrysanthemem coronarium* (Asteraceae)

krisantéma nichim — *Dendranthema morifolium* (Asteraceae)

k'ok' sat nichim — *Dianthus barbatus* (Caryophyllaceae)

mantzanilya — *Chamomilla recutita* (Asteraceae)

markarita

  cha'-lom markarita — *Leucanthemum vulgare* (Asteraceae)

  ch'ulul markarita — *Leucanthemum vulgare* (Asteraceae)

  k'ox markarita — *Leucanthemum vulgare* (Asteraceae)

  markaríta reyéno — *Leucanthemum vulgare* (Asteraceae)

  tzotziron markarita — *Leucanthemum vulgare* (Asteraceae)

markaríta tz'i'lel — *Aster bullatus* (Asteraceae)

  — *Sabazia sarmentosa* (Asteraceae)

markariton

  batz'i markariton — *Leucanthemum vulgare* (Asteraceae)

  tzotzin markariton — *Leucanthemum vulgare* (Asteraceae)

nube — *Gypsophila elegans* (Caryophyllaceae)

  — *Gypsophila paniculata* (Caryophyllaceae)

pilix

  k'ox pilix — *Melampodium divaricatum* (Asteraceae)

  — *Simsia sanguinea* (Asteraceae)

  sakil pilix — *Aldama dentata* (Asteraceae)

  — *Viguiera dentata* (Asteraceae)

pompom

  batz'i pompom

    k'anal pompom — *Dendranthema morifolium* (Asteraceae)

    moraro pompom — *Dendranthema morifolium* (Asteraceae)

    sakil pompom — *Dendranthema morifolium* (Asteraceae)

  muk'ta pompom

    k'anal muk'ta pompom — *Dendranthema morifolium* (Asteraceae)

    moraro muk'ta pompom — *Dendranthema morifolium* (Asteraceae)

    sakil muk'ta pompom — *Dendranthema morifolium* (Asteraceae)

sakramentual nichim — *Helenium scorzoneraefolia* (Asteraceae)

snichim san-lukax — *Zinnia elegans* (Asteraceae)

tontikil putzul — *Taraxacum officinale* (Asteraceae)

tzajal nichim

  batz'i tzajal nichim — *Pelargonium hortorum* (Geraniaceae)

  ik''ik'-lo'an tzajal nichim — *Pelargonium hortorum* (Geraniaceae)

  sak-vayan tzajal nichim — *Pelargonium hortorum* (Geraniaceae)

  sakil tzajal nichim — *Pelargonium hortorum* (Geraniaceae)

volita — *Tanacetum parthenium* (Asteraceae)

tzib

  batz'i tzib — *Pteridium aquilinum* (Pteridophyta)

  ik'al ok tzib — *Adiantum andicola* (Pteridophyta)

  — *Adiantum concinnum* (Pteridophyta)

  — *Adiantum poirettii* (Pteridophyta)

  — *Anemia adiantifolia* (Pteridophyta)

  — *Anemia phyllitidis* (Pteridophyta)

  — *Anogramma leptophylla* (Pterido-

210

phyta)

	Cheilanthes hirsuta (Pteridophyta)
	Cystopteris fragilis (Pteridophyta)
jamal anal tzib	*Elaphoglossum latifolium* (Pteridophyta)
	Elaphoglossum paleaceum (Pteridophyta)
kilajtik tzib	*Asplenium monanthes* (Pteridophyta)
	Campyloneurum angustifolium (Pteridophyta)
	Campyloneurum xalapense (Pteridophyta)
	Phlebodium aureum (Pteridophyta)
	Pleopeltis munchii (Pteridophyta)
	Polypodium adelphum (Pteridophyta)
	Polypodium alfredii (Pteridophyta)
k'ox tzib	*Cystopteris fragilis* (Pteridophyta)
	Dryopteris nubigena (Pteridophyta)
	Thelypteris deflexa (Pteridophyta)
	Thelypteris oligocarpa (Pteridophyta)
	Thelypteris resinifera (Pteridophyta)
	Thelypteris rudis (Pteridophyta)
muk'ta tzib	*Acrostichum danaeifolium* (Pteridophyta)
	Ctenitis equestris (Pteridophyta)
	Dryopteris nubigena (Pteridophyta)
	Marattia weinmanniifolia (Pteridophyta)
	Phanerophlebia remotispora (Pteridophyta)
	Polystichum distans (Pteridophyta)
	Woodwardia spinulosa (Pteridophyta)
muruch' tzib	*Cheilanthes farinosa* (Pteridophyta)
	Cheilanthes lendigera (Pteridophyta)
	Cheiloplecton rigidum (Pteridophyta)
	Llavea cordifolia (Pteridophyta)
	Notholaena candida (Pteridophyta)
	Notholaena sinuata (Pteridophyta)
tzajal tzib	*Polystichum distans* (Pteridophyta)
tzatzal ok tzib	*Lophosoria quadripinnata* (Pteridophyta)
tzib ak'	*Lygodium venustum* (Pteridophyta)

"Tzukum Jobel Set" 263

akan jobel	*Panicum hirticaule* (Poaceae)
	Paspalum botterii (Poaceae)
	Paspalum plicatulum (Poaceae)
	Polypogon elongatus (Poaceae)

	Polypogon viridis (Poaceae)
ik'al jobel	*Juncus dichotomus* (Juncaceae)
	Juncus ebracteatus (Juncaceae)
	Juncus effusus (Juncaceae)
	Juncus marginatus var. *setosus* (Juncaceae)
	Juncus microcephalus (Juncaceae)
kakaxon jobel	*Chloris virgata* (Poaceae)
	Cynodon dactylon (Poaceae)
	Dactyloctenium aegyptium (Poaceae)
	Eleusine indica (Poaceae)
konejo jobel	*Zeugites munroana* (Poaceae)
krus jobel	*Carex polystachya* (Cyperaceae)
	Cyperus canus (Cyperaceae)
	Cyperus hermaphroditus (Cyperaceae)
	Cyperus manimae (Cyperaceae)
	Cyperus niger (Cyperaceae)
	Cyperus pallens (Cyperaceae)
	Cyperus virens (Cyperaceae)
	Rhynchospora ciliata (Cyperaceae)
k'otox jobel	*Zeugites americana* var. *mexicana* (Poaceae)
k'un-jobel	*Aegopogon centroides* (Poaceae)
	Arthraxon quartinianus (Poaceae)
	Muhlenbergia tenella (Poaceae)
mosote	*Cenchrus brownii* (Poaceae)
	Cenchrus pilosus (Poaceae)
puj-'akan jobel	*Arundinella deppeana* (Poaceae)
tzajal jobel	*Aristida schiedeana* (Poaceae)
	Bouteloua media (Poaceae)
	Elionurus tripsacoides (Poaceae)
	Muhlenbergia spiciformis (Poaceae)
	Rhynchelytrum repens (Poaceae)
tzukum jobel	*Oplismenus burmanni* (Poaceae)
	Setaria gracilis (Poaceae)
	Setariopsis auriculata (Poaceae)
tzuntzun jobel	*Brachiaria reptans* (Poaceae)
	Dichanthelium laxiflorum (Poaceae)
yisim be	*Cyperus hermaphroditus* (Cyperaceae)
	Cyperus virens (Cyperaceae)
	Oplismenus burmanni (Poaceae)
	Setaria gracilis (Poaceae)
	Sporobolus indicus (Poaceae)

"Uch'ul Vo' Set" 264

bukaro	
bukaro	
chijal bukaro	*Gladiolus hortulanus* (Iridaceae)
sakil bukaro	*Gladiolus hortulanus* (Iridaceae)
tzajal bukaro	*Gladiolus hortulanus* (Iridaceae)
k'ox bukaro	*Crocosmia* × *crocosmiiflora* (Iridaceae)

jol koy
  batz'i jol koy — *Tigridia pavonia* (Iridaceae)
  sakil jol koy — *Tigridia chiapensis* (Iridaceae)
  te'tikal jol koy — *Tigridia hallbergii* (Iridaceae)
jutuju — *Malaxis fastigiata* (Orchidaceae)
kola — *Govenia liliacea* (Orchidaceae)
kola tz'i'lel — *Govenia superba* (Orchidaceae)
me' putzul — *Sobralia decora* (Orchidaceae)
putzul — *Cypripedium irapeanum* (Orchidaceae)

radióla
  k'anal radióla — *Gladiolus hortulanus* (Iridaceae)
  moraro radióla — *Gladiolus hortulanus* (Iridaceae)
  sak-vilan radióla — *Gladiolus hortulanus* (Iridaceae)
  sakil radióla — *Gladiolus hortulanus* (Iridaceae)
tz'emeni'
  batz'i tz'emeni' — *Tinantia erecta* (Commelinaceae)
     Tripogandra disgrega (Commelinaceae)
     Tripogandra grandiflora (Commelinaceae)
     Tripogandra montana (Commelinaceae)
  k'ox tz'emeni' — *Aploleia multiflora* (Commelinaceae)
     Tripogandra angustifolia (Commelinaceae)
  muk'ta tz'emeni' — *Campelia zanonia* (Commelinaceae)
  o'lol tz'emeni' — *Cranichis trilobata* (Orchidaceae)
     Erythrodes secunda (Orchidaceae)
     Habenaria clypeata (Orchidaceae)
     Habenaria quinqueseta (Orchidaceae)
  tzajal tz'emeni' — *Epidendrum radicans* (Orchidaceae)
  yaxal tz'emeni' — *Commelina alpestris* (Commelinaceae)
     Commelina coelestis (Commelinaceae)
     Commelina diffusa (Commelinaceae)
     Commelina erecta (Commelinaceae)
     Cymbispatha commelinoides (Commelinaceae)
     Tradescantia crassifolia (Commelinaceae)
     Tradescantia guatemalensis (Commelinaceae)
uch'ul vo'
  kilajtik uch'ul vo' — *Epidendrum parkinsonianum* (Orchidaceae)
  k'ox uch'ul vo' — *Encyclia ochracea* (Orchidaceae)
  muk'ta uch'ul vo' — *Epidendrum arbuscula* (Orchidaceae)
  sakil uch'ul vo' — *Encyclia* sp. (Orchidaceae)
     Encyclia varicosa (Orchidaceae)

setajtik uch'ul vo' — *Meiracyllium trinasutum* (Orchidaceae)
uch'ul vo'al ba ton — *Odontoglossum bictoniense* (Orchidaceae)
yuch'ul vo' bolom — *Encyclia* spp. (Orchidaceae)
     Gongora spp. (Orchidaceae)
     Lycaste cruenta (Orchidaceae)
     Stanhopea spp. (Orchidaceae)
yuch'ul vo' j'ik'al — *Encyclia cochleatum* (Orchidaceae)
     Epidendrum ciliare (Orchidaceae)
yat kotom — *Cyrtopodium punctatum* (Orchidaceae)
yok' vakax — *Spiranthes aurantiaca* (Orchidaceae)
     Spiranthes cinnabarina (Orchidaceae)

"Vo'tus Set" 267
nochleb vonon — *Cuphea aequipetala* (Lythraceae)
tzitz — *Tagetes lucida* (Asteraceae)
tzitz pox — *Hypericum uliginosum* (Clusiaceae)
tzitz tz'i'lel — *Crusea diversifolia* (Rubiaceae)
     Linum nelsonii (Linaceae)
     Linum schiedeanum (Linaceae)
     Pectis prostrata (Asteraceae)
     Tagetes filifolia (Asteraceae)
tzutzub — *Brickellia scoparia* (Asteraceae)
     Linum mexicanum (Linaceae)
     Lythrum lanceolatum (Lythraceae)
vo'tus
  antzil vo'tus — *Tagetes erecta* (Asteraceae)
  kaxlan vo'tus — *Tagetes erecta* (Asteraceae)
  kelem vo'tus — *Tagetes erecta* (Asteraceae)
  k'ox vo'tus — *Tagetes elongata* (Asteraceae)
     Tagetes tenuifolia (Asteraceae)
vo'tus tz'i'lel — *Schkuhria pinnata* (Asteraceae)

"Yama Chauk Set" 269
chichik'uy — *Piqueria pilosa* (Asteraceae)
     Piqueria trinervia (Asteraceae)
enkaje — *Ammi majus* (Apiaceae)
     Conium maculatum (Apiaceae)
     Daucus carota (Apiaceae)
inojo — *Foeniculum vulgare* (Apiaceae)
jok'leb tzo'op tz'unun — *Digiticalia chiapensis* (Asteraceae)
keb chij — *Eryngium carlinae* (Apiaceae)
     Eryngium ghiesbreghtii (Apiaceae)
     Eryngium longirameum (Apiaceae)
krem pox — *Micropleura renifolia* (Apiaceae)
kulantu — *Coriandrum sativum* (Apiaceae)
kulantu ch'o — *Apium leptophyllum* (Apiaceae)
     Berula erecta (Apiaceae)
     Daucus carota (Apiaceae)

Daucus montanus (Apiaceae)
Donnellsmithia juncea (Apiaceae)
Parthenium hysterophorus (Asteraceae)

	Petroselinum crispum (Apiaceae)
perejil	*Petroselinum crispum* (Apiaceae)
sakil nichim te'	*Jasminum mesnyi* (Oleaceae)
	Jasminum sambac (Oleaceae)
tuturu	*Thalictrum guatemalense* (Ranunculaceae)
tzis chauk	*Tagetes nelsonii* (Asteraceae)
yama chauk	*Aralia humilis* (Araliaceae)

Arracacia bracteata (Apiaceae)
Arracacia nelsonii (Apiaceae)
Bocconia arborea (Papaveraceae)
Bocconia frutescens (Papaveraceae)
Coaxana purpurea (Apiaceae)
Dahlia coccinea (Asteraceae)
Digiticalia chiapensis (Asteraceae)
Equisetum myriochaetum (Pteriodphyta)
Pedilanthus tithymaloides (Euphorbiaceae)
Prionosciadium nelsonii (Apiaceae)
Thalictrum guatemalense (Ranunculaceae)
Valeriana sorbifolia (Valerianaceae)

alavena	
batz'i alavena	*Mentha pulegium* (Lamiaceae)
ch'ulul alavena	*Mentha citrata* (Lamiaceae)
alavéna tz'i'lel	*Borreria laevis* (Rubiaceae)

Heliotropium angiospermum (Boraginaceae)
Hyptis verticillata (Lamiaceae)
Lantana achyranthifolia (Verbenaceae)
Lippia nodiflora (Verbenaceae)
Lippia stoechadifolia (Verbenaceae)
Mimulus glabratus (Scrophurlariaceae)
Salvia misella (Lamiaceae)
Scutellaria dumetorum (Lamiaceae)
Verbena carolina (Verbenaceae)

arvajaka	
batz'i arvajaka	*Ocimum basilicum* (Lamiaceae)
k'ox arvajaka	*Ocimum americanum* (Lamiaceae)
	Ocimum micranthum (Lamiaceae)
arvajáka tz'i'lel	*Prunella vulgaris* (Lamiaceae)
chilchil tz'i'lel	*Lepechinia schiedeana* (Lamiaceae)
tzotzil jabnal	*Stachys radicans* (Lamiaceae)
yarvajáka me'on	*Stachytarpheta cayennensis*

(Verbenaceae)
Stachytarpheta frantzii (Verbenaceae)

yax-chel	
k'ox yax-chel	*Satureja brownei* (Lamiaceae)
muk'ta yax-chel	*Catoferia chiapensis* (Lamiaceae)
yaxal nich tz'i'lel	*Ageratum corymbosum* (Asteraceae)

Ageratum echioides (Asteraceae)
Ageratum houstonianum (Asteraceae)
Ageratum paleaceum (Asteraceae)

amapóla	*Papaver somniferum* (Papaveraceae)
aselka	
k'anal aselka	*Beta vulgaris* var. *cicla* (Chenopodiaceae)
yaxal aselka	*Beta vulgaris* var. *cicla* (Chenopodiaceae)
ba nab tz'i'lel	*Eichhornea crassipes* (Pontederiaceae)
chan-tzelav tz'i'lel	*Alonsoa meridionalis* (Scrophulariaceae)
	Leucocarpus perfoliatus (Scrophulariaceae)
chenek' tz'i'lel	*Desmodium palmeri* (Fabaceae)
	Phaseolus vulgaris (Fabaceae)
	Senna uniflora (Fabaceae)
	Rhynchosia minima (Fabaceae)
ech'	
antzil ech'	*Pitcairnea breedlovei* (Bromeliaceae)
	Vriesea werckleana (Bromeliaceae)
ch'ix ech'	*Pitcairnia breedlovei* (Bromeliaceae)
	Pitcairnia calderonii (Bromeliaceae)
	Pitcairnia heterophylla (Bromeliaceae)
	Tillandsia rodrigueziana (Bromeliaceae)
kilon ech'	
sakil kilon ech'	*Tillandsia violacea* (Bromeliaceae)
tzajal kilon ech'	*Tillandsia violacea* (Bromeliaceae)
krus ech'	*Tillandsia guatemalensis* (Bromeliaceae)
uma' ech'	*Tillandsia butzii* (Bromeliaceae)
	Tillandsia capitata (Bromeliaceae)
	Tillandsia caput-medusae (Bromeliaceae)
	Tillandsia dasyliriifolia (Bromeliaceae)
	Tillandsia fasciculata (Bromeli-

	Tillandsia flabellata (Bromeliaceae)
	Tillandsia plumosa (Bromeliaceae)
	Tillandsia vicentina (Bromeliaceae)
kilon uma' ech'	*Tillandsia butzii* (Bromeliaceae)
	Tillandsia caput-medusae (Bromeliaceae)
krus uma' ech'	*Tillandsia dasyliriifolia* (Bromeliaceae)
tzajal uma' ech'	*Tillandsia fasciculata* (Bromeliaceae)
	Tillandsia plumosa (Bromeliaceae)
	Tillandsia vicentina (Bromeliaceae)
vojton uma' ech'	*Tillandsia capitata* (Bromeliaceae)
vojton ech'	*Tillandsia ponderosa* (Bromeliaceae)
xulub chivo ech'	*Billbergia pallidiflora* (Bromeliaceae)
yech' joj	*Tillandsia seleriana* (Bromeliaceae)
jol koy	*Calyptocarpus wendlandii* (Asteraceae)
jonjolin	*Sesamum indicum* (Pedaliaceae)
kontiyerva	*Dorstenia contrajerva* (Moraceae)
krus tz'i'lel	*Chromolaena odorata* (Asteraceae)
k'anal nich	*Alloispermum scabrum* (Asteraceae)
	Bidens bicolor (Asteraceae)
	Bidens ostruthioides (Asteraceae)
	Melampodium montanum (Asteraceae)
	Melampodium perfoliatum (Asteraceae)
	Potentilla staminea (Rosaceae)
	Sanvitalia procumbens (Asteraceae)
	Sclerocarpus uniserialis (Asteraceae)
k'ask'as tz'i'lel	*Alternanthera laguroides* (Amaranthaceae)
	Blechum brownei (Acanthaceae)
	Cordia spinescens (Boraginaceae)
	Euphorbia graminea (Euphorbiaceae)
	Geranium seemannii (Geraniaceae)
	Iresine celosia (Amarahtaceae)
	Lopezia langmanniae (Onagraceae)
	Mirabilis jalapa (Nyctaginaceae)
	Rondeletia sp. (Rubiaceae)
	Ruellia parva (Acanthaceae)

	Russellia sarmentosa (Scrophulariaceae)
lechuka	
jich'il anal lechuka	*Lactuca sativa* (Asteraceae)
votzvotz lechuka	*Lactuca sativa* (Asteraceae)
lula	*Ruta graveolens* (Rutaceae)
marivana	*Cannabis sativa* (Moraceae)
mexa tz'i'lel	*Kallstroemia rosei* (Zygophyllaceae)
nap'-'us tz'i'lel	*Croton ciliatoglandulifer* (Euphorbiaceae)
nekeb pox	
krem nekeb pox	*Acourtia nudicaulis* (Asteraceae)
tzeb nekeb pox	*Iostephane trilobata* (Asteraceae)
nich nab	*Aster exilis* (Asteraceae)
	Berula erecta (Apiaceae)
	Cardamine flaccida (Brassicaceae)
	Eryngium carlinae (Apiaceae)
	Eryngium ghiesbreghtii (Apiaceae)
	Hydrolea spinosa (Hydrophylliaceae)
	Ludwigia peploides (Onagraceae)
	Mimulus glabratus (Scrophulariaceae)
	Polygonum punctatum (Polygonaceae)
	Rumex crispus (Polygonaceae)
	Sisyrinchium scabrum (Iridaceae)
bero nich nab	*Cardamine flaccida* (Brassicaceae)
ch'ix nich nab	*Eryngium guatemalense* (Apiaceae)
koko'on nich nab	*Aster bullatus* (Asteraceae)
	Mimulus glabratus (Scrophulariaceae)
	Polygonum punctatum (Polygonaceae)
kuchara nich nab	*Berula erecta* (Apiaceae)
pech'e-'ok nich nab	*Sisyrinchium scabrum* (Iridaceae)
nichim joj	*Zephyranthes brevipes* (Liliaceae)
	Zephyranthes carinata (Liliaceae)
pinsel	*Centaurea cyanus* (Asteraceae)
pochok'	*Juanulloa mexicana* (Solanaceae)
poxil chon	*Hybanthus verbenaceus* (Violaceae)
poxil chu'ul	*Spigelia nicotianaeflora* (Loganiaceae)
poxil lukum	*Turnera diffusa* (Turneraceae)
poxil me'-vinik	*Chamaecrista desvauxii* (Fabaceae)
poxil satil	*Diastatea micrantha* (Campanulaceae)
poxil sim-nak'al	*Crossopetalum parvifolium* (Celastraceae)
poxil yayijemal	*Gnaphalium attenuatum* (Asteraceae)
	Gnaphalium brachypterum (Asteraceae)

Gnaphalium roseum (Asteraceae)

Gnaphalium viscosum (Asteraceae)

puj

  antzil puj   Typha domingensis (Typhaceae)

              Typha latifolia (Typhaceae)

  vinik puj   Scirpus californicus (Cyperaceae)

              Scirpus validus (Cyperaceae)

sakil nichim   Fleishmanniopsis leucocephalum (Asteraceae)

sat pukuj tz'i'lel   Spigelia humboldtiana (Loganiaceae)

sat vet   Chimaphila umbellata (Pyrolaceae)

tan ka'   Desmodium amplifolium (Fabaceae)

        Desmodium aparines (Fabaceae)

        Desmodium chiapense (Fabaceae)

        Desmodium maxoni (Fabaceae)

        Desmodium nicaraguense (Fabaceae)

        Desmodium orbiculare (Fabaceae)

        Desmodium skinneri (Fabaceae)

        Desmodium strobilaceum (Fabraceae)

tenten pox   Osbertia stoloniferus (Asteraceae)

tut   Equisetum hymale var. affine (Fern ally)

        Equisetum myriochaetum (Fern ally)

tut nab   Sesbania emerus (Fabaceae)

tux-nuk'

  k'an-chik tux-nuk'   Gossypium hirsutum (Malvaceae)

  sakil tux-nuk'   Gosspyium hirsutum (Malvaceae)

tzon-te'

  pop tzon-te'

  tzon-te'al balamil   Thuidium delicatulum (Bryophyta)

  tzon-te'al krus   Tillandsia usneoides (Bromeliaceae)

  tzon-te'al te'

  tzon-te'al ton

tzun-jol tz'i'lel   Nama jamaicense (Hydrophyllaceae)

ventex chij   Lophospermum turneri (Scrophulariaceae)

voy mula   Valeriana densiflora (Valerianaceae)

        Valeriana sorbifolia (Valerianaceae)

        Valeriana urticaefolia (Valerianaceae)

xanxan

  xanxanil balamil   Lycopodium clavatum (Fern ally)

        Lycopodium taxifolium (Fern ally)

        Lycopodium thyoides (Fern ally)

  xanxanil te'   Lycopodium tuerkheimii (Fern ally)

  xanxanil ton   Selaginella pallescens (Fern ally)

xenxerva   Zingiber officinale (Zingiberaceae)

xinal pox   Melampodium montanum (Asteraceae)

xinal tz'i'lel   Porophyllum ruderale ssp. macrocephalum (Asteraceae)

yail tz'i'lel   Rumex crispus (Polygonaceae)

        Rumex obtusifolius (Polygonaceae)

yajan chuch

  batz'i yajan chuch   Conopholis americana (Orobanchaceae)

  tzajal yajan chuch   Helosis mexicana (Balanophoraceae)

yak'ubal us   Ageratina bustamenta (Asteraceae)

        Ageratina petiolaris (Asteraceae)

        Ageratina pringlei (Asteraceae)

        Fleischmannia pycnocephala (Asteraceae)

        Peteravenia phoenicolepis (Asteraceae)

        Stevia caracasana (Asteraceae)

        Stevia connata (Asteraceae)

        Stevia ovata (Asteraceae)

        Stevia serrata (Asteraceae)

yat nab   Polygonum portoricense (Polygonaceae)

        Polygonum punctatum (Polygonaceae)

yat tz'i' tz'i'lel   Lactuca graminifolia (Asteraceae)

"Alavanux Set"

The "**Alavanux** set" is comprised of five generics, cultivated and protected herbs, many with swollen, edible roots or with leaves suitable for greens.

1. **Alavanux** (**-tik**, **-altik**) (**rabano**, **rabanos***, **ravano**) refers to all of the cultivated forms of *Raphanus sativus* (7–7), the radish. They are widely cultivated by Chamulans and, to a lesser degree, by Zinacantecs in both temperate and highland communities.

Specifics: 5.

  a. **Ch'ix alavanux**, "prickly radish" (**-tik**, **-altik**) (**alavanux**), refers to small plants with rough, prickly leaves and tough, round, red tap roots. This variety has been replaced in great part by **kaxlan alavanux**.

The seeds are sown at the beginning of the rainy season. The radishes are harvested in August and sold in San Cristóbal and Tuxtla. The "cold" roots are eaten raw. They are served as hors d'oeuvres at *ladino* bars.

  b. **Kaxlan alavanux**, "castilian radish" (**k'ox kaxlan alavanux**, **ravanito**), refers to plants similar to **ch'ix alavanux** except that the leaves are not very prickly and the swollen tap roots are soft and mild in flavor. The term, **ravanito**, is now most commonly in use.

Formerly, radishes were grown only in the rainy season, but with the development of irrigation systems in the hamlets the growing season has been extended. Good drainage is required in the rainy season lest the plants yellow and the roots split. Furrows are scratched with a hoe in land that has been enriched with sheep manure or fertilizer. Leaf compost is said to cause yellowing. The rows are spaced from 20 to 40 cm apart. If the seedlings are too close they should be thinned and transplanted. The seeds are planted from May to September, producing a crop in one-and-a-half to two months. In the dry season they are planted starting in January, and are watered every three days. They are sold and resold at market.

The "cold" roots are eaten raw. Radishes are often served in cantinas as hors d'oeuvres. Cf. **elamonix**. Occasionally both the "cold" leaves and roots are boiled, seasoned with salt and chili.

c. **Muk'ta alavanux**, "large radish" (**muk'ta kaxlan alavanux**), refers to the giant forms of the radish, with very large, round, swollen, rather tasteless tap roots. The gigantism is expressed in the above-ground parts of the plants also, with these plants becoming vigorous herbs up to 1 m tall.

This variety is seldom cultivated by Zinacantecs. The seeds are sown in June and the roots harvested in October.

The "cold" greens and roots are boiled, seasoned with chili and salt.

d. **Natikil alavanux**, "long radish" (**muk'ta rabano**), refers to red radishes with long (up to 20 cm), fusiform tap roots.

A few Zinacantecs plant the seeds from June through September. The plants are hilled. The radishes produce in three months. They are sold at market.

The "cold" greens and roots are boiled, seasoned with salt and chili.

e. **Sakil alavanux**, "white radish," is the oriental radish or daikon, which has a white, fusiform, mild-flavored tap root.

It is planted by a few Zinacantecs, the same as the **natikil alavanux**.

The "cold" root is boiled and eaten, seasoned with salt and chili.

2. **Metabel** is the cultivated beet *Beta vulgaris* (1–2). It is grown by many Chamulans and by a few Zinacantecs in Sak Lum and in some of the highland communities.

The seed is sown in May and June. The harvest is in September and October.

The "cold" roots are rarely, if ever, eaten by Zinacantecs.

3. **Mustisya** (**mostasa, mostaza*, mustesya**), refers to black mustard.

Specifics: 2.

a. **K'ox mustisya**, "small **mustisya**" (**ch'ulul mustisya, sakil mustisya**), is the mustard *Brassica juncea* (3–7), an annual herb with terminal racemes of yellow flowers. The four petals are opposite each other in the form of a cross. The fruit is a narrow silique about 2–3.5 mm thick and 3–4 cm long, diverging from the stem at about a 45 degree angle. The main stem leaves are divided with 2 to 3 pairs of leaflets.

The seeds are sown in cornfields and corrals in some of the temperate and nearly all of the highland communities in May, and they produce flowers in November. They are sold at market.

The "hot" greens are boiled, seasoned with salt and chili.

b. **Muk'ta mustisya**, "large **mustisya**" (**ik'al mustisya**), is the black mustard *Brassica nigra* (1–2). The leaves and flowers are much like *B. juncea*. The fruits do not diverge from the main stem but are appressed to it and are 1–2 cm long.

It is grown in some of the temperate and all of the highland communities. The cultivation and use are the same as for **k'ox mustisya**.

4. **Napux** (**-tik, -altik**) (**nabo***) refers to field mustard and turnip.

Specifics: 3.

a. **Batz'i napux**, "genuine **napux**" (**ch'ix napux**), is field mustard *Brassica campestris* (9–13). Field mustard is very similar to *B. juncea*. The fruits are not as thick, 1–2 mm, and the leaves are not divided.

Although this mustard used to grow wild, it now is sown by many people in cornfields and corrals in most of the temperate and all of the highland communities. The seeds are scattered in May and the plants picked from June to August. When the cornfield is weeded care is taken not to disturb the plants. A second planting may made in November.

The "hot" greens are boiled, seasoned with salt and chili. Highland people occasionally barter field mustard for coffee in the temperate hamlets.

b. **Jolinom napux**, "tuberous **napux**" (**juljul nabo*, kaxlan napux, muk'ta kaxlan napux, volvol nabo***), is the turnip *Brassica rapa* (2–3).

A few people in some of the temperate and most of the highland communities plant the seeds in seed beds, transplanting the seedlings to a corral, spaced 20 cm apart. Turnip plants are hilled. Turnips are known to grow only for certain people. They produce in three months. "Cold" boiled turnips, seasoned with salt and chili are eaten, especially at the Fiesta of St. Sebastian.

c. **Kaxlan napux**, "castilian **napux**" (**ch'ulul napux**), is a glabrous form of field mustard *Brassica campestris*.

It is planted in most of the temperate and highland communities the same as **batz'i napux**.

The "cold" greens are boiled, seasoned with salt and chili.

5. **Sanorya** (**sanaorya**) is the carrot *Daucus carota* var. *sativa* (1–2). It is grown by Chamulans and by a few Zinacantecs in Sak Lum and in some of the highland communities.

The seeds are planted in May and June. Sheep manure is

provided. Young plants are thinned and replanted, producing bifurcating roots. The harvest is in September and October. Carrots are sold at market.

The "cold" roots are rarely, if ever, eaten by Zinacantecs.

"Bertulaka Set"

The "**bertulaka** set" is a grouping of four generics that are herbaceous plants with soft, succulent stems and edible leaves.

1. **Bero** (**-tik, -altik**) (**béro, berol, vok vo'**) refers to watercress *Rorippa nasturtium-aquaticum* (5–11), and *R.* × *sterilis* (1–1), which occur in still water in temperate and highland areas. They are perennial herbs with leaves pinnately divided into ovate leaflets. The flowers are white, racemose, and 2–3 mm across.

The plant is cultivated in Atz'am, Sak Lum, and in many highland communities by placing cuttings in sections of the streams where the water is slow moving.

The greens are eaten raw or boiled, seasoned with chili and salt. They are classed variously as "hot" and "cold." Women sell watercress in the market in San Cristóbal in the rainy season.

2. **Bertulaka** (**-tik, -iltik**) (**beltoraka, belturaka, bertu-raka**) refers to low, fleshy-leaved plants that occur in open places in temperate and lowland areas.

Specifics: 4.

   a. **Batz'i bertulaka,** "genuine **bertulaka**" (**beltura tz'i'lel, tzajal belturaka, veltura itaj**), is *Portulaca oleracea* (4–7), an abundant plant of disturbed and second growth areas. It is a prostrate herb with small, yellow flowers and succulent leaves and stems. Leaves are alternate, broad and rounded at the apex, narrowing to a wedge-shaped base, and are 1–2.5 cm long. The flowers have five yellow petals but only two sepals. The fruit is a small capsule, 5–9 mm high, which splits open along the circumference of the capsule. It is found throughout the township.

The "cold" tips are boiled and eaten as greens.

Extended range: *Bacopa repens* and *Mimulus glabratus.*

   b. **K'ox bertulaka,** "small **bertulaka**," is *Bacopa monnieri* (1- 3), succulent perennials with prostrate stems that root at the nodes and often form dense mats. The leaves are sessile and opposite, broadly rounded at the apex, attenuate at the base, 6–20 mm long. The flowers are axillary, purple or pink, and about 8 mm long. This occurs in wet ground in the temperate and lowland regions.

   c. **Muk'ta bertulaka,** "large **bertulaka**" (**yitaj jsoktom**), is *Boldoa purpurascens* (1–2). This is a tall coarse lowland herb with sticky alternate, thin, triangular-shaped leaves, 2–15 cm long. The flowers are very small, white or purple, borne in small clusters at the ends of the branched inflorescence. It is common in disturbed areas in the lowlands.

The "cold" tips are boiled with chili and salt and eaten as greens.

Extended range: *Boerhaavia diffusa.*

   d. **Yaxal bertulaka,** "green **bertulaka**," is *Talinum paniculatum* (1–2), a large, erect herb with alternate, elliptic, thick, succulent leaves and stems and openly branched terminal inflorescences of small, yellow flowers. The fruit is a small round capsule enclosing many lustrous black seeds. It is common in shady, disturbed areas, coffee groves, and along trails in lower temperate and lowland regions.

3. **Bilil itaj,** "slippery greens," is *Talinum triangulare* (2–5), a thick-stemmed herb very similar to *T. paniculatum* but with pink or white flowers and larger capsules. It is common on rocky slopes and disturbed areas in the lowlands.

The "cold" greens are boiled.

4. **Nex** refers to *Boerhaavia,* herbs with small, purple flowers and sticky, pubescent, round leaves.

Specifics: 2.

   a. **Kilajtik nex,** "sprawling **nex**" (**sakil nap'ap'**), is *Boerhaavia diffusa* (3–6), a sprawling, viscid herb, common in disturbed areas and sandy flats along streams in the lowlands. It is a perennial plant growing from a thick woody root. The leaves are oval, 2–5 cm long, broadly rounded at the apex and base. The tiny purple-red flowers are in small clusters at the ends of slender peduncles.

The "cold" young leaves are boiled, seasoned with salt and chili.

   b. **Va'ajtik nex,** "erect **nex**" (**nap'-'us tz'i'lel, putzul nichim**), is *Boerhaavia erecta* (3–4), a tall, thin-stemmed annual herb with many erect branches from the base. The leaves are oval, 2–6 cm long, much like those of *B. diffusa.* The flowers are tiny and white and occur in an openly branched inflorescence. It is a common plant in disturbed areas in the lowlands.

"Boraja Set"

The "**boraja** set" is comprised of two blue-flowered, gray-leaved, herbaceous groups.

1. **Boraja** (**boreja**) refers to two blue-flowered borages, which are pubescent-leaved herbs up to 1 m tall.

Specifics: 2.

   a. **Batz'i boraja,** "genuine borage" (**ch'ixal itaj***), is the garden borage *Borago officinalis* (1–2), known only in cultivation in yards in temperate and highland areas. It is an erect herb with showy blue flowers. The stems, leaves, and inflorescence are abundantly covered with stiff hairs. The leaves are alternate, elliptic to ovate, 4–10 cm long, with winged petioles broadly expanded at their base. The inflorescence is branched and open with large 5-petaled flowers to 3 cm across. It once grew in Zinacantán Center and is still grown by a few

Chamulans. The seeds are planted in the rainy season. Borage is sold at market in San Cristóbal.

In 1797 the priest of Zinacantán reported that borage "was a good catharctic for them" (de Leon y Goicoechea, 1797).

As a cough remedy, three tips are brewed for a "hot" tea. The tips may be brewed together with elderberry flowers.

Extended range: *Salvia urica.*

b. **K'ox boraja,** "small borage" (**tzotzin tz'i'lel**), is the weedy bugloss *Cynoglossum amabile* (2–4), a native of the Himalayan region. It is morphologically very similar to *Borago officinalis,* but much smaller, and appressed pubescent, the leaves are narrowly elliptic or oblong, without expanded petioles. The flowers are 1–1.5 cm across. The fruit is made up of four spinescent nutlets. This is a roadside weed throughout the highlands.

The flowers are sold at market.

2. **Poxil obal,** "cough medicine" (**bakal tz'i'lel, ch'ail pox, ch'ail tz'i'lel, poxil jik'ik'ul obal**), is *Salvia lavanduloides* (6–11), a suffrutescent plant with terminal clusters of blue flowers. It is characterized by square stems, opposite, elliptic, gray leaves, 3.5–8 cm long. The flowers are small, about 1 cm long, irregular in outline, and densely crowded in terminal spikes. It is a very common element in the understory of the pine-oak forests of temperate and highland areas.

The "hot" leaves may be chewed raw to reduce the tickling sensation caused by a cough or whooping cough. Three entire plants may be brewed for a bitter-tasting "hot" tea, taken before breakfast for three days to reduce coughing. A handful may also be brewed together with **mantzanilya,** and the tea drunk before meals for one or two days.

Extended range: *Hyptis suaveolens, Lepechinia schiedeana, Salvia leucantha, S. tiliifolia* var. *albiflora,* and *S. urica.*

"Chichol Set"

The "chichol set" is comprised of 13 generics, erect, herbaceous plants generally with leaves that can be used as potherbs or with edible fruits.

1. **Chichol** (-**tik,** -**altik**) refers to ground cherries, *Physalis,* and tomatoes, *Lycopersicon.*

Specifics: 2.

a. **Putzul chichol** refers to husk tomatoes.

(1) **Batz'i putzul chichol,** "genuine inflated **chichol**" (**batz'i chichol, pajal chichol**), is the ground cherry *Physalis philadelphica* (8–10), erect herbs with thin, alternate leaves, yellow axillary flowers, and fruits that are green berries enclosed in a papery, inflated calyx. They occur as plants of disturbed areas and rubbish heaps as well as in milpas in temperate and highland areas.

When the moon is full, the seeds may be scattered in the rainy season in the cornfield or between rows of kale, though usually ground cherry is allowed to reseed by itself. The fruits

are sold at market.

"Cold" ground cherries are husked, boiled, and seasoned with salt, chili, and coriander. They are used to flavor greens and jerked meat. They may be kept four to five months. They are eaten by the stewards, stewards-royal, and elders at Ch'ivit Krus, on the way to Atz'am on the Fiesta of Our Lady of the Rosary. As a remedy for mumps, a raw "cold" ground cherry is rubbed on the neck, and the cold blade of a machete may be applied also to reduce the swelling.

Extended range: *Lycianthes lenta, Physalis nicandroides,* and *P. pubescens.*

(2) **Muk'ta putzul chichol,** "large inflated **chichol,**" is the common cultivated jamberry *Physalis ixocarpa* (1–4) known mainly from *ladino* markets. It is an erect herb with yellow flowers, 1–1.5 cm across. The leaves are alternate, 2–5 cm long, and coarsely toothed along the margin. The fruit is a berry enclosed in a papery 10-ribbed calyx. Jamberries are sold at market in October, but are rarely bought by Zinacantecs. It occurs in waste ground in temperate hamlets.

b. **Tzajal chichol** refers to tomatoes.

(1) **K'ox tzajal chichol,** "small red **chichol**" (**k'ox chichol**), is the cherry tomato *Lycopersicon esculentum* var. *cerasiforme* (2–6), a common weedy and occasionally cultivated plant of temperate and lowland areas.

Cherry tomatoes are planted in many of the lower temperate communities in May and June. They may be planted in rows 60 cm apart in a seed bed or just scattered. In the lowlands they may be planted between the rows of corn or scattered nearby. The fruits may be prey to leafcutter ants. Although cherry tomatoes are available at market from November to April (All Souls' Day to Holy Week), they are primarily associated with the corn harvest (December and January). To remove the seeds for storage the tomatoes may be squashed between the fingers over a piece of paper or they may be rubbed on a corncob so the seeds will stick to it. Then the corncob is placed in the sun for a day and the seeds rubbed off. Formerly, cherry tomatoes were sold in the San Cristóbal market by Zinacantecs and the people of Acala.

"Cold" cherry tomatoes are boiled, seasoned with salt, chili, and onions. They are used to flavor jerked meat, iguana, snails, pumpkin squash, and cushaws. They are the standard fare of Zinacantecs in the dry season when they are working in the lowland cornfields. As a remedy for mumps, a "cold" cherry tomato is rubbed on the neck. For further medicinal use cf. **elamonix.**

(2) **Muk'tik tzajal chichol,** "large red **chichol**" (**muk'tik chichol**), is the common tomato *Lycopersicon esculentum* var. *commune* (2–5), a plant mainly cultivated by *ladinos* in lowland areas and sold in all the major markets.

It is grown in a few of the highland communities and in many

218

of the temperate communities where the seeds are sown in a seed bed at the full of the moon (lest the fruits fall) in May. In 30–40 days the seedlings are transplanted 1 m apart to fertile soil or are provided sheep manure. Some farmers stake the plants. When the plants are in flower they are hilled so that two pickings will be possible, the first in September, and the second in November. Lowland *ladinos* and Zinacantecs who have access to sandy irrigated plots along the Grijalva River also plant tomatoes in November, harvesting them in March.

> (3) **Telajtik tzajal chichol**, "long red **chichol**," is the Italian or pulp tomato, a recent hybrid of *Lycopersicum esculentum* var. *commune* with pulpy, oblong fruits. These are now common in the San Cristóbal market.

For use cf. **k'ox tzajal chichol**.

2. **Chichol ak'**, "chichol vine" (**putzul chichol ak', tzotzin sat mes, tzotzin tz'i'lel**), is *Gaya minutiflora* (1–1) and *Herissantia crispa* (4–6). The former is an erect herb with alternate, lanceolate leaves, 2–6 cm long, cordate at the base. The flowers are white and axillary. The fruit is similar to that of *Herissantia crispa*. The latter is a sprawling, downy-leaved herb with inflated, puffball-like fruits. The flowers are white and about 1.5 cm across. The leaves are heart-shaped. It occurs in disturbed places in the lowlands. It is classed variously as "vine" and "plant." These plants occurs in waste ground and second growth in the temperate and lowland regions.

Extended range: *Neobrittonia acerifolia*.

3. **Chichol ch'o**, "mouse **chichol**" (-**tik**) (**chichol moletik, chichol tz'i'lel**), is *Jaltomata procumbens* (6–11), an erect soft-stemmed herb with clusters of pendent flowers and fruits. The leaves are alternate, broadly elliptic to ovate, 4–13 cm or more long. The flowers are yellow, 1–2 cm across. The fruit is a juicy berry, purple or black, subtended by a widely spreading 5-lobed, purple and green calyx. The plant is common in moist, shady, disturbed places in yards and fencerows, in temperate and highland hamlets.

The tender shoots are boiled and the fruits are eaten raw. Both shoots and fruits are "cold."

Extended range: *Lycianthes arrazolensis, Physalis nicandroides, P. pubescens, Solanum candidum*, and *S. morelliforme*.

4. **Chichol te'**, "tomato tree" (**unen mu tz'i'lel, tuil te'**), refers to *Lycianthes lenta* (3–8) and *L. quichensis* (1–2), sparsely branched, thin-leaved shrubs with rotate, blue flowers and red, tomato-like fruits. The leaves are alternate and broadly ovate. They occur in the understory of the tropical deciduous forest of the lowland areas and in highland pine-oak forest. They are classed variously as "plant" and "tree."

The fruits are eaten raw.

Extended range: *Physalis* sp.

5. **Espináka** is New Zealand spinach *Tetragonia expansa* (2–2), a recently introduced plant that is cultivated by Chamulans and a few Zinacantecs. This is a decumbent, branching herb with alternate, fleshy, triangular-shaped leaves and very small sessile, yellowish flowers, about 2 mm across. A pesticide is scattered on the ground before hoeing to control june bug grubs. The leafy stems are sold in the market in San Cristóbal.

6. **Koko'on** (-**tik**) is Mexican tea *Chenopodium ambrosioides* (7–11), a tall, rank, ill-scented herb often protected in cornfields and common in disturbed situations throughout the township. The leaves are alternate, narrowly oblong or lanceolate with irregularly dentate margins. The minute flowers are clustered in glomerules on interrupted spikes.

It is grown in nearly every temperate and highland community.

The seeds may be sown in hoed ground. When dry, the plant may be hung up on the corral so that the seeds will scatter on their own. In hamlets like Sek'emtik, where it is scarce, it is fenced in. Mexican tea should not be pulled up indiscriminately, lest it rebel and not grow the following year. The plant may be kept dried for two months. It is taken to the lowlands for seasoning food.

The "hot" young tips are used as seasoning for chicken, iguana, snails, young pumpkin squash, young summer squash, **vokol ich ta chichol**, broad beans, scarlet runner beans, and **ibes**. Together with chili it is used to season a wide variety of mushrooms and wild birds, also gophers, rats, opossums, armadillos, and skunks. Together with mint and chili it is used to season land crabs. It may be sold in market. For use as a snakebite cure cf. **poxil yerva**. An infusion made of mashed roots that are soaked and then strained is drunk to stop a drinking habit. The use of Mexican tea as a vermifuge is not known. A thin, weak person may eat 13 land snails seasoned with salt, pepper, Mexican tea, and plenty of chili to restore strength. It is "hot."

Extended range: *Conyza canadensis* and *Iresine celosia*.

7. **Koko'on chij**, "deer **koko'on**" or "sheep **koko'on**" (**nichim jch'ul-me'tik valalupa, nichim valalupa, nichimal k'in valalupa, poxil chakal, poxil poslom, poxil vo'an, tzajal koko'on tz'i'lel**), is the very common, herbaceous perennial *Iresine celosia* (8–11). It is erect, soft-wooded, and has large, thin leaves often with a reddish tinge along the veins. The flowers are in a large, white turning reddish, feathery, terminal inflorescence. This plant occurs in second growth and exposed situations throughout the township.

Ladinos occasionally use the flowers for altar decoration on the Fiesta of Our Lady of Guadalupe.

As a remedy for **poslom**, the "cold" leaves are crushed and wrapped around the swelling. They may be combined with the leaves of **chikin ton** and **tzukum pox** (?).

The plant is eaten by sheep.

8. **Ob** (-**tik**) (**maruch itaj, sat ob, tz'ob**) refers to the pokeberries, *Phytolacca*. These are coarse, herbaceous plants up to 2 m tall that often occur in great expanses in moist, disturbed forest situations in temperate and highland areas.

The term **maruch itaj**, "Mary's greens," should be substituted for **ob** when picking the tips lest the greens taste bitter.

Because the greens give the tongue an unpleasant sensation they are not widely eaten. They are available for picking throughout the year. They were once sold at market. The berries were used formerly for laundry soap.

Specifics: 2.

 a. **Sakil ob**, "white pokeberry," is *Phytolacca icosandra* (7–12), a coarse, somewhat succulent herb, 1–2 m tall, with thin, alternate, narrowly elliptic leaves to about 10 cm long. The flowers are small, white, and in terminal and axillary racemes. The fruit is round, ribbed, and depressed in the center, green and red turning black.

The greens, classed generally as "cold," but also as "medium" and "hot," are seasoned with lime juice, salt, and chili. They are less bitter than **tzajal ob** greens.

 b. **Tzajal ob**, "red pokeberry," is *Phytolacca rugosa* (8–14), with generally reddish tinged flowers, stems, and leaves. In most other aspects, it is similar to *P. icosandra*.

9. **Pa' itaj**, "pa' greens," is *Cleome magnifica* (1–3), a coarse, perennial herb up to 3 m tall with strongly scented herbage and large, terminal racemes of pale yellow flowers. The leaves are palmately divided and the flowers are large with very long exerted stamens. The petals are about 2 cm long and stamens about 7 cm long. The fruits are long and slender resembling bean pods, 8–10 cm long. They are narrowed at the base into a long stalk, 8–10 cm long. It occurs in scattered locations in temperate pine-oak and montane rain forests. It is also cultivated in temperate and highland hamlets. This is one of the most frequently mentioned famine foods.

Slips or young plants are transplanted in the rainy season by a few people in some of the temperate and highland communities. Chamulans also plant it on the slopes of Huitepec. Many scorn these greens, claiming they must be boiled all day. Others say that two hours is sufficient, but that the water should be changed half way through the cooking process. The tips are classed generally as "cold," but also as "medium." The juice may be squeezed out and the greens placed in tortillas. They are sold, already boiled, by Chamulans in the Chamula market.

10. **Pich'*** (**pich' itaj, pich' tuluk', pich' tz'i'lel**) is pepper grass *Lepidium virginicum* var. *pubescens* (6–9), an erect, stiffly branched annual that occurs in disturbed situations such as cornfields and pastures in the highland area. It is characterized by terminal racemes of minute white flowers, small, narrow, irregularly toothed leaves and flat rounded dry fruits.

Some people boil the "cold" leaves and eat them as greens, but they cause stomach aches if eaten in quantities.

Extended range: *Aster exilis, Capsella bursapastoris, Conyza canadensis, C. sophiifolia,* and *Descurainia streptocarpa*.

11. **Sikil ton**, "cold rock" (-**tik**), is the sprawling herb *Parietaria debilis* (3–6). It has succulent stems and numerous, small, dark leaves. The flowers are minute and in clusters along the stem. It occurs in rock crevices and disturbed rocky slopes, usually in moist locations in temperate and highland hamlets. It is sometimes found in the crevices of church buttresses.

In 1797 the priest of Zinacantán reported that *parietaria* was used to "refresh the head" (de Leon y Goicoechea, 1797).

To reduce fever and the "heat" of **majbenal**, a large handful is bruised in cold water. Salt is added and a bowl of the infusion is drunk from one to three times. It is classed variously as "medium" and "cold." This same remedy, less the salt, is administered to sick chickens.

12. **Tz'ul itaj***, "tz'ul greens" (-**tik**) (**tz'uil itaj**), refers to the amaranths.

Specifics: 3.

 a. **Batz'i tz'ul itaj**, "genuine tz'ul greens," refers to *Amaranthus hybridus* (17–17) and *A. scariosus* (1–4). The former is a common plant of disturbed areas such as cornfields, waste ground, rubbish heaps, roadsides, etc., of the temperate and highland areas. The latter occurs in similar habitats in the lowlands. Both are stout, erect herbs, 1–2 meters tall. The leaves are alternate and ovate, 5–15 cm long. The inflorescence is branched and made up of spikes of densely crowded, spinescent flowers. Care is taken to leave the plants undisturbed at weeding. They are sold by Chamulans at market in San Cristóbal.

They are grown in a few highland and many of the temperate communities. When weeding the cornfield care is taken not to disturb the plants. The tips are gathered by women and children from June to August, before the plants flower.

The "cold" greens are seasoned with salt and chili, but the bitter juice of the highland form is squeezed out and discarded.

 (1) **Sakil tz'ul itaj**, "white tz'ul greens," refers to white-stemmed plants.

 (2) **Tzajal tz'ul itaj**, "red tz'ul greens," refers to red-stemmed plants. These are bitterer especially in the lowland populations, but this difference has very little genetic basis. Some women are said to have a knack with cooking this green so that it will not be bitter.

 b. **Ch'ixal tz'ul itaj**, "spiny tz'ul greens," is *Amaranthus spinosus* (3–5), a weedy plant of lowland areas characterized by long, yellowish nodal spines. The tiny flowers are crowded into nodal spinescent clusters and terminal spikes. The leaves are alternate, narrowly elliptic, 1.5–8 cm long, on long and short petioles. This plant occurs in disturbed ground such as roadsides and fallow fields in the temperate and lowland areas.

 c. **Tan tz'ul itaj**, "gray tz'ul greens" (**tan tz'i'lel**), refers to the nettle-leaved goosefoot *Chenopodium murale* (3–8), and *C. nuttalliae* (1–1). The former is a scurfy-leaved herb of scattered occurence in disturbed areas in the highlands especially waste ground and alley ways in and around towns. It is characterized by having alternate ovate or triangular-shaped leaves with a coarsely toothed margin, 2–6 cm long. The flowers are minute and are crowded into rounded clusters on the branched terminal and lateral inflorescences. The latter is very similar but the leaves are less scurfy, more uniform in size and the inflorescences occur at the tips of the branches. It has a similar distribution.

The "cold" greens are boiled, seasoned with salt and chili. They are sold occasionally at market.

11. **Uskun-te'** (**-tik**) (**kuskun-te'**, **uskun tz'i'lel**) is *Galinsoga quadriradiata* (6–10), a pubescent, annual erect herb commonly protected in cornfields, but also common in grassy situations in pine-oak forests and disturbed areas in temperate and highland hamlets. The leaves are opposite, ovate with a toothed margin, 2–6 cm long. The flowers are on long peduncles in an openly branched inflorescence, with central yellow disk flowers surrounded by white ray flowers.

The young tips classed generally as "cold," but also as "hot," are boiled as greens, seasoned with salt and chili. They are eaten raw by Chamulans.

Extended range: *Ageratina aschenborniana*.

"Ch'aben Set"

The "**ch'aben** set" includes eight generics, all erect, herbaceous plants, most of which have terminal clusters of yellow flowers, divided leaves and leguminous fruits.

1. **Chenek' chij**, "sheep bean" or "deer bean" (**chenek' ch'o, ch'aben antivo, ch'aben chij, ch'aben ka', ch'aben tz'i'lel**), refers to an annual *Lupinus elegans* (4–8) and *L.* sp. (1–1), the former an herbaceous, perennial plant with terminal racemes of blue pea flowers, 1–1.5 cm long. The leaves are alternate, small and palmately 6–7 foliate. The leaflets are oblanceolate, about 1.5–3.5 cm long. It is common in the pine-oak forests of temperate and highland areas.

2. **Ch'aben** (**-tik, -altik**) refers to *Crotalaria*.
Specifics: 2.

   a. **Batz'i ch'aben**, "genuine **ch'aben**" (**tz'unbalal ch'aben**), is *Crotalaria mucronata* (1–5). These are tall herbs with yellow pea flowers in terminal racemes. The leaves are alternate and trifoliate with elliptic to obovate leaflets, 2.5–4 cm long. The fruits dry as an inflated pod in which the seeds rattle. The *ladinos* of Chiapa de Corzo cultivate them in their yards and they occur in disturbed locations in temperate and lowland areas.

It is grown in the lowlands, in many of the temperate communities, in Jech Toch' and Pat Osil.

In the temperate hamlets the seeds are sown in the cornfield or in nearby hoed ground, and sometimes fertilized with chicken droppings. The planting coincides with the corn planting. The harvest is in three months. If planted in November, the harvest is in February. When weeding the cornfield, care is taken not to disturb the plants. In lowland irrigated land the planting is in Lent. The harvest occurs when the corn is in tassel (**balalik**).

The leafy stems, predominately classed as "hot," are broken off and boiled as greens, seasoned with salt and chili. They are sold at market. Some claim that if this plant is eaten in quantity, one's chayote flowers will drop off. Others maintain that if a person eats this plant and then goes out and looks at his crops, they will die. After eating **ch'aben**, care should be taken not to urinate near a chayote vine in flower. Care should also be taken not to toss the inedible stalks near flowering bean plants, chili plants, chayote vines, nor any squash vine. Deliberately placing them on the above plants will cause them to die. The stalks may be burnt in the fire so that the smoke will kill cockroaches.

Extended range: *Senna uniflora* and *Crotalaria cajanifolia*.

   b. **Tontikil ch'aben**, "rock-growing **ch'aben**" (**bik'it ch'aben, ch'aben antivo, ch'aben ch'o**), refers to the small, wild-occurring crotalarias *Crotalaria incana* (1–4), *C. pumila* (2–9), and *C. quercetorum* (1–2). These are all sprawling plants of the forest floor in pine-oak and tropical deciduous forests of lowland and temperate areas. They all have yellow flowers with irregular corollas and legumes, which are oblong and somewhat inflated. *Crotalaria incana* and *C. pumila* are both trifoliate. *Crotalaria incana* has broadly obovate leaflets to 6 cm long. *Crotalaria pumila* has much smaller and narrower leaflets to 3 cm long. *Crotalaria quercetorum* is unifoliate with linear leaves.

When the Virgin Mary was hiding in the banana grove with the Christ Child she lay him on a bed of this plant to change his diapers.

In Masan the seeds of these plants may be sown together with those of **batz'i ch'aben**. When they occur wild in the cornfields, care is taken not to disturb them during the weeding. They are ready to eat during the bean planting season (late August and September). The stalks, less the root, are boiled as greens, seasoned with salt, chili, and lime juice. They are predominately classed as "hot." On Epiphany when the musician, acting as a bonesetter, strikes the dude in the groin to test if the bone is properly set he exclaims, "**yaxbil te', yaxbil ton, tontikil putzul, tontikil ch'aben!**" "Green wood, green stone, rock-growing **putzul**, rock-growing **ch'aben**."

3. **Ch'aben ka'**, "horse **ch'aben**" (**ch'aben chij, ch'aben tz'i'lel**), is *Crotalaria acapulcensis* (3–4), a completely wild-occurring plant superficially very similar to **batz'i ch'aben**. The leaflets are narrower, seldom more than 1.5 cm wide, whereas those of *C. mucronata* are commonly 2 cm wide and rounded rather than acute at the apex. It occurs in second growth and dry slopes in temperate and lowland areas.

It is considered to be lethal, but can be distinguished from the edible form as it wilts rapidly after being picked.

4. **Mesob jol bakal**, "corncob broom," is *Marina scopa* (2–5), a tall, wiry-stemmed shrub with terminal, loosely branched racemes of deep purple flowers, 6–7 mm long, and finely divided leaves. The many leaflets are 3–10 mm long with minute black dots along the margins and lower leaf surface. It is common in second growth fallow fields and corn

stubble in temperate hamlets.

Five plants are tied together to make a broom to sweep the corncobs off the threshing platform.

Extended range: *Brickellia diffusa, Dalea foliolosa, D. leporina,* and *D. lutea* var. *gigantea.*

5. **Natz' amuch,** "frog necklace" (**joj tz'i'lel**), is *Lisianthus nigrescens* var. *chiapensis* (2–3), a tall, glabrous herb with long, tubular, glossy black flowers, 4–5 cm long. The leaves are opposite, sessile, perfoliate, broadly ovate to lanceolate, with acute to attenuate apices, 3–12 cm long. The fruit is a fusiform capsule containing many tiny angular seeds. It occurs on rock outcrops and second growth in temperate and lowland areas.

The "cold" plant is brewed and the water used to bathe the leg of a horse bitten by a tarantula.

6. **Poxil mako',** "cockroach poison" (**poxil mako' chon**), is *Haplophyton cinereum* (3–9), an erect herb with opposite, narrowly ovate leaves, 2–5 cm long. The flowers are yellow, solitary in the upper leaf axils, and composed of a tube flaring into five ovate lobes, 10–15 mm long. The fruit is a long and very narrow follicle, 6–8 cm long, about 2 mm wide, containing many tufted-haired seeds. It is a common element in the understory of tropical deciduous forests of lowland and lower temperate areas.

To rid the house of cockroaches, a bunch of leaves is ground with corn dough. The "hot" dough is placed under the eaves for the roaches.

7. **Poxil vayichil,** "dream medicine," is *Crotalaria sagittalis* (1–2), an erect herb with sessile or short petiolate, lanceolate and linear, or elliptic leaves that are pubescent above and below, 2–8 cm long. The flowers are yellow in terminal and axillary racemes, maturing into hollow oblong-ovate, glabrous pods, 2–3.5 cm long. It is a very common element in the grassy understory and adjacent, disturbed slopes in pine-oak forests in temperate and highland areas.

To relieve nightmares, a bunch is brewed and the patient's body is bathed with the water twice a day.

8. **Tzukum tz'i'lel,** "caterpillar plant" (**ch'ixal toj tz'i'lel, mes te', muk'tik sat mes, poxil sim-nak'al, tontikil ch'aben, tzukum nich tz'i'lel, tzukum te', tzuntzun tz'i'lel,** and **yixtol ch'o,** all in part), is a non-Linnaean grouping of plants having terminal clusters of flowers in the shape of a woolly caterpillar, *Acalypha arvensis* (2–6), *A. botteriana* (2–2), *A. setosa* (1–1), *A.* sp. (1–1), *Barleria micans* (1–1), *Dalea foliolosa, D. leporina* (1–1), *D. lutea* var. *gigantea* (3–5), *D. sericea* (2–2), *D. tomentosa* var. *psoraleoides* (1–2), *D. versicolor* (1–1), and *Hyptis suaveolens* (1–2). The more robust plants may be classed as "tree."

As a remedy for "white" dysentery, a small bunch of *D. versicolor* is brewed. The "cold" tea is drunk before breakfast for two days.

Extended range: *Lisianthus nigrescens* var. *chiapensis.*

"Ch'il Vet Set"

The **ch'il vet** set is composed of two generics, both referring to members of the genus of *Lantana* with terminal, round clusters of flowers, scabrous leaves, and fleshy hard-seeded fruits.

1. **Ch'il vet,** "fox rib" (**ch'elop vet, ch'il-te' vet, ch'ili vet, ch'ilim vet**), refers to white- and orange-flowered, slightly aromatic *Lantana.* They are classed variously as "tree," and "plant."

Specifics: 2.

a. **Ch'ix ch'il vet,** "spiny fox rib" (**muk'ta ch'il vet, tzajal ch'ili vet**), refers to the orange-flowered species *Lantana camara* (8–19), a small and creeping to large and sprawling shrub with hispid, square stems and orange flowers in terminal heads. The leaves are opposite, with crenate margins, 4–12 cm long. The fruit is a black, fleshy drupe. It is a very common plant in second growth disturbed ground throughout the township.

As a remedy for diarrhea, a handful is brewed and several bowls of the "hot" tea are drunk. The fruit is eaten by people, sheep, horses, and cattle.

Extended range: *Hemichaena rugosa, Lippia bracteosa, L. chiapasensis,* and *Verbesina crocata.*

b. **Sakil ch'il vet,** "white fox rib" (**ik'al sat tz'i'lel, k'ox ch'ilim vet, pimyénta tz'i'lel, poxil k'ak'al sik, poxil tza'nel**), refers to *Lantana hispida* (15–20), a densely branched subshrub with white, flowers in terminal heads, opposite, ovate leaves, 2–7 cm long, with crenate margins and purple-black, fleshy drupes. It is very common in second growth in temperate and highland areas.

As a remedy for diarrhea, bloody dysentery, stomach ache, "wind," and malaria chills a handful of tips or the entire plant is brewed in a covered pot. One cup of the "hot" tea is drunk before breakfast for three days. For malaria, the plant may be bruised in cold water. The infusion is "medium."

Extended range: *Lippia cardiostegia.*

2. **Ten-jol pox,** "matted hair medicine" (**bot'-jol tz'i'lel**), is *Lantana achyranthifolia* (3–9), a tall, aromatic shrub with soft, pubescent leaves, 4–11 cm long, with dentate margins, and an ellipsoid, terminal head of white and pink flowers presented on long peduncles up to 16 cm long. The fruit is a fleshy, lavender-pink drupe. It is very common in disturbed, wet ground such as roadside ditches and the margins of springs and seeps in temperate and lowland areas.

As a remedy for diarrhea, a bunch is brewed. One cup of the "medium" tea is drunk.

"Ch'ix Set"

The **"ch'ix set"** is comprised of three generics referring to thistles, sow thistles, and *Conyza,* pubescent herbs of grassy expanses in meadows and pine-oak forests.

1. **Chikaryo** (-tik, -altik) (**chikaro, chikeryo, chikorya, chikoryo**) is the sow thistle *Sonchus,* a hollow-stemmed herb with yellow, dandelion-like flowers and milky sap. Both species are introduced weeds from Europe.

Specifics: 2.

    a. **Batz'i chikaryo**, "genuine **chikaryo**," is *Sonchus oleraceus* (7–12), most common as a street weed in towns, but also found in disturbed areas throughout the highlands. It is an erect annual, with pinnately lobed leaves, the terminal lobe triangular in shape, the margins spinose-dentate. The upper leaves clasp the stem and the lower leaves are petiolate. The yellow flowers are borne in an open branched inflorescence. The heads are mostly 1–2 cm across. The achenes are light brown, flat, and with a white tuft of hairs.

The tender leaves and stalks are eaten raw or boiled by some people. They are classed variously as "hot," "medium," and "cold." They are eaten by sheep and horses. The owner of a lamb may cut the stalks and feed them to it.

    b. **Ch'ix chikaryo**, "spiny **chikaryo**," is *Sonchus asper* (1–3). This plant is coarser and more spinose than *S. oleraceus* but otherwise very similar to it. It occurs in moist, disturbed areas in the highlands.

It is eaten by sheep and horses.

2. **Chikaryo tz'i'lel**, "**chikaryo** plant," is *Conyza chilensis* (1–1), a slender erect herb with a simple stem below and a few branches above. The basal leaves are oblanceolate, 5–16 cm long, narrow, with the margins entire or wavy. The upper leaves are linear, 1–6 cm long. Flowering heads are clustered at the ends of the branches and are white-flowered, 1–2 cm across. The seeds are brown with a dirty white tuft of hairs. It occurs on grassy slopes in temperate and highland pine-oak forests.

3. **Ch'ix*** applies to thistles *Cirsium.* These are spinescent herbs to 2 m tall.

Specifics: 2.

    a. **Lo'balal ch'ix**, "edible spine" (-tik) (**ch'ixal itaj*, lo'bol ch'ix, sakil ch'ix, tzajal ch'ix**), is *Cirsium horridulum* (5–9), an acaulescent thistle that occurs in wet meadows in the highlands. It has long, narrow, dentate leaves with stout yellow spines. The flowers are purple or red purple in terminal heads surrounded by erect, lanceolate spinescent leaves, equaling or exceeding the heads.

In 1797 the priest of Zinacantán noted: "The thistle is a purgative and the wild one has a very active and efficacious root. It has a purple flower and otherwise is like the cultivated one" (de Leon y Goicoechea, 1797).

The "cold" underground section of the stalk is eaten in famines. The roots may be boiled and eaten to reduce stomach pain, but should be taken sparingly.

Extended range: *Argemone mexicana, Odontotrichum cirsiifolium,* and *Eryngium carlinae.*

    b. **Tomal ch'ix**, "conical spine" (**sakil ch'ix**), refers to

Cirsium mexicanum (1–1), *C. nigriceps* (1–1), and *C. subcoriaceum* (3–4), tall (up to 2 m) herbs of the pine-oak forests of temperate and highland areas. The three have pinnately lobed, spiny leaves, and flowers in terminal heads. *Cirsium mexicanum* and *C. nigriceps* have leaves that are deeply pinnatifid, purple, or white flowers, and several terminal heads, about 2–5 cm across. *Cirsium subcoriaceum* has shallowly pinnatifid leaves, red-orange or red-yellow flowers, and larger solitary heads, 6–10 cm across.

The young stalk is peeled, boiled and eaten.

"Ch'oliv Set"

The "**ch'oliv** set" is a grouping of five generics, all members of the sunflower family.

1. **Ch'oliv** (-tik, -altik) is the generic for the wild species of dahlia occurring in Zinacantán. These are all perennial herbs with tuberous roots and pinnately divided leaves.

Specifics: 3.

    a. **Batz'i ch'oliv**, "genuine **ch'oliv**," is the tree dahlia *Dahlia imperialis* (4–6); although technically an herb, it often obtains a height of 4 m. It has thick, hollow, water-filled stems to 10 cm in diameter. The flowers are large and showy lavender-purple, with a yellow center, 8–10 cm across, and are produced in the fall in great profusion at the tops of the stem. The leaves are bipinnate. The leaflets are ovate with a long acuminate apex, 4.5–12 cm long. They occur in large masses on moist slopes in pine-oak forests of the highlands.

The stems may be used as candlesticks at household altars on All Souls' Day. Thirsty people drink the water contained in the stems. This water is also taken to cure excessive urination. The flowers are gathered to decorate the graveyard crosses on All Souls' Day.

Extended range: *Cosmos crithmifolius.*

    b. **K'ox ch'oliv**, "small **ch'oliv**" (**ch'oliv tz'i'lel**), is *Dahlia australis* var. *chiapensis* (3–6), a species that attains a height of 0.5 m from tuberous roots. It has lavender flowers, 4–8 cm across, with yellow centers and bipinnatifid leaves and occurs on steep slopes in pine-oak forests in the highland hamlets.

    c. **Tzajal ch'oliv**, "red **ch'oliv**" (**ch'oliv chij, k'anal ch'oliv, te'tikal ch'oliv**), is *Dahlia coccinea* (7–11), a brilliant, red-flowered plant that grows to 2 m tall from a tuberous root. The red or occasionally yellow ray flowers are 2–4 cm long and the yellow central disk of flowers is about 2 cm in diameter. The leaves may be simple or pinnate. The stems are hollow, but usually contain no water. It occurs on hot, dry, often rocky or gravelly slopes in temperate and highland hamlets.

The flowers are used occasionally to decorate cemetery crosses on All Souls' Day. They are sold at market. The plant is eaten by sheep, horses and cattle.

2. **Dalya** (**-tik**) (**lalya**) is the cultivated dahlia *Dahlia pinnata* (16–5). These are extremely variable plants of garden origin with a wide range of color and double forms. During the 1960s they were widely cultivated by *ladinos*, but now are rarely seen.

In a dramatic tale of Thunderbolt's daughter, she appears first as a beautiful dahlia before transforming herself into a serpent (Laughlin 1977, T72).

The tubers are planted in May by a few people in many of the highland communities. The flowers were used by stewards and *ladinos* to decorate altars. They were sold at market.

Specifics: 14.

    a. **Ik'-lo'an pino dalya**, "purple fine dahlia": purple form.

    b. **Ik'-lo'an pinto pino dalya**, "purple spotted fine dahlia": spotted, purple form.

    c. **Ik'-lo'an potz pino dalya**, "purple thick fine dahlia: double, purple form.

    d. **K'an-set'an pino dalya**, "orange fine dahlia": orange form.

    e. **K'an-set'an potz pino dalya**, "orange thick fine dahlia": double, orange form.

    f. **K'anal pino dalya**, "yellow fine dahlia": yellow form.

    g. **K'anal potz pino dalya**, "yellow thick fine dahlia": double, yellow form.

    h. **K'ox sakil pino dalya**, "small white fine dahlia": small, white form.

    i. **Moraro dalya**, "purple dahlia": purple form.

    j. **Rosaro pino dalya**, "reddish fine dahlia": reddish form.

    k. **Sak-vayan pino dalya**, "pink fine dahlia": pink form.

    l. **Sakil pino dalya**, "white fine dahlia": white form.

    m. **Sakil potz pino dalya**, "white thick fine dahlia": double, white form.

    n. **Tzajal pino dalya**, "red fine dahlia": red form.

3. **Kampray** (**-tik**) is *Cosmos bipinnatus* (2–3), a slender, tall annual with profuse, lavender-pink flowers with yellow centers, 4–7 cm across, and delicate, finely divided leaves. It occurs in disturbed areas such as yards and cornfields in the temperate and highland hamlets.

The flowers are put in altar vases or set in handfuls at the feet of the saints, when going to church. The flowers are sold at market in Tuxtla.

4. **Matas** (**-tik**) refers to the beggar's ticks *Bidens*, annual or perennial herbs with pinnately divided leaves and white or yellow daisy flowers with spine-tipped, elongate leaves.

Specifics: 2.

    a. **K'anal matas**, "yellow **matas**" (**ch'oliv nichim, jjaral- me'tik, k'ak'al yuch' max, saju', tzitz saju', tzotzin matas**, all in part), refers to the yellow-flowered *Bidens aurea* (3–4), *B. bicolor* (2–2), *B. humilis* (1–1), *B. ostruthioides* (4–5), and *B. triplinervia* (3–6). These have a variety of habits, from sprawling to large perennial subshrubs, but all have bright yellow flowers. They occur in forest habitats and on grassy slopes in temperate and highland hamlets.

Children sell the flowers of *B. ostruthioides*. The full range of **k'anal matas** is eaten by sheep, pigs, horses, and cattle.

Extended range: *Dyssodia papposa, Melampodium linear-ilobum, Tagetes nelsonii,* and *Viguiera longifolia.*

    b. **Sakil matas**, "white **matas**" (**k'ak'al mach'ul, k'ox matas, mach'ul, matas sajo', matas tz'i'lel**), is the highly variable *Bidens pilosa* (13–14), a small, erect herb with white-rayed flowers and yellow centers. The leaves are pinnately divided into ovate or lanceolate leaflets with dentate margins. The achenes are narrow, black-ribbed, and about 1 cm long with three yellow or yellow-brown awns. It is an almost ubiquitous weed occurring at all elevations and in a variety of habitats from disturbed areas to evergreen cloud forest.

Chamulans and Tenejapans are known to boil and eat the tender leaves. The plant is used as horse fodder and pig food.

Extended range: *Cosmos caudatus* and *Sabazia sarmentosa.*

5. **Saju'** (**-tik, -altik**) (**sajo'**) refers to *Simsia,* which are coarse, rank, weedy herbs with small, dusty, yellow daisy flowers.

Specifics: 2.

    a. **Batz'i saju'**, "genuine **saju'**" (**muk'ta saju', sakil saju'**), is *Simsia amplexicaulis* (7–11), an annual erect herb, usually much-branched. The leaves are rough, pubescent and have irregular crenate or dentate margins. The leaves may be petiolate, sessile, and clasping or may have a narrowly winged petiole expanding into an clasping base. The flowers are yellow with a pubescent involucre and are borne in lateral-branched inflorescences. The achenes are black, 3–5 mm long, with 2 awns. It occurs in disturbed areas and waste ground, often forming stands of a hectare or more in abandoned cornfields in temperate and highland areas.

It is given to horses and pigs for fodder.

Extended range: *Anoda cristata, Aspilia purpurea, Bidens aurea, B. ostruthioides, B. pilosa, Eupatoriastrum nelsonii, Galinsoga quadriradiata, Melampodium montanum, Melanthera nivea, Milleria quinquefolia, Sanvitalia procumbens, Sclerocarpus uniserialis, Spilanthes americana,* and *Wedelia fertilis.*

    b. **Ch'ix saju'**, "spiny **saju'**" (**k'anal saju', tzajal saju'**), is *Simsia grandiflora* (2–5), a plant with viscid, smelly herbage and pustulate, irritating hairs. It is a coarse herb with branched stems. The upper leaves are alternate elliptic, small, sessile, and clasping. The lower leaves are opposite, larger, triangular, and petiolate. The flowers are yellow with a pubescent involucre and borne in a branched inflorescence. It occurs in similar situations as *S. amplexicaulis,* but at lower elevations.

"Ch'uch' Set"

The "**ch'uch'** set" is comprised of nine generics, thick-rooted, large, showy-flowered monocots. Most are cultivated for their cut flowers.

1. **Asasena** (**-tik, -altik**) (**asusena, pech'e-ok castillan nichim*, pech'e-ok nichim***) refers to cultivated, bulbous, showy-flowered lily relatives. All are planted one bulb to a hole, a yard's distance apart. In ritual speech, **asasena** is paired initially with **lavalèna**, pink, referring to a child.

Specifics: 5.

a. **Batz'i asasena,** "genuine lily," is *Lilium candidum* (1–5), the common, white, verticillate-leaved lily with flowers 4.5–6 cm long.

A few are planted in some of the highland communities during the rainy season. The soil is enriched with horse and sheep manure. Four pickings are possible.

Seven or eight dozen flowers are bought by the steward's assistants to decorate the litter on which the Christ Children are carried on Christmas Eve. Each steward provides three flowers for the above purpose on the eighth *Posada*. The flowers are used by the stewards as a substitute for calla lilies for altar decoration. Both flowers and bulbs may be resold and are sold at market.

Extended range: *Escobedia laevis*. The stewards' assistants gather these flowers for altar decoration.

b. **K'anal asasena,** "yellow **asasena**," is the tall, grass-leaved, yellow lily *Hemerocallis fulva* (2–5). The day lily is a tall plant with basal strap-shaped leaves, 8–21 mm wide, and long naked scapes bearing 6–15 yellow or orange flowers, 10–12 cm long. The flowers open for one day only.

This lily is planted by a few people in many of the highland communities in the rainy season.

The flowers are cut or purchased by stewards to decorate the church or home altar on Sundays and fiestas. They are used infrequently in hamlet chapel flower changes, as in Pasté.

c. **Sakil asasena,** "white lily" (**liryo**), is the large-clumped, white lily *Hippeastrum solandriflorum* (3–6), which is cultivated and also has escaped along streams. The leaves are strap-shaped, 35–50 cm long. Flowers are 2–4 in an umbel, funnelform, and 20–40 cm long.

A few people in some of the temperate and all of the highland communities plant this lily in the rainy season.

The flowers are used for altar decoration and are almost ubiquitous in hamlet chapel flower changes. Both flowers and bulbs are sold at market.

d. **Tzajal asasena,** "red lily" (**amarin**), refers to *Hippeastrum bifidum* (1–1), *H. vittatum* (1–1), and *Spreckelia formosissima* (1–1). The latter is a single, large, irregular, red-flowered lily arising from a long globose bulb, with a smooth, brown, papery bulb coat. The leaves are narrow and strap-shaped. The corolla is about 12 cm long. *Hippeastrum bifidum* and *H. villatum* are similar but the flowers are umbellate, bright red, and about 5 cm long in *H. bifidum* and red striped and about 15 cm long in *H. vittatum*.

The former is grown by a few people in many of the highland communities and the flowers sold at market, but they can not be transported any distance. The latter is used to decorate the Church of St. Lawrence during Holy Week.

e. **Yaxal asasena,** "blue lily" (**yaxal nich asasena**), refers to the blue lily of the Nile, *Agapanthus africanus* (1–1), a large robust plant, with long, linear, somewhat succulent leaves about 60 cm long. The showy blue flowers are umbellate on a long scape. The perianth is 3.5–5 cm long.

They are grown in many of the highland communities where they are prized for their ability to flourish on unproductive land. They are used to decorate the altar, but only infrequently in hamlet chapel flower changes. They are offered in Na Chij on the Fiesta of the Most Pure Virgin. Both flowers and bulbs are sold at market.

2. **Asaséna tz'i'lel,** "lily plant," is *Hymenocallis riparia* (1–1), a plant with strap-shaped leaves, bulbs, and umbellate large white flowers. The flowers are about 15–18 cm long, consisting of a long narrow tube that flares into a broad cup, bearing long linear petal-like extensions. The anthers are long and exerted from the cup. This lily occurs along streams in temperate and lowland areas.

3. **Asaséna vóla,** "round lily" (**bántera espanyol, bántera nichim, bot'-jol nichim, bugambilya, karolína nichim, sak-tanan pox, sat toj, vóla nichim**), is the cespitose *Kniphofia uvaria* (3–3), the orange-flowered plant known as the red hot poker. The leaves are linear and recurved, 1–1.5 cm wide, all basal. The inflorescense is a spike-like raceme of densely crowded orange-red, tubular flowers, about 2–3.5 cm long. The upper flowers are spreading, the lower flowers are reflexed.

A few people in Chaynatik, Joyijel, and many of the highland communities plant the bulbs in the rainy season. It is also cultivated by Chamulans.

It is used infrequently in hamlet chapel flower changes, especially in Chak Toj.

The leaves are brewed for a "hot" tea for diarrhea and whooping cough.

The flowers may be resold and are sold at market.

4. **Ch'uch'** (**-tik**) refers to *Calathea, Canna,* and *Maranta*. These have starchy, edible rhizomes and broad, thin, glabrous leaves. Zinacantecs are not aware of the edibility of the rhizomes.

Specifics: 2.

a. **K'ox chuch',** "small **ch'uch'** " (**ch'uch' tz'i'lel, sakil ch'uch'**), refers to *Calathea soconuscum* (1–1) and arrow root *Maranta arundinacea* (3–3). *Calathea soconuscum* is a leafy herb with terminal inflorescences of pale yellow flowers. The leaves are parallel-veined, large, 22–36 cm or more long, 13–17 cm or more broad. The inflorescence is a spike of spirally arranged bracts that subtend three or more flowers. The bracts are broadly ovate and rounded at the apex. It occurs in wet places in the understory of seasonal evergreen forests of the lowlands. *Maranta arundinacea* is a thin-stemmed, broad-leaved plant with white terminal flowers. The leaves are parallel-veined and alternate on the stems, ovate-lanceolate or lanceolate to 20 cm long, 8 cm wide or less. The inflorescence is branched and open. The flowers are white, the tube about 13 mm long, the petal lobes 8–10 mm long. The fruit is ellipsoid, 7 mm long, with pale, red, rough seeds. It occurs on dry, rocky slopes, often in disturbed situations in temperate and lowland areas.

b. **Tzajal ch'uch'**, "red ch'uch'," is *Canna edulis* (5–6), a tall, very broad, glossy-leaved plant with large, red flowers and papillate, fleshy capsules with round, hard, black seeds. It is cultivated, but requires a rich, damp soil. It is also found in wild situations with similar conditions.

A few people in nearly all the temperate and all but one of the highland communities plant the tubers in the rainy season.

The leaves were sold formerly to butchers in San Cristóbal (before the advent of plastic bags). Two or three leaves were required to wrap a kilo of meat. Half a leaf was needed for cracklings. The leaves are sold to tamale merchants in San Cristóbal to wrap fresh bean tamales. Zinacantecs use them for the same purpose on Holy Cross Day, but not for weddings. Five or six leaves may be gathered by the wife of a ritual assistant to wrap the chicken meat that is presented to a shaman after a curing ceremony. When a man goes to the lowlands, his wife may wrap a lump of **pozol** dough for him in four large leaves or six small leaves, tying them with a strip of palm. The leaves are also used to wrap cheese.

The flowers are children's playthings. Fifteen to twenty seeds are placed in a religious official's rattle before a handle is affixed.

Extended range: *Hedychium coronarium*.

5. **Kartucho** (-**tik**, -**altik**) (**kartucho nichim**) is the calla lily *Zantedeschia aethiopica* (4–9), a plant arising from a fleshy rhizome with large, cordate leaves and white flowers. It is cultivated and occasionally persisting in most of the temperate and all but one of the highland communities. Children are warned not to chew the leaves as they are poisonous.

Calla lilies are generally planted from April to June, after the flowers have fallen. Usually one tuber is planted to a hole, but some plant more if they are small. The distance varies from 0.5–1 m. Many planters enrich the soil with compost or sheep manure. Humid ground is required and, if in the highland hamlets, a shady location is preferred for frost protection. Wooden frame shelters with corn stubble roofs may be provided if there are only a few plants. The clumps are divided every 2–3 years. The first year the plant flowers for All Souls'

Day, the second, it begins flowering in June. If the ground is not humid, one cutting is provided until November, otherwise the season is extended to March.

An enemy may bury ground tobacco at the foot of one's calla lilies so that the tubers will rot.

Calla lilies are offered almost ubiquitously in the township for flower changes. For the Fiesta of Our Lady of the Rosary two vases filled with calla lilies, daisies or more recently, pompom chrysanthemums, and macaw feathers adorn the banquet table also on January 20th and 22nd, during the Fiesta of St. Sebastian. They also adorn the table in the Chapel of Esquipulas on Carnival Sunday, Monday, and Tuesday. They are taken temporarily to the cantor's house for the banquet table on Carnival Monday and Tuesday. The stewards carry these vases to Atz'am to decorate the banquet tables of the Stewards of Our Lady of the Rosary and the tithing man on the Fiesta of the Virgin. Two dozen lilies are provided by the senior stewards and two dozen by the junior stewards. Stewards buy or gather three dozen calla lilies for their household altars and six dozen for the church at each flower change. The flowers may be resold and are sold in Tuxtla, often in bunches of six flowers and one leaf. For New Year's Day each steward gives four dozen lilies for the Church of St. Lawrence. On Epiphany each steward provides four dozen lilies and each ensign-bearer provides two dozen lilies for both churches. On the fourth Lenten Friday each steward provides four dozen lilies, on Palm Sunday six bunches, on Sacred Heart Day three dozen lilies, on St. Peter's Day and St. Dominic's Day six dozen, on the Fiesta of Our Lady of the Rosary four dozen for Zinacantán Center and the same for Atz'am, on Nativity Day four dozen and on All Souls' Day six dozen. The ensign-bearers provide two dozen lilies apiece for Zinacantán Center on the Fiesta of Our Lady of the Rosary and on Nativity Day. On the Fiesta of the Immaculate Conception each of the Stewards of the Sacrament, the Holy Cross, and St. Dominic provide four dozen lilies. The outgoing publicans offer thirty dozen lilies for the decoration of the Chapel of Our Lord of Esquipulas at the year's end (December 28). Calla lilies are standard decorations in all chapel floral changes except in Chak Toj. They are used in Kelem Ton for the Holy Cross Day and St. Lawrence fiestas.

6. **Liryo** is *Amaryllis belladonna* (**karmenita**) (2–2), a naked-stemmed, pink-flowered plant. Flowers are funnelform, about 8–10 cm long. It produces strap-shaped leaves when there are no flowers.

It is cultivated in many of the highland communities. It is used infrequently in hamlet chapel flower changes. The flowers may be resold and are sold at market.

7. **Nichim ninyo**, "Christ Child's flower" (**xela nichim**), is *Hippeastrum vittatum* (1–5), a low, red-flowered, lily-like plant. The leaves are strap-shaped, 30–45 cm or more long, 3–4 cm wide. The flowers are funnelform, large, 15–20 cm long.

It is cultivated by a very few people in some of the highland communities. It is too fragile to market.

226

8. **Snichim koyta**, "Ocozocuautla flower," is *Crinum amabile* (1-1), a very large, purple-flowered lily. The leaves of this tall robust lily are 12 cm or more wide, with smooth margins. The flowering scape is 2–3 feet long with an umbel of many purple and white flowers. The flower tube is 16–18 cm long and the lobes are 14–15 cm long.

It is cultivated only in the lower temperate hamlet of Masan.

9. **Vojton tz'i'lel**, "corn ear plant," is the wild ginger *Costus sanguineus* (1-2), a tall (to 2 m), thick-stemmed herb with alternating broad leaves and a terminal, ellipsoid, dense head of red flowers. The leaves are elliptic to oblanceolate, about 20 cm long, 6–10 cm wide. The spike is made up of densely imbricated redish or green bracts, broadly rounded at the apex and subtending the red flowers, which are 5–6 cm long. The plants occur in rocky outcrops in wet forest situations in the lowlands.

"Ch'ulelal Nichim Set"

The "**ch'ulelal nichim** set" includes four generics, herbs and subshrubs with small, glossy, leathery leaves and small, bright flowers.

1. **Alajebal pox**, "birth medicine," is *Satureja mexicana* (1-1). This is a branched, square-stemmed herb with opposite, ovate leaves, 1–3.5 cm long. The flowers are axillary, tubular, 2–4 cm long, bright red with exerted stamens. It occurs on rock outcrops in highland pine forests.

Young plants are occasionally transplanted in the rainy season. It is sold at market by Chamulans and Huistecans.

When a woman feels the onset of labor pains, she takes a "hot" tea to give her extra strength.

2. **Ch'ulelal nichim**, "ghost flower," refers to two subshrubs with large, brittle stems and tubular, red flowers.

Specifics: 2.

a. **Batz'i ch'ulelal nichim**, "genuine ghost flower" (**ch'ulelal, ch'ulelal pox**), is *Salvia mexicana* (2-5), a perennial herb with opposite, small, dentate leaves, 1–3.5 cm long. The flowers are bilabiate, red, with a tube 2–3.5 cm long, stamens exerted solitary in the leaf axils. The plant has fragrant herbage and occurs in limestone outcrops in dry pine-oak forest in highland hamlets.

It is sold by Chamulans, the people of Chenalhó, and occasionally by Zinacantec women at market in San Cristóbal. The plant may be stored dry for a year. The young tips are brewed as a "hot" substitute for coffee. This herb is preferred for scenting the "flower water" for a newborn baby. It is usually gathered in anticipation of the birth. As a "hot" remedy, the tea is drunk for deafness caused by "cold." It is also drunk by a woman in labor pains. As a remedy for **majbenal**, a small cup is drunk each day for three days. A "medium" tea is drunk for stomach ache (**k'ux o'onil**). As a "medium" remedy for diarrhea (**sikil tza'nel**) and nausea and diarrhea (**xenel ch'utul**) burnt pieces of tortilla are soaked in the tea, and the tea drunk

2–3 times. For further medicinal use cf. **kontiyerva, k'ox yax-chel, lula**.

Extended range: *Cuphea intermedia*.

b. **Tzajal ch'ulelal nichim**, "red ghost flower" (**ch'ix tzib, kámpana pox, natz'il te', tzajal pom tz'unun te', ventex chij**), is *Fuchsia microphylla* ssp. *quercetorum* (5-7), a glossy-leaved shrub with bright red flowers. The leaves are small, elliptic, opposite or verticillate, 1–3 cm long. The flowers are small, red, 7–15 mm long, and occur in the axils of the leaves. The fruit is a black berry about 5–6 mm in diameter. It is a common plant in the understory of pine-oak and evergreen cloud forests in temperate and highland hamlets. It is classed variously as "plant" and "tree." The plants are sold in Tuxtla at Christmas time.

3. **Poxil sal tz'i'**, "mange medicine" (**-tik**), is *Erigeron karwinskianus* (9-13), perennial herbs with many slender branching stems. The leaves are small, 1–5 cm long, variable in shape. They may be linear with entire margins, or obovate with lobed margins. Flowers are small daisies, white and pink, terminal. It occurs on limestone outcrops in dry pine-oak forests and is weedy, occurring in crevices in old stone buildings in temperate and highland areas.

To remove facial blemishes, a few "medium" or "cold" flowers or leaves are rubbed on the affected part.

Extended range: *Aster bullatus* and *A. exilis*.

4. **Poxil t'ajel**, "abrasion medicine," is *Symphoricarpus microphyllus* (1-4), a small-leaved subshrub with small, 6–10 cm long, tubular, white flowers in the axils of the leaves. The leaves are small, short petiolate or subsessile, broadly elliptic, 8–20 mm long, and opposite. The fruit is globose, white, and juicy containing two seeds. It occurs on limestone outcrops in dry pine-oak forests of the highland hamlets.

Women whose legs are chafed by their skirts when they walk to Chamula or San Cristóbal rub the "hot" berries on the affected part two or three times for three days.

Extended range: *Fuchsia encliandra* ssp. *tetradactyla, F. microphylla* ssp. *aprica,* and *Ludwigia octovalvis*.

"Ich Set"

The "**ich** set" includes seven generics, five of which refer to herbaceous members of the Solanaceae. The other two are superficially similar to individual members of this set.

1. **Bioleta** (**-tik, -iltik**) refers to violets, the cultivated ornamental ground covers *Vinca major* (1-3) and *Viola nannei* (1-4) along with *V. odorata* (1-1). These plants are superficially similar to **yich joj**. The ornamental plants reproduce asexually and often persist near abandoned habitations and along trails. They all have bright blue flowers. *Vinca major* has long trailing stems with opposite ovate leaves, 2–6 cm long. Flowers are 3–3.5 cm long with a central tube expanded into five blue petals. In *Viola nannei* and *V. odorata* the flowers and leaves arise from the ground on long pedicels.

The leaves are rounded and cordate at the base. The flowers are 1–1.5 cm across in *V. nannei* and somewhat larger in *V. odorata*.

In 1748 the priest of Zinacantán listed the *violeta* among the local medicinal plants (Monrroy y Calcadilla, 1748).

2. **Chuchu'**, "breast" (**chu' ninyo, chu' ryox, xchu' jch'ul-me'tik**), is *Solanum mammosum* (2–5), a weedy or marginally cultivated plant of the lower temperate hamlets (Masan) and lowland areas. It is an herbaceous or shrubby plant characterized by bright yellow, leathery, breast-shaped fruits, 4–8 cm long. The stems and leaves are densely pubescent and armed with stout yellow prickles. The leaves are shallowly lobed and 10–25 cm long. The flowers are lateral and in groups of 1–4. The petals are purple and parted to near the base.

As the Virgin had no breasts, Our Lord gave her these fruits. They are the Christ Children's toys.

It is grown in the lowlands and in many of the temperate communities.

In Masan the seeds are sown in hoed ground and the patch surrounded by rocks to keep the chickens out. A few people plant the seeds in their lowland cornfields.

Thirty-six stemmed fruits (one dozen apiece) are provided by the Stewards of Our Lady of the Rosary and the Junior Steward of St. Dominic on the eighth *Posada* to decorate the trees that flank the creche. They are also used for creche decoration in Apas, Atz'am, Muk'ta Jok', Na Chij, Naben Chauk, Paste', and Sek'emtik.

Extended range: *Martynia annua, Solanum acerifolium, S. angustifolium,* and *S. torvum.*

3. **Ich*** (**-tik**) refers to chilies. General commentary is presented under **sakil ich**, for until recently that was the variety most frequently cultivated and eaten by Zinacantecs.

Specifics: 10.

    a. **Bak ich**, "thin chili" (**-tik**), is a cultivated *Capsicum annuum* with long, very thin, green fruits. It can be a shrub to 6 feet tall or an herb. The leaves are ovate, lanceolate or elliptic, often in pairs, 1.5–9 cm long. The flowers are small and white. The berry is red, with cream to yellow seeds within. It is grown in most of the lower temperate communities and in the lowlands.

Planting schedules and techniques are identical to those of **sakil ich**.

As an antidote for a black widow spider bite in the highlands, 13 of these chilies are ground into powder and mixed with water, providing a "hot" infusion. Should the bite occur in the lowlands the chili powder is boiled together with three brown pebbles.

Formerly, postpartum mothers avoided eating this variety of chili as it was said to be "colder" than **sakil ich**, but now, after the latter failed to produce well for a number of years, it has almost entirely supplanted **sakil ich**. Although it produces more fruit, the bite is so hot that it is not eaten raw with pleasure—a fact lamented by all.

    b. **Jlok'ol-chak ich**, "sagging bottom chili" (**o'lol tzo'**

mut ich), is a cultivated *Capsicum annuum* with small, ovoid, papery, dry fruits, 1–2 cm long. It is cultivated exclusively in and around Simojovel.

Once, it seems, a man from Apas was traveling through Simojovel and cut down a patch of chilies. When the owner discovered the theft he asked the plants what had happened. They told him to take to the road to pursue the thief. He followed their advice and when he reached Apas he saw the chilies in the thief's house. He returned home without saying a word. The next day the thief died.

Although this chili is available in the market in San Cristóbal it is rarely bought by Zinacantecs.

    c. **K'anal ich**, "yellow chili" (**naránja ich, po'on ich**), is the cultivated, shrubby *Capsicum pubescens*. These superficially resemble bell peppers, but the seeds are very hot in flavor. They differ from *C. annuum* in their purple flowers, black seeds, and rough (rugose) leaves. They are cultivated primarily by Chamulans and the people of Larraínzar.

This chili is planted by a few people in most of the highland and a few of the temperate communities. The seeds are usually planted in May in an old pot and the seedlings transplanted a month later. They are provided with compost and manure. The seedlings are transplanted to a fencerow, under a tree, or staked. They fruit in August through November, but sparsely the first year. To guard against frost a wooden frame may be built, roofed with corn stubble and elderberry branches, or the chilies may be planted in an old pot or box and kept under the roof overhang.

The "hot" flesh of these chilies is usually eaten raw. It may be eaten dried, but is very hot.

    d. **Morte ich** (**sak-mórte ich**) is a cultivated *Capsicum annuum* with the thick, fleshy skin of the serrano type.

This chili is planted by a few people in Zinacantán Center, in the lower temperate hamlets, and the lowland flood plain.

    e. **Natikil ich**, "long chili," is a cultivated *Capsicum annuum* with thin skins of the jalapeño type. It is grown in Santa Rosa and Totolapa.

    f. **Pujkan ich**, "hollow chili" (**-tik**) (**puj-'ut ich, pujan tzajal ich, pujkin ich**), is the small bell pepper *Capsicum pubescens*.

It is grown by a few people in Minax, Potovtik, and Santa Rosa. The seeds are sown in May and transplanted a month later. They fruit from October through December. This variety often becomes unproductive after the first year.

    g. **Sakil ich**, "white chili" (**-tik**), is a cultivated *Capsicum annuum* with thick, white or greenish white skin.

According to one tradition, when Our Lord was hiding in the banana grove with his mother he bumped his nose and got a nosebleed. He blew his nose and when the drops of blood landed on the ground up sprouted these chilies. Others say that they were created by the blood shed by Our Lord as he hung on the cross when he was stabbed by the blind man.

Chili and corn share the same soul, for if chili is mistreated the corn harvest will be poor. When seated around a fire, and chili is burnt, some people will begin coughing, and others will not be affected by the acrid smoke. It is customary to remark that the companion animal spirits of the coughers are near at hand, right behind the house. Chili, when eaten in large quantities, is believed to cause sexual excitation. A green chili should not be shared lest lightning strike. To cause the flowers of an enemy's chayote or watermelon squash vines to drop off, the young stems are cut off and eaten with a lot of green chilies. Even the owner of chayotes and watermelon squash should not eat chilies, lest the flowers of the former fall off, and the young fruits of the latter rot.

This chili is planted in most of the lower temperate communities and in the lowlands. The seeds are sown in seed beds or scattered in the cornfield in May or June. They should be planted in the full of the moon, lest the fruits drop. And they should be watered immediately so they will take root before the first heavy rain. To produce chilies with thinner skins, better for cooking and not too hot, the planter should be barefoot. To produce hot chilies he should "cure" the plants by spitting tobacco in the middle of the field and then pissing. Or he should piss around them when planting and when they are flowering. A "green thumb" (**sk'abal**) is required for a productive crop. Some say that chilies should be planted in the shade and well-hidden from *ladinos*. They are partial to sandy soil.

The seedlings are transplanted in a month in rows $1/2$–1 m apart. When the plants are in flower they should have coyol fruits spat upon them to increase productivity. If the owner's wife is pregnant he should light a cigarette or piss in a line around the plants, lest the fruits fall off. The harvest is from late August (few) through December of the first year. If all the fruits ripen the plant will die, so chilies are picked while some fruits are still green. In the temperate areas chilies do not fruit until the second year, and even in the lowlands the first year's crop is small. The second year there are three pickings, in June, August, and December, but if irrigated they may fruit throughout the dry season. The plants produce for three years. They are subject to attacks by leaf-cutter ants, iguanas, green jays, orioles, boat-tailed grackles, and deer. Only old plants are affected by excessive moisture (**uch**). The chilies are sold at market.

Chili leaves may be boiled and eaten as "hot" greens. Raw chilies should not be eaten by postpartum mothers as they are "cold." Dried chilies are "hot."

When the grandparents of those now in their forties used to trot long distances with towering loads, they would take along with them tortillas, salt, and a handful of ground dried chilis for their sustenance. The chilies served as a substitute for beans. Chilies are used to season the "blood" of the petate bull provided on Epiphany by the Stewards of Our Lady of the Rosary. If a newborn baby fails to cry, chilies are burnt next to it causing it to cough and cry.

A tale is told of a woman who refused her husband's advances. When he discovered her beeswax dildo, he rubbed it with chili, supplying a painfully effective remedy (Laughlin, 1977, T134).

A person who has been bitten by a snake should grab the snake and bite it three times. Not only will this serve as an antidote for the venom, but the chili in the victim's saliva will kill the snake.

For further medicinal use cf. **moy, sakramentual nichim.**

   h. **Tzo' mut ich**, "bird shit chili" (**tempich, tempich ich, tempran ich, tenpich ich, tinpich ich, yich mut**), is the wild *Capsicum annuum* var. *aviculare* with small, round fruits that occurs commonly in the lowland areas often in disturbed situations, but also in tropical deciduous forests. Two varieties are recognized:

Jipajtik ssat: with "downward hanging fruit."
Va'ajtik ssat: with "upright fruit."

The "hot" fruits are eaten raw or added raw to a dish. They are sold at market.

   i. **Volajtik ich**, "round chili" (**k'ux pevul ich, volvol ich**), is the cultivated cherry chili *Capsicum annuum*. The fruit resembles the fruit of *Solanum chrysotrichum*. These are grown in Chiapa de Corzo and Ocozocuautla.

   j. **Yich kurik**, "Tenejapans' chili" (**yich kulajtik, yich k'ank'uk', yich ulo'**), is a cultivated *Capsicum annuum* with a thin skin. The fruits are elongate and 4–6 cm long. It is cultivated by Chamulans, Tenejapans, and the people of Cancuc.

These chilies are available in the market of San Cristóbal.

4. **Unen mu**, "little delicious" (**-tik, -altik**), is the wild nightshade *Solanum americanum* (13–19). It is a slender, erect, thin-leaved annual, up to 2 m tall. Leaves are alternate, elliptic, 3–6 cm long. The flowers are in lateral umbellate clusters, white, and very small, about 5 mm across. The fruits are round and black, 4–8 mm in diameter.

It is grown in Santa Rosa and occurs wild in nearly all of the temperate and highland communities in second growth and disturbed areas as well as moist locations in pine-oak and evergreen cloud forests.

The seeds may be stored and sown in the corral or hoed ground in the rainy season. Young wild plants may also be transplanted. They are available for picking from May through December. They are sold at market in Tuxtla and San Cristóbal.

This plant should be handled with care. It should not be pulled up indiscriminately as it has caterpillars (**xchanul**) that sting. Their stings can only be cured if the offender eats the leaves raw. Some claim that if the plant is sold its soul will be lost and the crop will disappear.

The greens are boiled with salt and chili and are eaten by all Zinacantecs. It takes a good hand (**sk'abal**), however, to prepare the greens. For some cooks they always turn out bitter. They are generally classed as "hot." They should be eaten in moderation lest they cause diarrhea and hiccups.

As a remedy for dysentery, a tea is made by brewing the greens without salt. The berries are chewed raw for fever sores.

Specifics: 2.

    a. **Sakil unen mu**, "white little delicious," refers to light green-stemmed plants.

    b. **Tzajal unen mu**, "red little delicious," refers to plants with darker green leaves and maroon to blackish stems. When cooked, these are often bitter.

5. **Unen mu tz'i'lel**, "little delicious plant," is *Rivina humilis* (1–1), perennial herbs or subshrubs with narrow ovate leaves, 3–11 cm long, rounded at the base, long and acute at the tip, with long, narrow racemes of tiny, white or pink flowers. The fruit is round, bright red, about 4 mm in diameter. It occurs on moist shady banks in temperate and lowland hamlets in both second growth and forest situations. The thin edible leaves are very reminiscent of **unen mu**.

The "hot" greens are eaten, boiled.

6. **Ye aja-chon**, "rattlesnake's mouth" or "rattlesnake's teeth" (**k'anal ch'ix**), is *Solanum angustifolium* (2–3), a very spiny herb common in disturbed situations in lowland areas. The flowers are large, yellow, and showy. The leaves are deeply divided into many rounded lobes. Both leaves and stems bear many stout yellow spines. The arrangement of spines about the fruits is reminiscent of a rattlesnake's mouth.

To relieve mules suffering from a tarantula bite, the fruit is bruised in cold water and the "hot" infusion administered to the affected area. The fruits should not be stored at home lest they attract snakes.

7. **Yich joj**, "raven's chili" (**lo'bol joj**), is *Lycianthes ciliolata* (2–3), a slender herb to 1 m tall with black, tomato-like fruits. The stems are branched. The leaves are usually in pairs similar in shape but unequal in size. They are 3–10 cm long and ovate. Flowers are solitary, white and purple, with fused petals, 2.5–4 cm across. It occurs as scattered individuals in disturbed areas in temperate and lowland areas.

The "cold" fruits are eaten.

Extended range: *Ruellia lactea*.

"Is-ak' Set"

The "**Is-ak'** set" is comprised of two generics belonging to a group of tuberous rooted plants mainly made up of potatoes and sweet potatoes.

1. **Is-ak'*** (**-tik, -iltik**) refers to potatoes and sweet potatoes. Specifics: 3.

    a. **Batz'i is-ak'**, "genuine potato," is *Solanum tuberosum* (3–4), a small, tubered, probably locally derived form of the potato that has become very scarce. It is a perennial herb with straggling branches and erect stems about 1 m tall. The leaves are alternate ovate to elliptic, 2–5.5 cm long, acute at the apex, minutely pubescent below. The flowers are racemose with pedicels, 1.5–2 cm long. The corolla is rotate, 5-lobed, purple with five conspicuous yellow anthers, 5–6 mm long. In the past it occurred wild near the tops of the high peaks near San Cristóbal in evergreen cloud forest.

Some claim that potatoes were created when Christ squeezed milk from his mother's breast. Others maintain that Our Lord instructed Adam and Eve, before they had anything to eat, to boil three river pebbles. These, then, were transformed into potatoes. One should avoid digging potatoes at noon because at this time their souls are bathing.

Many people once grew these potatoes in their yards. The young potatoes were scattered when the ground was hoed before the onset of the rainy season. Or they were planted between the clumps of corn. New potatoes were harvested at the time or allowed to mature and harvested in August. They were so plentiful in Atz'am that during the hoeing season fieldhands would be given an *almud* of potatoes in addition to their pay. Formerly potatoes and cane liquor were a standard gift to the lowland landholders whose land was to be rented. They were sold at market.

These small potatoes are considered to be the most flavorsome. They are washed, boiled, and mashed into small pieces. "Cold" potatoes are seasoned with chili and salt, or also with coriander and onion. They may be eaten alone or mixed with a variety of foods (beans, cabbage, tomatoes, eggs, shrimp, fish, and beef). "Cold" potato greens may also be eaten, boiled.

These potatoes may be subdivided further:

    (1) **Sakil batz'i is-ak'**, "white genuine potato," refers to white-skinned potatoes.

    (2) **Tzajal batz'i is-ak'**, "red genuine potato," refers to red-skinned potatoes.

    b. **Tranjero is-ak'**, "foreign potato" (**tanjero is-ak'**), is *Solanum tuberosum* (2–4), a recently derived brown-skinned, large-tubered strain of the potato.

These potatoes are now grown by many people in a few of the temperate and all of the highland communities. They are planted from mid-April through June, and, if irrigation is available, from November through February. They should not be planted when the moon is young, lest the flowers drop. Small, whole potatoes or potatoes cut into 2–4 sections are planted in rows 40 cm apart. Whole potatoes produce tubers more readily. They are planted in corrals or hoed ground and provided with compost, sheep or horse manure, or fertilizer. Some hill the plants when they are 20 cm tall and again before they flower. Others wait until the plants are in flower. Failure to hill will prevent the plants from forming tubers. They may be dug when the plant is in fruit. This may vary from 3 to 5 months. They are sold and resold at market.

For culinary use cf. **batz'i is-ak'**.

These large potatoes may also be further subdivided:

    (1) **Sakil tranjero is-ak'**, "white foreign potato," is the white-skinned potato.

    (2) **Tzajal tranjero is-ak'**, "red foreign potato," is the red-skinned variety.

    c. **Tzajal is-ak'**, "red potato," is the sweet potato

Ipomoea batata (1–2), which is grown primarily by the people of Larraínzar. It is a perennial vine with heart-shaped leaves, about 4–10 cm long, 3.5–8 cm wide. The flowers are axillary, clustered at the ends of long peduncles. The corollas are lavender about 3–4 cm long. The fruit is a two-celled capsule.

The cultivation of sweet potatoes has been introduced recently in Santa Rosa and most of the temperate communities. A few people plant the tuber or cuttings in hills in May. The tubers are harvested in January.

Sweet potatoes are sold throughout the year in the San Cristóbal market. Most commonly they are sold in chunks after having been boiled with raw sugar. These "cold" sweet potatoes are considered to be a fruit (**lo'bol**) and are eaten as between-meal snacks.

2. **Is-ak' tz'i'lel**, "potato plant," is *Solanum morelliforme* (1–2). This is a slender epiphytic and saxicolous herb with terminal clusters of white flowers maturing into black, round berries, 1 cm in diameter. It occurs in pine-oak forests in the highlands.

"Itaj Set"

The "itaj set" is a group of cultivated plants that are all variations of *Brassica oleracea*. There are five generic terms. The colonial term **coles** appears to have referred both to kale and cabbage.

1. **Batz'i itaj** (**-tik**), "real greens" (**sakil itaj**), refers to *Brassica oleracea* var. *acephala*, non-curly kale. Kales usually have a simple erect stem, bearing larger broad leaves. Flowers are yellow borne in terminal racemes. It is grown in a few of the temperate and all but one of the highland communities. Non-curly kale and curly kale are grown together in vegetable patches. The slips are planted in the rainy season. If planted when the moon is young the leaves will be more tender. The slips are planted 40 cm apart. Replanting may occur. The leaves and tip are cut off so the plant will branch out. The plants are hilled so they will produce many leaves. It will live 2–4 years. The harvest is in September. The greens are sold at market in San Cristóbal. Both flowers and leaves are gathered by women. They are brewed with chili, salt, lime juice, and sometimes mint. The leaves may be eaten raw. They are "cold."

If one dreams of selling kale, one's sheep or mules will die.

2. **Jol itaj** (**-tik**), "head greens" (**coles***, **jolinom itaj**), refers to *Brassica oleracea* var. *capitata*, cabbage. The seeds are sown in the rainy season and transplanted after a month. They should be sown when the moon is full so the heads will be big. The plants are hilled so they will head. Recently the pesticide BHC3 is being used with perilous frequency. It is scattered on the ground before hoeing to control june bug grubs. Cabbage plants may also be sprayed after the first week. The harvest is in three months. It is "cold," seasoned as above. It is sold and resold at market. Cf. **elamonix**.

To dream of eating cabbage or seeing a cabbage head is a presentiment that one will be murdered on the trail.

Specifics: 2.

  a. **Muk'ta jol itaj**, "large head greens," refers to the round-headed form of cabbage. It is grown in Santa Rosa, many of the temperate and most of the highland communities.

  b. **Yo'on vakax itaj**, "cow heart greens," refers to an oblong-headed variety that is sweeter than the round-headed form. It is "cold."

    (1) **K'ox yo'on vakax itaj**, "small cow heart greens," refers to a small-headed variety that is bitterer than the larger form.

    (2) **Muk'ta yo'on vakax itaj**, "large cow heart greens," refers to a big-headed variety.

3. **Koliflor** is *Brassica oleracea* var. *botrytis,* cauliflower. This is a recent introduction into the highlands. It is grown in a few temperate and highland communities.

4. **Kolinábo** is *Brassica oleracea* var. *gongyloides,* kohlrabi. The swollen base of the kohlrabi stem looks something like a turnip and can grow as large as an orange. It can be green or purple. *Ladinos* plant the seeds in the rainy season.

Kohlrabi cultivation is just beginning in Chaynatik, Joyijel, and a few of the highland communities.

The "cold" greens are seasoned the same as cabbage and kale.

5. **Tzukum jol itaj**, "caterpillar head greens" (**kuruch' itaj, muruch' itaj**), refers to *Brassica oleracea* var. *acephala*, curly kale. It is grown in a few of the temperate and many of the highland communities. It is planted the same as **batz'i itaj**. The leaves may be seasoned with mint and coriander. The greens are classed variously as "cold" and "hot."

Specifics: 2.

  a. **Sakil tzukum jol itaj**, "white caterpillar head greens," is curly kale.

  b. **Tzajal tzukum jol itaj**, "red caterpillar head greens" (**kulix itaj**), is a hybrid of the curly and non-curly forms.

"Ixim Set"

The "Ixim set" with seven generics, comprises all the major grains, plus sugarcane, which is also a cultivated grass.

1. **Aros** is rice *Oryza sativa*. Until recently it was known to Zinacantecs only in the market, but is grown by *ladinos* in the region of Nueva Concordia and is occasionally adventive in distant lowland areas. Rice is an annual grass with erect culms to 1 meter high. The leaves are narrow, 1–1.5 cm wide. Panicles are oblong and somewhat flattened with ridges on the hard outer coat.

Rice is seldom eaten by Zinacantecs in their homes, but fried rice and rice gruel (uncooked rice, ground and mixed with water) are standard fare in market restaurants. "Hot" rice gruel may be drunk by women to induce lactation, followed by a sweat bath.

2. **Avéna** (**trigo jobel**) refers to wild oats *Avena fatua* (2–2)

and cultivated oats *A. sativa* (1–2), slender or coarse grasses with culms from 30 cm to more than 1 meter high. The leaves are narrow, 4–15 mm wide. The panicles are loose and the spikelets are nodding. Spikelets are enclosed in long-awned glumes, about 2.5 cm long. The awns are either bent as in *A. fatua* or straight in *A. sativa*. The seeds are sown by *ladinos* in the highlands in the rainy season. "Cold" oats are eaten by *ladinos*.

3. **Ixim*** (-**altik**) refers to maize *Zea mays*. Because of the long history of cultivation of this plant in this region and because it is the staple and single most important food crop to these people, it is quite understandable that the classification and variation of types (races) of the plant would be very complex. This is further complicated by the very dissected, sub-dialectal, dispersed hamlet nature of the human population, which is reflected in the terms they apply to maize. Yet another feature is that within the last two generations modern technology in the form of hybrid stock of maize and increased mobility of the populations due to roads and motorized vehicles has led to a mixing of once distinct restricted types of maize. In the course of this study many of these races have gone out of existence in Zinacantán. The determination of race was very kindly provided by Prof. P.C. Mangelsdorf, who examined the samples in 1967.

In the oral tradition of Zinacantán, corn was present from the earliest times when Our Lord was just a baby fleeing with his mother from the Jews. According to some it was Our Lord, and according to others, his mother, who caused the corn to mature overnight to confuse their pursuers (cf. Laughlin, 1977, T52). In ritual speech corn is referred to as "Our Lord's sunbeams and shadows" (**xxojobal snak'obal kajvaltik**). After the Flood, it was the raven that brought man each kind of corn, stealing it from one of the Earth Lord's caves (cf. Laughlin, 1977, T70). When Our Lord's older brothers climbed a tree to eat honey and only threw down the beeswax for him to eat, he fashioned a gopher from the chewings. After he had molded it well he stuck splinters of corn stubble in its mouth so that it would have strong teeth to gnaw the tree roots.

When a boy baby is born he is called "woman's luck," **yorail antz**, and when it is a girl baby she is "man's luck," **yorail vinik**. Both ensure a good crop of corn.

To dream of corn has a variety of conflicting interpretations (cf. Laughlin, 1976:7–9):

1. To drink corn gruel	become sick (common cold)
2. To drink sweet corn gruel	become sick (cold "wind" in stomach, diarrhea)
3. To give corn	become poor (loss of corn's soul)
4. To sell corn	one's child will die (soul-loss)
5. To receive corn	become prosperous (receive soul of corn)
6. To receive bowl of corn, stack of tortillas	have poor harvest
7. To receive woman visitor	become prosperous (receive soul of corn)
8. To see cornfield flourishing, corn in heaps	corn crop will fail
9. To see corn in heaps	harvest will be good
10. To see barren cornfield	cornfield will flourish, harvest will be good
11. To see horses in the cornfield	wind will flatten corn

Unless people eat tortillas they are not fully socialized and can not learn to speak Tzotzil (Vogt, 1976:50).

Highland corn, having smaller ears and round kernels, is preferred by *ladinas*, who pay one more peso per **kvarto** for it than for lowland corn. It is preferred by *ladinas* and some Zinacantecs for corn gruel, but Zinacantecs maintain that it is inferior to the flat-kernelled lowland corn for tortillas as tortillas made of highland corn do not puff up, they are crumbly or rubbery, and stick to one's hands when hot. Highland corn is said to be "women's corn," as it grows by the house and is often harvested by them. It is also said to be for corn on the cob—a snack rather than a staple. It is heavier to carry than lowland corn as the kernels are larger. Even lowland seed corn is flailed, but highland corn is often stored on the cob. It suffers less from weevils than lowland corn. When the cobs of highland seed corn are shelled, the kernels at the tips are ground and eaten. The cobs are tossed in a ravine or far off place so they will not be used for toiletry. If they have been stored in the husk, the cobs are placed back in the husk and hung from a tree tip down or placed in a tree crotch to rest as they are exhausted from having borne the corn. They should not be burnt or the cornfield will turn yellow. If the butt of a corncob stands on end a visitor will arrive.

Corn on the cob, whether roasted or boiled, is always eaten as a snack. Boiled corn on the cob together with tortillas are ingredients of the net of fruit presented by the elders to each of the scribes on the fiestas of St. Sebstian and St. Lawrence. It is an essential grave offering on All Souls' Day.

If a person is too choosy buying corn (smelling it and picking out the rotten kernels), or discards corn or sour corn gruel, steps on or burns corn, the corn's soul will complain to the Earth Lord and to Our Lord. The offender soon will become destitute or will be punished in the afterworld. A stingy person will suffer the same fate. If the corn's soul departs, then one's supply will be exhausted quickly, but if its soul remains, the corn will last a long time. The corn's soul is male. The swishing of corn in the corn bin indicates that its soul is going to divert itself on a Sunday or is leaving permanently because of the infidelity of the house owner or his wife.

In former times, when oxcarts used to pass through Atz'am on their way to the highlands, if an ox broke a leg or became exhausted it would be sold for 50–60 pesos or exchanged for 400–800 stalks of corn stubble. Corn stubble is used to make dove traps. Corn stubble is used in the highland hamlets for fencing and for roofing the shelters built to provide protection from frost. On the Fiesta of St. Sebastian corn stubble is piled on top of the Jaguar Rock and set afire. The junior Jaguar, when impersonating a shaman, carries a corn stubble staff. Judas' cigarette is made of corn stubble. Children place young stalks on the fire and then take them out and strike them with a rock to produce a loud bang.

Corn leaves are used to wrap tamales (**pisil vaj**), and to cover pumpkin squash, steamed cushaw, and watermelon squash.

Corn husks are used to stopper water gourds, soul-calling gourds, and bottles, especially of cane liquor. To test the strength of cane liquor a corn husk is dipped into it and placed over the fire to check the size and duration of the blue flame. Corn husks are also used to wrap **pozol** dough and dough for tamales. Chamulans occasionally tie up chicken eggs in corn husk leaves when they bring them to market.

During the famine of 1915, corn tassels were eaten and corn silk was mixed with corn dough to make tortillas. Today it is only eaten when it is still moist, in a ball, attached to a young ear of corn that is roasted. Corn silk may be stored in the house. It is brewed together with brown sugar for "cold" sicknesses. For further medicinal use cf. **inojo, mantzanilya**.

Corn kernels are used for certain monetary calculations, as when the stewards count the value of their chaplets. For the communal payment of the San Lucas band at the Fiesta of Our Lady of the Rosary in Atz'am the amount owed by each man is figured with corn kernels: one kernel per individual. If the individual is just a boy, who pays a half share, the kernel is cut in half. This method was in use in Zinacantán Center about 10 years ago for all communal payments. The bag of corn would be delivered to the man in charge, together with the money. Should one of the tax-payers die, a kernel was removed from the bag.

If women eat while they are making tortillas it is said that their tortilla gourds will never fill up. If there is a lot of corn smut in the corn, this indicates that the women have left the griddle on the fire while they are eating.

A sick person eats only white corn, lest he be struck by **majbenal**. Some maintain that all corn is "cold," others that yellow is "hot." Yellow and white corn may be planted in adjacent fields. They produce equally well (with the same percentage of rotten kernels). Some prefer yellow corn for corn gruel as it requires less sugar. If white corn must be used, then, brown sugar may be added to provide the proper yellow shade. Three ears of yellow corn may be used in the "flower water" for bathing newborn babies. Cf. **antzil aj, yich'ak mut**. Black corn is only used at ceremonial meals when necessary and never at an important meal. When Christ was crucified he wiped his wounds with white corn and it turned red. According to another tradition Thunderbolt offered his daughter to a man, Kusum, but when they were in the cornfield harvesting their corn he quarreled with her and struck her. She wiped her bloody nose with an ear of corn and so there is red corn to this day. Red corn, **xch'ich'el jch'ul-tottik**, "Our holy Father's blood," is the soul of a cornfield. It acts as guardian of the soul of the cornfield.

Though some say it is tastier, it is never used in ceremonial meals. It is considered to be good for *pozol*. Chickens will not touch red kernels, as they know it is Christ's blood. To reduce fever, a shaman may grind 13 kernels, mixing the powder with water for an infusion. A little white salt may be added. This same infusion may be taken for **majbenal**, measles, nausea, and diarrhea (**xenel ch'utul**). Red corn is never sold.

When a soul has been lost, the shaman buries 13 kernels of each of the four colors, together with 13 black beans at the place of soul loss.

Corn should not be planted on Sunday or the dogs will have a holiday and eat it, nor should it be planted during Holy Week or it will be infested with corn smut (the smoke from Judas' cigarette). Corn should not be harvested on Sunday either for that is when the corn's soul is off bathing and diverting itself. If the corn is harvested and brought inside its soul will remain outside and the supply of corn will run out fast.

To ensure a good crop, four chickens are killed and eaten before the corn is planted. Their feet are dipped in the seed corn of each worker. It is recommended to eat birds, iguanas, and armadillos, all of which have long toenails. Eggs, snails, or fish should not be eaten, lest the roots take their form and be unable to withstand the force of a strong wind. However if after eating snails you plant three shells in the first three holes the corn will take root firmly—unless you whistle while planting, calling down the wind.

Corn that has been boiled without lime and ground once is used to starch and strengthen thread, and to break in new pots.

Roasted dry corn on the cob is used as a starter for chicha.

Corn stalks are split and used as a cover for the bowls of pumpkin squash and watermelon squash that are presented by the stewards to the sacristans during the *Posadas*.

To ensure that corn gruel will not be spoiled by a pregnant cook all the cooks must bite a piece of brown sugar.

To rid the cornfield of june bug grubs two burnt fishbones are buried together here and there. Another method is to take two grubs and place them head to head or one across the other and bury them in that position in their tunnel. A third means is to take the greasy, old skirt of an old woman and, holding it aloft like a flag, walk around the field three times. To rid the cornfield of yellowing (**uch**), three pine tips are planted in the field: one in the center and one on each side.

There is a great variety of methods to prevent raccoons from entering the cornfield. A naked boy and a naked girl may walk around the edge of the field three times. An adult may scatter garlic and tobacco around the edge. The farmer may prepare a bed of straw six inches long on each side of the field for raccoons, or he may construct a platform in the trees at the edge of the field, lie down on it, and call out to the raccoons, "Let's sleep together!"

The ring-necked coffee snake, **ik'al jchabajom chon**, black corn farmer snake, and the banded coffee snake, **k'anal jchabajom chon**, yellow corn farmer snake, are believed to care for the fields of corn sharing their color. To kill one of these snakes is to risk having your field destroyed by wind.

To prevent wind damage, a strip of the palm fronds distributed on St. Peter Martyr Day is tied to the corn plants at the four corners of the field. To drive away the wind, the farmer may spit tobacco, cigarette tobacco, and/or cane liquor at it in a high wind, the owner may call out, **"Tzotzan me kunen chob mu me xalomik un!"** "Be strong my little corn plants, please don't fall down."

When corn is stolen from a field, the owner may make a cross of the corn stalks that have been stripped of ears and stand it in the center or in a corner of the field so that Our Lord will punish the thief with poverty and death. The same effect may be produced by drawing a cross on the thief's footprints. However, everyone is given an allowance of three ears of corn that may be snitched.

To prevent corn from being eaten by weevils, three small shot glasses of cane liquor should be poured in the shape of a cross on the top of the corn bin.

To prevent tamales (**chenek'ul vaj, pisil vaj**) from being spoiled by a pregnant cook, she must put three tamales in the pot first before anyone else puts them in. If a pregnant woman has not done so and the tamales do not cook properly, then she must stick her tortilla cloth or table cloth in the pot.

When a young man plants prickly pears, pears, avocadoes, apples, apricots, quinces, white sapotes, cypress, juniper, pine or oak trees, he should plant 13 kernels of white corn next to the roots as an offering to the Earth, lest the planter die. When a fiancé pays a visit to his fiancée on or around the fiesta of St. Lawrence, his father carries a small net of food to present to her father. On the bottom are placed 10 boiled ears of corn in pairs, alternately pointing left and right. On top of these are placed 20 oranges, and on the very top 10 plantains.

For corn divination (**k'el-'ixim**) 13 kernels are removed from one big ear of each color. They are put in a bowl of water. Each kernel that rises represents a part of the soul that has been lost (except for those that float right side up, **-nujul**). If the base of the kernel is on top—**javal**—then the patient fell in a stream—**tz'ajem ta vo'**. If the kernel is lying on its side—**tz'e'el**—then he fell on the path, was scared by a snake or by the tutelary gods. After the divination the kernels are placed in the gourd for calling the soul. After the soul has been called, the kernels are ground, toasted, and eaten by the patient. The four ears of corn are placed at the head of the bed and remain for three days till the flowers are removed and put in the crotch of a tree at the nearest shrine.

Mothers chew tortillas and give the chewings to babies that are just beginning to eat solid food.

Three tortillas a day are fed to one's dog. Cats are fed corn that has been ground once. Chickens, turkeys, and pigs are given corn daily. Horses that race at the Fiesta of St. Sebastian and the Fiesta of St. Lawrence are given a $1/2$ liter of corn early in the morning. Pack horses are fed a quart at dusk, and at midnight or at dawn. The gods and the dead are fed tortillas in the form of wax candles.

To trap mice and field rats for eating, a toasted corn kernel is tied to a string beneath a deadfall. To attract his prey, the hunter chews several toasted kernels and spits them out around the trap.

On All Saints' Day Eve, the Stewards of St. Anthony distribute corn gruel and one ear of corn to each person present.

If a person eats corn on the cob that has had corn smut rubbed off or if the ear has sour undeveloped kernels, then he will be unable to take a trip, postponing it at the last moment again and again for three days. Should a person eat corn on the cob with the husk still attached he is liable to be the target of someone's angry words.

A tortilla sticking to the griddle indicates that the cook will be falsely accused.

If corn gruel is touched with the finger when cooking, it will curdle.

Corn will provide a good yield if dirt is rubbed on one's hands right after a gopher has left its burrow. But eating a jesus christ lizard will prevent one's cornfield from growing.

When harvesting the corn, ears that are stunted, half-grown, with very thin kernels are selected out, boiled, and eaten on the cob or fed to the chickens.

Three kinds of ears of corn are considered to be of good luck and are stood up next to the corn bin cross. **Mayol**, "its father," or **tot ixim**, "father corn," or **chib lotol**, "paired," has two or three separate husks growing from the same node. **Sme'**, "its mother," or **me' ixim**, "mother corn," has two or three tips on one ear. It is eaten on St. Lawrence's Day.

Another form, **chikin t'ul**, "rabbit ear," a very large ear in the **ajan** stage with its upper leaf sheath spreading to suggest rabbit ears, is considered by some to be good luck. Others say it frightens and chases people.

Bad luck is assigned to a variety of malformed ears whose names often overlap: **jov-ch'ut**, "split belly," referring to an ear with several rows lacking kernels, **pik'-ch'ut**, "toothless belly," lacking kernels in the center of the row, **xcha'al**, "its metate," lacking kernels in one row, **jjuch'nom**, "grinder," lacking kernels at far end or with split cob, **joj**, "raven," split cob. When found at the harvest after the kernels are removed they are all broken. The "grinder" is thought to grind up all its companions and so is "killed." The "raven" is said by some to be a sign that one's corn will be stolen, others split the cob in two so that its "beak" will not be able to eat the corn.

Young corn plants are scratched up by raccoons, pacas, black robins, common bobwhites, yellow-throated brushfinches, and especially by red-eyed towhees and great-tailed grackles. Ripe, but not dry, ears of corn are eaten by dogs, coatis, raccoons, deppe's squirrels, unicolored jays, steller's jays, green jays, red-shafted flickers, orange-fronted parakeets, and great-tailed grackles. Dry ears of corn are eaten by coatis, collared peccaries, white-lipped peccaries, common ravens, red-shafted flickers, and great-tailed grackles. Magpie jays are renowned for entering fieldhouses to steal tortillas and corn dough that have been hung from the rafters.

Cutworms and webworms are believed to fall from the sky on hazy, sunny days in the lowlands, like drizzle. Some say that they are more prevalent where grass rather than broad-leaved plants grow. Corn earworms appear in the cobs of both lowland and highland corn, "like the worms in our teeth" (cavities). They are roasted in the coals and eaten.

To cure a dog of a severe cough, a collar of burnt corncobs cut into pieces is hung around its neck.

To cause measles to erupt, the patient drinks the "medium" water from corn that has been boiled without lime (**bul jux**) and dyed red with the fruit of **vo'ox**. As a remedy for athlete's foot (**xk'a' sk'al koktik**), corn dough is pushed between the toes with a stirring rod. Corn dough and white salt is given to sheep to reduce swell head. The scraps of dough that have fallen onto the *metate* platform may be rubbed on a burn to reduce the pain.

Corn on the cob is covered with corn husks when boiled to keep in the steam.

A person suffering muscular pain (a knot in the thigh after cutting one's leg) sprays salt water on his thigh and ties one leaf of corn husk around each toe.

Two corncobs may be placed on a woman's belly after childbirth.

Corncobs are used for bottle stoppers and for toiletry, as well as for rubbing the bristles off a slaughtered pig's hide. They are used for fuel when roasting watermelon squashes and pumpkin squashes in a pit, but if a corncob burns on the hearth one's child will become a snuffler. They are also used to fertilize unproductive cornfields. During major fiestas boys snatch up the discarded corncobs for missiles. Corncobs are ground and burnt and the powder used for gunpowder. The smoke of burning corncobs is an effective means for removing wasps nests from one's house. The powder of dried corn smut is used to stanch a cut.

When forests were still abundant, Zinacantecs preferred to fell the trees to make their milpas, for not only was the soil more fertile, but no weeding was required for two years. The large trees would be felled in December, leaving the smaller ones until after the Fiesta of St. Sebastian (January 18–23).

Heavy second growth will burn properly, but will produce a good corn crop for only one year. The next year the underbrush is too thin to burn well, and even with weed-killer will not produce. It takes four years for the undergrowth to become heavy again.

Flat land is also preferred for cornfields because the compost is not washed away and the field may be planted for eight years, but it is risky, for if the rains are heavy the corn roots will rot. The best compromise is a gentle slope, not too steep or flat and not stony. If the slope is steep the compost may be leached in two years. For this reason a steep slope is better for farming if it is rocky, as the rocks keep the compost in place. Typically rocky and steep, most temperate fields must be cleared with a billhook rather than a machete.

In the highlands a strip two arm lengths wide is cleared around the field to keep animals out. Highland fields and temperate fields not littered with rocks are hoed prior to planting.

When selecting seed corn, all healthy kernels of the highland corn, except those at the tip, are used. Because lowland corn is flailed no such distinction is made. Seed corn may be taken to the Church of St. Lawrence on Easter to be blessed.

Highland fields can be planted for 5–6 years, then left fallow for 2–3. However, if the farmer moves his sheep corral around on the highland slopes he may plant his land for 15–16 years, leaving it fallow for 1–2. When the field is "resting," **batz'i saju'**, **chichik'uy**, and **poxil yayijemal** grow on it. Temperate fields produce well for two years, then are allowed to rest one year before producing well for another two years, but some allow their fields to rest for as long as eight years. Lowland fields produce well for three years.

A very few Zinacantecs have access to lowland riverside plots, where they plant in mid-November. No beans are planted with the corn, but sand-loving plants such as melons, water-melons, tomatoes, and chilies may be associated. The ground is watered after the weeding, once a week. The irrigation is done communally, sometimes by *ladinos* and Zinacantecs together. The field must be watched or the corn will be stolen by parakeets and grackles. The harvest is in March. The land may be used every year.

When planting, 4–6 kernels are placed in each hole, 4–5 sandal lengths apart. Planting begins first in Selva on the slopes of Muk'ta Vitz on 1 March, next in Naben Chauk on March 10, in San Mikulax on 19 March, and in P'ij on 1 April. If rain has fallen, planting may begin in early April in the highland communities, but usually is delayed until 25 April or the first two weeks of May. Temperate communities also begin on 25 April. In Atz'am, where the soil is drier, planting may continue from late May as late as 20 June, depending on the arrival of rain, but if planted later, it will be scratched up by grackles, towhees, and racoons that have been attracted to the fields that were planted earlier. Corn is planted in the lowlands from 25 May to 1 July, except near Concordia, where it may begin in April. Seed corn may be bought or exchanged often from lowland *ladinos*.

People are cautioned not to plant corn if there is no moon, or if the moon is waning, lest the seeds fail to sprout properly or the plants become spindly. Nor should one plant from Holy Wednesday to Easter, for the pain suffered by the planter will be borne by Christ.

The seed corn may be soaked for one night so it will sprout in three days rather than five.

If only 1–2 plants emerge in a clump, 2–4 kernels are added.

Formerly, when weeding was done by hoe, the fields were weeded first in mid-June and again in mid-July. Now herbicides have replaced that technique almost everywhere and are applied just once. If grass is thicker than broadleaf weeds, grass-killer is applied first. The weeding is done working from east to west.

Chemical fertilizer is applied when the corn is knee-high and at weeding time. There are those who claim that after its use the land wears out and must lie fallow for four years. Others maintain that hybrid corn wears out after 3–4 years of use, but that the native corn loves it, **lek xa'i,** and grows well, "just like a well-fed, well-dressed person."

When the corn is head high the Chamulans hill their corn, a practice once shared by many Zinacantecs. Now a very few continue to hill their corn after the weeding so the roots will hold firm.

Much more frequent than hilling is "doubling," but this is practiced only by industrious, **baxbol,** people who care for, **xk'uxubin,** their corn. In the lowlands in September, at bean planting time, and in the highlands in late November, the stalk is bent over at the halfway point to reduce moisture damage. If the stalk breaks it is hung back up. Care is taken to insert the tip under the leaves that are brushed together so that each clump is separated from the next. Some assert that doubling should be done at full moon lest the bugs hiding under the leaves come out to sting workers during the day.

Highland corn is harvested in December and early January, except in the northern end of Pat Osil where, as with temperate corn, the harvest comes in late January, February, and early March. Lowland corn is harvested from mid-November to late February, except near Concordia where it may begin in early November.

Some harvest from west to east so weeds will die and corn increase.

In the lowlands the corn-threshing floor should be in a wide, flat place where a truck can reach it. Here the whole group of farmers sets up their camp. The corn to be eaten or sold is flailed before the seed corn. Highlanders who raise corn on the temperate slopes also flail their corn for transport home by mule.

Many believe that the corn should be flailed when the moon is full, lest it be weevil-eaten. If the moon is waning, the corn is set aside for eating or quick sale. Smoke drives weevils away from seed corn. Ashes may be added to the bags of corn or a poison pill wrapped in cloth may be attached to each corner of the bag for four days.

Although the specific names for corn may include the generic, **ixim,** they generally do not.

Specifics: 26.

In describing the varieties of corn, several elements are taken into account, some of which are employed as names to distinguish those varieties:

1. cultivated by the ancestors: **ba'yi tz'unubil,** "first seed."
2. hybrid: **ivriro.**
3. plant size: **enáno,** "dwarf."
4. time of planting: **sakramentual,** "Corpus Christi."
5. place of planting: **olon osilal,** "lowland," **vitztikal,** "mountain" or "temperate."
6. speed of growth: **kvarentáno,** "forty days," **ba'yi,** "first," **tz'akal,** "later."
7. size of ear: **muk'ta,** "large," **bik'it, k'ox,** or **chimpo,** "little."
8. thickness of cob: **jich'il bakal,** "thin cob," **yijil bakal,** "thick cob."
9. shape of kernel: **ton,** "stone" or "round," or **pimil sat,** "thick kernel," **latz** or **pacha,** "flat," **ye tz'i',** "dog's tooth," **ch'ix,** "spiny."
10. color of kernel: **ik',** "black," **k'on,** "yellow," **sak,** "white," **tzoj,** "red," **k'ob tz'i',** "dog's paw," or "spotted," **pinto,** "spotted," **xch'ich'el jch'ul-tottik,** "Our Lord's blood," for any red ear or for white corn with streaks of red.

The major distinction between varieties of corn derives from a combination of habitat and kernel shape. Highland corn has round kernels, whereas lowland corn has flat kernels. Anyone can distinguish highland ears from lowland ears, but temperate corn, which is a mix of the two, is difficult to identify ex locus with ear in hand.

HIGHLAND

Highland corn plants, except for **sakramentual ixim** and **ye tz'i',** have downy stalks and round-kernelled ears.

Specifics: 25.

a. **Bik'it sak,** "small white" refers to a variety of races: Imbricado mix, Nal-Tel Blanco, Nal-Tel Blanco mixed with Oloton, and Tierra Alta Quicheño. The ear has 14 rows of kernels.

b. **Chix te',** "cherry" (**chak tojal ixim, tzajal ixim**), refers to Imbricado mix, Quicheño Rojo, and Nal-Tel Rojo. It is grown by a few people in highland and temperate communities, away from the house. It is very slow-growing, with small ears, providing corn on the cob for the Fiesta of St. Sebastian (January 18–20). There is a danger that it will be damaged by frost. The red kernels are produced on 10–14 irregular rows, on a thick, hard cob that is especially suited for making into gunpowder.

c. **Ik'al ixim,** "black corn," refers to corn of the Negro de Chimaltenango race. In highland and temperate communities it is grown by few people and even then will produce for a smaller chosen few. It grows to the same height as white corn ($1^1/2$ m) except in the corral where it grows taller. The ear has 10–12 rows of kernels.

d. **K'anal chix te',** "yellow cherry" (**bik'it k'on, chix te' k'on, k'anal chak toj, tz'akal k'on**), refers to Imbricado mix, Quicheño, Quicheño mixed with Nal-Tel. Cultivated in highland and temperate communities, this yellow corn has the same properties and uses as **chix te'.**

e. **Muk'ta k'on,** "big yellow" (**ba'yi k'on, yut mokal ixim**), refers to Quicheño, Oloton, Quicheño mix, and Oloton mix. This corn, producing ears with 10–12 rows of kernels, is ready for harvest in November.

f. **Muk'ta sak,** "big white," refers to Oloton, Serrano, and Nal-Tel mixed with Oloton. The ear has 12–14 rows of kernels.

g. **Pinto ixim**, "spotted corn" (**k'ob tz'i'**), refers to Nal-Tel Blanco or Serrano mixed with Negro de Chimaltenango. This tall-growing corn is planted in highland and temperate communities. It is recognized to be a crossing of black and white corn. The kernels are not lined up in straight rows on the thick cob. The term **k'ob tz'i'** is used only in the highlands.

   (1) **Ik'al pinto ixim**, "black spotted corn," refers to cobs with just a few red and white kernels.

   (2) **Sakil pinto ixim**, "white spotted corn," has a larger proportion of red and white kernels.

h. **Sakramentual ixim**, "Corpus Christi corn" (**ch'ix ixim**), refers to Imbricado and Imbricado mix. This corn, with smooth stalks, a very thin cob, and irregularly placed long, pointed white kernels, occurs now only in Zinacantán Center, where it appears sporadically. Formerly it was planted on Corpus Christi. It is a fast-growing plant that grows only head high. This corn is not sold.

i. **Ye tz'i'**, "dog's tooth" (**ch'ix ixim**), refers to Imbricado, very similar to Palomero Toluqueño. This corn, similar to **sakramentual ixim**, has pinkish cream kernels. Its distribution and use are identical to **sakramentual ixim**.

TEMPERATE

Temperate corn plants have stalks with sparse down.

j. **Vitztikal bik'it k'on**, "temperate small yellow," refers to Olotillo and San Marceño mixed.

k. **Vitztikal bik'it sak**, "temperate small white," refers to Nal-Tel Blanco mixed with Dzit-Bakal, Olotillo, Quicheño, and Quicheño modified by Teocinte.

l. **Vitztikal muk'ta k'on**, "temperate big yellow," refers to Comiteco, Quicheño mixed with Teocinte, and San Marceño mixed.

m. **Vitztikal muk'ta sak**, "temperate big white," refers to Nal-Tel Blanco mixed with Dzit-Bakal, Olotillo, and Olotillo mixed with Sal-Por. The ears may be very large.

LOWLAND

Lowland corn plants have smooth stalks and flat-kernelled ears.

n. **Bik'it sak**, "small white," refers to Olotillo mixed with Nal-Tel.

o. **Enáno**, "dwarf," is a dwarf hybrid corn bought from the government. It grows waist to head high, producing corn in 60–70 days. The white kernels are arranged in 18–20 rows on a thick cob. Three *lonas* of ears provide 12 *almudes* of grain.

p. **Ik'al ixim**, "black **ixim**," refers to Negro de Tierra Caliente. The corn silk is very black; the kernels appear in 8–10 rows.

q. **Ivriro**, "hybrid," refers to corn of the Vandeño race that grows 10 feet tall. It is preferred because it gets few rotten spots, but it is hard to harvest as the stem does not break easily and the husk is hard to pull off.

   (1) **Bik'it ivriro**, "small hybrid" (**ivriro 250**), has 12 or more rows of white corn on a thick cob.

   (2) **K'anal ivriro**, "yellow hybrid," produces corn in 60 days.

   (3) **Muk'ta ivriro**, "big hybrid" (**ivriro 580**), has 16–17 rows on a thick cob with kernels to the very tip. It requires fertilizer. Three *lona* bags of ears provide 12 **almudes** of grain.

r. **Krema** refers to Vandeño mix. The plant grows about 10 feet tall, the corn is borne breast high. The kernels, which are yellow with a white end, are placed on 12 rows on a fairly thick cob. This is a popular variety now.

s. **Kvarentáno** (**chimpo, chimpu, kvarentányo**) refers to Zapalote Grande. The plant grows head high. The ears are borne low on the plant. The white kernels are placed in 12–16 rows on a fairly thick cob. The small ears are produced in 40 days, but because it ripens early no one is in the cornfields to protect it from predators and robbers. It has nearly disappeared, even though it brings a high price.

t. **Napalu** (**ba'yi tz'unubil, napalu'**) refers to Dzit-Bakal, Olotillo, and Olotillo mixed with Nal-Tel. This plant, though cultivated from early times, is still planted by many people. The plant grows so tall, on a thick stalk, and the ears are borne so high that doubling or harvesting must be done by whacking the stalk with a stick and breaking it. Its height and slow growth make it susceptible to wind damage. The kernels are arranged in 8–16 rows on a fairly thick cob having a reddish tinge. Three *lonas* of ears provide 12 *almudes* of grain.

   (1) **K'anal napalu**, "yellow **napalu**," has yellow kernels.

   (2) **K'ox k'anal napalu**, "small yellow **napalu**," has small ears of yellow corn.

   (3) **Sakil napalu**, "white **napalu**," has white kernels.

   (4) **Tzajal napalu**, "red **napalu**," has red kernels.

u. **Pacha**, "flat" (**ba'yi tz'unubil, latz, olotìyo**), refers to Olotillo. It grows about 10 feet tall. It has a very thin red cob. This variety, associated with lowland *ladinos*, has nearly disapeared. Three *lonas* of ears provide 13 *almudes* of grain.

v. **Pinto ixim**, "spotted **ixim**," refers to Dzit-Bakal mixed with Negro de Tierra Caliente.

w. **Rokame** (**brokame**) refers to Olotillo. Because the plant does not grow tall it is less susceptible to wind damage. The yellow kernels, white at the end, are arranged in 10–14 rows on a thick reddish cob. Three *lonas* of ears provide 14 *almudes* of grain.

x. **Teralényo** refers to Vandeño mix. The kernels, which have a white top and a pink cast, are placed on 12 rows. This variety is planted by very few people.

y. **Tuspényo** (**suspényo**) refers to Vandeño. This corn grows head high, bearing the corn fairly low so that it is subject to predation by animals. However, because it produces in 90 days, it is preferred for planting with bush beans. The white kernels are placed in 14–16 rows, covered with a tough husk that makes harvesting especially difficult. Three *lonas* of ears provide 12 *almudes* of seed. The kernels are heavier than those of **ivriro** and **napalu**. The seeds, when purchased, are painted with poison. The plants require fertilizer. This variety, unknown twenty years ago, is planted now by many people.

Three additional varieties, **jarócho**, **povlano**, and **vajole-péna**, have not been identified.

4. **Triko** (**-tik**, **-altik**) (**castillan ixim***) is wheat, *Triticum aestivum* (1–4). Wheat was the major crop in Zinacantán during the colonial period, but has not been cultivated here within living memory.

In 1797 the priest of Zinacantán reported: "They sow several bushels of wheat, which, if well-cared for will produce over a hundred, using 3 or 4 laborers /Chamulans/ who are neighbors of the town. They have a competent irrigation system. And one small plot that the priest sowed provided 16 bushels from ³/₄ of a bushel—what more can one say!" (de Leon y Goicoechea, 1797).

It is grown now by Chamulans, Huixtecs, and Amatenangeros. The seeds may be sown at any time of year. Plants are robust annual grasses with terminal spikes. The spikelets are about 8 mm long, sessile, and crowded on the rachis, making the inflorescence appear cylindrical. The outer glumes of the spikelet are very long awned.

Eaten only in the form of bread, it is not classed as "hot" or "cold."

5. **Tukum j'ik'al**, "spook's **tukum**," is sorghum, *Sorghum bicolor* (3–4), a robust annual grass. The inflorescence is a compact panicle made up of purplish, ovate spikelets about 5 mm long. Leaves may be as much as 5 cm wide. This plant was introduced probably very early into the New World. Now mostly grown for fodder, it was once a major food crop. It is cultivated by *ladinos* in lowland areas. The seeds are planted in June with the aid of a digging stick, two to a hole.

The "cold" grain is rarely eaten, toasted on the griddle. It is sold at market. It is also sold by *ladinos* in a candy confection.

Extended range: *Lasiacis ruscifolia*.

6. **Vale'*** (**-tik**, **-altik**) is sugarcane, *Saccharum officinarum* (3–5), a plant introduced into the New World in the 16th Century. It is a tall perennial grass to about 4 meters high with a large, silver or pinkish, plume-like inflorescence. The nodding branches of the inflorescence are made up of individual spikelets, which are 4–5 mm long and have a ring of long silky hairs at the base. It is propagated asexually from buds at the base of the plant, thus preserving types with desirable characteristics.

Sugarcane is planted by a few people in Santa Rosa and many of the temperate communities in May and June, and, if irrigation is available, in February and March. A slip 1 m or 3–4 nodes long is scraped at both ends and planted 30 cm deep at an angle, 30–40 cm apart in rows an armspan apart. When newly planted, it takes 1¹/₂–2 years to produce, and after that, yearly. The harvest is from September through December.

Two sugarcane stalks adorn the chapel of Sak Lum on the fifth Lenten Friday. Two sugarcane stalks are also provided on the eighth *Posada* by the Stewards of Our Lady of the Rosary to flank the creche door. They are used similarly in Apas, Atz'am, and Sak Lum. Thirty sections are placed in the bottom of the net of fruit given by the fiancé to his fiancée. A smaller number are included in the net of fruit presented by the elders to the scribes on the fiestas of St. Sebastian and St. Lawrence.

The "hot" stems of sugarcane are eaten raw and roasted. They are also used for brown sugar, *chicha*, and cane liquor. Cf. **ixim**, **sakramentual nichim**. A charred piece of sugarcane is used as a starter for *chicha*. "Hot" brown sugar and now increasingly "cold" refined sugar are used to sweeten coffee, pinole, corn gruel, and mature squashes.

Sugarcane is sold at market, particularly before All Souls' Day.

On the Fiesta of St. Sebastian, the entertainers, and at Carnival the cantors, serve barrels of *chicha* to all participating officials. During Carnival kids and sometimes older men go from house to house at night with pitchers, begging for *chicha*. This *chicha* is made with pineapples, sugarcane, and brown sugar. To drink *chicha* in one's dream portends a common cold, cold "wind" in one's stomach, swollen stomach, or diarrhea.

Some people credit the birth of cane liquor to the elders who decided that *chicha* was for the hot sun, not for our Lord's fiestas. When they invented cane liquor fiestas, at last, they were fun (Laughlin, 1977, T98). Others credit the Devil, who gave the liquor its strength by pissing around the pot three times while Our Lord's back was turned. Then the Devil got Him drunk on it so His children, unwatched, could learn to reproduce. Here is a third version:

"Drink water!" said (Our Lord). He left water, that's what was left long ago. There were no fiestas, no fiesta of any kind, none. The musicians drank water, but they didn't sing, no, no. There wasn't anything. They just drank water, because there was nothing. There wasn't anything, no.

But it wasn't really Our Lord who came, who knows? "What are you doing?" he said. "How come you don't hold fiestas?" he said.

"No, we never hold fiestas, no," they said.

"How come you don't make a sound, you don't sing?" he said.

"No," they said.

"Ah!" he said. "But why?" he said. "But how come?" he said.

"But we don't know how to," they said.

"Ah," he said. "I've come," he said. "I've come to see you. I hear the fiesta never makes a sound. I hear there's no fiesta at all. How come?" said (Our Lord). "Well," he said. "Ah," he said. "Doesn't anyone have any sugar, doesn't anyone have any sugarcane?" he said.

"Of course they do," they said.

"Ah, well, that's fine," he said. "Calm down then, I'm coming, I'll give the orders, I came to see you, too. I came to see you. But there's sugarcane somewhere. Have them boil it!" he said. "Have them boil it, grind it well, have them boil it!" he said.

"All right," they said.

Sonofabitch, but you see they followed the orders about how to make cane liquor. They obeyed, they boiled it.

"Is it good?" asked (Our Lord).

"It's just the same, it's as sweet as it always is, it's as sweet as sugar as we say. It's just the same, it's just the same."

"How could that be?" said Our Lord who had come. "But why? But what can we do?" he said.

The devil came, too. That's why if you drink a lot of it we say, "The devil is interfering." He came.

"Well, compadre," they said to each other.

"How is it, compadre?" said (the devil). "What are you doing?" he asked.

"I'm boiling sugar because I want cane liquor," said (Our Lord).

"How come you all don't know what to do?" said (the devil).

"We don't," they said.

"Ah," said (the devil). "But wait and see!" he said. "Turn your backs for a long time!" they were told. Turn your backs!" he said, indeed.

But he went right away and pissed three times around the place where (the sugar) was boiled. When they turned around, "Taste it, I guess, to see how it is!" It was cane liquor now. It was cane liquor now. "Well, you all drink it, I guess," said (the devil). They drank it. Lord! "Drink a whole shot, we'll see what it does!" he said.

Well, they drank. Eh, it warmed up their veins. They were happy now.

Well, give it to your musicians. I guess we'll see what happens," he said. They gave it to their musicians. Eh, the musicians began to feel no pain now. "That's it, that's what I told you!" said (the devil). "I did it by myself," he said.

Don't you see, god has one word, the devil has the other.

The devil blessed it. That's the way it was left up to now.

That's how cane liquor was left. That's why if you drink too much, you feel the devil interfering, whether it's because we get into trouble from it or beat up someone because of it or die from it. But Our Lord and (the devil) talked to each other the same way, because they made the good stuff. See here, as for cane liquor, wherever you go, where you hear there's a fiesta, there's cane liquor, there's a little bit of something for us to chat over.

The perils of cane liquor are dramatically and humorously exposed in many tales (Laughlin, 1977, T1, T87, T127, T141).

Cane liquor is served at nearly every secular and religious celebration, at curing ceremonies, requests for loans, and indeed for any request. Its use as a social lubricant in Zinacantán has been documented in too many contexts to list here.

When an ensign-bearer enters and leaves office, the musicians ask his ritual tutor to spray their instruments with cane liquor so that the instruments will not break and will have a good tone throughout the fiesta. This is also done at a wedding.

At Holy Cross Day ceremonies the mortar is used as a shot glass for one round of drinks so that no accidents will occur.

It is said jokingly that one can make a nor'easter lift by drinking cane liquor.

Undiluted cane liquor serves as an antidote for black widow spider bites. A person who has been bitten may drink as much as a quart of cane liquor without feeling the effects of the liquor. Cf. **kampor**.

Cane liquor, distilled from brown sugar by bootleggers in a few hamlets, is sold year round, but it is not considered to match the quality of Chamulan cane liquor. A bonesetter sprays cane liquor on the leaves used in bone setting.

When corn gruel is made for the stewards royal, publicans, ensign-bearers, and elders, a bottle of cane liquor is taken to the mill and drunk by those men and women who have taken the corn. When the ground corn is mixed with water, three rounds of cane liquor are served (at the beginning, middle, and end) in a large shot glass to the cooks, and again when the corn gruel is being boiled. If a cook does not not want to drink the cane liquor she may pour it in the corn gruel. A pregnant cook should drink a shot of cane liquor and take three bites of every chunk of sugar she puts in the pot. When the prefects (**j'ilvanej**) arrive they are served a round of cane liquor in a small shot glass.

Three rounds of liquor are also drunk by the cooks preparing tamales (**pisil vaj** and **chenek'ul vaj**) for ritual meal.

Formerly, cane liquor was a standard gift to the lowland landholder whose land was to be rented.

To dream of drinking cane liquor portends a common cold, cold "wind" in one's stomach, or that one's children will get sick. Alternatively, it means the dreamer will become wealthy. Cf. **kokov**.

The leaves are used for horse fodder.

Specifics: 3:

a. **Sakil vale'**, "white sugarcane," is a form of sugarcane with greenish white stems having only a few reddish purple stripes. The stem is generally coarser, tougher and the taste harsher than the red type. It has a hollow center. This type is grown by *ladinos* in Pujiltik where it is available year round and processed into refined sugar and cane liquor. Zinacantecs once worked in Pujiltik, but claiming the sugar caused them sickness, abandoned their jobs. Another form of white-stemmed sugarcane is grown in the temperate hamlets and by *ladinos* in Acala, San Lucas, and Ixtapa. The temperate sugarcane has more ribbing. The stem of this form is chewed as well as being used for brown sugar, **chicha,** and cane liquor. Sugarcane is sold and resold at market, particularly before All Souls' Day. The leaves are used for horse fodder.

b. **Tzajal vale'**, "red sugarcane," is a variety of sugarcane with red-purple stems. It is grown in the temperate hamlets and by *ladinos* in Acala, San Lucas, and Ixtapa.

This form, preferred for chewing, is also used for brown sugar, **chicha**, and cane liquor. Sugarcane and sugar is sold and resold at market as above. Mothers chew the stems and give them to their babies when they are just beginning to eat solid food.

c. **Vale' j'ik'al**, "spook's sugarcane," is a variety of sugarcane that grows only a little over 1 m tall. Its stem is soft and very sweet. The stem and leaves are tinged dark maroon.

It is planted in the yard in Chikinibal Vo', Jok' Ch'enom, Masan, Muk'ta Jok', and Potovtik. The stems are especially sweet for chewing, but are not sold at market.

7. **Ximo'** (**ximo**) refers to members of *Tripsacum,* a perennial, tall, clumped grass with an inflorescence similar to maize.

Specifics: 2.

a. **Batz'i ximo'**, "genuine **ximo'**" (**xchob antivo**), is *Tripsacum laxum* (4–8) and *T. maizar* (1–3), coarse, tall plants to 2 m high. The male portion of the inflorescence hangs like a tassel over the dense, hard clusters of female flowers. This is an occasional plant in grassy, open pine-oak and tropical deciduous forests in temperate locations. According to tradition this was the ancestor's corn, but it was very fussy. Some say that it demanded to be weeded three times, others, that it complained to Our Lord three times because the people stepped on it and did not weed it. Our Lord, exasperated, said that there was pardon for the people and banished it to the wilds. According to another tradition corn was turned into **ximo'** during the Flood. The stem can be chewed just as that of corn.

b. **Bik'it ximo'**, "small **ximo'**" (**chak'ak'**, **jobelal avarto**), refers to the smaller-leaved, more clumped plants of *Tripsacum*: *Tripsacum manisuroides* (3–5).

They are usually about 1 m tall. They are sparingly branched and have leaf blades 1–1.8 cm wide. The inflorescence is a somewhat stiff spike with florets sessile or embedded in the rachis. The florets are narrowly oblong with acute apices. They occur in similar habitats with *T. laxum*. The people of the temperate hamlets cut the stalks with an ax or billhook and pound them to make packsaddles.

"K'ojom Set"

The "**k'ojom** set" is a grouping of eight generics, herbs and subshrubs with elliptic leaves, mostly pink flowers, and small, dark, round fruits.

1. **Akuxa tz'i'lel**, "needle plant," refers to *Erodium* and *Geranium,* closely related plants with divided leaves, pink flowers, and 5-parted fruits with an elongate, stylar column.

It is likely that one of the following plants corresponds to *alfilerillo,* cited by the priest of Zinacantán in 1797 as a remedy for quinsy or tonsilitis "which is epidemic from time to time among the children here" (de Leon y Goicoechea, 1797).

Specifics: 3.

a. **K'ox akuxa tz'i'lel**, "small needle plant" (**akux tz'i'lel, akuxa jabnal, akuxa tz'i'lel, jich'il akuxa tz'i'lel**), refers to *Erodium cicutarium* (4–6) and *E. moschatum* (1–3), herbs with pinnately divided opposite leaves and the style column 2–3 cm long. The flowers are small, pink, with five petals about 7 mm long. They are scattered weeds of disturbed ground in the highland hamlets.

To dry out a boil (**chakal**), the plant is brewed and the "hot" water used to bathe the boil. The leaves and fruits are put over a fire and the smoke used in the cure for **k'asel**.

Extended range: *Alchemilla pectinata, A. sibbaldiaefolia,* and *Lamium amplexicaule.*

b. **Muk'ta akuxa tz'i'lel**, "large needle plant" (**akuxa, tzajal pox**), is *Geranium goldmanii* (4–6), a sprawling herb with magenta flowers, with five petals, 10–15 mm long, and a stylar column less than 1 cm long. The leaves are orbicular or triangular in outline, palmately divided to the base. The leaves, petioles, and stems are softly pubescent. It occurs on rocky slopes in pine-oak forests of temperate and highland hamlets.

As a remedy for barrenness, women take a "hot" tea of the root. For other uses cf. **k'ox** and **sakil akuxa tz'i'lel**.

c. **Sakil akuxa tz'i'lel**, "white needle plant" (**kajtzanob bek'et, poxil yayijel, tzajal tz'i'lel**), is *Geranium seemannii* (10–11), a thinly branched herb with palmately divided leaves, the stylar column less than 1 cm long. The flowers are white or pale lavender with five petals, 7–10 mm long. This herb is very common in disturbed areas and second growth in temperate and highland hamlets. When termed **tzajal tz'i'lel** it is classed as **sme'**, "female," to distinguish it from the

240

"male" form, otherwise known as **yich'ak ch'o.**

To stanch wounds, the root is dried on the fire, pulverized, and the powder applied. As a remedy for swelling, the root is boiled and the patient bathed with the "hot" water. For other uses cf. **k'ox** and **muk'ta akuxa tz'i'lel.**

2. **Chintuli' jobel,** "bobwhite grass," is *Plantago linearis* (1–2), a caespitose herb of rock outcrops in highland areas. The inflorescence and flowers are much like *P. australis* ssp. *hirtella* and *P. major* (see **yak' tz'i**). The leaves are numerous and linear, 5–15 cm long, 1–2 mm wide.

The leaves are brewed and the "hot" tea drunk to soothe stomach pains (**k'ux ko'ontik**).

3. **K'ojom (-tik)** (**ch'upak' tz'i'lel, k'ojom jobel, poxil chuvaj, poxil sep'**) is *Ranunculus petiolaris* (5–7), a perennial herb with palmate, basal, divided leaves and a loosely branched inflorescence with bright yellow flowers, 17–25 cm across. The fruit is an aggregate of black achenes about 2 mm long, each with a slender curved beak. It is common in meadows and in the grassy understory of pine-oak forests in highland hamlets.

As a remedy for mange, the "hot" leaves are crushed and applied to the affected part, or the leaves are first toasted and ground into powder. The mange is bathed with **k'ox pak' chak** tea and the powder rubbed on. As a remedy for tarantula bite, the plant is boiled together with **ch'upak' joj** and the bite bathed with the liquid. For further medicinal use cf. **arvajáka tz'i'lel.**

Extended range: *Bletia reflexa* and *Micropleura renifolia.*

4. **Poxil chuvaj,** "madness medicine" (**yaxal nich tz'i'lel** in part), refers to *Polygala chiapensis* (1–4) and *P. costaricensis* (2–5), perennial herbs with alternate elliptic leaves from 2.5–6 cm long and terminal racemes of blue or lavender flowers. The flowers are irregular in shape, resembling pea flowers, 5–11 mm long. The fruit is a flattened, oval pod. They occur in brushy second growth, thorn woodland, and tropical deciduous forest in lowland and temperate areas.

To cure madness, the plant is burned over the fire while the patient is forced to inhale the smoke. If this is not effective, the patient is held down and warm water, in which the plant has been crushed, is poured in his nostrils. It is a "hot" cure.

Extended range: *Monnina chiapensis.*

5. **Poxil pat ka',** "mule's back medicine" (**ch'ail pox, piménta tz'i'lel, pox ka', poxil sim-nak'al**), refers to *Psychotria erythrocarpa* (6–7), soft-wooded shrubs to 2 m tall with opposite glossy, elliptic leaves pubescent beneath, 3–8 cm long, and terminal cymes of small, white flowers and small, fleshy, red or black fruits. Each fruit contains two ribbed seeds, 6–8 mm long. They are common elements in second growth and in the understory of tropical deciduous forests of lowland and temperate areas.

To cure pack sores, the leaves are burned on the griddle and pulverized. The "hot" powder is applied to the sore. Alternatively, the leaves may be brewed and the water applied to the sore. As a remedy for stomach ache, "white" dysentery,

swollen stomach, and nightmares, the plant is brewed and the "hot" tea drunk.

Extended range: *Psychotria pubescens.*

6. **Poxil sep',** "mange medicine" (**ch'ail jobel, k'ox klavel, poxil chakal, tzuk' ch'en**), is *Pinaropappus spathulatus* var. *chiapensis* (3–5), a caespitose herb with long, linear leaves and scapose, pink flowers in a head, similar to a dandelion flower. It occurs on rock outcrops in pine-oak forests of the highland and temperate hamlets.

To cure mange, the "cold" leaves are smashed to a paste and rubbed on the affected area. The leaves may also be brewed and the water used to bathe the affected area. The leaves may be either boiled or crushed in cold water as a "cold" remedy for both mange and fingernail distress (**unen k'obol**).

7. **Poxil yerva,** "tarantula medicine," is *Elytraria imbricata* (3–5), a wiry-stemmed herb with basal, elliptic pubescent leaves, 3.5–15 cm long, and compact, terminal spikes of small, ephemeral blue flowers, 3–6 mm long. The peduncles are covered with small lanceolate, imbricate bracts, which continue into the inflorescence. It is a common plant in disturbed and second growth situations and in the open understory of tropical deciduous forest in the lowland and lower temperate areas.

To cure horses that have been bitten by a tarantula, the entire plant is brewed together with **sakil sal-te'.** The "hot" tea is given to the animal to drink once. As a remedy for snakebite, it is brewed with the roots of **koko'on** and of **kururin** and drunk once. To ease pain in the legs (**k'ux koktik**), the patient's family cuts a small bunch and boils it and, when it is warm, bathes the affected part.

8. **Yok' tz'i',** "dog tongue" (-tik) (**chikin chij, lan te' tz'i'lel, poxil k'ok, poxil majbenal, poxil sep'** in part, **yok' tz'i' tz'i'lel**), refers to *Plantago australis* ssp. *hirtella* (8–11), and *P. major* (1–2), caespitose herbs with parallel-veined leaves and small flowers in a dense spike. The flowers are 4-merous with brownish membranous petals about 1–2 mm long, densely crowded on the elongated spike. The leaves are basal, elliptic, 1.5–3.5 cm wide in *P. australis* ssp. *hirtella* and broadly ovate, 4–8 cm wide in *P. major*. These are very common plants in grassy, disturbed areas in the highland hamlets.

To reduce the heat of **majbenal,** six leaves are crushed and mixed with cold water. A half cup of the "cold" infusion is drunk once in the morning or afternoon. A "cold" tea serves the same purpose and is also a remedy for measles. To relieve heartburn (**me'-vinik**), the plant is crushed in cold water and the "cold" infusion drunk. As a remedy for mange, a small bunch is crushed and bound to the affected part once daily for three days. As a remedy for mumps, three leaves are bound to the neck. To lessen muscular reflex pain (**nelub**), a leaf is bound to the affected part: neck, arm, hand, or thigh. It is also used to remove boils (**chakal**). The leaves are pulverized and administered to stanch cuts.

Extended range: *Ruellia nudiflora.*

"Moy Set"

The "**moy** set" is a group of five generics, soft-wooded shrubs and coarse herbs mostly with trumpet and bell-shaped flowers and elliptic, softly pubescent leaves.

1. **Kámpana nichim**, "bell flower," refers to plants with trumpet- or bell-shaped, white or red flowers.

Specifics: 5.

  a. **Batz'i kámpana nichim**, "genuine bell flower" (**kampana**), is the single-flowered *Datura candida* (6–8), large, soft-wooded shrubs with pendent, elongate, white, trumpet-shaped flowers, 15–20 cm long. The leaves are alternate, ovate, with an acute or acuminate apex, 15–30 cm long. It is classed as "tree." *Ladinos* use the flowers for altar decoration. It is grown in many of the temperate and all but one of the highland communities. In the highland hamlets a few people plant slips in their yards in the rainy season. In the temperate hamlets slips are planted in fencerows in the dry season.

The "hot" leaves are applied to a bone break. Children play with the flowers.

  b. **Bik'tal kámpana nichim**, "small bell flower" (**kámpana ch'ulelal, kámpana tz'i'lel**), is *Escobedia guatemalensis* (5–7), a coarse, brittle-stemmed herb with large, axillary, spreading, white flowers, 14–15 cm long. The calyx is tubular, 5–7 cm long, enclosing the lower half of the flower tube. The leaves are opposite, distichous linear-lanceolate, 5–15 cm long, 6–15 mm wide. The roots are thick and bright orange. The plant occurs in moist places such as grassy seepages and meadows in temperate and highland hamlets.

  c. **Cha'-koj kámpana nichim**, "two-tiered bell flower," refers to the double-flowered forms of *Datura candida* (1–1) (see above). *Ladinos* use the flowers for altar decorations.

  d. **Sakil kámpana nichim**, "white bell flower" (**k'ox kámpana nichim**), is *Bouvardia longiflora* (3–8), a brittle-stemmed shrub to 1 m tall, with long, erect, tubular, white flowers in terminal clusters. The flower tube is narrow, 1.5–2 mm wide, 5–7.5 cm long, expanding into four elliptic petal lobes about 12–18 mm long. The leaves are opposite, narrowly ovate, 2–5 cm long. It occurs in second growth in temperate and highland hamlets.

Children sell the flowers on the roadside.

  e. **Tzajal kámpana nichim**, "red bell flower" (**kola venáro, tzajal kampana**), is the garden hibiscus *Hibiscus rosa-sinensis* (3–7), a red-flowered shrub cultivated in lowland and temperate *ladino* house gardens. The flowers are large and showy with petals 7–9 cm long and a characteristic column of fused stamens exerted from the corolla. The leaves are alternate, broadly ovate, coarsely dentate along the upper two-thirds of the margins, rounded at the base, about 5–10 cm long. It is classed as a "tree." *Ladinos* use the flowers for altar decorations.

2. **Kámpana tz'i'lel**, "bell plant," refers to coarse herbs with large flowers in terminal inflorescences.

Specifics: 3.

  a. **K'anal kámpana tz'i'lel**, "yellow bell plant" (**kachímpa tz'i'lel**), is *Ludwigia octovalvis* (2–1) and *L. peruviana* (2–2), coarse herbs of wet places with large, open, yellow flowers with four spreading petals about 15–30 mm long. The corolla and calyx are above the obpyramidal inferior ovary, which develops into stout, many-seeded fruits, which split longitudinally along the many small ribs. The leaves are opposite, narrowly elliptic to ovate-elliptic, 2–11 cm long. It occurs in temperate and lowland areas.

  b. **Tzajal kámpana tz'i'lel**, "red bell plant," is *Lonicera pilosa* (1–2), a thin, brittle-stemmed, sprawling plant with capitate clusters of long, orange, tubular flowers, 4–5 cm long. The leaves are alternate, short petiolate, oblong-oval, 3–7 cm long. Those directly below the inflorescence are fused into a disc. The fruit is a red berry about 7 mm in diameter. It occurs in pine-oak and evergreen cloud forests in temperate and highland hamlets.

Extended range: *Oenothera kunthiana.*

  c. **Yaxal kámpana tz'i'lel**, "blue bell plant" (**tz'ubal nich**), refers to *Achimenes cettoana* (2–2), *A. grandiflora* (1–2), *A. longiflora* (1–2), *Ruellia hookeriana* (1–2), and *R. nudiflora* (1–2), plants with large, terminal inflorescences of trumpet-shaped, bilabiate, purple to magenta flowers. They occur on shaded banks and along streams in temperate and lowland areas.

3. **Malva** (**kámpana nichim, malvarisko, natz' alperes, poxil k'ak'et**) is *Mirabilis jalapa* (6–12), the four o'clock, a large, soft-wooded shrub grown by *ladinos* in temperate, highland, and lowland gardens and occasionally occuring wild in fencerows and on waste ground throughout the townships. The tubular magenta, purple, or white flowers occur in terminal clusters. The perianth is 3–5.5 cm long. The leaves are opposite, broadly ovate or triangular-ovate, 3–12 cm long. The capsule is ovoid, about 1 cm long, somewhat wrinkled or roughened between the five sutures.

To heal burns, a bunch of the entire plant is brewed. The burns are bathed with the water three times daily until healed. The remedy is classed variously as "medium" and "hot." A person suffering from a black eye brews three or four tips and bathes the bruise with the decoction or rubs the flowers on the bruise. For swelling or when the blood rushes to the heart after a person has fallen from a truck or been struck by a car, the "hot" tea is taken.

Extended range: *Anoda cristata, Bouvardia leiantha, Heli-*

otropium indicum, and *Justicia* sp. A small bunch of *Justicia* is crushed and applied to burns once daily for three days. It is "cold."

4. **Moy** (-**tik**) (**bankilal, moy pox, yanal moy**) is tobacco *Nicotiana tabacum* (4–6), a rank, viscid, tall, annual plant to 2 m tall with tubular-salverform pink or white flowers, 3.5–4.5 cm long and about 2 cm across, arranged in a panicle. The leaves are alternate and variable. They may be ovate, obovate, or elliptic, sessile and decurrent or amplexicaul. The larger leaves are at least 5 cm long. The fruit is a capsule 1.5–2 cm long partially enclosed by the accrescent calyx. Zinacantecs recognize that seed from the same plant will produce both forms. They attribute greater strength to the pink form. Tobacco is cultivated in most of the temperate and all but one of the highland communities and occurs as an occasional weed in rubbish heaps and waste ground. In Zinacantán Center a few households keep a plant sheltered under the roof so that tobacco leaves will still be available after winter frosts.

The epic tale of the Zinacantec merchants who used to travel to Tabasco to buy tobacco to sell in Guatemala—and their fateful reception across the border—is known to all (Laughlin, 1977, T150). In a lighter vein is the story of the young man who, while buying a load of cigars in San Juan el Bosque, won a bride for just a liter of cane liquor (Laughlin, 1977, T92). Tobacco is considered to be a wild plant, but because of its power as a guardian against evil spirits, young plants are frequently transplanted to the yard. It is dangerous, however, to have tobacco growing too abundantly in one's yard. Its excessive heat will cause the household to starve or it will bring sickness to the house (**spay jchameltik**). However, tobacco must not be cut down, or its invisible caterpillars (**sbuluk' satil**) will bite the offender when he is walking in thick underbrush. The wound will not heal until he eats a mashed, green tobacco leaf.

Tobacco must not be denied to a person who asks for it, nor should it be sold, lest it die. It should not be scolded, nor should one give thanks for it, lest the person become stupid or die. A woman once went to get tobacco for her husband. She said, "Thank you," to the first person who sold it to her. Then she went to a second person, who gave her some more. She said, "Thank you." Now she was scolded for saying that. She was told that one must not do that. It was true. She arrived home and her stomach swelled up until she died. But if you eat a bit of the leaf, that will save you.

No other plant in the flora of Zinacantán is accorded the magical power, both for good and evil, as that assigned to tobacco. Although this power is focused on chewing tobacco, it is also present in the mere leaf. Tobacco is referred to as **bankilal**, elder brother, as it is the elder brother of Thunderbolt. The elder brother scolded Thunderbolt for striking us so much and if we rub tobacco on our body we will be safe from Thunderbolt. Chewing tobacco may be termed **muk'ta mol**, "great old man," and when specially prepared in a mixture for curing **poslom** it is termed **ojov**, "lord."

In preparing chewing tobacco, the leaves are placed in a wooden trough or the underside of a log stool set by the front door and pounded with a billhook handle. The leaves are squeezed by hand to remove the juice, then pounded again together with lime and sometimes camphor and orange rind. (Camphor is only added if the tobacco is to be used as a medicine). The "hot" tobacco is stored in special gourds. It is chewed now primarily by old men, but is an essential ingredient of many cures, though not used by all shamans. According to tradition the value of tobacco was not known by *ladinos.* Long ago when the men went to work in the coffee fincas they took their tobacco along with them. They slept together in a big room. They left the door open. Those who had tobacco gourds put them next to their heads. One night the owner of the coffee finca peered in with evil thoughts. He saw flames dancing on the ground next to the gourds. He came in and woke the men up. "What have you hidden?" he asked.

"Nothing."

"What's in the gourds?"

"Elder brother."

"Sell me some!" he says.

"No!"

Finally they agreed and he bought some, so now *ladinos* know the value of elder brother.

Long ago a man went to the coffee fincas. He took his net along with him to work. He set it down and took out his tobacco. He put some in his mouth.

The owner of the finca saw him. "Why do you eat horse shit?" he asked.

"No, this is medicine."

The owner said, "No, it's just horse shit." They worked until two in the afternoon. The owner went home. He fell sick. He felt worse and worse. Then he sent for them and begged them to cure him. At last they agreed, on condition that he give them two days of rest, because in those days the workers weren't paid. They gave him the tobacco to take, but in a bowl of urine. After they urged him and urged him to drink it, he swallowed it down. He let a big fart and got well. He bought their tobacco and respected it from then on.

Should a *ladino* foreman on the coffee plantations not let his workers rest, they may sprinkle tobacco on his back when he is asleep. This will cause him nausea and diarrhea, laying him up for a least a day.

Long ago the Tenejapans were taught by the people of Simojovel to protect themselves from the long-haired Lacandon highwayman with tobacco medicine (Laughlin, 1977: 297–301). Zinacantecs learned that it was protection from the ravages of Spooks (Laughlin, 1977:183–186). In these tales and in everyday discourse tobacco is shown to have the power to stupefy, paralyze, or blind an adversary. To drive a strong wind away from the cornfield the farmer may spit tobacco and cane liquor at it or sprinkle tobacco on the ground. Shamans bury chewing tobacco at the spot where a person has suffered soul-loss, to incapacitate the Earth Lord. They also spit tobacco juice on the ground to scare the witch off, and rub the patient's body with tobacco at bedtime. This last may be done by anyone who has been frightened during the day. A person who is being pursued by a rainbow may protect himself by scattering tobacco on the ground. If he meets a snake on the trail he should spit tobacco juice at it. To protect his cornfield from the depredations of raccoons he should scatter tobacco and garlic around it. Cf. **chenek'**.

As a remedy for the aching of one's leg or foot that is caused by an evil spirit (**poslom**), blood-letting is followed by massaging the limb with a mixture of garlic, tobacco, and woman's urine and binding it with the piece of an old skirt. More simply, the limb may be bandaged with tobacco leaves that have been wilted on the fire or rubbed with a mixture of tobacco and camphor. Wilted leaves are also used for bonebreaks. Tobacco and camphor may be used for gangrene (**mos**), and applied to mange (**sep'**.) The "hot" tobacco-garlic-urine potion may be taken for constipation or urinary stoppage (**makel**). For painful urination, tobacco may be mixed with cane liquor and drunk.

The remedies are legion: Chewing tobacco is rubbed on a snakebite to draw off the poison. To rid oneself of intestinal worms, leaves are placed on one's stomach in the shape of a cross to turn the worms around (**chjoyp'ij o sni'**). As a remedy for a swollen stomach (**pumel**), a person may chew the tobacco and swallow the juice or rub the juice on his stomach. He may also soak the tobacco in water and drink the infusion. To cure "wind," chewing tobacco is eaten or mixed with warm water and drunk. The same warm infusion may be drunk to vomit up tuberculosis (**sak-'obal**). As an abortive, tobacco may be drunk with cold water. The "worm" that causes toothache is killed by eating chewing tobacco. Juice from a tobacco leaf is applied to the eye if a yellow spot appears on the white of the eye.

For a stomach ache, tobacco and dried chili may be ground and mixed in water. The "hot" infusion is drunk.

For animal ailments the following remedies have been reported. A sheep suffering "wind" in its belly has its belly rubbed with a tobacco leaf. Alternatively, the leaf is pounded and mixed with ashes from the hearth and rubbed on its belly. A mule suffering from "wind" in its legs is forced to drink hot water or cane liquor in which tobacco has been sprinkled. For further medicinal and magical use cf. **axux, ixim, k'ox yax-chel, lula**.

Extended range: *Cerastrium nutans, Martynia annua,* and *Rechsteineria warscewiczii.*

5. **Poxil aja-chon**, lit. "lordly snake medicine," i.e., "rattlesnake medicine" (**chenek' aja-chon, chenek' chon**), is *Martynia annua* (3–4), a rank, viscid weed with profuse, white and maroon, pendent, tubular-campanulate flowers, 4–5.5 cm long, and woody, beaked capsules, 2 cm long. The leaves are broadly triangular or broadly angular ovate, cordate at the base, palmately veined, 5–23 cm long, 5–22 cm wide. It occurs in disturbed areas and waste ground in the lowlands.

As a remedy for snakebite, the bean is boiled and the tea is drunk.

"Nok'ol Sik'ol Set"

The "**nok'ol sik'ol** set" is comprised of two generics. Both are parasites and members of the mistletoe family Loranthaceae. They have brittle leaves and/or stems and attach to trees by means of a holdfast.

1. **Nok'ol sik'ol**, "**nok'ol** cigarette" (**nap'ux te', nop'ol sik'ol**).

Specifics: 2.

    a. **Nok'ol sik'ol**, "**nok'ol** cigarette," refers to *Phoradendron annulatum* (3–6), *P. falcatum* (2–3), *P. nervosum* (4–10), *P. quadrangulare* (1–2), *P. robustissimum* (1–2), *Struthanthus deppeanus* (3–5), and *S. tacanensis* (2–6). These are coarse parasites, often forming vine-like mats over the host trees. In Tenejapa, *S. intermedius* Kuijt ined. is a pest, often killing or seriously affecting the production of oranges and other citrus trees. In Zinacantán it is noted on peach trees and **chikin-ib**. The plants have leathery, lance ovate leaves and small flowers in axillary spikes or clusters. The fruit is a muscilaginous berry. These plants are common in forests and on cultivated trees throughout the township. *Struthanthus* is classed as a "vine."

The name of these plants is derived from the way they stick to a tree as a cigarette does to one's mouth. At the time of the Flood the monkeys were transformed into mistletoe.

For a bone break three leaves are bound to the break for three days. For this purpose, *Struthanthus* is classed as **stot**, "male," and *Phoradendron*, **sme'**, "female." The former is considered to be more potent. As a remedy for whooping cough, the leaves are brewed with **tzon-te'al krus**, for a "hot" tea. The leaves are also used in the "steam cure."

Extended range: *Aristolochia maxima* and *Psittacanthus calyculatus.*

    b. **Nok'ol sik'ol j'ik'al**, "spook's **nok'ol** cigarette," is the common lowland parasite of tree legumes and other plants *Psittacanthus calyculatus* (4–10). It is a coarse plant often as large as the trees that it parasitizes. The flowers are red-orange and 6–10 cm long, and make large displays on the host. The petals are linear, long and narrow, fused into a tube at the base but spreading above. The stamens are long and exerted from the corolla. The leaves are opposite, coriacious, lanceolate to oblong, 6–15 cm long. It is classed variously as "plant" and "vine."

2. **Yikatz toj**, "pine's burden" (**k'anal nok'ol sik'ol, nap'ux te', tzon-te'al toj**), is *Arceuthobium globosum* (4–8), a leafless parasite on pines. They are small, much-branched and have jointed stems and connate scales instead of leaves. It occurs in the higher elevation pine forests.

As a remedy for whooping cough, a "hot" tea may be prepared. The plant is also used in the "steam cure."

"Pak' Chak Set"

The "**pak' chak** set" is comprised of five generics, small-flowered, leathery-barked, wiry-stemmed, weedy herbs.

1. **Pak' chak,** (**pak' chak abnal***) refers to *Malva* and *Kearnemalvastrum,* herbs with soft, pubescent, large, ovate leaves.

Specifics: 2.

    a. **K'ox pak' chak,** "small bottom patch" (**tz'oban tz'i'lel**), refers to *Malva nicaeensis* (4–6) and *M. parviflora* (6–8), common weeds of waste ground, roadsides, and yards in the highlands. The leaves are round-reniform, shallowly lobed, palmately veined, long petiolate, 1.5–2.5 cm long in *M. nicaeensis*, 2–7 cm long in *M. parviflora*. The flowers are pink, lavender, or white, 8–10 mm broad, and are arranged in axillary clusters. The fruit is disk-shaped, made up of many joined carpels, and resembles a wheel of cheese.

To relieve constipation, a small handful of tips is brewed. One cup of the "hot" tea is drunk before breakfast and in the afternoon. The same tea is taken for diarrhea caused by worms, provoking the patient to vomit them up. The liquid is used to bathe the patient afterwards. The "hot" leaves are brewed and the decoction used to bathe festering cuts. The leaves may be applied to bone breaks or ground into powder to stanch bleeding. For further medical use cf. **k'ojom, poxil yayijemal.**

Extended range: *Anoda cristata, Modiola caroliniana,* and *Sida rhombifolia.*

    b. **Muk'ta pak' chak,** "large bottom patch" (**mol pak' chak**), is *Kearnemalvastrum lacteum* (4–8), a tall, tough-stemmed, branched herb to 2 m high with clusters of small white flowers. The leaves are palmately 3- to 5-lobed, 3–5 cm long, 3–13 cm wide, and softly pubescent above and below. It is a common plant in disturbed situations, roadsides, and waste ground in the highlands.

The leathery bark is used to secure the rock in a deadfall for rats.

2. **Pem-k'ulub,** "**pem** grasshopper," refers to *Verbena, Crusea,* and *Borreria.* These have thick, opposite leaves with impressed nerves, square stems, and terminal, white or pale blue flowers.

Specifics: 2.

    a. **Batz'i pem-k'ulub,** "genuine **pem** grasshopper" (**bik'it pem- k'ulub, sakil pak' chak**), refers to *Verbena carolina* (6–7) and *V. litoralis* (4–5), branched herbs with small flowers in terminal spikes. The leaves are opposite, elliptic to narrowly obovate with serrate margins and prominently veined beneath, 1.5–8 cm long. *Verbena carolina* generally has smaller leaves than *V. litoralis*. The inflorescence and flowers of both are similar. They may be blue, lavender, or white, 1.5–3 mm long, and are crowded into terminal spikes. These are common in disturbed areas and waste ground as well as the understory of pine-oak forest in temperate and highland hamlets.

As a remedy for madness (**chuvaj**), a small bunch is brewed. A spoonful of the "hot" tea is forced down the patient's nose once a day for three days. The parents of a child that throws tantrums crush a handful of the plant in cold water, or brew it. The child is forced to drink a cupful of the "cold" liquid so that he will vomit his evil. As a remedy for anger (**k'ak'al o'onil**) the plant is crushed and then mixed with cane liquor. It is "cold." As a remedy for malaria, the plant is brewed to provide a "hot" tea. The same tea may be taken for diarrhea. If it is for worms it is sweetened with brown sugar. The leaves may be ground and the powder applied to a wound to stanch bleeding. The "hot" leaf is also applied to a bone break.

Extended range: *Buchnera pusilla, Salvia misella, S. reptans.*

    b. **Sakil pem-k'ulub,** "white **pem** grasshopper" (**k'ox jabnal, poxil k'ux k'abil, poxil makel, poxil tza'nel, xanxan, xanxanil be**), refers to *Borreria laevis* (3–5), *Crusea calocephala* (1–2), and *C. parviflora* (1–3), small-branched herbs with white or lavender flowers in head-like clusters, which may be terminal or axillary and always closely subtended by two or four leaf-like bracts. The leaves are opposite, narrowly elliptic to narrowly obovate, widely spaced on the stems, 11 cm long or less. The flowers are funnelform, very small, about 2–15 mm long. The heads and flowers are much larger in *C. calocephala* than *C. parviflora* and *B. laevis*. The heads are 1.5–2.5 cm broad in *C. calocephala* and 7–13 mm broad in *C. parviflora* and *B. laevis*. They occur in disturbed situations, such as cornfields and roadsides in the temperate and highland hamlets.

As a remedy for constipation and urinary stoppage a "hot" tea of *B. laevis* is taken. To cure diarrhea, a bunch is brewed together with the roots of **krus jobel**. A half cup of the "hot" tea is taken twice a day. *Borreria laevis* is brewed and the "hot" liquid used to bathe a tarantula or a snake bite. The leaf of *Crusea* sp. is brewed and the "hot" tea taken to relieve painful urination. As an antidote for jimson weed poisoning, the leaf of *B. laevis* is ground on a stone and mixed with water, which is administered to the poisoned dog.

3. **Poxil jolol,** "hair medicine" (**sat mes poxil ka', tz'itesob jolol**), is *Anoda cristata* (6–5), a lavender-flowered herb common in disturbed ground such as cornfields and places around habitations at all elevations. The flowers are terminal or axillary, with five lavender petals, 2–2.5 cm long, and a column of fused stamens in the center. The leaves are alternate and triangular with two or four triangular lobes at the base. The fruit is a pubescent star-shaped disk, about 1.5 cm across, made up of fused carpels. It is subtended by the accrescent 5-lobed calyx.

To induce their hair to grow longer, women grind the tips of the plants on a rock and mix them in cold water, bathing their hair with the "cold" infusion.

4. **Sat mes,** "**sat** broom" (-**tik**), refers to *Sida, Waltheria, Melochia,* and *Turnera.* These are superficially similar, stiff, erect plants, all occurring in disturbed situations as in yards, along roadsides, waste ground, or fallow fields.

Specifics: 3.

    a. **K'anal sat mes,** "yellow **sat** broom" (**k'anal pak' chak, k'ox sat mes**), refers to *Sida barclayi* (12–14) and *S. rhombifolia* (5–7), which together are almost ubiquitous weedy herbs, with *S. barclayi* being common in lowland areas and *S. rhombifolia* widespread in temperate and highland situations. These have small ovate or oblong-ovate leaves on stiff, leathery-barked stems, a characteristic that makes them very suitable for brooms. They have small, pale yellow flowers, 12–18 mm broad, solitary in the axils or in groups of two or more.

As a remedy for falling hair, the plant is mashed and soaked for a day, placed outside overnight, and the infusion used as a rinse the following day. To burst boils (**chakal, vo'an**) and kill their "animals," the leaves are crushed and rubbed on, sometimes with crushed matasano pit and tallow, or the leaves may be boiled together with marigold (**vo'tus**) of any kind and the steam applied. This is a "hot" remedy. The plants are cut, tied with a vine, and used to sweep the yard, the threshing floor, or wherever corn is spread out to dry.

Extended range: *Chamaecrista nictitans* ssp. *disadena* var. *pilosa, C. rufa, Hybanthus verbenaceus,* and *Marina spiciformis.*

    b. **Sakil sat mes,** "white **sat** broom" (**muk'ta sat mes, putzul chij tz'i'lel**), refers to *Corchorus siliquosus* (1–1), *Melochia tomentosa* (1–1), *Sida acuta* (2–5), *Turnera ulmifolia* (3–7), and *Waltheria americana* (5–10), plants with gray, soft, pubescent leaves and pale yellow or white flowers that are much more bushy than those of **k'anal sat mes.** They occur in second growth of temperate and lowland regions.

As a remedy for horses suffering diarrhea, the plant is brewed and the "hot" tea administered.

5. **Xtalaj tz'i'lel,** "antlion plant," is *Pavonia schiedeana* (1–1), a stiff herb with pubescent branches, alternate elliptic or narrowly obovate leaves, 5–17 cm long, with crenate-dentate margins. The flowers are clustered at the end of a long peduncle. They are pink or lavender, with five petals, 10–13 mm long. Its spiny seed, which sticks to clothing, is likened to an antlion. This plant occurs in the disturbed understory of seasonal evergreen forest of temperate and lowland areas.

"Petok Set"

The "**petok** set" is a grouping of six generics, all cacti.

1. **Chikin ton,** "rock ear," refers to three cacti that inhabit crevices in rock surfaces. All have young stems covered with stiff white spines; however, **batz'i chikin ton** and **muk'ta chikin ton** mature into flattened, elongate, sometimes spineless stems, whereas **bik'it chikin ton** remains round and covered with spines.

Specifics: 3.

    a. **Batz'i chikin ton,** "genuine rock ear" (**poxil k'ak'et**), is *Epiphyllum crenatum* var. *kimnachii* (7–6), a clustered, pendent orchid cactus with large, white and pink trumpet-shaped flowers, 14–20 cm long, and flattened, succulent stems with wavy margins. It occurs in crevices on sheer limestone cliffs in temperate and highland areas. *Ladinos* use the flowers for altar decoration.

To relieve the pain of a burn, the outer surface of the leaf is scraped off and the leaf is rubbed on the burn. This "cold" remedy may also be applied for **poslom.** The "cold" fruit is eaten by people and birds.

    b. **Bik'it chikin ton,** "small rock ear," is *Mammillaria eriacantha* (1–1). These cacti are small, globose or short-cylindrical, with watery sap. The surface is densely covered with white spines. The spines are arranged in clusters with one central stout spine and many finer spines radiating at its base. The flowers are magenta, about 8–10 mm long. It occurs in crevices in limestone outcrops in the highland and temperate regions.

    c. **Muk'ta chikin ton,** "large rock ear" (**kola lakarto**), is *Hylocereus undatus* (6–8), a terrestrial or epiphytic cactus with arching, triangular stems. Each rib of the triangle is flattened into a thin, broad, green surface. The margins of the stem are wavy with spiny nodes 2–4 cm apart. The flowers are very large, as much as 30 cm long, and white. The fruits are 6–12 cm long, red, and contain numerous black seeds. It is cultivated by lowland *ladinos* and by Zinacantecs in Kelem Ton, Masan, Sak Lum, and Santa Rosa. It is planted in Masan in May and June. The "cold" fruit is eaten raw.

2. **Chorísyo ch'ix,** "sausage spine" (**koryon ch'ix, tzukum ch'ix**), is *Opuntia pubescens,* (1–2) a spiny leafless shrub with sausage-shaped segments, bearing spines with sheaths that make them extremely difficult to remove from the skin. The flowers are yellow and occur on the ends of the segments. The juvenile segments are reminiscent of a woolly caterpillar. This cactus occurs on rocky slopes in thorn woodland in the temperate and lowland regions.

Extended range: *Stenocereus eichlamii.*

To relieve the pain of caterpillar stings, the plant is smashed and the juice applied.

3. **Ch'ixal amuch,** "frog spine" (**kola lakarto**), is *Acanthocereus horridus* (2–2), a sprawling, three-sided, succulent vine with large clusters of spines to 6 cm long and long, white, tubular flowers, 18–25 cm long, and a sweet, succulent, spinescent fruit. It is common in lowland second growth and primary tropical deciduous forest. It is also planted by *ladinos*

in fencerows.

4. **Ne bolom**, "jaguar tail" (**kola lakarto, sne bolom, sne lakarto**), is *Selenicereus grandiflorus* (3–6), a sprawling vine-cactus with ribbed stems, 2–4 cm in diameter, and covered with stout, star-shaped spines. The flowers are white and very large. The fruit is red or pink, juicy, and covered with long, ferruginous hairs. Lowland *ladinos* plant the stems at an angle or lying down in fences. The plants are often epiphytic or saxicolous. The fruit that ripens in September is rarely eaten by Zinacantecs, who claim it causes malaria.

5. **Petok** (-**tik**, -**altik**) refers to the erect, shrubby, flat-stemmed cacti *Nopalea* and *Opuntia*.

The name **petok** is explained in this way:

> Clouds (**tok**) gathered and formed inside a fence long ago, leaving behind the prickly pear, but when the people tried to transplant it, it would not fruit until they planted 13 corn kernels with it. It was the opossum's and the coyote's fruit long ago. They went to get some. Opossum wanted to climb up to eat the fruit, but he couldn't because of the spines. He's too short, too, to pick them. Then Coyote came. They spoke to each other, as we say, "Please pick me one of the fruits to eat," said Opossum.
>
> "Okay," said Coyote. Quickly he stood up to pick it. "Open your mouth wide!" Opossum was told. He didn't open his mouth. He just caught it in his paws. "And now eat it," he was told. They ate and ate them. (Opossum) felt his paws itching now, with the spines you understand. Opossum's paws certainly itched. Quickly he threw it away. He felt bad.
>
> And then, "Well, why did you throw it away?" asked Coyote.
>
> "As for me, I'll eat it. See, it's good to eat!" said Coyote, too.
>
> He ate again.
>
> Well, it was that Coyote who finished eating it, because it was his fruit long ago. When they finished Opossum said, "You trick us." He was squatting there looking at his paw. He left. He was distracted by it, he didn't eat the fruit, he threw it away. It was Coyote who finished eating it. That's the end. Each one went off by himself. That's the story about the prickly pear.

Extended range: *Mammalaria* sp.

Specifics: 4.

    a. **Batz'i petok**, "genuine **petok**" (**lo'balal petok**), refers to *Opuntia ficus-indica* (3–6), large plants, to 2 m tall, with elongate, elliptic, thick , prickly pads, 3–6 dm long, and orange or yellow campanulate flowers, 4–8 cm long, with many white anthers.

The leaves are planted by a few Zinacantecs in yards and fencerows in many temperate and all highland communities. Some claim that it is dangerous for young people to plant it. If it causes sickness it should be "killed" with a machete. Many say that it may be planted throughout the year, though others maintain that it will rot if planted in the rainy season. To fruit well it should be planted in compost with 13 kernels of highland white corn or 13 corn kernels and 13 highland black beans. Cf. **ixim**.

As a fixative for whitewash, the leaves are chopped up finely and soaked for a day before adding the lime to the water. For medicinal use cf. **elamonix**. The fruits are harvested from late August through October. Before eating these "cold" fruits, the spines are rubbed off with weeds.

    b. **Ik'-lo'an petok**, "purple **petok**," is *Opuntia ficus-indica* (1–3), a large plant, to 3 m tall, with rounded, very long, spiny, thick pads and purple campanulate flowers. It is cultivated by *ladinos* in highland areas, fruiting at the same time as **batz'i petok**.

    c. **Te'tikil petok**, "wild **petok**," refers to the low-branched highland *Opuntia* sp. 640 (1–2), and the lowland *Opuntia* sp., both occurring on exposed, dry, rocky slopes. The fruits are eaten by birds.

    d. **Tzajal petok**, "red **petok**" (**ch'ieb ch'uj***, **te'tikal petok**), is *Nopalea cochenillifera* (3–5), a tall plant, to 4 m, with large, flat, pointed pads with small spines. The flowers are red and tubular. It is widely common in the understory of tropical deciduous forest. Formerly this cactus was grown as it served as a host for cochineal bugs, which produced red dye. Lowland *ladinos* and Zinacantecs in many temperate communities commonly plant it in fencerows. The fruits are "cold."

6. **Yoyal vinajel**, "sky post" (-**tik**) (**orkana**), refers to *Cephalocereus maxonii* (3–6) and *Stenocereus eichlamii* (4–7). Both are large tree-like cacti with columnar stems, which are 6–10 ribbed. In *Cephalocereus* the areoles are soft-hairy and the ends of the stems are covered with long hair-like bristles. Flowers are pink, about 4 cm long. The fruit is about 3.5 cm broad and naked except for a few scales. *Stenocereus* is characterized by its brown felty areoles and stout spines. The flowers are white fading to red and 6–7 cm long. They occur in tropical deciduous forest in the lowlands. *Ladinos* plant them in lowland fencerows.

It is classed as a "tree."

"Pimil Anal Set"

The "**pimil anal** set" is comprised of seven generics, thick, succulent-leaved herbs that are saxicolous or epiphytic.

1. **Pimil anal**, "thick leaf," refers to *Sedum* and *Pilea microphyla*. All are leafy-stemmed succulents.

Specifics: 3.

    a. **Batz'i pimil anal**, "genuine thick leaf," is *Sedum praealtum* (1–4), a plant that occurs mostly in cultivation or on the roofs of buildings. It is a succulent herb with small, sessile, fleshy obovate leaves, 1–2 cm long. The flowers are bright yellow with 4–5 petals, 5–8 mm long, and are numerous in a short-branched terminal inflorescence. It occurs in a few locations on limestone cliffs, where it appears to be in the wild state. It is grown in Chaynatik, Joyijel, Petz Toj, and Sak Lum, and in all the highland communities.

A few Zinacantecs grow sedum in their yards. Although slips may be planted, it is more common to transplant young plants in the rainy season. Compost may be supplied.

Each steward provides half a large basket of sedum on the first *Posada* to adorn the litters of Joseph and Mary and to decorate the churches of St. Lawrence and St. Sebastian. A small basket is gathered to decorate each steward's altar. For the eighth *Posada,* half a large basket is provided by each steward to decorate the creche. The plants are tied in vertical strips on the roof, alternating with geraniums and mountain palm or holly fern. The elders provide a small basket for their Christmas altar. The publicans provide two small baskets to adorn the Chapel of Our Lord of Esquipulas. They are offered in Elan Voʻ for the New Year, in Naben Chauk for Epiphany, in Atz'am for Monday of Holy Week, in Elan Voʻ and Naben Chauk for the first *Posada.* They are widely used to decorate hamlet creches.

To cure fever sores, a handful of the "cold" leaves is chewed before breakfast for one to two days, or for nine days. The "cold" leaves may be rubbed on the neck as a remedy for mumps. A person with a headache may rinse his hair and rub the leaves on his head. As a remedy for deafness caused by "heat," the leaves are bruised in water and the infusion applied to the ear.

Extended range: *Echeveria bella.*

b. **K'ox pimil anal**, "small thick leaf," is *Sedum guatemalense* (1–2), a saxicolous and occasionally epiphytic herb with very small, succulent, linear leaves, 5–14 mm long, arranged along thin stems. The flowers are pink or white with petals 5–6 mm long and are arranged in a terminal panicle. It occurs in pine-oak forest and evergreen cloud forests of the highlands.

c. **Tontikil pimil anal**, "rock-growing thick leaf" (**k'un-tz'iʻlel**), is *Pilea microphylla* (2–4), a very dense-matting, succulent herb that is common on rocks in temperate and highland areas both in forest and disturbed situations. The leaves are very small, broadly elliptic to broadly obovate, 2–8 mm long, and numerous on the slender-branched stems. The flowers are minute in tiny clusters in the axils of the leaves. Zinacantecs note its appearance after the burning of the fields.

It may be used as a substitute for sedum at Christmas time.

2. **Poxil chin**, "exema medicine" (**poxil balamil**, and **poxil nuk'ul** in part), refers to *Echeveria acutifolia* (1–2), *E. mucronata* (1–3), *E. sessiliflora* (1–2), and *Villadia albiflora* (2–3), rosette-leaved succulents of rock outcrops and limestone cliffs of the temperate and highland hamlets. The flowers are orange in scapose racemes.

As remedy for exema, a bunch of the "cold" *Echeveria* leaves is crushed and applied to the affected part once each morning for three days. Alternatively, the leaves may be crushed in water and the infusion used to bathe the skin. To cure mumps, the "cold" leaves are crushed and bound to the neck. As a remedy for soul-loss (**balamil**), *V. albiflora* is placed over the fire and the patient's clothing smoked. It is crushed in cold water and the patient bathed.

3. **Poxil eal**, lit. "mouth medicine," i.e., "fever sore medicine" (**pimil anal, pimil anal tz'iʻlel**), is *Pinguicula moranensis* (4–5), an insectivorous, acaulescent plant with a basal rosette of leaves occuring in crevices of rock outcrops and sheer cliffs. The leaves are thick and covered with a sticky substance. They are obovate, rounded at the apex, 2–10 cm long, 1–6 cm wide. The flower is scapose, solitary, and bright magenta with a long slender spur at its base. It occurs in temperate and highland hamlets.

The plants may be used as a substitute for sedum at Christmas time. As a remedy for fever sores, a few "cold" leaves are chewed once a day for two days.

Extended range: *Echeveria bella.*

4. **Poxil yat chij**, "sheep penis medicine" or "deer penis medicine," is *Echeveria bella* (1–2), a small saxicolous plant with a basal rosette of succulent, oblong obovate, acute leaves, 1.5–3 cm long. The flowers are yellow and orange with five acute petals, about 7–10 mm long, borne on a terminal raceme. It occurs on rock outcrops in pine-oak forest on the high ridges surrounding San Cristóbal.

As a remedy for **chin** skin disease, the leaves are crushed and the "cold" juice applied.

5. **Sentavo tz'iʻlel**, "penny plant" (**meryo tz'iʻlel, pimínta tz'iʻlel**), is *Peperomia campylotropa* (3–6), a bulbous acaulescent herb with round, coin-shaped leaves, 8–28 mm in diameter, which appear each rainy season. The petioles are long and slender, 3–8 cm long, and attach to the center of the blade, forming an umbrella-like leaf. The spikes are long and slender, much exceeding the leaves. The plants are locally abundant in the grassy understory of pine-oak forests in highland areas.

Extended range: *Alchemilla pectinata.*

6. **Vixobtakil** (**-tik**) refers to *Peperomias* with narrow, thick, succulent leaves.

Specifics: 3.

a. **Batz'i vixobtakil**, "genuine **vixobtakil**," is *Peperomia galioides* (5–11), an epiphyte with sessile-linear-oblanceolate or narrowly oblong leaves in whorls of four to six leaves at a node. They are mostly 1–2 cm long and 1-nerved below. The inflorescence is a narrow spike 1–1.5 mm wide with microscopic flowers and poppy-seed-like seeds. It is common in pine-oak and evergreen cloud forests of temperate and highland hamlets. It is grown by a few people in four temperate and most of the highland communities.

It is a basic ingredient of "flower water." A large handful of the "cold" plant is used. The plant is also used to adorn the patient's bed. It is rarely used to decorate crosses. To relieve headaches and overheating or to calm fever, the plant is crushed in cold water. The patient's head is bathed with the infusion once or twice a day. To calm fever, a small bunch may also be brewed and a half cup of the "cold" tea drunk before meals twice a day, for one day. The "cold" leaf is chewed for fever sores. For further medicinal use cf. **antzil aj, k'ox aja-te'es.**

Extended range: *Villadia albiflora.*

> b. **Muk'ta vixobtakil**, "large **vixobtakil**" (**tzajal vixob-takil** in part), refers to *Peperomia humilis* (2–4) and *P. liebmannii* (2–5), saxicolous and epiphytic plants with broad, thick, three-veined, opposite, pubescent leaves, 3–4 cm long. They are very common plants on limestone outcrops and occasionally as epiphytes in pine-oak forests of temperate and highland areas.

> c. **Setajtik vixobtakil**, "round **vixobtakil**" (**tzajal vixob-takil** in part), refers to *Peperomia deppeana* (3–6) and *P. quadrifolia* (2–6), similar elliptic-ovate, whorled quadrifoliate epiphytes common in pine-oak forests of temperate and highland areas. The inflorescence is a slender terminal spike of minute flowers.

To relieve the "heat" of **majbenal**, a small bunch of the "cold" plants is crushed in water and the patient's head is bathed with the infusion. For fever sores, the leaves are crushed and rubbed on the sore.

7. **Vixobtakil chon**, "snake **vixobtakil**," is *Peperomia heterodoxa* (1–1), an erect, stout herb, branched above, with four leaves whorled at the nodes. The basal leaves are very short petiolate, thick and succulent oval, elliptic or obovate, 8–20 mm long, pubescent or gray-granular, rounded at the apex. The upper leaves are usually larger (8)12–50 mm long, thin, on slender petioles about 4 mm long, elliptic to obovate, acute at the apex. The spikes are terminal, solitary or clustered. It occurs on rocky ledges in oak forests of the temperate zone.

"Pitzak' Set"

The **pitz'ak** set consists of 10 generics, low herbaceous plants, many of which are mat-forming.

1. **Alpajo** (**-tik, -altik**) (**alfajo, ve'el vakax**) is alfalfa *Medicago sativa*, a plant occasionally cultivated for forage by *ladinos* in highland pasture valleys. It is an erect perennial herb with very deep roots. Leaves are 3-foliate, with obovate leaflets, 1–2 cm long. The flowers are 5–6 mm long, blue or violet, and in short clusters. The legume is twisted into a spring-edged spiral. At the present time it is very rare. The seeds are mixed with sand and sown in rows in February.

As a remedy for liver damage caused by excessive drinking, a handful is brewed and the tea is drunk before breakfast for three or nine days.

Extended range: *Melilotus alba* and *M. indica.*

2. **Chak'ak'** (**-tik, -ultik**) (**chak'ak' tz'i'lel, ch'upak' mut, k'anal nich, k'anal nich poxil k'ok', k'ox chak'ak', muk'ta poxil k'ok', poxil sal-tz'i'**) is the common herb *Spilanthes americana* (14–9), which occurs in grassy places of forests and

disturbed areas of temperate and highland hamlets. It is usually prostrate, rarely erect, with opposite ovate or elliptic leaves from 2–6 cm long, the apex acute, the base broad and rounded or wedge-shaped. Flowering heads are on long naked peduncles, one or sometimes more at a node. The central disk is yellow and either conical or globose, surrounded by 8–14 bright yellow petal-like ray flowers.

For **sal-tz'i'** blemishes, a small bunch is crushed and applied to the affected part once daily for two days. To cut fever, a bunch is brewed with refined sugar or crushed and mixed with cold water. Both the tea and the infusion are "cold." Sheep eat the plant.

Extended range: *Anagallis arvensis, Perymenium ghiesbreghtii, Scutellaria dumetorum,* and *Tridax procumbens.*

3. **Chikin ch'o**, "mouse ear" (**chikin ch'o pox, meryo pox, poxil k'ok'**), is *Dichondra argentea* (7–9), a sprawling herb that occurs as mats in exposed, grassy fields and on rocky slopes of temperate and highland regions. The leaves are small, round, and covered with a gray velvet pubescence, 1–2 cm wide. Flowers are solitary at a node white, deflexed, and inconspicuous, about 3 mm across.

To cut fever and the heat of **majbenal skventa kajvaltik**, a bunch is crushed and mixed in (1) cold water, (2) cold water sweetened with refined sugar, or (3) warm salt water. The infusion is "cold." For a mild case of chills and fever (**sik k'ok'**), a tea is taken. For a severe case it is brewed together with **tzotzil jabnal.**

4. **Ch'aben tz'i'lel**, "ch'aben" plant" (**xaxib ch'o** in part), refers to *Indigofera miniata* (2–4), *I. mucronata* (2–4), *Melilotus alba* (7–9), and *M. indica* (1–4). These highland herbs are very similar in general appearance to alfalfa. They differ in having elongate inflorescences of yellow, salmon, or white flowers, smaller leaflets, and an elongate or rounded legume, rather than a twisted one. They grow in yards and in disturbed areas.

They are eaten by sheep, cattle, and horses.

5. **Mail tz'i'lel**, "watermelon squash plant" (**tz'omol tz'i'lel**), is the diminutive sprawling herb *Houstonia serpyllacea* (5–8). The stems are greatly elongate, often forming dense mats, or sometimes hanging pendent from banks. The leaves are very small, 4–6 mm long, and are crowded along the stems. Flowers are solitary in the leaf axils, tubular, white, and less than 1 cm long. The capsule is oblong, 4 mm long. It occurs in dense, grassy pastureland of temperate and highland regions.

The plant is chewed to relieve toothache. Children play with the berries.

Extended range: *Oxalis albicans.*

6. **Pitzak'** (**-tik, -altik**) (**pitzak, trebol***) refers to clover and burclover.

Specifics: 3.

> a. **Batz'i pitzak'**, "genuine clover" **k'ox pitzak', pitzak' chitom**), is the common, wild-occurring clover *Trifolium amabile* (10–15), a sprawling herb of grassy

fields and second growth in temperate and highland hamlets. The flowers are white or pink in small clusters about 1–1.5 cm across. The leaflets are small, obovate, and 6–13 mm long.

Children mash the roots and roll them into pellets. Two are dropped into an elderberry stem. The stem is pounded on the ground, "exploding" one of the pellets to the height of a rooftop. To find a four-leaved clover reputedly brings good luck. Sheep eat the leaves.

b. **Muk'ta pitzak'**, "large clover" (**ch'aben vet**), is the coarse, herbaceous clover *Trifolium repens* (5–7), a creeping perennial herb with white flowers in large clusters, 1.5–3 cm tall. The leaflets are large, broadly obovate to almost round, 1.3–4 cm long. It is often cultivated by *ladinos* for pasture and occurs in wet pastures and along streams of the highlands as a naturalized plant. For use cf. **batz'i pitzak'**.

c. **Tzajal pitzak'**, "red clover" (**ch'ix tz'i'lel, k'anal pitzak', trejo**), refers to burclover and yellow sweet clover *Medicago polymorpha* (4–7) and *Melilotus indica* (1–1), common weeds of yards and cornfields in temperate and highland areas. Both are low-growing clover-like plants with small leaflets and very small yellow pea flowers borne on either elongate or head-like inflorescences.

It is eaten by sheep.

7. **Poxil chuvaj**, "madness medicine," is *Anagallis arvensis* (1–1), a slender sprawling herb with small opposite, ovate leaves, 8–13 mm long. The flowers are salmon-colored, axillary, 6–10 mm broad, and on long pedicels. The fruit is a round capsule about 5 mm in diameter. This is a weedy plant of the temperate and highland regions.

The "hot" leaves are crushed and inserted in the nose and ears of a crazy person.

8. **Poxil me'-vinik**, "mother man medicine," is *Oxalis frutescens* ssp. *angustifolia* (1–1), a somewhat shrubby herb with pinnately divided leaves crowded on the stems. The leaflets are elliptic and usually three, 1–2.5 cm long. The yellow flowers are borne on axillary peduncles in groups of three to about six. The corolla is 6–12 mm long. This plant occurs in exposed situations in the temperate and lowland areas.

To relieve heartburn, the plant is crushed in cold water. The sour-tasting infusion is "cold."

9. **Tzotz-ni' tz'i'lel**, "downy-tipped plant" (**nekebal pox, poxil yayijemal, tzotzin tz'i'lel**), refers to *Hieracium abscissum* (1–1) and *H. stuposum* (5–6), woolly-leafed perennials occurring in temperate and highland pine-oak forests. The oblong leaves of *H. stuposum* are in a basal rosette until flowering when one or more stems appear bearing many small yellow composite flowers in an openly branched inflorescence. The stems may be 60 cm tall. Seeds are like dandelion seeds with white hairs at the apex which aid in dispersal. *Hieracium*

abscissum is very similar but has a tuft of tan hairs at the apex of the seed.

To stimulate lactation, four or five roots are crushed and brewed with white pepper to provide a "hot" tea. As a remedy for "wind" and for barrenness, the plant is brewed with brown sugar, pepper, and chili. This tea is also "hot." The leaves may be applied to cuts to stanch the bleeding.

10. **Vala-pojov**, "bent milky sap" (**-tik**), refers to fleshy stemmed begonias and tuberous-rooted *Oxalis*.

Specifics: 3.

a. **Batz'i vala-pojov**, "genuine bent milky sap" (**vanal pojov**), refers to the purple-flowered, tuberous-rooted, herbaceous plants *Oxalis galeottii* (4–4) and *O. latifolia* (6–9). In both, the leaves and flowering peduncles arise without stems directly from the underground tuber. The leaves are on long petioles, up to 30 cm long, and are palmately divided into three or four heart-shaped leaflets. The base of the leaflet is acute, the tip is lobed. Flowers are pink or purple, funnel-shaped, and range from 8–20 mm long. They are borne in an umbellate inflorescence at the end of a long peduncle usually equaling or exceeding the leaves. They occur on exposed grassy slopes and cultivated fields throughout the township.

The "sweet" roots may be eaten raw. The stem may be chewed to quench thirst. As a remedy for fever sores, the "cold" stem is crushed and rubbed on the lips. A tea is taken to cure hiccups.

b. **K'ox vala-pojov**, "small bent milky sap," refers to the yellow-flowered, fibrous-rooted herbs *Oxalis albicans* (1–1), *O. corniculata* (1–1), and *O. frutescens* ssp. *angustifolia* (1–1). All have elongate stems, with many small 3-foliate leaves. Flowers occur in pairs at the end of a rather long peduncle. They are funnelform and about 12 mm long or smaller. The fruit is a cylindric capsule to about 20 mm long. They are weedy plants of roadsides and cornfields and exposed rocky slopes of temperate and highland areas.

The plant is crushed in cold water for a "cold" infusion to reduce fever.

c. **Muk'ta vala-pojov**, "large bent milky sap" (**poxil eal**), refers to the fleshy-stemmed, tuberous-rooted plants *Begonia biserrata* (1–2), *B. fischeri* var. *tovarensis* (1–1), and *B. oaxacana* (1–2). These occur in protected shady ravines of montane rain forest and pine-oak forest in cold, temperate, and some lowland areas. All have alternate, palmately veined leaves, and male and female flowers, which may be white, pink, or red. *Begonia biserrata* has leaves that are large, about 6–13 cm long, and coarsely lobed. The leaves of *B. fisheri* var. *tovarensis* and *B. oaxacana* are not lobed, but rather rounded, cordate in the former and asymmetric and broadly ovate in the later.

The "cold" stems are rubbed on the lips for fever sores.

"Pojov Tz'i'lel Set"

The "**pojov tz'i'lel** set" includes six generics, herbs with thick leaves and white, sticky sap.

1. **Jol olol**, "child's head" (**bankilal jol olol**), is *Dalembertia triangularis* (4–8), a tuberous-rooted herb common on rocky second growth slopes in temperate and lowland areas. The leaves are alternate, triangular, rounded at the base, subcordate, 3.5–7 cm long. The minute flowers are arranged in a dense, ovoid terminal spike. The capsule is 3-lobate, about 12 mm broad.

Some Zinacantecs skin the "cold" root and eat it raw for quenching thirst. Though it is available year round, similar to chayote root, it is best in December and January, becoming tough and fibrous in February.

Extended range: *Acalypha botteriana, A. langiana, A. vagans, Anoda cristata,* and *Euphorbia graminea.*

2. **On te' pox**, "madrone medicine," refers to white-flowered, erect milkweeds with opposite leaves and terminal umbels of white and maroon flowers.

Specifics: 2.

    a. **Bik'it on te' pox**, "small madrone medicine" (**poxil nuk'ul**), refers to *Asclepias contrayerba* (1–1) and *A. oenotheroides* (1–4), erect herbs with small, terminal, or axillary umbellate white flowers with recurved petals and an exerted group of modified stamens that occur in disturbed ground. The leaves are opposite, pubescent, ovate or oblong, 4–12 cm long. The many flowered umbels are usually shorter than the leaves. The fruit is a follicle, 6–11 cm long, usually pubescent enclosing the long, silky-haired seeds. These plants occur in the grassy understory of the pine-oak forests in the temperate and highland regions.

As a remedy for mumps, the "cold" leaves of *A. oenotheroides* are crushed and bound to the neck. To speed the mending of a wound, the leaves of *A. contrayerba* are boiled and the "hot" decoction used to bathe the wound.

    b. **Muk'ta on te' pox**, "large madrone medicine" (**ik'al pojov tz'i'lel, muk'ta primon, yat tz'i' te'**), is *Asclepias similis* (2–3), an erect, single-stemmed, perennial herb with terminal umbels of creamy white and maroon flowers. The leaves are opposite, elliptic to narrowly obovate, darker above than below, 7–15 cm long, 2–8 cm wide. The fruit is a follicle about 13 cm long enclosing seeds with white, silky hairs. It occurs in the open understory of pine-oak forests of temperate and highland hamlets. It is classed variously as "plant" and "tree."

As a remedy for "wind," the plant is boiled and the patient bathed with the "hot" decoction.

3. **Pojov tz'i'lel**, "milky sap plant," refers to milkweeds and spurges. They are both erect herbs with opposite leaves and milky sap.

Specifics: 2.

    a. **Batz'i pojov tz'i'lel**, "genuine milky sap plant" (**cholchol nich** and **poxil lukum** in part), refers to *Chamaesyce densiflora* (1–2), *C. hirta* (1–2), *C. hypericifolia* (1–2), *C. hyssopifolia* (1–2), *Euphorbia dentata* (1–5), *E. francoana* (2–5), *E. graminea* (5–7), *E. heterophylla* (5–8), and *E. macropus* (2–3). These are thin-stemmed herbs with minute flowers, opposite leaves, and 3-parted fruits, which occur mostly in disturbed and second growth situations, but also in open places in dry pine-oak and tropical deciduous forests of highland, temperate and lowland areas.

The "cold" root of *E. macropus* is toasted and applied to burns.

Extended range: *Begonia plebeja.*

    b. **Tzajal pojov tz'i'lel**, "red milky sap plant" (**nichim ch'ulelal, tz'ibom tz'i'lel**), is *Asclepias curassavica* (4–6), an erect herb often with many stems from the base with terminal umbels of red-orange flowers, with recurved petals about 5–8 mm long and an everted group of modified stamens. The leaves are opposite, narrowly elliptic, 4–11 cm long. The fruit is a follicle, fusiform, 6–10 cm long. The seeds are brown, 6 mm long, with a tuft of long, silky white hairs. It occurs in wet, disturbed areas and marshes in temperate and lowland areas.

4. **Poxil chin**, "exema medicine" (**tzajal te', ve'el sak-ch'ut mut**), is *Phyllanthus mcvaughii* (3–5), a thin-stemmed sub-shrub much-branched, with small alternate broadly ovate to orbicular leaves, 0.8–4 cm long. The flowers are axillary and very small, 1–2 mm broad. The fruit is a capsule, about 6 mm in diameter, which splits into three parts each containing one seed. This grows in the second growth of the temperate regions. It is classed as "tree."

5. **Poxil chu'ul**, "breast medicine," is *Euphorbia anychioides,* a small, erect perennial herb with numerous branches and small opposite, serrate, oval leaves, 3–8 mm long. The minute flowers are terminal. The capsule is about 1.5 mm broad. It occurs in the grassy understory of pine-oak forests in the temperate and highland regions.

The sap is applied to the nipples of a nursing mother whose baby has bitten her.

6. **Poxil ti'ben lukum**, "worm bite medicine" (**tzun te' jol**), is *Chamaesyce hyssopifolia* (2–5), a slender herb with a dense cluster of tiny flowers that occurs in second growth and disturbed situations in temperate and highland hamlets. The leaves are opposite, sessile or very short petiolate, elliptic, ovate or obovate, 1–3 cm long, on stems that are often dark red or purple. The small dense inflorescences are terminal or axillary. The 3-parted capsule is about 1.5 mm broad.

To cure sores on the bottom of one's toes, a handful of "hot" tips are crushed and bound to the affected part. They are changed every three days until the sores are healed. For a head cold (**simal obal**), a "hot" tea is taken.

Extended range: *Chamaesyce hypericifolia*. The "cold" sap is applied to minor cuts.

"Pok'ok'" Set"

The "**pok'ok'** set" is comprised of three generics, all terrestrial aroids with thick stems, rhizomatous roots and large, glossy leaves.

1. **Pamal jabnal**, "incense leaf" (-**tik**) (**japob kantela me'eletik, japob kántela tz'i'lel, snichim me'eletik**), refers to *Anthurium schlechtendalii* (7–10), a plant of rock outcrops in deep forest conditions. It has thick caudices and large, leathery, glossy, lance-elliptic leaves up to 1 m long. It occurs in moist pine-oak, montane rain, and tropical deciduous forests of temperate and lowland areas.

The assistants of the elders and the ensign-bearers of St. Dominic and of the Holy Cross gather eight leaves apiece on Thursday before the first Lenten Friday and on Monday before the fourth Lenten Friday. Two leaves, tied at the base with a string, encase each candle that is borne to the Church of St. Lawrence by the old women who serve as candlebearers every Lenten Friday and during Holy Week. The first set of leaves is placed in water so that it will last for three Fridays, and the second set so that it will last for Holy Week.

Extended range: *Anthurium huixtlense, A. seleri, Elaphoglossum latifolium,* and *Spathiphyllum phryniifolium*.

2. **Pi** (-**tik**), *Xanthosoma violaceum* (2–2), is similar to *X. robustum*. Its heart-shaped leaves are from 20–50 cm long and are on long petioles. The flowers are densely crowded on a central cylindric spike about 2 cm thick, surrounded by a showy spath. The spath is about 25–30 cm long, yellowish white, and tinged with purple. It is known mostly from cultivation in temperate and lowland areas.

Zinacantecs from the highland hamlets are totally unaware of the existence of this plant, never having heard of its name. The tubers are transplanted in most of the temperate communities in the dry season, one to a hole, a meter apart. It produces in one year. People from the temperate hamlets maintain that it neither flowers nor fruits. The leaves are known to be poisonous to eat. Four or five tubers are produced around the main tuber and it is these that are dug up in February and March for eating.

The "cold" tubers are prepared in a variety of ways. They may be boiled and eaten alone as a snack, similar to a chayote, or they may be boiled with sugar and eaten also as a snack, as if they were sweet potatoes. They may be ground, boiled, and seasoned with salt and coriander or salt and mint, or they may be eaten in **vokol ich**.

Specifics: 2.

    a. **Sakil pi**, "white **pi**," is a variety with green leaves.

    b. **Tzajal pi**, "red **pi**," is a variety with reddish leaves.

3. **Pok'ok'** (-**tik**) (**kekex, pokok, xpoko', xpokok, xpok'ok'**) is *Xanthosoma robustum* (5–9), the giant, elephant-ear-like plants arising from a thick starchy stem. The leaves are up to 1 m long. The flowers are in spathes up to 20 cm long,

with a thick, fleshy fruit enclosed. It occurs along slow-moving streams and wet, adjacent flats in temperate and lowland areas.

In case of necessity the "cold" root may be boiled, seasoned with salt and chili.

Extended range: *Anthurium chamulense* and *Monstera deliciosa*.

"Pom Tz'unun Set"

The "**pom tz'unun** set" is a diverse grouping of 14 generics, herbs and subshrubs with large, showy, tubular flowers.

1. **Ba ikatzil**, "top load," is *Fuchsia splendens* (1–1). It is a suffrutescent, epiphytic, or saxicolous shrub with opposite, ovate, sometimes subcordate leaves, 5–15 cm long, with serrate margins and petioles 2–6 cm long. The flowers are red, tipped with green, tubular, axillary, solitary, 3–5 cm long, drooping, on pedicels about equaling the petals. The fruit is a purple, fleshy, oblong, edible berry 3–6 cm long. Its Tzotzil name is derived from its clambering habit. It occurs in the evergreen cloud forest of the highlands.

It is eaten by sheep.

2. **J'ak'-'uch**, "cause of yellowing" (**bot'-jol nichim, bot'-jol tz'i'lel, poxil balamil, sóltaro pox, yak' uch**), is *Castilleja arvensis* (8–9), a hemi-parasite of *Zea mays* and many other plants. It is a scapose herb up to 3 dm tall with a terminal, ellipsoid cluster of tubular, red flowers and lanceolate leaves 8 cm long or less. It is common, but scattered in cornfields and fallow ground in temperate and highland hamlets.

The yellowing of corn plants is attributed in part to the influence of this plant when it grows in the cornfield. Children pull up the plants and pretend that they are the flowers of a curing ceremony. As a remedy for soul-loss, two or three stalks are brewed. A half cup of the "hot" tea is drunk before breakfast. If a child is looked at by a pregnant woman, suffers "embarrassment" and subsequently gets nausea and diarrhea (**apon**), a tea is made of a bunch of this plant together with **tan pox** and half a chopped up seed of **itzompi**.

Extended range: *Castilleja integrifolia* and *Gomphrena decumbens*.

3. **Latzbil tonal pox**, "stacked rock medicine" (**k'ox sak-nich te', suk mok**), is *Salvia lasiantha* (1–2), a large shrub with pale orange flowers that is common in second growth in temperate hamlets. The stems, leaves, and inflorescences are pubescent. The leaves are ovate, acute at the apex, rounded at the base, with serrulate margins, 2–9 cm long. The flowers are 2–2.5 cm long and are arranged in an interrupted spike.

The name, "stacked rock medicine," is restricted to Atz'am, where it is known to grow along a stone wall that a *ladino* built many years ago. When a person is suffering from headache, nausea, and swelling as a result of being sold to the Earth, this plant is brewed and the "hot" tea is drunk before each meal. A large bowlful of this very bitter tea should be drunk in one gulp. Its odor is so foul that the Earth Lord is reputed to order the soul of the affected person out of his domain, telling him, "**Yan avik'**!" "You stink!" The branches are used in brush fences.

4. **Nap'ap' tz'i'lel**, "sticky plant" (**-tik**), is a non-Linnaean grouping of herbs with very sticky foliage, either as a result of curved or barbed hairs or of viscid, oily hairs. These include: *Ageratum houstonianum* (1–4), *Bastardia viscosa* (1–2), *Conyza chilensis*, *Cuphea cyanea* (4–5), *C. leptopoda* (1–2), *Desmodium amplifolium* (1–1), *Galium uncinulatum*, *Galium* sp., *Gnaphalium* sp. (2–2), *Mentzelia aspera*, *Priva lappulacea*, *Salvia misella*, *Siegesbeckia jorullensis*, and *Stevia polycephala*. Some speakers subdivide these further.

Specifics: 5.

a. **Batz'i nap'ap' tz'i'lel**, "genuine sticky plant," is *Siegesbeckia jorullensis* (4–6), a viscid herb of moist, disturbed areas in wet pine-oak and evergreen cloud forest in the highland hamlets. It has small, yellow daisy flowers, subtended by five linear glandular phyllaries, 6–14 mm long. The leaves are triangular ovate to lanceolate, 3–12 cm long. The upper leaves are sessile, the lower with winged petioles. It sticks to one's clothes.

b. **Bik'it nap'ap' tz'i'lel**, "small sticky plant" (**kilkil tz'i'lel**), refers to *Galium orizabense* (1–1) and *G. uncinulatum* (1–3), small, sprawling, herbaceous perennials with bur-like seeds about 1.5–2 mm in diameter. The flowers are minute in open, panicles. The leaves are small, obovate to narrowly elliptic 7–25 mm long, in whorls of four at a node. They occur on rocks in pine-oak forests of temperate and highland hamlets.

As a remedy for **chin** skin disease, a "cold" bunch is mashed and applied once to the affected part.

c. **K'anal nap'ap' tz'i'lel**, "yellow sticky plant" (**muk'ta nap'ap' tz'i'lel, noch'och' tz'i'lel, tzeb tz'i'lel**), is *Mentzelia aspera* (5–12), a sprawling herb with leaves and fruits covered with barbed hairs that catch on almost any surface. The flowers are orange with petals about 12 mm long. The fruit is a cylindrical capsule covered with barbed hairs, enclosing grayish yellow rough seeds. The leaves are alternate, ovate, and often 3-lobed, with serrate or dentate margins, 3–10 cm long. It is a very common plant in second growth and disturbed situations in temperate and lowland areas.

If a boy sticks some of this herb on the back of a girl's blouse she will fall in love with him and not be able to get him out of her mind.

d. **K'ox nap'ap' tz'i'lel**, "small sticky plant" (**poxil k'ok'**), is *Salvia misella* (3–6), a blue-flowered, viscid, low herb of disturbed ground in temperate and lowland areas. It has square stems and opposite ovate leaves. The tubular blue flowers are verticillate on the spikes and are about 4–6 mm long. The calyces stick to one's clothing.

To relieve fever, a "cold" tea of the leaves may be taken.

e. **Yaxal nap'ap' tz'i'lel**, "blue sticky plant" (**ik'al nap'ap' tz'i'lel, ik'al tz'i'lel, k'ox nap'ap' tz'i'lel**), is *Priva lappulacea* (4–11), a small, blue-flowered herb with round, inflated, bur-like fruits, 5–6 mm in diameter, which easily attach themselves to one's clothing. The leaves are opposite, ovate with crenate-dentate margins, 3.5–14 cm long. The flowers and fruits are arranged in long, thin, terminal spikes. It is a common plant in disturbed areas and second growth in temperate hamlets.

5. **Nochleb buluk' sat**, "hornworm perch" (**buluk' sat tz'i'lel, ik'al pom tz'unun, ik'al tz'i'lel, k'ox yaxal pom tz'unun**), is *Salvia tiliifolia* (9–9), a tall herb with numerous, pale blue flowers verticellate in a terminal spike and round, strongly veined opposite leaves, 2.5–9 cm long. It is a common plant in disturbed ground and second growth situations of temperate and highland hamlets.

As an antidote for snakebite, the "hot" leaves are applied directly to the wound, or are boiled before application.

Extended range: *Hyptis suaveolens*.

6. **Pom tz'unun**, "hummingbird nectar" (**-tik, -altik**), refers to a variety of plants with opposite, densely pubescent leaves and tubular flowers.

Many are associated with unproductive land.

Specifics: 7.

a. **K'anal pom tz'unun**, "yellow hummingbird nectar" (**nap'ap' nich, nap'ap' tz'i'lel, nuk' xchil ulo', poxil antz tz'i'lel, poxil ch'ich', poxil ch'ich' tza'nel, poxil ch'ulelal, poxil sim- nak'al, poxil tza'nel, tzajal pom tz'unun**), is *Cuphea cyanea* (11–11), a spreading subshrub with sticky pubescence and ovate leaves, 2–5 cm long, with an acute apex and rounded base. The flowers are yellow and orange, 2–2.5 cm long, in terminal racemes. It is very common on rock outcrops in second growth and pine-oak forest situations in temperate and highland hamlets.

As a remedy for **majbenal**, diarrhea, and bloody dysentery, a small bunch is brewed. One cup of the "hot" tea is drunk in the afternoon for two days. The same tea is also classed as "cold" and, for diarrhea, should be drunk before breakfast for two days.

Extended range: *Cuphea leptopoda* and *C. pinetorum*.

b. **Muk'ta pom tz'unun**, "large hummingbird nectar," is *Hemichaena rugosa* (2–2) a woody shrub, 2–3 m tall, with showy, axillary, orange flowers, 3.5–4.5 cm long, with long exerted stamens. The leaves are bullate, sticky pubescent, ovate with serrate or dentate margins, about 2–5 cm long or longer. This plant occurs on limestone cliffs in the highlands.

As a remedy for **poslom**, the plant is brewed together with wax myrtle and **nap'ap' tz'i'lel** (specific not designated) to provide a "hot" tea.

c. **Puj-'akan pom tz'unun**, "hollow-stemmed hummingbird nectar" (**ik'al pom tz'unun, jom akan, muk'ta** pom tz'unun, tzajal pom tz'unun, ve'el k'ovix), is *Priva aspera* (5-8), a tall herb with square stems, stiff, prickly pubescence, and lavender flowers in long terminal racemes. The flowers are funnelform, 8-10 mm long. The fruit is a globose capsule, about 5-6 mm in diameter. The leaves are broadly ovate with acuminate apices, about 3-15 cm long. It is a common plant in moist second growth situations in temperate hamlets.

d. **Sakil pom tz'unun,** "white hummingbird nectar" (**chivo te', ik'al pom tz'unun, poxil tz'akob-bail** and **yaxal pom tz'unun** in part), refers to *Hyptis mutabilis* (1-2), *H. tomentosa* (2-2), and *H. urticoides* (3-6). *Hyptis tomentosa* is classed as **te',** "tree." These are erect branched suffrutescent plants with square stems, ovate leaves and clusters of blue, lavender, or white flowers 10-13 mm or 4-5 mm long in terminal or axillary inflorescences. *Hyptis tomentosa* is densely pubescent on the leaves, stems, and inflorescence and has larger flowers than *H. mutabilis* and *H. urticoides*. These plants occur in waste ground and second growth throughout the township.

As a remedy for diarrhea and stomachache a "hot" tea of *H. tomentosa* is taken.

e. **Tzajal pom tz'unun,** "red hummingbird nectar" (**ik'al pom tz'unun, muil pom tz'unun, muk'ta pom tz'unun, muk'ta poxil k'ok', sakil pom tz'unun, xinal tz'i'lel,** all in part), refers to *Kohleria elegans* (2-4), *Salvia chiapensis* (2-5), *S. cinnabarina* (1-1), *S. coccinea* (1-1), *S. excelsa* (7-11), *S. holwayi* (4-8), and *S. karwinskii*. All have red or orange tubular flowers and are subshrubs in second growth and in the understory of pine-oak and evergreen cloud forests of temperate and highland areas.

Some members of this group are used in the "steam cure."

Extended range: *Centropogon grandidentatus, Lamourouxia viscosa,* and *Stachys coccinea.*

f. **Yax-'ulan pom tz'unun,** "purple hummingbird nectar" (**bik'tal pom tz'unun, ik'al tz'i'lel, moraro nichim, nochleb tz'unun, tz'utz'un tz'unun**), is *Salvia urica* (5-7), a coarse, hairy herb of disturbed ground in temperate hamlets. The stems are 4-sided and pubescent. The leaves are ovate, 5-15 cm long, pubescent. The flowers are blue, and arranged in verticellate clusters on the spike.

Extended range: *Salvia cacaliaefolia.* This is planted occasionally and the flowers sold. Bunches are used in the "steam cure." The leaves are crushed in cold water and the infusion taken to end barrenness.

g. **Yaxal pom tz'unun,** "blue hummingbird nectar" (**ch'ix pom tz'unun, ik'al pom tz'unun, lixton vérte, tzajal pom tz'unun, tzitz jobel,** all in part), refers to *Salvia polystachya* (4-7), *S. purpurea* (2-8), *S. reptans* (2-3), and *S. rubiginosa* (3-5), perennial herbs or shrubs with blue flowers in densely crowded or verticillate spikes, opposite leaves, and 4-sided stems. These occur in second growth and open understory in the pine-oak forests of temperate and highland regions.

Salvia rubiginosa may be used in the "steam cure."

7. **Poxil k'ok',** "fever medicine," is *Loeselia mexicana* (5-8), a tall subshrub with tubular red flowers, about 2 cm long, with exerted stamens. The leaves are alternate, elliptic to ovate, 1.5-6 cm long, acutely serrate. The flowers are clustered in the axils of the leaves. It is a common element in second growth on dry slopes in temperate hamlets.

To allay a fever, a handful is crushed in cold water. One cup of the "medium" infusion is taken before breakfast. Alternatively, a handful of tips may be brewed and a cup of the "medium" tea drunk before breakfast.

Extended range: *Capraria biflora* var. *pilosa, Hedeoma costatum, Loeselia glandulosa,* and *Russelia sarmentosa.*

8. **Poxil majbenal,** "beating medicine," is *Cuphea pinetorum* (1-1), branched herbs with deep purple or maroon, tubular flowers, 15-20 mm long, arranged in a terminal raceme. The leaves are lanceolate, opposite, sessile or very short petiolate, 1.5-6 cm long. It occurs in the second growth and open understory of pine-oak forests in the highland and temperate regions.

A tea of this "hot" plant is brewed as a remedy for **majbenal** and for bloody dysentery.

9. **Primon** (**-tik, -altik**) (**kámpana ch'o tz'i'lel**) refers to *Centropogon grandidentatus* (1-1) and *Lobelia laxiflora* (6-9), large herbs with tubular, axillary orange flowers, 2-4 cm long, and alternate, lanceolate or narrowly elliptic leaves from 3-20 cm long. The fruit is fleshy and round in *Centropogon* and capsular in *Lobelia*, common in pine-oak and evergreen cloud forests of temperate and highland areas.

The sap is applied to an embedded thorn or wounds to cure infection. The plant is eaten by sheep.

Extended range: *Fuchsia splendens* and *Lobelia cardinalis* ssp. *graminea.*

10. **Sten uch,** "opossum's granary" (**ik'al pom tz'unun**), is *Stachys coccinea* (2-5), a hispid herb with tubular, red flowers, 2-2.5 cm long, verticillate in a long, terminal spike. The stems are angular and pubescent with erect hairs. The leaves are opposite, cordate-ovate, with crenate margins. They are 2.5-7 cm long. It occurs in wet, open areas in pine-oak and evergreen cloud forests in temperate and highland hamlets.

A large handful is used as one of the ingredients of the "steam cure."

11. **Tentzun,** "goat" (**tentzun pox, tentzun tz'i'lel, tzunjol tz'i'lel**), is *Ruellia inundata* (4-10), a brittle-stemmed subshrub common in gravelly deposits along lowland streams and rivers. It has terminal clusters of lavender tubular flowers, 4-4.5 cm long. The inflorescence is axillary, dichotomously branched, and leafy with many lanceolate bracts, 3-8 mm long. The leaves are opposite, long petiolate, and ovate, 3-15 cm

long. The fruit is a club-shaped capsule, 7–11 mm long, containing 2–6 flat, ovate, seeds, which are mucilaginous when wet.

In 1797 the priest of Zinacantán cited *yerba del toro,* which is most likely this plant, as a remedy for "flux" (de Leon y Goicoechea, 1797).

This plant is of sufficient medicinal importance now that shamans may store it at home. As a remedy for "wind," three stems are brewed or bruised in cold water. The "hot" tea or infusion is taken 2–4 times. For further medicinal use cf. **kururin, vako' ak'.**

Extended range: *Bonplandia geminiflora, Bouchea prismatica, Carlowrightia* sp., *Cuphea leptopoda, Justicia clinopodium, Loeselia glandulosa, Marsypianthes chamaedrys,* and *Ruellia nudiflora.*

12. **Tzajal kampana,** "red bell" (**luchleb tz'unun, primon, rosáryo roxa, snich pok' ulo'**), is *Lamourouxia viscosa* (5–8), a tall, brittle-stemmed, long, tubular, red-flowered herb of second growth situations in temperate hamlets. The leaves are sessile, dentate, oblong, acute at the apex, rounded at the base, 3–7 cm long. The flowers are 3.5–5 cm long and in a dense raceme. The capsules are black, ovate, and 8–10 mm long.

Children sell the flowers on the roadside.

13. **Yalem bek'et,** "fallen flesh" (**cholchol nich, k'anal nich primon, tzalub kelem**), is *Castilleja integrifolia* (5–7), a brittle-stemmed herb with tubular red-orange and yellow flowers, about 3 cm, long in a terminal raceme and narrow linear, viscid leaves, 4 cm long or less. It is common on exposed rock outcrops in pine-oak forests of temperate and highland hamlets.

14. **Yich'ak ch'o,** "rat claw" (**natz'il tz'i'lel, poxil simnik'al, tzajal tz'i'lel**), is *Hamelia patens* (6–10), a large, soft-wooded shrub with terminal clusters of red-orange tubular flowers, 1.5–2 cm long. The leaves are elliptic or ovate, 6–20 cm long, softly pubescent below. The fruits are erect, fleshy, ellipsoid, 6–10 mm long, 4–6 mm thick, red turning to black. It is a very common element in second growth in temperate and lowland areas. When termed **tzajal tz'i'lel** it is classed as **stot,** "male," to distinguish it from the "female" form also known as **sakil akuxa tz'i'lel.**

To cure "white" dysentery, a handful of tips is brewed. The "medium" tea is drunk before breakfast and in the evening. To cure bloody dysentery, the tips are crushed in cold water and the "medium" infusion taken as above. As a remedy for heartburn (**me'-vinik**), a "cold" tea or infusion may be taken.

"Poxil Apon Set"

The "**poxil apon** set" is comprised of two generics, both evening primroses.

1. **Orisyon tz'i'lel,** "dusk plant" (**putzul pepen, putzul unetik**), refers to the evening primroses *Oenothera kunthiana* (1–1) and *O. pubescens* (3–5), slender herbs with white or yellow flowers and alternate, oblong-lanceolate leaves with sinuate, dentate margins. The flowers are solitary in the upper leaf axils. The capsules are cylindric or clavate. These are common plants in disturbed areas and cornfields of the highlands. The flowers open at dusk.

2. **Poxil apon,** "embarrassment medicine" (**-tik**) (**poxil k'ok'**), is *Oenothera rosea* (15–20), low, slender, wiry herbs with oblanceolate or obovate, alternate leaves that are sinuate-dentate and sometimes pinnately lobed at the base, 1.5–3 cm long. The flowers are delicate and pink with broadly obovate petals, 5–10 mm long, axillary, forming slender racemes. The capsules are obovoid, 8–10 mm long, 4-angled, and narrowed at the base into a pedicel. It is a common plant in disturbed areas and roadsides in the highlands. It is sometimes classed as **stot,** "male," whereas *O. kunthiana* is **sme',** "female."

As a remedy for "embarrassment," a handful is bruised in cold or warm salt water. The infant is given the "cold" infusion and its body is massaged with the plants. To counter the effects of "evil eye," a small bunch is brewed and half a cupful of the "cold" tea drunk before breakfast for three days. Both infants and adults suffering from "evil eye" may take the salt infusion twice a day. The shaman also sprays it on the elderberry branches he uses to "sweep" the child. The mother drinks the infusion so that her milk will help cure her baby. The "cold" tea also relieves fever. For further medicinal use cf. **batz'i chijil te'** and **j'ak'-'uch.**

Extended range: *Gaura tripetala, O. kunthiana.*

"Sakaton Set"

The "**sakaton** set" is comprised of six generics, large, clump-forming, perennial grasses.

1. **Ana-jobel,** "ana grass" (**-tik, -altik**), is the rat-tail muhly *Muhlenbergia macroura* (4–8), a large, clumped grass growing up to 2 m across with long, narrow, dense inflorescences up to 1 m tall. It is common and often dominant in bunch grassland communities of highland areas.

This grass is cut with an ax and used for thatching in the highland hamlets. Although some claim that this is the best grass for thatching, others maintain that there is too much stalk and too few leaves, that the wide leaves fall off quickly. It is woven and twined to make slings. It is eaten by horses.

2. **Ch'ix jobel,** "spiny grass" (**-tik**) (**jobelal na**), refers to *Festuca amplissima* (1–2), *Muhlenbergia breviligula* (1–5), *M.* cf. *emersleyi* (1–3), *M. robusta* (3–5), and *M. stricta* (1–4). These attain clumps to 2 m across and have feathery inflorescences. They occur in bunch grassland in the highlands and in pine-oak forests in highland and temperate hamlets.

The clumps are cut with a billhook for thatch in the temperate hamlets and for thatching fieldhouses. Though this grass cuts the hands, it is the kind most widely used in the temperate hamlets. The flower stalks are used for pack saddles. For further use cf. **lo'balal met.** It is eaten by horses.

Extended range: *Erianthus trinii, Muhlenbergia macroura,*

and *Rhynchelytrum repens*.

3. **Jobelal xalma**, "pack saddle grass," refers to the beard grasses *Andropogon bicornis* (1–4) and *A. glomeratus* (1–2). These are few-stemmed, clumped, perennial grasses up to 1–5 m tall with dense, plume-like inflorescences. They are common in temperate hamlets, especially on dry slopes with pines. *Ladinos* use the grass for pack saddles.

It is used occasionally for thatch.

4. **Limon jobel**, "lime grass," applies to grass-like plants with lemon-scented leaves and rhizomes.

Specifics: 2.

   a. **Batz'i limon jobel**, "genuine lime grass" (**te' limon**), is the cultivated lemon grass *Cymbopogon citratus* (3–5). It is a native of southern India and Ceylon and is a clumped perennial similar in appearance to **jobelal xalma**.

Young plants are transplanted by a few people in the rainy season in the lowlands, in all of the temperate and all but one of the highland communities.

As a "cold" substitute for coffee, the leaves are brewed with refined sugar. As a "hot" cough remedy and for sore throat, the tea is drunk sweetened with honey. The leaves are sold at market.

   b. **K'ox limon jobel**, "small lime grass," refers to *Scleria bourgeaui* (1–2), *S. hirtella* (1–2), and *S. pterota* (1–2), perennial plants with strongly lemon-scented, slender, creeping rhizomes, strap-shaped leaves, and terminal spikes of small apetalous flowers. The fruit is a round, smooth, white or brown nutlet. The plant is grass-like in appearance. They are common in moist meadows in highland and temperate hamlets.

5. **Ne chuch**, "squirrel tail" (**-tik**) (**ne chuch jobel**), refers to *Piptochaetium virescens* (1–2) and *Stipa ichu* (4–6), large, clumped, perennial grasses with feathery inflorescences rising up to 1 m above the clumps. The former is common and often dominant in bunch grassland in highland areas.

When one of the survivors of the Flood was transformed into a squirrel, he was given a plume of this grass for his tail.

The clumps are cut with an ax or, if in a rocky area, with a sickle. Those who prefer the rat-tail muhly for thatching claim that this grass is too soft, that weeds grow on it, and that it rots too fast. The stems are twined to make house lashing, and woven and twined to make slings. The inflorescences were once used for bodkins. They are sold for altar decoration at Christmastime. The plant is eaten by horses.

6. **Sakaton** (**-tik**) refers to *Panicum bulbosum*, *P. maximum*, and *Sorghum halepense*. These are rhizomatous, erect, few-stemmed, tall grasses to 1.5 m high. They have diffuse, terminal inflorescences and small, dense, round, millet-like seeds. Both specific classes were introduced for forage from the Mediterranean region.

Specifics: 2.

   a. **Batz'i sakaton**, "genuine **sakaton**" (**bik'it sakaton, k'ojom jobel, muk'ta sakaton, o'lol sakaton, sakil sakaton**), refers to *Panicum bulbosum* (2–3) and *P. maximum* (2–7). These are variable, commonly cultivated and somewhat naturalized, tall, thick, rhizomatous grasses of lowland and temperate areas. *Ladinos* broadcast the seeds in the cornfields in the rainy season. The roots are sold to those who have no seeds. The grass is used as fodder for donkeys, horses, and cattle even while in pasture.

This grass, together with cane leaves, may be used for thatching fieldhouses.

   b. **Tzajal sakaton**, "red **sakaton**" is *Sorghum halepense* (1–2), a tall coarse grass of disturbed ground and occasionally cultivated by *ladinos* in lowland areas.

"Tan Pox Set"

The **tan pox** set includes six generics, plants with small, scurfy, gray leaves. Many have aromatic herbage.

1. **Bot'-jol tz'i'lel**, "swollen-headed plant" (**poxil simnak'al**), is *Gomphrena decumbens* (2–5), a sprawling or prostrate herb with gray elliptic or obovate leaves, 1.5–5 cm long, and a dense, white, elliptic, terminal inflorescence, made up of numerous acute, membranous bracts. The head is about 1 cm wide. It is cultivated by *ladinos* in their yards and is common in disturbed situations in temperate and lowland areas. *Ladinos* use the flower for altar decoration.

A handful of the plant may be bought when suffering from dysentery. A large bowlful of the "hot" tea is drunk before breakfast.

2. **Mixto** (**mixtu', nixto**) is *Salvia microphylla* (1–2), a soft-wooded shrub with small, gray, aromatic, opposite, oblong-ovate leaves, 12–20 mm long, and red tubular flowers, about 2 cm long, verticillate along a terminal raceme. It is commonly cultivated in *ladino* yards in temperate and highland areas.

Zinacantecs occasionally plant slips near their houses.

For a woman in difficult labor, a handful is brewed. She should drink one or two gourdfuls of the "hot" tea. The flower is used for altar decoration.

3. **Oregano** is oregano *Origanum vulgare* (1–3), a gray-leaved, aromatic herb occasionally cultivated in temperate and highland areas. The leaves are ovate, 1–3 cm long, whorled at the nodes. The flowers are white or lavender, tubular, about 6 mm long, in a terminal raceme. *Ladinos* and Chamulans sow the seeds in their yards in the rainy season. *Ladinos* use the leaves for seasoning chicken and turkey. The plant is classed variously as "medium" and "hot."

4. **Tan pox**, "gray medicine" is *Helianthemum glomeratum* (5–8), a wiry-stemmed subshrub with clusters of inconspicuous, yellow flowers. The leaves are small, 1–2.5 mm long, gray pubescent, and numerous along the stems, giving the plant a totally gray appearance. It occurs on grassy, often overgrazed slopes in pine-oak forests of temperate and highland hamlets.

As a remedy for diarrhea, a handful is brewed together with

tzitz pox to provide a "hot" tea. As a remedy for "white" dysentery, the plant is brewed alone for a "medium" tea. For bloody dysentery the plant is bruised in cold water and a small cup of the "medium" infusion taken. Alternatively, the plant may be brewed together with half of the pit of itzompi. The tea is taken before a meal two or three times. For further medicinal use cf. j'ak'-'uch.

Extended range: *Alchemilla sibbaldiaefolia, Krameria revoluta,* and *Lithospermum distichum.* The root of *L. distichum* is brewed for a "hot" tea for headache.

5. Tomyo (spoxil kaxlan) is garden thyme *Thymus vulgaris* (1–2), a low-growing, gray-leaved, aromatic herb occasionally cultivated in temperate and highland areas. The leaves are small and verticillate at the nodes. The flowers are small, pinkish, and tubular, borne in rounded or ovoid terminal clusters.

A few people sow the seeds in their yards in the rainy season. The "cold" shoots are sold at market in San Cristóbal and are used by *ladinos* to season chicken, turkey, and pork. Some believe, however, that if the plant is sold it will lose its soul and disappear.

6. Tz'i' nichim, "dog flower" (aleli), is stock *Matthiola incana* (1–4), a gray-leaved herb cultivated by highland *ladinos* for its colorful, fragrant flowers. The leaves are oblanceolate, obtuse at the apex, 2–10 cm long. The flowers are in terminal racemes, purple or pink, with four petals about 2.5 cm long, and occur in single and double formations. The long narrow pods are 6–7.5 mm long and 4 mm thick. The seeds are planted in pots and transplanted in the rainy season.

Stock was present as a medicinal plant in the gardens of Zinacantán in 1748, as reported by the priest (Monrroy y Calçadilla, 1748:2); however, only recently have Zinacantecs begun planting stock seed in temperate fields, 60 cm apart in rows. The flowers, sold at market in San Cristóbal, are used by *ladinos* for altar decorations.

"Tuix Set"

The "tuix set" is comprised of eight generics including a tuberous-rooted agave, bulbous, grass-leaved plants in the lily family, and small rosetted lilies.

1. Axux* refers to garlic.

Specifics: 2.

a. Batz'i axux, "genuine garlic," is the common white garlic *Allium sativum* (1–2), cultivated by Chamulans, but not by Zinacantecs. This is a stout plant with leaves 2.5–3.5 cm wide and a flowering stalk, 8–10 mm in diameter. The pink flowers have six acute petals about 6 mm long and are borne in a large, globose, head-like inflorescence, 7–9 cm in diameter.

"Hot" garlic is rubbed on the limbs of a child suffering soul-loss. It is also buried at the spot where the child is believed to have lost its soul. As a remedy for poslom, garlic is mixed with tobacco and woman's urine and rubbed on the patient's legs. Formerly, garlic was ground, seasoned with salt and chili and eaten. Now it is only eaten by Chamulans and *ladinos.* For further uses cf. ixim, lula, moy.

b. Yaxux ka', "horse's garlic" (axux ka', tuix ka'), is a giant variety of garlic *Allium scorodoprasum* (2–4), often called giant garlic or sand leek.

The bulbs are planted by Chamulans and by Zinacantecs in many of the highland communities.

In Zinacantán its use is only medicinal. As a remedy for "wind" and swollen stomach, a clove may be rubbed on the affected part, or if the whole body is affected, 3–4 cloves. Garlic flowers and leaves may be used for the same purposes. Or a clove may be crushed on a rock, brewed, and the very "hot" (k'ok') tea drunk. Alternatively, the clove may be crushed with dry chili and mixed in hot water to which a little salt is added. This infusion is both drunk and rubbed on the body. For madness, a clove is rubbed on the patient's head.

There are many garlic prescriptions for poslom. Two cloves may be crushed and rubbed on the affected part. The garlic may be crushed and mixed with cane liquor. A cloth is immersed in the solution and bound around the leg for four days to burn away the illness. This is also a cure for gangrene (mos). Or, crushed garlic and tobacco may be brewed, then cane liquor and a man's urine mixed in before the bandage is immersed in the liquid. This is also effective for a horse suffering "wind." Finally, crushed garlic may be mixed with cane liquor or a woman's urine and the bandage immersed in the solution.

A horse suffering "wind" may have its stomach rubbed with garlic flowers and leaves so that it will break wind. Alternatively, the horse's belly may be rubbed with crushed garlic cloves and then slapped three times with a woman's sash. All of the above remedies are classed as very "hot" (k'ok').

Extended range: *Schoenocaulon officinale.*

2. Ch'upak'* is the cultivated form of the tuberous-rooted agave *Agave brachystachys* (2–6). It is acaulescent with soft, thin, lance linear leaves, 2–4 cm wide, 25–35 cm long. Zinacantecs maintain that this agave, unlike its wild form, tub chil, never flowers. It is cultivated by a few Zinacantecs in most highland hamlets, in the hamlets of the Atz'am valley, and in one other temperate community.

As the foam produced by the root is neither bitter nor smelly (xin), it is used to launder the clothing of saints and patients. It is also used for shampoo. The roots may be dug up, saved, and sold to those in need of them.

Extended range: *Anthericum vestitum, Calochortus ghiesbreghtii, Echeandia macrocarpa, Nothoscordum bivalve, Schoenocaulon officinale,* and *Spiranthes aurantiaca,* all tuberous-rooted, lily-like plants of grassland situation.

3. Ch'upak' joj, "raven ch'upak'" (k'anal tub chil, k'ox tub chil), refers to the small rosetted lilies *Anthericum eleutherandrum* (1–4), *A. vestitum* (2–3), *Echeandia macrocarpa* (5–7), *E. macrophylla* var. *longifolia* (1–2), and *E. parviflora* (1–2). These plants have many elongated tubers and are acaulescent with a rosette of long, narrow, thin, linear leaves. The flowers are yellow or white, borne in a simple

raceme or branched inflorescence up to 1 m long. The fruit is an oblong or ovoid capsule that is 3-sided or 3-lobed. They are common in second growth, rocky slopes, and cornfields of temperate and lowland areas.

As a remedy for tarantula bite, the root may be brewed and the tea administered. Or the root may be crushed and mixed with cold water together with **k'anal nich** (*Potentilla* sp.) for an infusion. For further medicinal use cf. **arvajáka tz'i'lel**.

Extended range: *Hypoxis decumbens*.

4. **Pech'e-'ok jobel**, "flat-stemmed grass" (**pech'-'ok**), refers to *Orthosanthus, Sisyrinchium,* and *Schoenocaulon,* grass-like lilies and irids that occur in savanna and grassland situations.

Specifics: 3.

    a. **Batz'i pech'e-'ok jobel**, "genuine flat-stemmed grass" (**k'ox palma, nichim uch, pech'ajtik jobel, pech'e-'ok, pech'e-'ok tz'i'lel, xanxan jobel**), is *Orthosanthus chimboracensis* var. *centro-americanus* (5–7), a tufted rhizomatous plant with equitant leaves, 1 cm wide or less, and a branched inflorescence with terminal clusters of bright blue flowers with perianth segments, 1–1.5 cm long. The capsule is 3-sided, oblong, 9–16 mm long. It is common in exposed areas in the moist highland forests.

Extended range: *Carex donnell-smithii*.

    b. **K'anal pech'e-'ok jobel**, "yellow flat-stemmed grass" (**pech'e-'ok chon, xik' kukay**), refers to *Sisyrinchium angustissimum* (3–7), *S. convolutum* (7–10), *S. scabrum* (2–4), and *S. tinctorium* (1–4), grass-like plants with bright yellow flowers or blue with yellow stamens in *S. scrabrum*. The flowers are terminal and fasciculate with spreading petals, 6–12 mm long. The leaves are mostly 8 mm wide or less. The capsules are subglobose and contain numerous seeds. They are common in second growth and disturbed situations (including cornfields) and grassy slopes in temperate and highland hamlets.

As an antidote for snakebite, *S. convolutum* is boiled and the "hot" liquid used to bathe the bite. The plant is also used for altar decoration.

    c. **Sakil pech'e-'ok jobel**, "white flat-stemmed grass" (**k'axib jobel, nichim joj, sakil nich pech'-'ok, tuix jobel**), is *Schoenocaulon officinale* (3–4), a bulbous plant with a tall dense spike of white flowers that is common in savannas and disturbed, grassy slopes in temperate and lowland areas. The bulb is covered with an outer coat of long black interwoven fibers. The scape is up to a meter long. The flowers are white, with perianth parts about 5 mm long and long exerted stamens.

5. **Tub chil**, "cricket spit," is the wild-occurring form of **ch'upak'**, *Agave brachystachys* (2–2). The flowers are greenish yellow, fading brownish pink, 3.5–4 cm long, arranged in a long spike, 1–2 meters tall. It occurs in grassy savannas and second growth in temperate and lowland areas. Their tubers produce a very itchy lather that is a remedy for dandruff.

6. **Tuix*** (-**tik**, -**altik**) (**sevulya, tuvix**) refers to onions and shallots. The term, **sevulya**, until recently was restricted to the common garden onion, but now has been extended to include all onions and shallots.

Specifics: 4.

    a. **Batz'i tuix**, "genuine onion" (**tzajal sevulya, tzajal tuix**), is a cultivated local onion *Allium cepa* (1–2) with a small, red head and long flower stalk.

This onion is widely planted by Chamulans and by a very few Zinacantecs in many of the temperate and highland communities. Although seeds are occasionally sown in a seed bed and the seedlings transplanted, it is more common to plant the bulbs. These may be bought from Chamulans. The onions are planted 20–30 cm apart in rows 40–50 cm distance in hoed ground or in a corral. Sheep manure is provided. Planting occurs in the rainy season and, if water is available for irrigation, in the beginning of the dry season (November).

The entire "cold" plant may be eaten raw or roasted. It is used to flavor beef, pork, chicken, beans, cushaw and pumpkin squash seeds, potatoes, chayote root, tomatoes, and chili sauce. It is also used to flavor bull's blood and the "blood" of the *petate* bull on Epiphany (provided by the Stewards of Our Lady of the Rosary). It is sold at market.

    b. **J'alnom tuix**, "postpartum mother onion" (**j'alnom sevulya**), is the cultivated shallot *Allium ascalonicum* (1–2). This group differs from the common onion in that its bulbs multiply and produce lateral bulbs. It has a long flowering stalk with a globose head of white, 6-petaled flowers.

Shallots are planted by Chamulans and by a very few Zinacantecs in the highland hamlets. Planting schedules and techniques are the same as those for **batz'i tuix**.

The entire shallot plant is eaten and used for culinary purposes as above.

    c. **Sakil tuix**, "white onion" (**muk'tik tuix, sakil sevulya, soktomal sevulya**), is the common white garden onion *Allium cepa* (1–4), formerly cultivated by the people of Chiapa de Corzo, but now widely cultivated by Chamulans.

A very few people in the temperate and highland hamlets plant the bulbs in the rainy season. They are cultivated in the same way as **batz'i tuix**. They are sold at market.

The "cold" bulbs are used to flavor fried beans and **yo'on tuluk'** mushrooms. Cf. **kokov**.

    d. **Te'tikil tuix**, "wild onion" (**k'ox tuix, te'tikil sevulya, xulub tuix**), is the wild-occuring native onion *Allium kunthii* (1–2). It occurs in temperate and highland areas often in pine forest and near milpas. This onion is a slender plant with many bulblets forming a mass of stalks. Its inflorescence is small and laxly umbellate. The flowers are pink, lavender, or white, with acuminate petals, 6–7 mm long. The bulbs are white. In Tenejapa, unlike Zinacantán, this onion may be cultivated. Wild onions are sold by Chamulans at market. They are eaten in the same ways as **batz'i tuix**.

7. **Tuix jobel**, "onion grass," is *Nothoscordum bivalve* (1–1), a slender lily with an open umbel of white flowers with acute, oblong perianth segments, 9–11 mm long. The pedicels are long, 2–5 cm. The bulb is white. This plant closely resembles *Allium* but has no onion odor. It occurs in wet places in the pine-oak forests of the highlands.

As a remedy for mange (**sep'**), the "hot" plant may be crushed, boiled, or dried on the fire and applied to the affected part to kill "its animals."

8. **Tuix tz'i'lel**, "onion plant," is *Calochortus ghiesbreghtii* (1–2), a white and reddish brown-flowered lily scattered in the grassy understory of pine-oak forests in temperate and highland areas. The flowers are terminal on long naked peduncles, 6–16 cm long, with obovate petals, 11–18 mm long, hairy near the base. The bulb is ovoid with a thick netted outer coat. The fruits are linear-oblong and 3-angled, 3–4.5 cm long.

9. **Ve'el k'ovix**, "towhee food," is *Hypoxis decumbens* (1–1), a slender plant arising from a globose or subcylindric corm. The leaves are 10–40 cm long, 2–12 mm wide. The flowers are yellow with lanceolate perianth segments, 4–10 mm, on a slender, few-flowered scape. It is a very common plant in the grassy understory of pine-oak forests of the temperate and highland hamlets.

"Tzajal Nichim Set"

The "tzajal nichim set" is comprised of 20 generics, which are mostly plants cultivated for their cut flowers and are primarily members of the daisy family.

1. **Altamixa** (**jjalal-me'tik, jjaral-me'tik**) is *Ambrosia cumanensis* (6–11), a rank-smelling herb with dissected leaves, 3–10 cm long, that is common in disturbed ground and fallow fields in highland hamlets. The flowers are either male or female and are greenish yellow. The male flowers are sessile or on short pedicels, 3–4 mm broad, in a long dense spike or raceme. The female flowers are similar in size but fasciculate in the upper leaf axils. The fruit is obovate, with 4–7 short spines.

This herb may be stored dry. To induce abortion, a small bunch is brewed and a cup of the "hot" tea is drunk twice for one day. To prevent postpartum hemorrhaging, a cup of this tea may be drunk before the mother's first meal. Chamomile may be added to it. The same tea may be taken by people suffering from "wind," swollen stomachs, or **poslom**. The affected part is bathed also with a liquid. Postpartum mothers may bathe themselves with this liquid rather than taking a sweat bath. The leaves are applied to a sprain or broken bone.

2. **Espáyder** (**xelajtik krisantema**) is the "spider" type of florists' chrysanthemum, "Spiders and Spoons" (2–3), *Dendranthema morifolium*.

It is grown only in cold frames in Pat Osil and Zinacantán Center. It takes four months to flower and flowers for one month.

It is sold in market.

Specifics: 3.
    a. **K'anal espáyder**, the yellow variety.
    b. **Moraro espáyder** (**paylíyo**), a magenta variety.
    c. **Sakil espáyder**, the white variety.

3. **Jjaral-me'tik**, "our holy lady" (**nichim jjaral-me'tik, snichim jch'ul-me'tik**), is the feverfew *Tanecetum parthenium* (5–10), which is cultivated and adventive around habitations in highland and temperate areas. This chrysanthemum relative has small heads, about 1.5 cm broad, with white rays and a yellow central disk. The leaves are bipinnate, 2.5–4.5 cm long.

A few people in many of the temperate and highland communities sow the seeds or transplant the young plants in May. The flowers are sold occasionally at market. This herb may be stored dry.

As a remedy for "wind" and stomach ache, three or six tips are brewed and a cup of the "hot" tea is drunk before breakfast and supper. Postpartum mothers suffering pain or hemorrhage take this same tea or may combine feverfew with chamomile.

The flowers are used for altar decoration.

Extended range: *Bidens triplinervia, Hofmeisteria urenifolia,* and *Parthenium hysterophorus*.

4. **Kartolina** is a small double hybrid chrysanthemum, "Jewel Box" (2–3), *Dendranthema morifolium*. It has flowers 3 cm across on stems 60 cm tall. It is grown by slip, outside, in Pat Osil. It is sold in market.

Specifics: 3.
    a. **K'anal kartolina**, the yellow variety.
    b. **Moraro kartolina**, a lavender variety.
    c. **Sakil kartolina**, the white variety.

5. **Klavel** (**-tik**) is the cultivated carnation *Dianthus caryophyllus* (8–3), another extremely variable plant of garden origin. It was among the flowering plants sent by Fray Jordán de Piamonte in Oaxaca to the first Dominican friars in Zinacantán in 1545 (Ximènes, 1929, 1:423).

It is grown in a few temperate and all of the highland communities.

Carnations were planted formerly by seed, but now are planted almost exclusively by slip in the highland hamlets and in Atz'am. They are planted when the moon is new, so that they will grow tall and not mature too fast. The slips are planted very close together in seed beds in February and watered every three days. The slips are transplanted in June to flat land where they are planted 40 cm apart in rows 50–60 cm apart. Two handfuls of sheep manure are provided to each plant. Replanting may occur. Some prefer to plant the slips in the rainy season without the use of a seed bed. Irrigation is common. The flowers raised commercially are grown principally in Naben Chauk. The plants take six months to flower. The flowers are picked every three days. The plants are replaced after 2–3 years. If there are just a few plants they may be protected from frost by a wooden frame roofed with corn stubble or they may be planted in an old pot or box and kept under the roof overhang. Carnations, unlike daisies, are prey to rabbits. When a foot high they are hilled so the roots will take firm hold and the stalks remain erect not pushing against adjacent plants.

They are almost ubiquitous in hamlet chapel flower changes. Carnations are used to decorate the graveyard crosses on All Souls' Day. They adorn the creche in Sak Lum. They may be resold and are sold in San Cristóbal and Tuxtla. One small basket of carnations is taken to church when begging pardon. Cf. **batz'i tz'oban.**

Specifics: 6.
- a. **Ik''ik'-lo'an klavel,** "purple carnation," a dark red form.
- b. **Korona klavel,** "crown carnation," a red-centered, white-edged form.
- c. **Rosaro klavel,** "pink carnation," a deep pink form.
- d. **Sak-vayan klavel,** "pink carnation" (**saksak-vilan klavel**), a pale pink form.
- e. **Sakil klavel,** "white carnation," a white form.
- f. **Tzajal klavel,** "red carnation," a red form. As a remedy for dysentery, the flower may be brewed for a "hot" tea or bruised for a "cold" infusion. Stewards, stewards-royal, and elders may substitute red carnations for geraniums for altar decoration. This substitution is always made in Bik'it Joyijel and Kelem Ton.

Extended range: *Dianthus chinensis* and *Pinaropappus spathulatus* var. *chiapensis.*

6. **Klavelina (-tik) (klavelito)** is the garden pink *Dianthus caryophyllus* (1–3).

It is cultivated in all but one of the highland communities, as above. It is offered occasionally in hamlet chapels, especially in Chak Toj for flower changes. In ritual speech, it is called **lavaléna** or **lavalína.** Paired in final position with **nichim**, flower, or **asasena**, lily, it refers to a child.

7. **Kopita** is candytuft *Iberis simplex* (1–1). It is a much-branched, linear-leaved herb with terminal head-like clusters of 4-petaled, pink flowers, 10–15 mm long. The fruits are flattened, ovoid, 8–10 mm long.

A very few people in the highland hamlets raise this flower to sell.

8. **Krisantema (florejvána, krisante)** is the crown daisy *Chrysanthemum coronarium* (2–3), an occasionally cultivated plant in highland areas. The flowering heads are about 2–4 cm broad, and yellow. The leaves are numerous and bipinnately lobed.

A few people in many of the highland communities plant the seeds or transplant the young plants in the rainy season. The flowers may be resold and are sold at market and used for altar decoration, especially on All Souls' Day. Because of their cost their use is infrequent in hamlet chapel flower changes.

Specifics: 3.
- a. **K'anal krisantema,** the yellow form.
- b. **Rosaro krisantema,** the pink form.
- c. **Sakil krisantema,** the white form.

9. **Krisantéma nichim,** "krisantéma flower" (**rais, rais ta komitan**), is the florists' chrysanthemum *Dendranthema morifolium* (3–5). The flowering heads are large, 4–9 cm broad. The leaves are pinnately lobed, 2.5–7 cm long. It is raised by *ladinos* in Comitán and sold in the San Cristóbal market for All Souls' Day decorations. Very recently, Zinacantec flower merchants have been purchasing this chrysanthemum in Oaxaca for resale.

10. **K'ok' sat nichim,** "hot-faced flower" (**jvanita, pirik' nichim**), sweet william, is *Dianthus barbatus* (1–1), a relative of the florist's carnation. The opposite, lance-oblong leaves, 6–11 cm long, are crowded at the base of the plant, becoming shorter and more widely spaced near the top. The flowers are pink, showy, 2–2.5 cm long, and crowded into terminal headlike clusters, 4.5–6 cm broad.

A very few people in the highland hamlets, transplanting the seedlings, raise this flower to sell.

11. **Mantzanilya (mantzaninya, mantzaniya)** is chamomile, *Chamomilla recutita* (2–2), an aromatic, finely branched herb, which is cultivated and often adventive around houses in the highland areas. The leaves are 3–6 cm long, bipinnate with filiform segments. The ray flowers are white, the central disk yellow, solitary at the ends of the branches, 6–8 mm broad.

A few people in many of the temperate and most of the highland communities scatter the seeds in October (Fiesta of Our Lady of the Rosary) so that the plants will flower for Holy Week. Planting may continue into November. The flowers are sold at market in Chamula and San Cristóbal.

This herb may be stored dry. It has a wide variety of medicinal uses. The "hot" tea may be taken for deafness caused by cold and for heartburn (**me'-vinik**). The tea mixed with cane liquor may be used for a hangover or for fever. Alternate remedies for heartburn include a tea to which basil is added, or an infusion of the seeds bruised in warm water, either alone or with fennel leaves. As a remedy for cough and laryngitis, two stalks are brewed together with basil, brown sugar, and tallow, or brewed in cane liquor, or brewed with basil in which a shot of cane liquor is added. To ease heart pain (**k'ux o'onil**), a tea of this herb brewed with corn silk and three red pine splinters is taken. As a remedy for "wind" and diarrhea, two stalks are brewed and cane liquor, in which camphor has been soaked, is added to it. One cup of the "hot" tea is drunk before breakfast for three days. For diarrhea (**k'ak'al tza'nel**), salt may be added to the tea. For further medicinal use cf. **altamixa** and **jjaral- me'tik.**

On Good Friday the elders hand out bunches of blessed chamomile. For the Lenten Fridays, except the fourth Friday, each steward provides four bunches of chamomile to decorate the saints' litters. Six bunches are provided on the fourth Friday. Each ensign-bearer provides five bunches for the first, second, and third Lenten Fridays and seven bunches for the fourth, fifth, and sixth Fridays. Half a small basket is provided by each steward on Tuesday of Holy Week and Good Friday. The publicans provide two small baskets to decorate the Chapel of Our Lord of Esquipulas on Lenten Fridays. Chamomile is widely used for Lenten decoration in the hamlets: San Mikulax on the fourth Lenten Friday and Maundy Thursday, Elan Vo' the fourth Lenten Friday and Palm Sunday, Paste' for Holy Week, Naben Chauk for Lenten Fridays, and Sek'emtik for the sixth Lenten Friday. The flowers are used to decorate the creche in Apas.

For ritual use cf. **tzajal nichim**.

Extended range: *Chamomilla suaveolens*.

12. **Markarita** (-**tik**, -**iltik**) (**margarita**) is the ox eye daisy *Leucanthemum vulgare* (8–5). This is a variable garden plant.

It is grown in a few temperate and all of the highland communities.

Formerly daisies were planted by seed, but now young plants or slips are planted in the upper temperate and highland hamlets in May and again in November. They are set 40 cm apart in rows 40–60 cm apart. They require full sun. Sheep manure is sometimes provided. The flowers may be resold and are sold in San Cristóbal, Tuxtla, and Arriaga throughout the year.

Daisies are used for altar decoration by people begging pardon in church. They may also be used to decorate the well crosses on Holy Cross Day. They are used with some frequency for flower changes in hamlet chapels. For ritual use cf. **kartucho**.

Specifics: 5.

  a. **Cha'-lom markarita**, "two level daisy," is the most preferred form, as it is semidouble and has two levels of ray florets presented continually. Its thick stem permits the grower to cut a bunch more quickly. They are sold in bunches of 15 or 20 flowers.

  b. **Ch'ulul markarita**, "smooth daisy" (**o'lol markarita**), is a smooth-stemmed, medium-sized daisy that was introduced in 1975. It propagates by seed. The number of flowers to a bunch are not counted.

  c. **K'ox markarita**, "small daisy," is the variety first cultivated in Zinacantán, but has been supplanted by the larger varieties. The number of flowers to a bunch were not counted.

  d. **Markaríta reyéno**, "full daisy," is a fully double form very recently introduced and grown only in Pat Osil. There are 12 flowers to a bunch. This is the most expensive variety.

  e. **Tzotziron markarita**, "downy daisy" (**o'lol markarita**), is a downy-stemmed, medium-sized daisy. The number of flowers to a bunch are not counted.

Extended range: *Astranthium purpurascens, Cosmos diversifolius*, and *Gaillardia pulchella*.

13. **Markaríta tz'i'lel**, "**markaríta** plant," refers to *Aster bullatus* (1–1) and *Sabazia sarmentosa* (1–1), perennial herbs with white daisy flowers. The stems are branched and the leaves are either linear in *Aster* or ovate in *Sabazia*. The flowering heads are about 1.5–2 cm broad. The plants occur along streams (*Aster*) and on moist slopes (*Sabazia*) in pine-oak and evergreen cloud forest in the highlands.

14. **Markariton** (-**tik**) (**muk'ta markarita**) refers to the large varieties of ox eye daisy *Leucanthemum vulgare* (4–4).

It is cultivated as above.

Specifics: 2.

  a. **Batz'i markariton**, "genuine **markariton**," is a smooth-stemmed form that was cultivated at the same time as **k'ox markarita**, but in much smaller numbers. It is cultivated by few people today. A bunch contains 12 flowers.

  b. **Tzotzin markariton**, "downy **markariton**," is a downy-stemmed form that is seldom cultivated, as the flowers wilt very quickly. A bunch contains 12 flowers.

15. **Nube**, "cloud" (**sakil boton**), is baby's breath, *Gypsophila elegans* (1–1) and *G. paniculata* (1–1), herbs with delicate white or pink flowers in large-branched inflorescences.

It is cultivated in many of the temperate and in highland communities, planted in the dry season. It is sold at market.

It is used to decorate the creche in Sak Lum, and is used in hamlet chapel flower changes in Atz'am and Sak Lum.

16. **Pilix** (-**tik**) (**p'ilix, yok ne sibak**) refers to herbaceous or subshrubby sunflowers with yellow, terminal flowers.

Specifics: 2.

  a. **K'ox pilix**, "small **pilix**," refers to *Melampodium divaricatum* (1–4) and *Simsia sanguinea* (1–1), two delicately branched, small, purple or yellow-flowered sunflower herbs occurring in disturbed areas in temperate and lowland regions. Both have opposite leaves that are rough to the touch. Leaves of the purple-flowered *Simsia* are trilobate, narrowly linear or triangular ovate. The leaves of *Melampodium* are broadly ovate to oblong-lanceolate and entire. The heads are 1–1.5 cm broad in *Melampodium* and 1.5–2.0 cm broad in *Simsia*.

  b. **Sakil pilix**, "white **pilix**" (**bik'it sun**), refers to *Aldama dentata* (2–6) and *Viguiera dentata* (3–9), two tall subshrubs with stiff, straight stems. Both have yellow flowers in open branched inflorescences with ray flowers, 7–15 mm long. The leaves are ovate to lanceolate acute at the apex, 3–12 cm long. They are common in disturbed areas and fallow ground in temperate and lowland areas. Because of the stiffness of the stems, the plants are classed variously as "tree" and "plant." The stems are sold in bundles by the people of Laguna Grande and Totolapa to the fireworks makers in San Cristóbal.

A handful of the stems may be tied together in the middle and used as a torch.

17. **Pompom** is the term for all double chrysanthemums. Two major segregations are made with several color forms in each.

  a. **Batz'i pompom**, refers to large and giant double chrysanthemum, "Super Jet" (2–3) *Dendranthema morifolium*, only cultivated originally in cold frames in Pat Osil and Zinacantán Center, but now grown outside in Atz'am, Pat Osil, Sak Lum, and Zinacatán Center.

It is sold in market, and despite its expense it is used occasionally in flower changes, especially for banquet vases.

    (1) **K'anal pompom**, the yellow variety.

    (2) **Moraro pompom**, a rosy lavender variety.

    (3) **Sakil pompom**, the white variety.

    b. **Muk'ta pompom**, "large **pompom**" (**espúma del-mar**), is a hybrid giant football chrysanthemum, "Royal Highness" (2–3) *Dendranthema morifolium*, grown only in cold frames in Zinacantán Center. To start, cultivation plants with roots are bought. Planting is begun in February to produce plants 80 cm to 1 m tall, flowering in May for three weeks to one month. A second planting occurs at the end of July and beginning of August to produce flowers for All Souls' Day. The sprouting tips are cut off and the stumps pulled up. The tips are planted very close in flats, to which are added chemical fertilizer (enraysone plus). After 2–3 weeks these seedlings are transplanted to rows 15 cm square. In mid-November a third planting is sometimes practiced, but it risks frost damage. An alternative method is to plant slips directly. If this is done, the plants vary in height, reaching $1^{1}/2$ meters. They take an extra month to flower, produce fewer flowers, but continue flowering for 5 to 6 months.

They are sold at market.

    (1) **K'anal muk'ta pompom**, the yellow variety.

    (2) **Moraro muk'ta pompom**, a rosy lavender variety.

    (3) **Sakil muk'ta pompom**, the white variety.

18. **Sakramentual nichim**, "sacrament flower" (**-tik**), is *Helenium scorzoneraefolia* (3–7), a perennial herb with creeping rhizomes and scapose, yellow daisy flowers. The basal leaves are oblanceolate, 20–30 cm long, decurrent on the petiole. The cauline leaves are shorter and not decurrent. The flowers have a disk about 2.5 cm broad and rays about 2–3.5 cm long. It is common in moist, grassy places in pine-oak woodland of highland areas.

As a remedy for "wind," six roots are brewed, and a small cup of the "hot" tea is drunk before breakfast. The tea is also drunk to induce an abortion and to stop postpartum hemorrhaging.

To warm the belly of a postpartum mother, a man (who is not "cold") grinds the root on a **metate**. The juice is mixed with black pepper, dried chili, and brown sugar. The mother drinks the "hot" infusion.

One small basket, half geraniums and half **sakramentual nichim**, is provided by each steward to decorate the churches on Corpus Christi. The publicans decorate the Chapel of Our Lord of Esquipulas similarly. The elders decorate their altars in the same way. On Corpus Christi these flowers are also used in Elan Vo', Paste', and San Mikulax.

19. **Snichim san-lukax**, "St. Luke's flower" (**snichim san-tukax, snichim xan-lukax, tzajal ch'ix nichim, tzajal nichim ta olon osil, tzajal olonal nichim**), is the garden zinnia *Zinnia elegans* (4–5), which is commonly cultivated by *ladinos* in temperate and lowland yards and occasionally grown in highland *ladino* communities. The *ladinos* of San Lucas (El Zapotal) plant zinnia seeds in May. *Ladinos* and stewards use the flowers for altar decoration. They are sold at market.

Extended range: *Zinnia peruviana*.

20. **Tontikil putzul**, "rock-growing **putzul**" (**sputz'taob xavon k'oxetik, stubtaob xavon k'oxetik, tut tz'i'lel**), is the dandelion *Taraxacum officinale* (5–6), which is common in disturbed ground and near habitations in the highland areas. It is a rosetted herb arising from a thick tuberous root. The flowers are yellow and in a head at the end of a hollow stalk. The leaves are pinnately lobed and 10–15 cm long.

Children bruise the stem and flowers in water, producing a foam that they blow at each other.

21. **Tzajal nichim**, "red flower" (**-tik, -altik**) (**batz'i nichim, potzalal nichim**), is the garden geranium *Pelargonium hortorum* (7–7), grown very commonly around houses in temperate and highland hamlets. This is an extremely variable plant known only in cultivation and derived from several South African species of *Pelargonium*. As this hybrid could not have been introduced to Zinacantán prior to 1850, its central importance is probably the result of the replacement of a wild flower, possibly *konkon*.

Specifics: 4.

    a. **Batz'i tzajal nichim**, "genuine red flower," has a blossom uniformly bright red with the flowers in tight clusters.

The geranium is the quintessential flower of Zinacantán. Rarely, if ever, is it used in the neighboring Indian towns. Retaining its bright red color for weeks, it is the principal flower for religious decoration. This color, it seems, dates back to when Christ was suffering from a bloody nose and used the flower to stem the flow. A shaman was heard to refer to it as **batz'i nichim**, the genuine flower.

It is grown in a few of the temperate and all of the highland communities. In the highland hamlets geranium slips are planted generally, but not exclusively, in the rainy season. In the temperate hamlets they are planted in the dry season, lest they rot. Some plant the slips very close together in rows an armspan apart. Others plant the slips 20 cm apart or $^{1}/2$ m apart or one meter's distance. Manure is seldom provided.

As a remedy for fever sores, three "medium" leaves or three flowers are chewed and rubbed on the lips. For a headache, six flowers are crushed in warm water and the patient's head bathed with the "hot" infusion. To relieve a fever, the flower may be crushed in warm water together with fennel leaves. The head is bathed with the "cold" infusion. Three "hot" flowers are a basic ingredient of "flower water." During a major curing ceremony, when blood is drawn from the neck of the sacrificial chicken, the shaman dips a geranium into the bowl and daubs the blood on the patient's forehead and forearms in the form of crosses. In order to recover a person's soul, the shaman beats the ground where the soul allegedly has been lost with oak, yellow pine, and geranium tips. For a major curing ceremony, a large basket of geraniums is required to decorate the crosses. For a minor ceremony a small basket is required. For further medicinal use cf. **antzil aj, tilil, tzis uch**, and **yich'ak mut**.

Sour orange leaves and geranium blossoms are gathered by the wedding petitioner, tied in bouquets, and distributed to the wedding guests at the dance. When a coffin is carried to the cemetery, the procession makes stops to rest during which a geranium blossom is dipped in water and the water sprinkled on the corpse's lips.

For the biweekly flower changes, each steward provides one large basket of geraniums. The geraniums provided by the senior stewards are used to decorate the Church of St. Lawrence, and the geraniums provided by the junior stewards are taken to the Church of St. Sebastian. One small basket is needed to decorate the steward's altar. One large basket is provided by the stewards royal every other Saturday to decorate the Chapel of Esquipulas. One medium-sized basket is required by the elders on alternate Saturdays to decorate the altar of the grand alcalde. Geraniums are offered for flower changes in all chapels except in Bik'it Joyijel and Kelem Ton. On Lenten Fridays, Tuesday and Wednesday in Holy Week, and on Good Friday each steward provides a small basket of geraniums and chamomile flowers, which are tied to the saints' litters. Each ensign-bearer offers a bunch of geraniums on the fourth, fifth, and sixth Fridays of Lent. On Good Friday, the elders, holy elders, and any stewards, ensign-bearers, or former elders who so desire offer a small basket with candles, geraniums, and chamomiles at the base of the cross in the Church of St. Lawrence. On Corpus Christi each steward provides a small basket of geraniums and **sakramentual nichim**. On Holy Cross Day each of the stewards of the Holy Cross provide a large basket of geraniums. On the Fiesta of Our Lady of the Rosary and on All Souls' Day, one large basket of geraniums and marigolds is provided by each steward. For the first *Posada* each steward brings a large basket of geraniums and **pimil anal** to decorate the litters of Joseph and Mary. A small basket of the same is used to adorn their household altars. On the eighth *Posada* a large basket of geraniums and sedum is provided by each steward for the roof of the creche, which is embellished with vertical rows of geraniums separating the rows of greenery. When a new house is inaugurated geraniums are tied to each of the three pine tips planted in the corners of the house. Geraniums are used to adorn the creche in Apas, Atz'am, Chak Toj, and Naben Chauk. Geraniums are used to decorate the well crosses on Holy Cross Day and to decorate house entrance crosses on all major fiestas. Three geraniums are tied to the cross on the roof of a newly constructed house and to the corn bin cross. Geraniums are used to decorate the graveyard crosses on All Souls' Day. Though not sold at market, geraniums are bought locally by religious officials for altar decoration.

b. **Ik''ik'-lo'an tzajal nichim**, "maroon red flower," has a dark red bloom. It is cultivated by *ladinos* and by a very few Zinacantecs.

c. **Sak-vayan tzajal nichim**, "pink red flower," has a pink blossom. It is cultivated by *ladinos* and by a very few Zinacantecs.

d. **Sakil tzajal nichim**, "white red flower," has a white blossom. It is cultivated by a few *ladinos*.

Extended range: *Begonia oaxacana* and *Spigelia splendens*.

22. **Volita** (**bolita, jjaral-me'tik saju', volita nichim**) is the fully double form of the feverfew *Tanecetum parthenium* (3–3).

It is grown in all but two of the highland hamlets.

A recent introduction, this plant was cultivated originally by seed, but now by slip. There may be three plantings: (1) May–June, (2) late August–September, (3) November. The slips are set 20–60 cm apart in rows 40–60 cm distance. Sheep manure is provided by some. Replanting may occur. The plants are hilled. Pesticide may be applied monthly. Two pickings are possible.

A handful of this plant may be brewed for a "hot" tea for chest pain (**k'ux o'onil**).

The flowers are used for altar decoration. These flowers are used very frequently in hamlet chapel flower changes. They may be resold and are sold at market.

"Tzib Set"

The "**Tzib** set" is a grouping of two generics and together refer to the ferns. It is clear from the collecting effort that any fern (there are about 600 species that are known to occur in Chiapas) presented to the Tzotzil would be placed in this group.

1. **Tzib** (**-tik**) refers to virtually all of the ferns.

Specifics: 9.

a. **Batz'i tzib**, "genuine **tzib**" (**tzajal tzib**), is bracken, *Pteridium aquilinum* (1–2), a terrestrial fern with long, hairy, creeping rhizomes. The blade is 2–4 pinnate, and the margins of the segments are reflexed to cover the sori. The frond can attain a length of 2 m. It occurs in many habitats throughout the township.

It is associated with unproductive land.

b. **Ik'al ok tzib**, "black-stemmed **tzib**" (**poxil sarampyo**), refers to maidenhair ferns and other small, delicate, terrestrial ferns with black stems. Included are *Adiantum andicola* (1–4), *A. concinnum* (1–2), *A. poirettii* (2–3), *Anemia adiantifolia* (1–2), *A. phyllitidis* (1–4), *Anogramma leptophylla* (1–1), *Cheilanthes hirsuta* (3–5), and *Cystopteris fragilis* (1–1). These occur on moist, shaded banks in pine-oak and evergreen cloud forests of temperate and highland areas.

c. **Jamal anal tzib**, "wide-leaved fern," refers to *Elaphoglossum latifolium* (2–3), *E. paleaceum* (1–4), and several species determined only *Elaphoglossum* spp. These have simple fronds with various types of pubescence. They are epiphytic or terrestrial and have short-creeping rhizomes. They occur on shaded, steep slopes as epiphytes and on rock faces in highland areas.

  d. **Kilajtik tzib**, "pendulous fern" (**tzibal k'a'-te'**), refers to *Asplenium monanthes* (1–4), *Campyloneurum angustifolium* (2–2), *C. xalapense* (1–2), *Phlebodium aureum* (1–1), *Pleopeltis munchii* (1–2), *Polypodium adelphum* (1–1), *P. alfredii* (1–2), and probably several other species. These are epiphytic ferns in pine-oak and evergreen cloud forest in temperate and highland areas. The blades are either entire and linear as in *Campyloneurum* or once pinnate. All have rounded sori and arise from rhizomes and hang down from the branches on which they are perched.

The rhizome of *Polypodium adelphum* is crushed in cold water with white salt and administered to sheep suffering "wind."

  e. **K'ox tzib**, "small fern," refers to *Cystopteris fragilis* (1–1), *Dryopteris nubigena* (1–1), *Thelypterus deflexa* (1–1), *T. oligocarpa* (1–1), *T. resinifera* (1–1), and *T. rudis* (1–1). These are terrestrial ferns with twice pinnate fronds. They occur on wet banks in montane rain forest, pine-oak-arbutus forest, and evergreen cloud forest.

Thelypterus sp. is sold in Tuxtla at Christmas time.

  f. **Muk'ta tzib**, "large fern" (**ch'ib tzib** in part, **mol tzib**, **palma tzib** and **yaxal tzib** in part), refers to the large, terrestrial, clumped ferns *Acrosticum danaeifolium* (1–1), *Ctenitis equestris* (1–1), *Dryopteris nubigena* (1–2), *Marattia weinmanniifolia* (1–1), *Phanerophlebia remotispora* (1–2), *Polystichum distans* (1–2), and *Woodwardia spinulosa* (2–5). They occur in the understory of moist pine-oak and evergreen cloud forests of temperate and highland areas.

They are sometimes used as a replacement for pine decorations on the crosses, and adorn the creche in Chak Toj. The swollen, starchy rhizome of *M. weinmanniifolia* was eaten during the famine.

  g. **Muruch' tzib**, "kinky fern" (**tzibal ton**), refers to highland and temperate rock-growing ferns with finely dissected, pubescent fronds, *Cheilanthes farinosa* (1–2), *C. lendigera* (1–2), *Cheiloplecton rigidum* (1–2), *Llavea cordifolia* (1–5), *Notholaena candida* (1–1), and *N. sinuata* (3–6).

  h. **Tzajal tzib**, "red fern" (**tzotzil tzib**), is *Polystichum distans* (2–5), a clumped, terrestrial fern that is very abundant in the understory of evergreen cloud forest in highland areas. It arises from a stout scaly rhizome and has large bipinnate fronds, 40–100 cm, long with round sori on the undersurface.

Holly ferns were used formerly to decorate the roof of the creche and the Church of St. Sebastian on Christmas Eve. The Stewards of Our Lady of the Rosary provided 150 plants on the eighth *Posada*. They adorn the creche in Atz'am, Sak Lum, and San Mikulax.

  i. **Tzatzal ok tzib**, "strong-stemmed fern" (**mol tzib**, **sakil ok tzib**, **sakil tzib**), is *Lophosoria quadripinnata* (2–6), an immense fern arising from red scaley rhizomes with fronds to 3 m long, which are usually tripinnate with small, lanceolate, pinnatifid segments. It occurs on shaded, moist banks in wet pine-oak and evergreen cloud forests of highland areas.

2. **Tzib ak'**, "fern vine" (**ak'il tzib**), is *Lygodium venustum* (3–4), a viny fern occurring in second growth of lowland areas. The fronds are divided into many basally lobed leaflets with finger-like projections along their margins. It is classed as a "vine."

As a remedy for fever, it is brewed with refined sugar and the "cold" tea allowed to cool before drinking.

"Tzukum Jobel Set"

The "**tzukum jobel** set" is a diverse grouping of 13 generics, grasses and grass-like herbs.

1. **Akan jobel**, "stem grass" (**-tik**) (**ak' jobel** and **ve'el t'ul** in part), refers to *Panicum hirticaule* (1–2), *Paspalum botterii* (1–1), *P. plicatulum* (1–2), *Polypogon elongatus* (1–1), and *P. viridis* (1–2). These are branching, sprawling, and often rooting at the node grasses with tall inflorescences that occur very commonly in disturbed and second growth throughout the township and are especially common in cornfields. Because of their persistent root system they are very difficult to remove from cultivated land.

They are used for horse fodder.

Extended range: *Andropogon glomeratus*, *Arundinella deppeana*, *Digitaria leucites*, *Muhlenbergia tenella*, *Oplismenus burmanni*, and *Sporobolus indicus*.

2. **Ik'al jobel**, "black grass" (**nichim jobel**), refers to the rushes *Juncus dichotomus*, *J. ebracteatus*, *J. effusus*, *J. marginatus* var. *setosus*, and *J. microcephalus*. These are rhizomatous perennials with green, stiff, round stems and clustered, terminal inflorescences that become dark red-brown to black in fruit. They are common in moist ground in temperate and highland areas.

3. **Kakaxon jobel**, "palm grass" (**potz-nich jobel**, **sakil jobel**, **salya jobel**, **ti' ba vakax**, all in part), refers to *Chloris virgata* (2–5), *Cynodon dactylon* (1–1), *Dactyloctenium aegyptium* (3–6), and *Eleusine indica* (1–3), sprawling, mat-forming grasses with digitally compound inflorescences. They are common plants in disturbed areas throughout the township.

They are used for thatch when roofing grass is scarce.

4. **Konejo jobel**, "rabbit grass" (**vale' tz'i'lel**), is *Zeugites munroana* (1–2). It is a miniature bamboo-like grass with broad round leaves and delicate terminal inflorescences that occurs on moist slopes of pine-oak and evergreen cloud forest of the highlands.

264

It is eaten by sheep.

5. **Krus jobel,** "cross grass" (**chikin t'ul jobel, k'otox, poxil sim-nak'al, tuil yisim jobel, tzisan kotz, ve'el ka' jobel, xanxan tz'i'lel, xojob xoto-chak,** all in part), refers to the sedges *Carex polystachya* (1–1), *Cyperus canus* (1–4), *C. hermaphroditus* (7–11), *C. manimae* (1–1), *C. niger* (1–1), *C. pallens* (1–3), *C. virens* (1–1), and *Rhynchospora ciliata* (1–3). These are erect, coarse, grass-like plants with angled stems and terminal, branched inflorescences of apetalous flowers. They are common in moist, disturbed areas throughout the township.

As a remedy for dysentery, 5–6 "hot" roots of *C. hermaphroditus* are brewed or bruised in cold water. (This remedy proved to be extraordinarily effective for one of the authors of this book). Pregnant women who feel "cold" pains brew it together with black pepper. For further medicinal use cf. **sakil pem k'ulub.**

Extended range: *Carex jamesonii.*

6. **K'otox jobel** is *Zeugites americana* var. *mexicanus* (1–1), a slender grass with alternate, ovate, petioled leaves, 1.5–2.5 cm long, and an open panicle with florets at the ends of its branches. This grass grows on moist slopes of pine-oak and evergreen cloud forest of the highlands.

7. **K'un-jobel,** "soft grass" (-**tik**), refers to *Aegopogon cenchroides* (1–1), *Arthraxon quartinianus* (1–1), and *Muhlenbergia tenella* (2–6). All are delicate, low-growing, feathery-flowered grasses that often occur in dense colonies in open areas in temperate and highland hamlets.

They are eaten by sheep, horses and cattle.

8. **Mosote** (-**tik, -altik**) (**mosote jobel**) is the sand bur *Cenchrus brownii* (4–6) and *C. pilosus* (1–4), a tall grass with a dense, terminal inflorescence with seeds that have stiff spines that can make walking in sandals very painful. It is common in savannas, open slopes, and cornfields in temperate and lowland areas.

It is eaten by horses and cattle.

9. **Puj-'akan jobel,** "hollow-stemmed grass" (**puj-'ut jobel**), is *Arundinella deppeana* (2–3), a tall, few-stemmed grass with a large, feathery inflorescence that is common on open slopes and disturbed ground or second growth in temperate hamlets.

It is eaten by horses.

10. **Tzajal jobel,** "red grass" (-**tik**) (**tzajal nich jobel**), refers to *Aristida schiedeana* (1–2), *Bouteloua media* (1–3), *Elionurus tripsacoides* (1–4), *Muhlenbergia spiciformis* (1–2), and *Rhynchelytrum repens* (4–7), all delicately branched grasses with feathery inflorescences and a reddish tinge to the foliage and flowers. They are common in savannas and disturbed, grassy slopes in temperate and lowland areas.

Aristida schiedeana, B. media, and *M. spiciformis* are used for thatching fieldhouses. They are eaten by sheep, horses, and cattle.

11. **Tzukum jobel,** "caterpillar grass" (**koryo tzukum jobel, pech'ajtik tzajal jobel, yisim be jobel**), refers to

Oplismenus burmanni (2–2), *Setaria gracilis* (3–4), and *Setariopsis auricualta* (1–1). These are slender, weedy grasses with short, dense, terminal inflorescences that resemble woolly caterpillars and stick to one's clothing. They are common in disturbed and second growth situations throughout the township.

Extended range: *Sporobolus indicus.*

12. **Tzuntzun jobel,** "messy-haired grass" (**k'ik'i jobel, tzatzal t'ul jobel**), refers to *Brachiaria reptans* (1–6) and *Dichanthelium laxiflorum* (1–4), small, tufted grasses with a delicate inflorescence of small, round florets. They are very common in the grassy understory of pine-oak forest of temperate and highland areas.

Extended range: *Arthraxon quartinianus.*

13. **Yisim be,** "path whiskers" (-**tik**) (**yisim be jobel**), is a non-Linnaean alliance that includes *Cyperus hermaphroditus* (1–3), *C. virens* (1–2), *Oplismenus burmanni* (1–1), *Setaria gracilis* (1–3), and *Sporobolus indicus* (1–1). These grasses or grass-like plants with terminal clusters of spikes, or a long dense terminal spike of grass florets, occur throughout the township.

"Uch'ul Vo' Set"

The "**uch'ul vo' set**" is comprised of 11 generics. These plants are mostly characterized by tuberous roots, terminal inflorescences, and parallel-veined leaves.

1. **Bukaro** (-**tik, -altik**) (**bukero, radióla**) refers to the gladiolus and its relative *Crocosmia.*

Specifics: 2.

   a. **Bukaro** is the common gladiolus *Gladiolus hortulanus* (3–5). This name refers to the unimproved form with small flowers and short flower stems (105 cm).

For planting techniques and use see **radióla,** which has largely replaced **bukaro.**

   (1) **Chijal bukaro,** "striped gladiolus," with intense red flowers streaked and speckled with yellow.
   (2) **Sakil bukaro,** with white flowers.
   (3) **Tzajal bukaro,** (**batz'i bukaro**) with red flowers.

   b. **K'ox bukaro,** "small gladiolus" (**chak-lakan te' nichim, nichim chak-lakan te', santa lusi'ya, vach' nichim**), is *Crocosmia* × *crocosmiiflora* (2–4), an orange-flowered, equitant-leaved plant that is cultivated occasionally and is commonly escaped and established in wild situations in moist, temperate, and highland locations.

It is usually large and erect with numerous strap-shaped leaves, 1–2 cm wide. The inflorescence is a spike of orange-red flowers, 3–4 cm long, with a slender curved tube and spreading lobes.

The bulbs are planted in the rainy season in all but one of the highland communities.

The flowers are used for altar decoration and infrequently in hamlet chapel flower changes, especially in Paste'. They are sold at market in San Cristóbal and Tuxtla.

2. **Jol koy**, "**koy** tuber" (**koykoy, koyoy**), refers to *Tigridia*. These all have long, plicate leaves and spherical corms.

Specifics: 3.

a. **Batz'i jol koy**, "genuine **koy** tuber," is the Mexican shell flower *Tigridia pavonia* (9–12), conspicuous with its large, mottled, bright-orange flowers. The leaves are linear, plicate, and about 13–25 mm wide. The flowers are long pedicellate and 6–7 cm across. The fruit is a capsule about 3–5 cm long, 1 cm broad. *Ladinos* cultivate it ornamentally. It does not occur in the wild but is often adventive around dwellings in temperate and highland localities.

A few people transplant the roots along streams.

Men and women gather the "cold" bulbs, but they should be careful to refer to the plant as **is-ak'**, "potato," rather than its real name, lest the bulbs become bitter. These are boiled with salt and chili or are roasted. They may also be mixed with potatoes for **vokol ich**. Occasionally the "cold" tender leaves are boiled as greens, seasoned with salt and chili.

Children play with the flowers, carrying them around in bunches and tearing them to shreds. The flower stem makes a good whistle. The tepal is called **xchikin**, "its ear," and in Chamula children are warned not to play with the flowers, lest their ears get infected.

Extended range: *Rigidella orthantha*.

b. **Sakil jol koy**, "white **koy** tuber," is *Tigridia chiapensis* (1–2), a plant with white flowers that is locally abundant in meadows in the highlands. The flowers are several in each spathe with perianth segments about 2 cm long, white, spotted with yellow and purple. The capsules are 2.5 cm long. The leaves are narrow, 0.6 cm wide.

c. **Te'tikal jol koy**, "wild **koy** tuber" (**jok'leb vonon, jol koy ch'o**), is *Tigridia hallbergii* (2–2), a plant with a pendulous, purple flowers occuring in the temperate and highland pine-oak forests. The leaves are narrow, about 6–18 mm wide, perianth segments are 15–20 mm long.

3. **Jutuju** (**orkíya**) is *Malaxis fastigata* (1–1), a bulbous, terrestrial orchid with a terminal cluster of small, green flowers. This small orchid has one or two broadly ovate or broadly elliptic leaves, which sheath the stem below and expand near the middle. The flowers are in an umbrella-shaped raceme on pedicels, 13–15 mm long. It occurs in the grassy understory of pine-oak forests in temperate and highland areas.

As a remedy for boils (**chakal, vo'an**), the leaves are smashed and ground, burnt in a bowl, and applied hot.

4. **Kola**, "glue" (**kola tz'i'lel, kolail vob, palma nichim, sera tz'i'lel**), is *Govenia liliacea* (5–9), a terrestrial orchid with a thick, fleshy tuber and white flowers. Several brown papery sheaths surround the base of the stem from which the two large leaves arise. The leaves are elliptic or oblanceolate, acute at the tip, plicate, 21–45 cm or more long. The peduncle also arises from the basal sheaths and is as long or longer than the leaves. The flowers are white, 1.5–3 cm long, in a terminal cylindrical raceme. It occurs on shady slopes in pine-oak and evergreen cloud forests.

As a glue used in making fiddles and guitars, 2–3 roots are boiled in water laced with a bit of cane liquor. Or to glue musical instruments and paper, the root is peeled and the juice smeared on where needed.

Extended range: *Bletia* sp. and *Cranichis trilobata*.

5. **Kola tz'i'lel**, "glue plant" (**p'uk, skolail svob antivo**), is the large terrestrial orchid *Govenia superba* (4–6). It has a thick, fleshy tuber, plicate leaves, and dirty-yellow flowers in a terminal raceme. It differs from *G. liliacea* in flower color in having a more elongated raceme with many more flowers. It is similar in all other aspects. It occurs on wet slopes in pine-oak and evergreen cloud forests in temperate and highland areas.

It was once used for glue, as above.

6. **Me' putzul**, "mother inflated" (**orkíya nichim**), is *Sobralia decora* (2–6), a long, woody-stemmed orchid with large, terminal, sessile purple flowers, 5–6 cm long. The leaves are alternate, ovate and plicate, clasping at the base, 15–25 cm long. It occurs around rock outcrops in steep ravines in temperate hamlets. It is sold by children along the highway.

Extended range: *Bletia reflexa*.

7. **Putzul**, "inflated," is *Cypripedium irapeanum* (2–5), the ladies' slipper orchid. It is a tall plant arising from a dense tuber. The leaves are ovate and plicate, alternate on the stem, 5–15 cm long; the flowers are large, 8–11 cm long, yellow, and inflated, borne in the axils of the leaves. It occurs in the grassy understory of pine-oak forests of temperate hamlets.

The flowers are gathered and sold. Children turn the flower inside out and inflate it.

Extended range: *Calceolaria tripartita*.

8. **Radióla** (**-tik**) is the improved form of the common gladiolus *Gladiolus hortulanus* (1–1). When first introduced it was termed "**pino bukaro**," "fine gladiolus," but that name has been superseded by **radióla**.

Gladiolas are extensively cultivated in most of the temperate and all but one of the highland communities between the rows of corn and in separate hoed ground. The tubers are dug up in January and left to dry in the sun for 1–2 weeks. The skins are removed so the tuber will not rot. The tuber is allowed to sprout before planting. Some say the bulb should be planted at the full of the moon so it will continue to be strong and not rot after flowering.

There is great variation in planting schedules and techniques. Gladiolas planted in late April or May provide two pickings: (1) July, (2) August. Gladiolas planted in midsummer provide flowers for All Souls' Day. People with access to irrigation also plant in the dry season (November–February). Most gardeners do not provide fertilizer, though some enrich the soil with compost, sheep manure, and ashes to prevent the june bug grubs from eating the tubers. The tubers are planted anywhere from 15–40 cm apart in rows 20–40 cm distant. A few

266

gardeners hill the plants. Two pickings are possible.

These flowers are used by ordinary people and religious officials to decorate the altar. Each steward gives the sacristans funds to buy gladiolas for Sacred Heart Day decorations. They are almost ubiquitous in hamlet chapel flower changes. The flowers are sold at market in San Cristóbal and Tuxtla. "Fine" gladiolas are the principal flower bought by Zinacantecs in Mexico City for sale in Tuxtla.

Specifics: 5

    a. **K'anal radióla**, the yellow form, grown locally and seldom bought in Mexico City.

    b. **Moraro radióla**, the magenta form.

    c. **Sak-vilan radióla** (**rosaro radióla**), the pink form.

    d. **Sakil radióla**, the red form.

9. **Tz'emeni'** (**-tik**) (**tz'emeni**) refers to sprawling herbs with bright flowers and clasping, parallel-veined leaves. They are all spiderworts (Commelinaceae) and orchids.

Specifics: 6.

    a. **Batz'i tz'emeni'**, "genuine **tz'emeni'** (**sakil tz'emeni'**), refers to *Tinantia erecta* (2–3), *Tripogandra disgrega* (3–6), *T. grandiflora* (1–2), and *T. montana* (2–3). These are thick-stemmed herbs with purple or white flowers, often rooting at the nodes and spreading to cover large areas of disturbed ground in temperate and highland areas. The leaves are alternate, parallel-veined, sheathing the succulent stem, ovate, elliptic to oblong-lanceolate. The inflorescences are terminal and umbellate or subumbellate, with 3-petaled flowers, 10–30 mm broad.

To stop hair from falling out, *Tinantia erecta* is bruised in cold water and the "cold" water used to bathe the hair.

    b. **K'ox tz'emeni'**, "small **tz'emeni'**," refers to *Aploleia multiflora* (1–4) and *Tripogandra angustifolia* (1–5). These are very delicate herbs with white or purple flowers that occur on rocky slopes in exposed areas of temperate hamlets. The trimerous flowers are in terminal inflorescences. The leaves are parallel-veined, sheathing, and either linear as in *T. angustifolia* or oblong-lanceolate or oblong ovate in *A. multiflora*.

    c. **Muk'ta tz'emeni'**, "large **tz'emeni'**," is *Campelia zanonia* (1–5), a tall, erect herb with strap-like leaves clasping the stem, 10–35 cm long, and large, purple, fleshy berries. The flowers are fasciculate, subtended by two bracts. They are trimerous, white, lilac or pink, with petals 9–10 mm long. It occurs in the understory of tropical deciduous forest in lowland and temperate areas.

    d. **O'lol tz'emeni'**, "medium **tz'emeni'**" (**tz'emeni'al ba ton** in part), refers to *Cranichis trilobata* (1–5), *Erythrodes secunda* (1–1), *Habenaria clypeata* (1–1), and *H. quinqueseta* (1–3), tuberous-rooted, white-flowered, terrestrial orchids of the grassy understory of pine-oak forests of temperate and highland areas. The leaves are alternate, sheathing, distributed along the stem or basal as in *Erythrodes*. The small flowers are

borne in terminal spikes.

    e. **Tzajal tz'emeni'**, "red **tz'emeni'**" (**kilajtik uch'ul vo'**, **tz'emeni'al ch'en**), is *Epidendrum radicans* (2–3), a succulent-leaved, spreading (with stems to 2 m long) orchid with terminal clusters of red-orange flowers. It occurs in second growth and on cliffs in temperate hamlets.

The stalk is used as a toy whistle by shepherds.

    f. **Yaxal tz'emeni'**, "blue **tz'emeni'**" (**ik'al tz'emeni'**, **uch'ul vo' tz'i'lel**, **bik'tal tz'emeni'**, **mis tz'i'**), refers to *Commelina alpestris* (2–2), *C. coelestis* (4–8), *C. diffusa* (4–5), *C. erecta* (3–5), *Cymbispatha commelinoides* (4–7), *Tradescantia crassifolia* (1–2), and *T. guatemalensis* (1–2), spreading or erect herbs with terminal trimerous blue or lavender flowers and alternate thin, elliptic, parallel-veined clasping leaves. They occur in second growth, disturbed ground, and in the understory of pine-oak and evergreen cloud forests in temperate and highland areas.

In 1748 the priest of Zinacantán noted that **mataliste** (*C. erecta*) was used as a medicinal herb (Monrroy y Calcadilla, 1748).

To induce a sick child to nurse, a small bunch of *Commelina diffusa* is brewed and the child is bathed with the "cold" water twice a day for two days.

10. **Uch'ul vo'**, "water receptacle" (**-tik**, **-altik**) (**uch'ob vo'**), refers to the fleshy pseudo-bulbed orchids. It appears that any of 100+ species of these plants would receive this designation. The pseudo-bulb, a fleshy storage organ that is really a swollen stem contrasts with the true-bulbed, terrestrial orchids. These are always treated differently, i.e., **jutuju**, **kola**, **kola tz'i'lel**, **yok' vakax**. The pseudo-bulb species are epiphytic or saxicolous.

Specifics: 8.

    a. **Kilajtik uch'ul vo'**, "pendent water receptacle" (**chi uch'ul vo'**, **volajtik uch'ul vo'**), is *Epidendrum parkinsonianum* (2–3), a large pendent epiphytic orchid. The pseudobulbs are one-leaved and enclosed in a translucent sheath. The leaves are fleshy, linear lanceolate, up to 5 dm long, 1–3.5 cm wide. The flowers are large, showy and fragrant. The spreading petals are white and yellow, linear lanceolate, and 5–8 cm long. The flowers are in groups of 1–3 on a small peduncle enclosed within the leaf sheaths. It occurs in the pine-oak forests of the temperate and highland regions.

    b. **K'ox uch'ul vo'**, "small water receptacle" (**volajtik uch'ul vo'**), is *Encyclia ochracea* (5–6). This is a slender, ascending epiphytic orchid, 7–35 cm tall, with narrow leaves, 6–15 mm wide. The flowers are yellow, about 10–15 mm long, in a many-flowered raceme. The capsule is ellipsoid with three narrow wings, 12–20 mm long. It occurs in the pine-oak forests of the temperate and highland regions.

Thirsty shepherds chew the "cold" bulb.

Extended range: *Leochilus pygmaeus* and *Pitcairnia breed-lovei.*

c. **Muk'ta uch'ul vo',** "large water receptacle," is *Epidendrum arbuscula* (4–3). This is a loosely branched epiphytic orchid with purple or reddish brown flowers. The leaves are clustered at the ends of the branches and are spreading, elliptic in shape, up to 16 cm long, 2–5 cm wide. The flowers are 2.5–3 cm long, in a terminal raceme. The capsules are ovoid, 6-ribbed, about 5 cm long. It occurs in the pine-oak forest and evergreen cloud forest of the temperate and highland regions.

Children play with the flowers.

Extended range: *Encyclia chondylobulbon* and *Smilacina scilloides.*

d. **Sakil uch'ul vo',** "white water receptacle" (**tzajal uch'ul vo'**), refers to *Encyclia* spp. (1–1) and *E. varicosa* (1–3). The latter is a perennial epiphytic or terrestrial orchid with narrow, acute, distichous leaves, 4–12 cm long, 4–12 mm wide. The leaf sheaths are black-dotted and completely cover the stem. The delicate white and brown-maroon flowers are in panicles and 1.5–2.5 cm long. They occur in the pine-oak and evergreen cloud forests of the temperate and highland regions.

The bulb is boiled by school children and used for glue.

Extended range: *Stelis* sp.

e. **Setajtik uch'ul vo',** "disk-shaped water receptacle," is *Meiracyllium trinasutum* (1–4). This small magenta-flowered orchid is prostrate and creeping on large branches of trees. The small broadly elliptic to orbicular leaves are sessile, 2–4 cm long, 2–2.5 cm wide, and very fleshy. The several terminal flowers are on a short peduncle about 1 cm long. The petals are elliptic, acute, and about 10 mm long, 3 mm wide. The capsule is narrowly ellipsoid, about 1.5 cm long. It occurs in the pine-oak forests of the highlands.

f. **Uch'ul vo'al ba ton,** "rock top water receptacle" (**yuch'ul vo' bolom**), is *Odontoglossum bictoniense* (1–3). This is a slender, white, lavender- or pink-lipped orchid with long linear leaves, 1.5–5.5 cm wide. The flowers are showy and numerous, about 3–3.5 cm long, produced on a long, uncrowded raceme. It occurs on rock outcrops and as an epiphyte in pine-oak forsts and evergreen cloud forest in the highlands.

Extended range: *Bletia* sp.

g. **Yuch'ul vo' bolom,** "jaguar's water receptacle" (**k'anal uch'ul vo'** in part), refers to large-bulbed *Encyclia, Gongora, Lycaste,* including *L. cruenta* (1–4), and *Stanhopea* that occur in montane rain forest and pine-oak forests, mostly in the temperate regions. The bulbs are not considered to be good for quenching thirst.

h. **Yuch'ul vo' j'ik'al,** "spook's water receptacle" (**yuch'ul vo' antivo, yuch'ul vo' chuch**), refers to *Encyclia cochleatum* (1–2) and *Epidendrum ciliare* (1–1). The former is a stout orchid with 1–3 oblong lanceolate leaves, 15–30 cm long or more, 1.5–9.5 cm wide. The flowers are racemose and showy. The sepals and petals are linear lanceolate and yellow and brown, about 2.5–7 cm long. The broad entire lip is deep. The capsule is ellipsoid, 2–4 cm long, with three wings, and is usually recurved or pendent. *Epidendrum ciliare* is a white and yellow-flowered orchid with narrow linear-lanceolate petals and conspicuous oblong bracts subtending the flowers, which are arranged alternately in the raceme. These orchids occur in the rock outcrops of montane rain forest and pine-oak forest of the temperate zone.

Extended range: *Maxillaria variabilis.*

11. **Yat kotom,** "coati's penis" (**-tik, -altik**) (**stz'itesob at, vale' tz'i'lel**), is *Cyrtopodium punctatum* (4–5), a terrestrial or rock-growing orchid with a long, fleshy pseudobulb up to 1 m long and an elongate inflorescence of large, yellow and purple or red blossoms with petals, 10–15 cm long. The leaves are linear, plicate, distichous. The capsule is oblong oval up to 8 cm long, 3–5 cm in diameter. It occurs in tropical deciduous forest of lowland and temperate areas.

During weeding and clearing, care should be taken not to disturb these orchids, because if they die, so will the corn farmer. The "hot" pseudobulbs are chewed once a day for three days by boys who want to lengthen their penises. The pseudobulbs may also be rubbed on one's coccyx for the same purpose. To increase one's virility, 13 shavings may be cut off the bulbs and soaked in cold water. The amount of water in the bowl should just cover the first knuckle of one's finger. If more than this amount is drunk, the potion will cause sex madness. They are considered to be more effective than wild yams.

Extended range: *Lasiacis sorghoidea.*

12. **Yok' vakax,** "cow tongue" (**uch'ul vo'al ton, k'anal pech'e-'ok, nichim joj**), refers to *Spiranthes aurantiaca* (1–2) and *S. cinnabarina* (5–5), orange-flowered, fleshy, gray-green-leaved orchids of grassy slopes in temperate hamlets. Spikes of large, pubescent, tubular flowers, 2–2.5 cm long, and sub-tended by a foliaceous bract, are characteristic of *S. aurantiaca.* The leaves are clasping and sheathing the stem, elliptic oblong, 2.5–5 cm wide. *Spiranthes cinnabarina* is smaller in stature, has smaller flowers, 1.2–2.0 cm long, shorter spikes, and shorter narrower leaves.

They are eaten by cattle and horses.

"Vo'tus Set"

The "vo'tus set" is comprised of seven generics, narrow or finely divided-leaved herbs, often very rank smelling.

1. **Nochleb vonon,** "bumblebee perch" (**-tik**) (**jipleb vonon, luchleb vonon, nakleb vonon, nochleb tz'unun tz'i'lel**), is *Cuphea aequipetala* (14–17), a wiry-branched herb frequently

prostrate or decumbent with tubular, purple flowers characteristically visited by bumblebees. The tubular calyx is about 11–15 mm long and pubescent with rather stiff black hairs. The leaves are sessile, opposite or verticillate, narrowly ovate, 8–28 mm long. This plant is common on grassy slopes and disturbed ground in temperate and highland areas.

It has a variety of medicinal uses: As a remedy for nightmares, the shaman brews a small bunch. A cup of the "hot" tea is drunk before breakfast for three days. A half cup of this same tea is taken before breakfast by a child, for stomach ache. For diarrhea, too, a cup is drunk before breakfast and lunch, or before each meal. A tea of the plant, brewed together with its roots, and sometimes with **poxil tza'nel**, relieves "white" dysentery. A cup is drunk before breakfast for three days. For bloody dysentery, the plant is bruised in cold water and the infusion drunk. To remove a dark scar or the black patches that appear on some women's faces after childbirth, a handful of flowers is rubbed seven or eight times on the blemish.

Extended range: *Buchnera pusilla, Castilleja integrifolia, Cuphea wrightii, Gaura tripetala, Justicia clinopodium,* and *Lopezia racemosa.* As a remedy for diarrhea and nausea, a small bunch of *J. clinopodium* is brewed. A half cup of the "hot" tea is drunk before breakfast for three days.

2. **Tzitz** (-**tik**) (**tzitzal ul, tzitzil ul**) refers to *Tagetes lucida* (13–19), perennial herbs with thin, wiry stems, strongly scented, narrow leaves, 5–10 cm long, and flat-topped, terminal clusters of orange-yellow daisy flowers about 1 cm broad. These are common in the grassy understory of pine-oak forests in temperate and highland areas.

In the colonial dictionary the friar gives **batz'i tzitz** and **tzitz** as terms for "wild fennel," which perhaps denoted this plant.

> Well, there was a bird that lived in the woods. Maybe the bird was like a person.
>
> Well, it traveled in the woods carrying its flower. "What kind of flower are you carrying?" it was asked.
>
> "I'm not. It isn't a flower," it said.
>
> "What is it, what is it?"
>
> "It isn't a flower. This is just a plant," it said.
>
> "But it has to have a name," said (the person).
>
> "It does indeed!"
>
> "But what kind of plant is it?"
>
> "This can be eaten."
>
> "Ah," he said, "How is it eaten?"
>
> "It is soaked in water," it said.
>
> "Ah, tell me what it's called."
>
> "Listen, I'll tell you," it said. "**Tzijtzij ul, tzijtzij ul**," it said as it went off.
>
> "Ah, **tzijtzij ul** is its name."
>
> "**Tzijtzij ul**, indeed!"
>
> "Is it eaten in corn gruel?"
>
> "Ah, it's eaten in corn gruel, soaked in water," it said.
>
> "Well, do you know how to eat it?"
>
> "I do."

> "What do you eat, do you drink that **tzijtzij** gruel?"
>
> "As for me, I just take this along. Everybody hears what I say as I go."
>
> "What do you eat, then?" he asked.
>
> "I don't eat anything much. I eat bugs." It said that it flicked up leaves, that that was where it found bugs. It just swallowed one after another.
>
> "Well, then you don't eat what you are carrying then?" it was asked.
>
> "I don't eat it, I just show it around," it said.
>
> "Isn't it edible?"
>
> "Why shouldn't it be edible?"
>
> "But what's it like, I can't see it."
>
> "Well, I'll give you one to see. I'll give you a sign," it said.
>
> "What kind of a sign?"
>
> "I'll give you its flower," it said.
>
> "Well, what's its flower like?"
>
> "I'll give it to you," it said. Quickly it drew one. (The junco) drew it. It turned out red and yellow just like a marsh marigold.
>
> "Ah," he said. "Well, all right, then, I'll take it," said the person who had received it.
>
> "Take it, try it out, soak it in water," it said.
>
> "Ah, fine!" he said. He soaked it in water. Eh, don't you see the wonderful fragrance of the marsh marigold remained....

Tagetes lucida is occasionally transplanted to the yard in the rainy season.

A handful or three plants are ground on the **metate**, soaked in water, and added to corn gruel, but if the cook is too liberal with this "hot" seasoning one may fall ill. The flavor is similar to cinnamon. It may also be brewed and sweetened with sugar as a coffee substitute. It may be kept dried for 4 to 5 weeks for convenience as it grows in few places. It is sold at market.

3. **Tzitz pox**, "**tzitz** medicine" (**chikin ba, poxil tza'nel, spoxil yul j'alnom, vach' t'ul**), is *Hypericum uliginosum* (6–8), a thin-stemmed herb with small opposite, linear appressed leaves, 1–2 cm long, and terminal clusters of bright yellow flowers. The capsule is ovoid, acute at the apex, 5–6 mm long. These are common on overgrazed, grassy slopes in highland areas.

As a remedy for malaria, a "hot" tea of this plant is brewed. The same tea may be taken for swelling. A small cup is drunk from one to three times a day. It may be taken over a period of a month. As a remedy for "cold wind," a handful of stems is brewed together with brown sugar, rue, and **tan pox**. A bowlful of the "hot" tea is drunk before meals for three days. A postpartum mother may be given corn gruel, unsweetened, but seasoned with this herb and chili. For further medicinal uses cf. **tan pox**.

Extended range: *Centaurium brachycalyx, Gymnolaena chiapasana,* and *Linum schiedeanum.*

4. **Tzitz tz'i'lel**, "**tzitz** plant" (**tzitz tzoj tob** in part), refers to

Crusea diversifolia (1–2), *L. nelsonii* (1–2), *L. schiedeanum* (1–2), *Pectis prostrata* (1–1), and *Tagetes filifolia* (1–2), very delicate, low-growing herbs of the grassy understory of pine-oak forests of temperate and highland areas. They have terminal, yellow and white flowers.

As a remedy for stomach ache (**k'ux o'onil, k'ux ch'util**), a small bunch of *C. diversifolia* is brewed with brown sugar. One or two spoonfuls of this "hot" tea are taken before meals for one day.

Extended range: *Cuphea utriculosa.*

5. **Tzutzub** (**lok'esob jolobil, poxil majbenal, skventa jtaleltik, tzitz te',** and **tz'itz'op nich,** all in part) refers to *Brickellia scoparia* (1–1), *Linum mexicanum* (3–6), and *Lythrum lanceolatum* (6–7), three superficially similar plants with tall (to 1 m), thin, tough stems, linear leaves and perennial, underground rootstocks. They all occur in open areas in pine-oak forests of temperate and highland areas.

Women cut the stems and scrape off the bark for use as bodkins. *Lythrum lanceolatum* may be brewed and the "cold" tea taken to relieve **majbenal.**

6. **Vo'tus** (**-tik, -altik**) refers to marigolds, *Tagetes.*

Nearly every temperate and highland household cultivates marigolds on a small scale. The dry plant may be hung on a corral post or on a peach tree in the corn field so that the seeds will scatter. Marigold seeds are scattered in the corral, in burnt or hoed fallow ground and between the rows of corn in the cornfield in the rainy season (primarily in June). When the cornfield is weeded care is taken not to disturb the marigolds.

Specifics: 4.

   a. **Antzil vo'tus,** "female marigold" (**potzan, tzeb vo'tus, tzebal vo'tus**), refers to the double-flowered forms of *Tagetes erecta* (3–2). The two predominant color forms are recognized as **k'anal,** "yellow" and **tzajal,** "red."

To relieve a child's night sweats, a tea made from the yellow flowers is drunk or the child is bathed. A "hot" tea of the leaves may be taken for constipation (**makel**). No shaman is required. For decoration, these double-flowered forms are much preferred. On All Souls' Day three bunches of yellow marigolds are tied to the household cross and one bunch to the grave cross. These marigolds are used by the elders, stewards, and stewards-royal for the flower change on All Souls' Day. Each steward provides a large basket, half "red" marigolds and half geraniums, for the Fiesta of Our Lady of the Rosary. Two small baskets of "red" marigolds are provided by the publicans to decorate the chapel of Our Lord of Esquipulas. The elders adorn their altar with one small basket. "Red" marigolds are also used for the Fiesta of Our Lady of the Rosary in Atz'am, Elan Vo', Na Chij, Paste', and Sek'emtik. In Atz'am one bunch is provided by each of the elders and stewards to adorn the censers that are lowered into the salt well.

Yellow marigolds replace the "red" marigolds in Zinacantán Center for All Souls' Day. They are used in Apas, Atz'am, Bik'it Joyijel, Chak Toj, Elan Vo', Na Chij, Naben Chauk, Paste', and Sak Lum.

The flowers may be resold and are sold at market.

For further use cf. **k'anal sat mes.**

   b. **Kaxlan vo'tus,** "castilian marigold" (**muruch' potzil nichim**), refers to the modern yellow pompom types of *Tagetes erecta* (2–3) that are cultivated especially by *ladinos* in their yards.

They are grown by a few people in Atz'am and are used to adorn the altar, especially on the Fiesta of Our Lady of the Rosary, but also on All Souls' Day. They are sold at market.

   c. **Kelem vo'tus,** "boy marigold" (**krem vo'tus**), refers to the single-flowered forms of *Tagetes erecta* (3–2). These are cultivated and also occur naturally in cornfields and disturbed ground. **K'anal,** "yellow," and **tzajal,** "red" varieties are recognized.

To relieve a cough, the leaves are brewed with orange rind. The flowers have the same use as those of **antzil vo'tus,** though they are considered to be decidedly second-rate. A smart merchant will mix them together with the double variety.

   d. **K'ox vo'tus,** "small marigold" (**vo'tus ulo', vo'tus ch'o**), is *Tagetes elongata* (5–8) and *T. tenuifolia* (2–4), wild-occurring species of open areas in pine-oak and evergreen cloud forests. This marigold is branched above, with pinnate leaves, 6–12 cm long. The leaflets are elliptic, about 1–4 cm long, serrate. The flowers are bright yellow, terminal, with rays 8–10 mm long and the involucre 1.5–2 cm long.

Extended range: *Dyssodia papposa* and *T. foetidissima.*

7. **Vo'tus tz'i'lel,** "marigold plant," is *Schkuhria pinnata* (1–3), a delicately branched herb with yellow flowers similar to *Tagetes.* The leaves are alternate, filiform, 8–25 mm long. The flowers are terminal at the ends of an openly branched inflorescence. The heads are 6–8 mm long, 6–8 mm broad. It is common in disturbed areas in the highlands.

"Yama Chauk Set"

The "**yama chauk** set" is a grouping of 13 generics, herbs and large subshrubs, most of which have umbellate inflorescences, large, bipinnately dissected leaves, and hollow stems.

1. **Chichik'uy** (**-tik, -altik**) (**chichik'u', chichik'ul, chichilk'un**) refers to *Piqueria pilosa* (2–7) and *P. trinervia* (7–12), erect herbs with thin branches and terminal, flat-topped clusters of small, white flowers, about 2–3 mm broad. The leaves are opposite, short petiolate ovate with serrate margins, 2.5–7 cm long. It is very common in second growth and disturbed ground, especially in yards and cornfields in temperate and highland areas.

As a remedy for rabies, the tips are brewed. A cup of the "cold" tea is drunk once a day for three days. As a remedy for athlete's foot (**chi okol**), a small bunch of the "cold" plant is placed between the toes. To cure a rabid dog, a small bunch is bruised in salt water, and the "cold" infusion administered three or four times a day for two days. A poisoned dog may be given the same infusion to which lime juice has been added, after which the dog is bathed in the remaining water. As a remedy for "wind" in sheep, the plant is crushed in cold water and administered. The leaves are used for bone break. Flower growers wrap their bundles of flowers in this plant for protection during transport.

Extended range: *Sabazia sarmentosa.*

2. **Enkaje** refers to *Ammi majus* (1–2), *Conium maculatum* (1–2), and *Daucus carota* (1–1), tall, hollow-stemmed herbs with finely divided leaves and terminal, flat-topped umbellate inflorescences with small white flowers. They occur as weeds in disturbed ground in highland areas. No recognition of the poisonous properties of *C. maculatum* was recorded or that *D. carota* were feral plants of garden carrot (**sanorya**).

A few Zinacantecs in Apas, Na Chij, and Naben Chauk occasionally sow the seeds of *A. majus* in their yards. The flowers of each species are used for altar decoration.

3. **Inojo** (**castillan tzitz***, **inajo, inejo**) is fennel *Foeniculum vulgare* (5–7), a tall, aromatic herb with hollow stems, very finely divided leaves with an expanded, clasping petiole. The inflorescence is a terminal umbel with rays from 2.5 to 7 cm long. The flowers are very small and yellow. It occurs as a weed along roadsides and disturbed ground in temperate and highland areas.

Fennel was one of the plants introduced into Zinacantán 1545, sent by Fray Jordan de Piamonte from Oaxaca (Ximenes, 1929, 1:423).

A few people in Santa Rosa, most of the temperate, and all of the highland communities transplant young fennel plants to their yards or corrals in the rainy season. They may protect them from chickens with a stake encirclement. Young plants should not be cut, lest they die.

Possibly when the priest of Zinacantán noted the use of **eneldo**, or dill, as a remedy for "wind" in 1797, he was referring to the closely similar fennel, as dill is unknown here now (de Leon y Goicoechea, 1797).

Fennel has a variety of medicinal uses. As a remedy for **majbenal**, caused by anger, the tips are brewed with white salt. One cup of the "medium" tea is drunk. A half cupful of this same tea may be taken for heartburn (**me'-vinik**), before breakfast for three days. For **majbenal**, one cup of "cold" tea, without salt, may also be taken at bedtime and again before breakfast. Alternatively, for anger (**sk'ak'al ko'ontik**), fennel may be brewed together with corn silk and sweet lemon leaves. It may also be brewed in cane liquor for a "medium" tea or bruised in cane liquor for a "cold" infusion. As additional remedies for heartburn, cane liquor may be added to fennel tea or the fennel tips may be brewed with refined sugar and burnt tortillas. For further medicinal uses cf. **batz'i chijil te', tzajal nichim**. Occasionally fennel may be bought at the market.

4. **Jok'leb tzo'op tz'unun**, "hummingbird nest perch" (**korneta, tan ok tz'i'lel**), is *Digiticalia chiapensis* (3–3), a tall, hollow-stemmed, glabrous herb common in second growth in temperate hamlets. The leaves are large, 6–12 cm long,

lobed into triangular or oblong lobes. The inflorescence is a large terminal panicle of white flowers, 6–7 mm broad.

To reduce fever, a small bunch is brewed and a half cup of the "cold" tea is drunk before breakfast and lunch for one day.

5. **Keb chij**, "deer burp" or "sheep burp" (**ch'ix tz'i'lel, ch'ix vo tz'i'lel, poxil chakal, sakil ch'ix**), refers to *Eryngium carlinae* (3–3), *E. ghiesbreghtii* (3–6), and *E. longirameum* (1–1). These are perennial herbs with cordate-based triangular-ovate leaves, 10 cm long or less, on long petioles. The minute flowers are crowded into a subglobose head subtended by rigid, acute, bluish silver lanceolate bracts; *E. carlinae* is very similar but the leaves are oblanceolate or obovate, 3–10 cm long, attenuate at the base, and sharply serrate. The flowering heads are conic or subglobose subtended by white or bluish spine-tipped bracts. They are common in the grassy understory of pine-oak forests of temperate and highland areas.

As a remedy for boils (**chakal**), a small bunch of *E. ghiesbreghtii* is brewed. The "hot" liquid is used to bathe the affected part three times daily for two or three days. As a remedy for mange (**sep'**) the leaves are dried on the fire and applied to the affected part to kill "its animals." It is considered dangerous to handle these leaves without washing one's hands before eating. This plant and, to a lesser degree, the two other species, may be fatal to sheep if eaten.

Extended range: *Adenocaulon lyratum.* The leaves may be ground and the powder used to stanch bleeding. As a remedy for gangrene (**mos**), the leaves are dried on the fire together with those of **k'axib jobel** and **k'ox klavel**. These, together with the dried bodies of a false chameleon, a marsh alligator lizard, and a blue-bellied lizard, are applied to the affected part.

6. **Krem pox**, "boy medicine" (**loj-'at pox, mémela tz'i'lel**), is *Micropleura renifolia* (3–7), a small, perennial herb with kidney-shaped leaves, 2–7 cm wide, and terminal, umbellate, minute greenish flowers. The fruit is somewhat kidney-shaped, 2 mm long, 3–4 mm wide. It has one to five fusiform tuberous roots. It is common on grassy slopes in pine-oak forests of highland areas.

A "hot" tea may be taken for swelling, but the main focus of this plant is for women, lacking sons, who do not want to be beaten by their husbands. To induce the birth of sons by warming his wife's uterus, a man may gather a bowlful of tubers. These are ground on the **metate** and brewed with six chilies and two pieces of brown sugar. A cup of the "hot" tea is drunk by his wife before breakfast for three days. Or he may gather nine tubers that are ground, and brewed with brown sugar, black pepper, and 13 chilies. One bowl of the "hot" tea will cause the woman to give birth to nine sons. The leaves are ground into a powder to stanch bleeding.

7. **Kulantu** (**-tik**) is coriander *Coriandrum sativum* (2–5). It is a branched herb with dissected leaves, the segments linear. The small white flowers are arranged in umbels, 2.5–5 cm broad. The fruits are ovoid or globose, about 4 mm long, ribbed. It is a cultivated herb in yards and gardens in Santa Rosa, in all but one of the temperate, and all of the highland

communities. The seeds may be sown in the dry season in corrals, fallow land far from chickens, and in the cornfields. Although some scatter the seeds, most claim that they grow better if planted in rows like radishes, with compost or sheep manure. If planted in the yard they must be fenced in as protection against the chickens. They should not be pulled up by the roots, lest they disappear, and they should not be allowed to go to flower. The plant is available for picking from May to October, but its season may be extended by watering. It is sold and resold at market.

Some used to call this plant **antun,** "anthony." The "cold" leaves are used together with chili to season beef, and a wide variety of wild animals including rats, mice, squirrels, skunks, raccoons, coatis, opossums, rabbits, peccaries, deer, and snails. They are also used, together with chili, to season young watermelon squash, young pumpkin squash, young summer squash and their flowers and tips, young chayotes, potatoes, chayote root, tomatoes, kale, cabbage, beans, and fresh cow peas. The leaves may also be eaten raw. The plants may be kept dried for one month. The seeds are ground and used in the dry season to season corn gruel. Cf. **alavena.**

8. **Kulantu ch'o,** "mouse coriander" (**kulantu tz'i'lel**), is a non-Linnaean alliance of plants resembling coriander. It includes *Apium leptophyllum* (6–8), *Berula erecta* (3–6), *Daucus carota* (wild form) (2–2), *D. montanus* (2–4), *Donnellsmithia juncea* (1–1), *Parthenium hysterophorus* (1–1), and *Petroselinum crispum* (1–1). These are weedy plants occurring throughout the township.

9. **Perejil*** is parsley *Petroselinum crispum* (2–2), an annual or biennial from a fusiform root. The leaves are pinnately divided into pinately lobed ovate leaflets. The flowers are yellow or white and umbellate. It is cultivated in the highlands.

The seeds are sown in November and December, but parsley is a new addition to the market.

10. **Sakil nichim te',** "white-flowered tree," refers to *Jasminum mesnyi* (1–3) and *J. sambac* (1–2). The former is a sprawling, soft-wooded shrub with opposite pinnately compound leaves with three elliptic to lanceolate leaflets, 2–4 cm long. The flowers are large, about 4–4.5 cm broad, yellow, with broad rounded petals. The latter is an erect shrub with opposite entire leaves that are broadly oblong-obovate to broadly elliptic, 3–6 cm long, rounded at the apex. The white, fragrant flowers are densely clustered at the ends of the branches, about 2 cm long and broad. Highland and lowland *ladinos* cultivate these shrubs in their yards and in fencerows. The slips are planted in the rainy season. They use the flowers for altar decoration. The flowers are sold at market. This shrub is classed as a "tree."

11. **Tuturu** (**tzis chauk**) is *Thalictrum guatemalense* (3–4), a large, perennial herb with leaves to 1 m across that are finely dissected like the frond of a fern. The leaflets are broadly obovate to orbicular, lobed at the apex, rounded to subcordate at the base, about 1–3 cm long. The flowers are small, green or

yellowish, the stamens long-exerted, the anthers 5–9 mm long. The fruit is an achene, 4–5 mm long. These occur in moist, open plains in pine-oak and evergreen cloud forests of highland areas.

As a remedy for fever (**k'ok'**) a bunch is brewed and left to cool. A half cup of the "cold" tea is taken. To cure sick chickens, the leaves are bruised in cold water for a "cold" infusion. Children play with the tips.

12. **Tzis chauk,** "thunderbolt fart" (**-tik, -iltik**) (**tzis chitom**), is *Tagetes nelsonii* (7–14), a highland, soft-wooded shrub with very strongly scented herbage, divided leaves with 5 to 15 narrowly elliptic leaflets and flat-topped, terminal clusters of yellow flowers with rays to 15 mm long. It is common along roadsides and in disturbed areas.

As a remedy for "cold" in the limbs, the "hot" plant is bruised in water that may be warmed before bathing the patient with it. As a remedy for soul-loss (**balamil**), the patient may be bathed with a cold infusion of water in which the "hot" plant has been brewed. Its foul odor also serves to drive away the Earth Lord.

Extended range: *Bidens laevis, B. squarrosa,* and *Dyssodia appendiculata.*

13. **Yama chauk,** "thunderbolt's flute" (**-tik, -altik**), is a non-Linnaean alliance including *Aralia humilis* (1–2), *Arracacia bracteata* (3–7), *A. nelsonii* (1–1), *Bocconia arborea* (2–5), *B. frutescens* (3–5), *Coaxana purpurea* (2–4), *Dahlia coccinea* (6–4), *Digiticalia chiapensis* (1–2), *Equisetum myriochaetum* 91–2), *Pedilanthus tithymaloides* (1–4), *Prionosciadium nelsonii* (4–5), *Thalictrum guatemalense* (6–10), and *Valeriana sorbifolia* (1–1). These are tall (to 2 m) herbs or subshrubs with large, hollow or pith-filled stems and pinnately divided, lobed or dissected leaves. They occur in second growth throughout the township.

A man suffering venereal disease gathers 12 plants of *Arracacia bracteata.* They are brewed and the "medium" tea drunk before breakfast for as many days as necessary. The tips may be used in the "steam cure."

"Yax-chel Set"

The "**yax-chel** set" is comprised of nine generics. All are mints or mint-like with opposite, aromatic leaves.

1. **Alavena** (**-tik, -altik**) (**castillan tuil nichim***) refers to the true mints *Mentha.* These are early Spanish introductions from Europe.

Specifics: 2.

    a. **Batz'i alavena,** "genuine mint" (**-tik**) (**ch'ix alavena**), is penny royal *Mentha pulegium* (2–3), a coarsely pubescent-leaved herb once common in adventive situations. It is decumbent with ovate to orbicular, opposite leaves, about 2 cm long, with serrate margins. Zinacantecs note that it neither flowers nor fruits.

In 1797 the priest of Zinacantán noted that **poleo** was used to stanch bleeding (de Leon y Goicoechea, 1797).

It is grown in the lowlands in all but one of the temperate and all of the highland communities. Young plants are transplanted any time of the year, but if in the dry season they should be watered in the late afternoon. If watered they may continue into the rainy season. They may be given sheep manure and ashes when they are planted either in the corral or the yard. They may be planted in an old pot or box and kept under the roof overhang. Penny royal is known to grow for only certain people.

Penny royal must not be refused to a person who asks for it, nor must it be sold, lest its soul depart and the plant die. It was once bartered for mangoes in San Lucas. The disappearance for many years of wild-growing penny royal was caused, according to some, by the sale of the plant to people of San Lucas. Others claim that visitors from San Lucas, Acala, and Chiapa de Corzo stole its soul. Still others maintain that its soul went to the afterworld. It is beginning to reappear now. The "hot" tips are used to flavor beef, pork, **vokol ich chitom**, snails, cabbage, kale, and the mushrooms **bililux** and **chakat'ob**. Together with chili it is used to season snails, peccary, raccoon, squirrel, coati, opossum, armadillo, young watermelon squash, young pumpkin squash, and young summer squash. Together with chili and coriander it is used to season venison, snails, beef, kale, and cabbage. It is also used to flavor bull's blood and the "blood" of the **petate** bull on Epiphany (provided by the Stewards of Our Lady of the Rosary). Farmers traveling to the lowlands may take it along for seasoning. It may be kept dried for 1 to 2 months. The flavor of penny royal is preferred to that of bergamont mint and is said to last longer when dried.

    b. **Ch'ulul alavena**, "smooth mint" (-**tik**), is bergamont mint *Mentha citrata* (1–2), a smooth, glabrous-leaved herb. The leaves are opposite, ovate, about 1.5–3.5 cm long, short petioled, and serrate margins. The stems are 4-sided and reddish or purple.

Bergamont mint is planted in Santa Rosa and in all but one of the temperate and highland communities. Its cultivation and use is identical to that of penny royal except that there is no restriction on its sale.

2. **Alavéna tz'i'lel**, "mint plant," is a non-Linnaean grouping of wild-occuring plants that are similar to mints. Included are *Borreria laevis* (1–1), *Heliotropium angiospermum* (1–4), *Hyptis verticillata* (1–2), *Lantana achyranthifolia* (1–2), *Lippia nodiflora* (1–1), *L. stoechadifolia* (1–2), *Mimulus glabratus* (1–1), *Salvia misella* (1–2), *Scutellaria dumetorum* (1–2), and *Verbena carolina* (1–2). These plants occur throughout the township usually in second growth or disturbed situations.

Zinacantecs note that *L. stoechadifolia* is very resistant to herbicides.

3. **Arvajaka** (-**tik**) (**avrajaka**) refers to the basils *Ocimum*. Specifics: 2.

    a. **Batz'i arvajaka**, "genuine basil," is the introduced and totally cultivated European basil *Ocimum basilicum*

(2–3). It is an annual herb, densely branched with aromatic, opposite elliptic to ovate leaves, 2–4 cm long. The flowers are white or purple-tinged, about 4–5 mm long, borne in whorls in simple terminal racemes. *Ladinos* sow the seeds in the temperate and lowland areas in the rainy season. They use the plants for altar decoration.

It is grown in a few of the temperate communities.

When the saints from Ixtapa and San Lucas visit Zinacantán Center, basil plants are brought along and placed at the feet of the saints in the Church of St. Lawrence. Likewise, when Zinacantec saints return the visit, basil plants are bought and offered in the churches there. Also, a shaman who attends a fiesta in Ixtapa or San Lucas may buy a bunch of basil to bring back and store at home. Basil is offered in Bik'it Joyijel at the Fiesta of Our Lady of the Immaculate Conception, and for every flower change. Basil may be bought at market in San Cristóbal and Tuxtla.

As a remedy for "wind," a bunch may be brewed. A cup of the "hot" tea is drunk before breakfast. As a remedy for earache, the tips are brewed. A wad of cotton is soaked in the decoction and put in the ear. For further medicinal uses cf. **kontiyerva**, **mantzanilya**, and **k'ox yax-chel**.

    b. **K'ox arvajaka**, "small basil" (**sve'el tuch'ich'**), refers to the wild-occurring *Ocimum americanum* (4–6) and *O. micranthum* (1–6), common weeds in temperate and lowland areas that are very similar in fragrancy and habit to the European basil. Both have opposite ovate leaves and terminal racemes of verticillate blue or lavender tubular flowers. *Ocimum micranthum* has larger leaves and flowers than *O. americanum*.

As a remedy for malaria (**pasmo**), two or three plants are bruised in cold water or brewed. A "hot" cupful is drunk before breakfast for one or two days. For other medicinal uses cf. **batz'i arvajaka** and **ch'ail pox**.

Extended range: *Gongylocarpus rubricaulis*.

4. **Arvajáka tz'i'lel**, "mint plant" (**alavéna tz'i'lel, bot'-jol nichim, bot'-jol tz'i'lel**), is self-heal *Prunella vulgaris* (5–7), a plant of moist, grassy slopes and meadows in the highland areas. It is a procumbent or erect herb with opposite ovate to oblong leaves, 3–8 cm long, and terminal bracted spikes of blue or purple bilabiate flowers. The flowers are crowded and verticillate forming an oblong head-like spike, 2–10 cm long.

As a remedy for malaria, a "hot" tea is taken. To reduce fever, the tips are bruised in water. The "cold" infusion is used to bathe the head. As a remedy for embarrassment suffered by young children who have accompanied their mothers to market in San Cristóbal, young tips are smeared on their face and head two times each morning for three days. For sheep suffering swellhead, the plant is brewed together with **ch'upak' joj** and **k'ojom** and the head bathed.

5. **Chilchil tz'i'lel**, "rattling plant" (-**tik**) (**ch'akil tz'i'lel, na p'ilix, nochleb p'ilix, poxil k'uxben chon, tub pilix, yisim uch**), is *Lepechinia schiedeana* (7–10), a coarse, spreading

herb with terminal interrupted spikes of verticillate, pale blue, tubular flowers. The calyx is tubular with spinose-tipped acute lobes, the stems and leaves are pubescent. The leaves are opposite, oblong or oblong-ovate with crenate margins, 4–6 cm long. When in fruit, the seeds rattle in the dry, tubular calices. It is very common on overgrazed, grassy slopes in highland pine forests.

To cure toothache, the plant is brewed and the tea taken to rinse the mouth, or the leaf is chewed raw. Children eat the "cold" fruit.

6. **Tzotzil jabnal**, "woolly leaf" (**-tik**), is *Stachys radicans* (1–4), a woolly-leaved, purple flowered herb common in wet ground along streams and in wet, disturbed areas and in meadows in the highland areas. The leaves are opposite, sessile or short petiolate, oblong-ovate to ovate, 12–30 mm long. The flowers are purple or pink, bilabiate, 10–15 mm long, and verticillate in an interrupted spike.

To relieve a person suffering from **majbenal skventa kajvaltik**, a variety of remedies classed as both "medium" and "cold" are available: (1) the tender tips are bruised in cold water together with **sikil ton**, and a small cup of the infusion is taken, (2) the tips are brewed in salt water and the warm tea drunk, (3) the tips are bruised and cold salt water and the infusion drunk. For chills and fever, a tea may be taken.

Extended range: *Drymaria gracilis, Lamium amplexicaule, Stachys agraria, S. coccinea,* and *S. rotundifolia.*

7. **Yarvajáka me'on**, "pauper's basil" (**muk'ta jol choy tz'i'lel, ne ch'o tz'i'lel**), is *Stachytarpheta cayennensis* (1–1) and *S. frantzii* (3–3). These are common roadside and second growth plants of the temperate and lowland regions with long, terminal rat-tail inflorescence, 2–3 mm in diameter, of deep-blue tubular flowers, 10–16 mm long. The leaves are opposite, elliptic or oblong ovate, decurrent on the petioles, serrate, 3–10 cm long.

As a remedy for earache, the plant is brewed and the "hot" tea drunk.

Extended range: *Achimenes grandiflora.*

8. **Yax-chel**, "green **chel**" (**-tik**), refers to *Satureja* and *Catoferia*, two similarly aromatic plants.

Specifics: 2.

a. **K'ox yax-chel**, "small green **chel**" (**k'ox jabnal, poxil jabnal, poxil k'ok'**), is *Satureja brownei* (10–15), a tiny, spreading herb with bilabiate, lavender flowers, 6–10 mm long. The leaves are opposite, short petiolate, broadly obovate, with cordate or subcordate bases, 5–12 mm long. It is very abundant on grassy slopes and in meadows in the temperate and highland areas.

This plant is a "hot" remedy for a great number of ailments: Women whose eyesight dims following childbirth (**yax-chel**), take a cup of the tea before breakfast for as many days as necessary, or the leaves may be bruised in cold water that is used to bathe the patient's head. As a remedy for swelling (**pumel**) a small bunch is brewed together with basil and **ch'ail**

pox. The tea is drunk as above. As a remedy for "cold wind," a small bunch is brewed with **ch'ulelal** and a pinch of tobacco. This tea is also drunk as above. To relieve headaches, cure **majbenal**, and to cause measles to erupt, a handful is bruised in warm water. One cup of the infusion is drunk. To relieve headaches, a handful may also be heated and smeared on the head two or three times a day for two days. To relieve earaches, a few stems are pushed into the ear. As a "cold" remedy for madness, the plant may be bruised in cold water and the infusion poured into the ears and nose or used to bathe the patient's head.

Extended range: *Anagallis arvensis, Bouchea prismatica,* and *Salvia longispicata.*

b. **Muk'ta yax-chel**, "large green **chel**" (**yax-chelul**), is *Catoferia chiapensis* (4–10), a soft-wooded shrub with large, terminal dense spikes of white and lavender tubular flowers, 1.5–2 cm long, with very long exerted stamens, three times as long as the corolla. The leaves are opposite, ovate, acuminate at the apex, decurrent at the base, 10–18 cm long, softly pubescent below. It occurs on rocky second growth slopes in temperate hamlets. It is classed as a "tree."

This plant has many of the medicinal uses described to **k'ox yax-chel**. The "hot" remedies are: A tea is taken for dimmed eyesight following childbirth. For pregnant or postpartum mothers suffering "stomach" pains, a midwife directs smoke from the leaves towards her patient. To relieve headaches, a handful is brewed and the water used to bathe the head twice a day. As a remedy for insomnia, four leaves are bruised and mixed with cold water. A drop is placed in the nostrils. Or, the "medium" leaves are ground and placed in the nostrils at bedtime for three nights.

Extended range: *Aphelandra deppeana, Barleria micans, Croton draco, Justicia fulvicoma,* and *Miconia oligotricha.*

9. **Yaxal nich tz'i'lel**, "blue-flowered plant" (**chivo pox, muk'ta yalem bek'et** and **nap'ap' tz'i'lel** in part), refers to *Ageratum corymbosum* (3–3), *A. echioides* (1–2), *A. houstonianum* (2–4), and *A. paleaceum* (1–1). These are opposite, pubescent-leaved herbs with fuzzy, terminal clusters of blue flowers. They are common in the grassy understory of pine-oak forest, in grassy savannas, and also weedy in fallow fields and cornfields.

Extended range: *Bartletina hylobia, Bonplandia geminiflora, Commelina alpestris, C. diffusa, Fleischmannia imitans, F. pycnocephala, Hyptis suaveolens, H. verticillata, Prunella vulgaris,* and *Salvia urica.*

Isolates

1. **Amapóla** is the opium poppy *Papaver somniferum*, a stout herb often up to a meter tall. The flowers are large and showy with bluish white, pink, or red petals darkened at the center, 4–5 cm long. The leaves are alternate, glaucous, clasping the stem with irregularly incised margins. The fruit is

a capsule, glabrous and globose, 2–3 cm in diameter, with a disk at its apex. This is a common weed of the stock yards of the highlands, widely distributed in highland gardens by means of the manure.

On 26 August 1983 *El Periodico* of Tuxtla Gutiérrez headlined *"Enorme Plantío de Amapola Destruyeron,"* reporting that 5760 poppy plants in San Mikulax were burnt by the Mexican army. It seems that a nameless foreigner had donated the "turnip and lettuce seeds" whose crop he advised could be sold for a good price in Tapachula. In 1985 a second planting was reported in Sek'emtik. Despite the heavy penalties announced regularly on the radio, Zinacantecs are fascinated with the high price paid for the gum. A Paste' truck driver, working in the Lacandón jungle, was tempted by a million peso sale of gum, which he was told would be speedily bought up by *gringos* for astronomical figures.

2. **Aselka** (**-tik**) is *Beta vulgaris* var. *cicla* (2–2), swiss chard, a green very recently introduced into Bik'it Joyijel and in many of the highland communities. It is a biennial plant from a large branched root with large leaves with a thick midriff.

A few people sow the seeds in seed beds in May, transplanting them after a month within a corral. Where irrigation is possible they are planted in December. This is preferred as they do not suffer mildew. They are provided with sheep manure. They are ready to pick in a month-and-a-half. They are sold at market.

Specifics: 2.

   a. **K'anal aselka**, "yellow **aselka**," is the variety with reddish leaves.

   b. **Yaxal aselka**, "green **aselka**," has white stalks and green leaves.

2. **Ba nab tz'i'lel**, "lake-top plant," is *Eichhornea crassipes* (1–1), the water hyacinth that grows in the Presa de Angostura. This is a floating herb with short stems, numerous roots, and showy lilac flowers, with a flower tube 1.5–2 cm long and lobes about 3 cm long. The leaves are round-reniform with broad petioles, 2–30 cm long, which are often inflated. The fruit is a capsule about 1.5 cm long containing seeds that are narrowly 10-winged. It also occurs in roadside ditches and slow moving water in the lowlands.

3. **Chan-tzelav tz'i'lel**, "four-ridged plant," refers to *Alonsoa meridionalis* (1–1) and *Leucocarpus perfoliatus* (1–1), two figworts with prominent, 4-angled stems and yellow or orange tubular flowers, 12–20 mm long, in terminal racemes. The leaves are opposite, narrowly ovate, with serrate margins, 3–7 cm long and petiolate in *Alonsoa* and narrowly oblong-obovate or narrowly elliptic, with serrulate margins, 7–18 cm long and perfoliate in *Leucocarpus*. The fruit is a conical or globose capsule, 10–15 mm long. They occur in wet, exposed places in evergreen cloud forest of highland areas.

4. **Chenek' tz'i'lel**, "bean plant" (**chenek' ch'o**, **xinal tz'i'lel**, and **yol lum** in part), refers to *Desmodium palmeri* (1–1), *Phaseolus vulgaris* (2–2), *Rhynchosia minima* (1–1), and *Senna uniflora* (4–5). The last is an erect herb with pendent segmented legumes, 2–4 cm long, and yellow flowers. The leaves are pinnate into pubescent, elliptic leaflets, 2–5 cm long. *Desmodium palmeri, P. vulgare,* and *R. minima* are all trifoliate with leaflets ranging from broadly ovate to narrowly ovate, with rounded to attenuate apices, 1.5–6 cm long. The flowers may be orange, yellow, white, or purple, small and in terminal or axillary racemes. These are very abundant in the understory of tropical deciduous forest and in disturbed ground in lowland areas.

5. **Ech'** (**-tik**) refers to bromeliads. These are clumped plants with fibrous leaves in a tight rosette forming a bowl that can hold water. The flowers are racemes on thick stems arching from the center of the rosette.

Specifics: 8.

   a. **Antzil ech'**, "female bromeliad" (**mol ech', sakil ech', tontikil ech', yech' j'ik'al**), refers to *Pitcairnea breedlovei* (3–5) and *Vriesea werckleana* (2–3), rosetted plants that occur on limestone cliff faces. The leaves are broad sheathing, triangular-linear, to 10 dm long, and the inflorescence is very tall (to 1 m), a simple raceme or branched. The flowers are green or yellow, secund, 2.5–5 cm long. They occur in temperate and highland areas.

The leaves were once used to wrap **pozol** when traveling to the lowlands. In major curing ceremonies the "cold" plants are used to decorate a patient's bed. In Jok' Ch'enom the plant is an ingredient of "flower water."

Extended range: *Catopsis nutans* and *Pitcairnia calderonii*.

   b. **Ch'ix ech'**, "spiny bromeliad," refers to *Pitcairnia breedlovei* (2–2), *P. calderonii* (1–3), *P. heterophylla* (2–2), and *Tillandsia rodrigueziana* (1–2). These are epiphytic and saxicolous, rosetted plants with very narrow leaves, often with spines at the leaf bases or along the margin of the leaves. They occur in temperate and highland areas.

As a remedy for stomach ache *Pitcairnia* sp. is boiled and the stomach bathed with the "hot" liquid.

   c. **Kilon ech'** (**-tik**), "pendulous bromeliad" (**kiletel ech', kilkil ech'**), is *Tillandsia violacea* (5–8), a giant (to 1 m across), rosetted epiphyte with an immense, pendulous inflorescence to 3 m long consisting of alternate subsessile spikes, 9–15 cm long, 4–6 cm wide. The spikes are flattened, blue-flowered with conspicuous, densely imbricated, coriacious bracts subtending the flowers. It occurs in pine-oak forests of temperate and highland areas.

They are used to adorn the creche in Apas and Atz'am. Formerly on Monday of Holy Week, each of the stewards provided four inflorescences. This number was reduced to three and now to two. The inflorescences are hung on the two pine trees that flank the cross on Good Friday. The same use is made in Naben Chauk. These bromeliads are also used for decoration in Sak Lum on the fifth Lenten Friday and in Chak Toj and Elan Vo' on Good Friday.

This plant may be subdivided further:

(1) **Sakil kilon ech'**, "white pendulous bromeliad," refers to plants with young flower stalks.

(2) **Tzajal kilon ech'**, "red pendulous bromeliad," refers to plants whose flower stalks have reddened with aging. They are preferred to the young flowers, which become gray after they are cut.

d. **Krus ech'**, "cross bromeliad" (-**tik**) (**batz'i ech'**, **k'ox ech'**), is *Tillandsia guatemalensis* (4-7), an epiphyte with numerous leaves, about 4 dm long, forming an urn-shaped bowl. The flowers are blue in an openly branched red bracteate inflorescence. The floral bracts are about 13-15 mm long. It is a common element in evergreen cloud forest and moist pine-oak forest in the highland areas. Some people in the highland hamlets now transplant these bromeliads to the forks of trees in their yards.

This "cold" plant is a basic ingredient of "flower water" in the highland hamlets. A single plant is used. Three plants are used to decorate the house cross and each shrine at a curing ceremony. For each flower change the stewards gather 900 plants. Eight hundred plants are provided by the senior steward in charge; 500 hundred of these to decorate the Church of St. Lawrence. Forty plants are provided by each of the other senior stewards. Sixty plants are provided by the senior steward to decorate his coffer. This bromeliad is gathered also by the stewards-royal every Saturday to decorate the Chapel of Espuipulas and their coffers. The elders decorate the altar of the grand alcalde every two weeks. Forty plants are provided by each steward on the eighth *Posada* to decorate the creche. On Christmas Eve the Christ Children are placed under an arch of this bromeliad and bamboo palm in the Church of St. Sebastian These bromeliads are used to decorate the creche in Apas, Na Chij, Naben Chauk, Paste', and San Mikulax. They are used in the hamlet chapel flower changes in about half the hamlets. The plants are sold by the people of San Felipe at Christmas time in San Cristóbal, Chiapa de Corzo, and Tuxtla. For further uses cf. **antzil aj, ch'ib, ik'al toj, tzis uch, yich'ak mut.**

Extended range: *Tillandsia flabellata.*

e. **Uma' ech'**, "mute bromeliad" (-**tik**) (**sonso ech', yech' antivo** in part), refers to *Tillandsia butzii* (1-2), *T. capitata* (2-4), *T. caput-medusae* (1-2), *T. dasyliriifolia* (1-2), *T. fasciculata* (3-8), *T. flabellata* (1-1), *T. plumosa* (2-4), and *T. vicentina* (1-4). These are common, often abundant epiphytes of pine-oak forests in temperate and highland areas.

Children should avoid putting this plant in their mouths lest they become mute or begin to stutter. The plants are sold in Tuxtla at Christmas time.

They may be further subdivided:

(1) **Kilon uma' ech'**, "pendulous mute bromeliad"—*T. butzii, T. caput-medusae*. Both plants have long sheathing leaves with inrolled margins with bases that are suborbicular or broadly elliptical. The scapes are erect with imbricated foliaceous bracts. The inflorescence is either simple or branched, consisting of linear, flattened, bracted spikes of lavender or blue flowers.

2. **Krus uma' ech'**, "cross mute bromeliad"—*T. dasyliriifolia*, a very large stemless epiphyte with strap-shaped leaves, 7-9 cm long and to 6 cm wide at the base. The scape is erect, elongate, paniculate. The floral bracts are broadly ovate, coriaceous, and shorter than the flowers. The flowers are white or greenish with petals 3-4 cm long.

(3) **Tzajal uma' ech'**, "red mute bromeliad"—*T. fasciculata, T. plumosa, T. vicentina. Tillandsia fasciculata* and *T. vicentina* are epiphytes with long rosulate leaves with sheaths 2-3 cm wide and stout scapes, which are simple or branched. The spikes are composed of deeply imbricated bracts subtending the flowers. The bracts are 2-4 cm long in *T. fasciculatum*, subtending flowers about 6 cm long. The bracts are 2-2.5 cm long, subtending flowers 4-5 cm long in *T. vicentina. Tillandsia plumosa* is much smaller with many rosulate, linear leaves with sheaths 1-2 cm wide. The scapes are several and slender. The floral bracts are red, about 5 cm long; the flowers are blue about 7 cm long.

(4) **Vojton uma' ech'**, "ear of corn mute bromeliad"—*T. capitata*, a stemless epiphyte with leaves about equaling the inflorescence, narrowly triangular with large sheaths about 4-5 cm wide. The scape is curved with large foliaceous scape bracts exceeding the ellipsoid inflorescence. The floral bracts are ovoid, orange subtending the blue flowers, with petals 35-55 mm long.

Extended range: *Pitcairnia breedlovei* and *P. karwinskyana.*

f. **Vojton ech'**, "ear of corn bromeliad" (-**tik**) (**sot' ech', tzajal ech'**), is *Tillandsia ponderosa* (2-6), an epiphytic, urn-shaped plant with an enormous, thick, brilliant red inflorescence up to 50 cm tall. The floral bracts are densely imbricate, about 5.6 cm long. The flowers are purple with petals 4-5 cm long. It is a common plant in pine-oak forests of highland areas. Some people in the highland hamlets now transplant these bromeliads to the forks of trees in their yards.

For major curing ceremonies, 15 plants are gathered: Three "cold" plants are for the "flower water." One is placed at the altar of each of the three churches in Zinacantán Center, one at each of the six mountain shrines, one on the house entrance cross, and two at the top of the arch at the entrance to the patient's bed. The number used may, however, vary.

Two hundred plants are taken by the stewards to Atz'am on the Fiesta of Our Lady of the Rosary. To make the roof cross of the creche, three plants are gathered by the stewards on the

276

sixth *Posada* and stored in the church for two days. The red leaves and flowers are alternated with white corn husk leaves. They are bound to a small, wooden cross. One plant was placed formerly at each corner of the roof of the creche. They are used to adorn the creche in Chak Toj and Naben Chauk. The plants are sold by Chamulans and the people of San Felipe in San Cristóbal during the Christmas season. At this time, too, a large group of people from Chiapa de Corzo march in procession with the image of a Christ Child, *El Niño Florero*. Until recently they intoned prayers in the otherwise forgotten Chiapanec language. Proceeding through Muk'ta Jok' and Sek'emtik, they visit the church of Naben Chauk before gathering these bromeliads on the steep slopes of Naben Chauk, Yaleb Taiv, and San Felipe. Heavily laden, they return home to decorate their altars in Chiapa de Corzo. For further uses cf. **tzis uch.**

Extended range: *Tillandsia seleriana.*

    g. **Xulub chivo ech',** "goat horn bromeliad," is *Billbergia pallidiflora* (1–2), an epiphyte with few leaves in a tight rosette forming a horn-shaped bowl and a long, narrow, pendent inflorescence. The inflorescence is many-flowered and densely cylindric. The flowers are green with petals up to 52 mm long. It occurs in tropical deciduous forest of lowland areas.

    h. **Yech' joj,** "raven's bromeliad," is *Tillandsia seleriana* (1–2), a clustered epiphyte with the leaves closed over the top of the bowls. The enclosed hollow is often a favorite nesting site for a species of stinging ants. The inflorescence is branched into 3 to 7 spikes. The floral bracts are 20–28 mm long. The flowers are blue or violet with petals about 3.5 cm long. It is common in dry pine-oak forests of temperate areas.

The plants are used as flowers in a baby's curing ceremony.

6. **Jol choy,** "fish head" (**jol choy tz'i'lel**), is *Calyptocarpus wendlandii* (5–11), a common, sprawling herb with small, yellow, terminal daisy flowers and spine-tipped fruits about 1 cm broad, which are very painful when they get lodged in one's sandals. The leaves are opposite, broadly elliptic, serrate, 2–7.5 cm long. It occurs in the wet understory of tropical deciduous forest along streams.

It is eaten by horses.

7. **Jonjolin** is sesame *Sesamum indicum,* an erect herb to 1 m tall with finely pubescent stems, leaves, and fruits. The lower leaves are opposite, and the upper, alternate. They are ovate to oblong, 5–15 cm long, 2–6 cm wide. The flowers are solitary, white, and 2–3 cm long. The corolla is two-lipped. The capsule is oblong, 2–3 cm long, with four longitudinal grooves. The seeds are ovate and cream-colored or tan, 2 mm long. It is commonly cultivated by *ladinos* in the Central Depression and is a fragrant roadside weed. This plant has been introduced recently to six lower temperate communities.

8. **Kontiyerva** (**konchiyerva**) is *Dorstenia contrajerva* (3–6), a perennial acaulescent herb with basal palmately lobed or triangular cordate scabrous leaves and a hand-shaped, disk-like inflorescence of minute flowers. The leaves are long petiolate, 10–15 cm long, the disk-like inflorescence is 2–5 cm broad. It occurs in the understory of tropical deciduous forest and seasonal evergreen forest of lowland areas.

This plant has a variety of medicinal uses. Corn farmers suffering from "wind," diarrhea, or loss of energy gather three or four roots. They are crushed and soaked in cold water. One bowlful of the infusion is drunk. If taken this way the patient may continue to drink cold water and does not need to remain in quarantine. The roots may also be brewed for a "hot" tea. For "wind" and swelling, the roots are brewed with basil. For diarrhea, they are brewed with **batz'i ch'ulelal nichim,** but this treatment proscribes the drinking of cold water and demands a two day (or some say) a one month quarantine, lest a slow death ensue. A bowl of the "hot" tea is drunk, in any case, before breakfast for one or three days. For "cold" in the stomach there are two additional prescriptions. Three roots are ground raw and brewed with brown sugar, or to make a "hotter" potion, the roots are first dried. The "tea" is very thick. For postpartum women who feel "cold" in the stomach one month after delivery, the tea may be taken. To relieve the pain of wasp stings, a bath of this herb is effective.

Extended range: *Iostephane trilobata.*

9. **Krus tz'i'lel,** "cross plant," is *Chromolaena odorata* (1–1), a coarse shrub, with drooping or recurved branches. The leaves are opposite, ovate, variable in size and shape, 3-nerved from the base, acute or attenuate at the apex. The inflorescence is large and broad, made up of cylindric dandelion-like heads of lavender or white flowers. The branches that bear the flowers diverge at right angles from the main stem. This plant occurs in second growth of the temperate and lowland regions.

10. **K'anal nich,** "yellow flower," is a non-Linnaean term referring to a number of yellow-flowered weedy plants including *Alloispermum scabrum* (1–1), *Bidens bicolor* (1–1), *B. ostruthioides* (1–1), *Melampodium montanum* (2–2), *M. perfoliatum* (1–1), *Potentilla staminea* (1–1), *Sanvitalia procumbens* (1–1), and *Sclerocarpus uniserialis* (1–1), which occur throughout the township usually in second growth or weedy situations.

11. **K'ask'as tz'i'lel,** "brittle plant" (**k'ask'as nichim** and **tut nichim** in part), is a non-Linnaean grouping of many unrelated shrubs with brittle stems: *Alternanthera laguroides* (1–2), *Blechum brownei* (1–1), *Cordia spinescens* (1–3), *Euphorbia graminea* (1–1), *Geranium seemannii* (1–1), *Iresine celosia* (3–2), *Lopezia langmenniae* (1–2), *Mirabilis jalapa* (1–1), *Rondeletia* sp. (1–4), *Ruellia parva* (1–3), and *Russelia sarmentosa* (2–4).

12. **Lechuka** (**lechuga***) is lettuce *Lactuca sativa* (2–2), a plant recently introduced to Zinacatán.

Lettuce is cultivated in Bik'it Joyijel, Sak Lum, and all the highland communities. The seeds are sown in the rainy season in a corral. Lettuce is rarely, if ever, eaten by Zinacantecs. It is sold at market.

Specifics: 2.

a. **Jich'il anal lechuka**, "narrow-leaved lettuce," refers to the loosely heading lettuce varieties.

b. **Votzvotz lechuka**, "clumped lettuce," is head lettuce such as "iceberg."

13. **Lula (ruda*)** is rue *Ruta graveolens* (4–7), a very strongly scented subshrub often cultivated by *ladinos* in highland, temperate, and lowland yards. The leaves are alternate, divided into narrowly elliptic leaflets, 6–30 mm long. The inflorescence is a terminal raceme of yellow flowers with fringed petals about 6–7 mm long. The fruit is a capsule about 7–8 mm long with four acute lobes at the apex.

In Santa Rosa, a few people plant rue in their yards. It is planted in many temperate and all highland communities, but it is known to grow for only certain people. Seeds, slips, or seedlings are planted in the rainy season. The plants need no fencing, as chickens will not touch them.

Rue has a very wide variety of medicinal uses. For laryngitis (**makal jnuk'tik ta sik**), a "hot" rue tea, brewed with cane liquor, is taken. Rue tea is taken by nursing mothers to stimulate lactation. To cause measles to erupt, three shoots are brewed. The shaman bathes the child in the "hot" water. As a remedy for stomach ache, a handful is brewed. The patient drinks two spoonfuls mixed with cane liquor. As a remedy for **majben utz kolo'**, a bunch of rue is bruised and mixed with white salt and cane liquor. One shot glassful is drunk and the whole body bathed with the infusion. Alternatively, three or six tips may be brewed with **batz'i ch'ulelal nichim** and a pinch of tobacco. One cup is drunk, and the remainder used to bathe the patient's arms, legs, chest, forehead, back, and sides. Or, a handful may be mixed with garlic and tobacco and rubbed on the knees, calves, and thighs. Or if the pain is at the base of the spine, it may be massaged with the same potion. A person who has been tormented by the Earth Lord in his dreams brews three shoots. He is bathed with the "hot" water for three days to a week. As a remedy for soul-loss (**balamil**), rue is crushed and rubbed on the body at bedtime for three days. Just the wrists and ankles may be rubbed or the whole body. In addition 12–13 tips may be buried erect, surrounded by three cloves of garlic in the place where soul-loss was suffered. These are considered to serve as the substitute for the startled person. Also as a remedy for soul-loss, rue tea may be drunk. If the leaves are rubbed on the body, garlic may be added to the rue to prevent the Earth Lord from approaching. An additional use was noted by the priest of Zinacantán in 1797: "for the ears" (de Leon y Goicoechea, 1797). For further use cf. **kururin, tzitz pox.**

14. **Marivana (marivano tz'i'lel)** is marijuana *Cannabis sativa* (1–3), a large plant from 6–12 feet tall. The leaves are alternate and palmately divided into 3–7 narrowly lanceolate segments, about 4–15 cm long, with serrate margins. The male flowers are borne in very long panicles. The female flowers are in short leafy spikes about 2 cm long. In the 1950s and early 1960s, it occurred as a weed in the lowlands.

Marijuana was cultivated by a few people in the 1970s, but this was ended abruptly by their jailing. In 1985 there was renewed talk of its clandestine cultivation. In 1987 two Zinacantecs were jailed for planting what they call "weeds."

It is widely believed, as they have been told by *ladinos,* that marijuana will drive a person mad.

Extended range: *Leonurus sibericus.* As a remedy for paralysis, a handful is brewed together with basil for a "hot" tea.

15. **Mexa tz'i'lel**, "table plant" (**manya chenek' tz'i'lel**), is *Kallstroemia rosei* (2–5), a prostrate herb with axillary yellow-orange flowers, about 2 cm broad, and opposite pinnately divided leaves with ovate or broadly elliptic leaflets, 5–20 mm long, which occurs in waste ground, roadsides, and disturbed fields in lowland areas. The fruit is conical and ribbed, about 6 mm long, with an attenuate beak about 6 mm long.

As a remedy for stomach ache, (**k'ux o'onil**), a bunch is brewed. One cup of the "medium" tea is drunk before breakfast for three days. It is also used for pig fodder.

16. **Nap'-'us tz'i'lel**, "gnat sticking plant" (**poxil sep', tzotzin te', tzuntzun tz'i'lel**), is *Croton ciliatoglandulifer* (3–7), a gray-leaved subshrub with long, gland-tipped hairs on the stems and margins of the leaves. The leaves are alternate, ovate or broadly ovate with an attenuate apex and rounded base, 1.5–6 cm long. The flowers are small, white, and in terminal clusters. It is common in second growth and fallow fields in lowland areas. It is used as a cure for "mange."

17. **Nekeb pox**, "shoulder medicine," refers to *Acourtia* and *Iostephane*, two acaulescent perennial herbs with flowers produced from the rosette on long naked peduncles. They both occur in the understory of pine-oak forest in the highland and temperate regions.

Specifics: 2.

a. **Krem nekeb pox**, "boy shoulder medicine," is *Acourtia nudicaulis* (1–2). These are perennial, acaulescent herbs with toothed ovate or oblong ovate leaves on long petioles. They are acute at the apex, rounded and then decurrent on the petiole or cordate at the base. The flowers are white and dandelion-like in an open panicle at the end of a long scape. It occurs in the understory of pine-oak forests in the temperate hamlets.

The root is brewed and the tea drunk by women who want to have boy babies.

b. **Tzeb nekeb pox**, "girl shoulder medicine," is *Iostephane trilobata* (1–2). These are erect scapose herbs with basal triangular ovate or trilobate leaves, 5–10 cm long. The lobes are broadly rounded and the blade is decurrent on the petiole and scabrous above and below. The flowers are solitary at the ends of the long peduncles and are daisy-like with yellow rays, 9–15 mm long. It is a common plant in the grassy understory of pine-oak forests of highland and temperate areas.

The root is brewed and the tea drunk by women who want to

have girl babies.

18. **Nich nab**, "lake flower" (**-tik**), is a non-Linnaean grouping of many unrelated herbs that occur in or near water. These include *Aster exilis, Berula erecta, Cardamine flaccida, Eryngium carlinae, E. ghiesbreghtii, Hydrolea spinosa* (1–1), *Ludwigia peploides* (1–2), *Mimulus glabratus, Polygonum punctatum, Rumex crispus* (1–1), and *Sisyrinchum scabrum*. Because of genuine or suspected toxic properties responsible for killing sheep, many speakers segregate the following.

Specifics: 5.

a. **Bero nich nab**, "watercress lake flower" (**sakil nich nab**), is *Cardamine flaccida* (3–6), a slender, perennial, branched herb with abundant leaves. The alternate leaves are pinnately divided into small ovate or orbicular, crenate leaflets, 0.4–1.5 cm long. The small white flowers are racemose. The fruit is a narrow silique about 22 mm long and 1 mm wide. This plant grows on the edges of standing water in the highlands. It is considered to be particularly toxic.

b. **Ch'ix nich nab**, "spiny lake flower," is *Eryngium guatemalense* (1–1), a coarse, stout perennial, with long linear leaves, 10–30 cm long, with spine-like lobes on the margins. The inflorescence is umbellate with conical or globose heads of purple flowers, 1.5–2 cm broad, subtended by an involucre of narrowly triangular, spine-tipped bracts. This plant grows on exposed grassy slopes on the highest ridges. It is fatal to sheep. This and the other "lake flowers" toxic to sheep are believed to grow in their livers after being ingested.

c. **Koko'on nich nab**, "mexican tea lake flower" (**tzajal nich nab**), refers to *Aster bullatus* (1–1), *Mimulus glabratus* (2–2), and *Polygonum punctatum* (4–6), which all grow along streams or in very wet soil in the highlands. They are glabrous-leaved and have succulent, turgid stems.

d. **Kuchara nich nab**, "spoon lake flower" (**kulantu tz'i'lel, tzib nab**), is *Berula erecta* (5–8), a slender herb with long pinnate leaves, growing in moist pasture land or along creeks in the highlands. The leaflets are oblong ovate, serrate, 1–4 cm long. The tiny white flowers are borne in terminal umbellate inflorescences. It is not considered as lethal as the other members of this complex.

e. **Pech'e-'ok nich nab**, "flat-stemmed lake flower," is *Sisyrinchium scabrum* (4–3), a blue-flowered member of the iris family with narrow, grass-like leaves and a terminal cluster of blue flowers, 8–12 mm long. The fruit is a globose capsule about 5–8 mm long. It is common on moist grassy slopes in the highlands. See also **pech'e-'ok jobel**.

19. **Nichim joj**, "raven flower" (**nich joj**), refers to *Zephyranthes brevipes* (2–5) and *Z. carinata* (1–4), bulbous lilies with large, funnel-shaped, pink flowers, 4–6 cm long in *Z. carinata* and 5–12 cm long in *Z. brevipes*. The leaves are narrow, 5–7 mm wide. They are common in grassy fields and meadows of highland areas.

Children play with the flowers.

20. **Pinsel** (**-tik**), *Centaurea cyanus,* which is known commonly as bachelor's button, is a slender annual with wiry stems. The leaves are alternate, entire, 5–10 cm long, and 5 mm wide. The lower leaf surface and young stems are cottony. The flowers are usually blue but can be purple or pink and are 3.5 cm across. The involucre is made up of spinescent bracts, which are 4–9 mm long.

This commercial flower has been grown by a few Zinacantecs in Atz'am, Naben Chauk, and Zinacantán Center since about 1980. The seeds are planted in flats in August. After three weeks, the seedlings are transplanted 35 cm apart in rows 40 cm apart. The plants flower in three months and are pinched back so they will flower abundantly in six months. The flowers are picked once a week, but the tough stems must be cut with clippers. Though the plant flowers for a year and a half, Zinacantecs prefer to collect the seeds to begin a new crop after a year of flowering.

It is sold at market in San Cristóbal and Tuxtla.

21. **Pochok'** is *Juanulloa mexicana* (1–1), an epiphytic herb arising from a tuberous root with sprawling stems and large, ovate, woolly pubescent leaves. The flowers are orange with an angled tube up to 8 cm long and clustered at the end of the leafless branches. It occurs in oak forest of the temperate hamlets.

22. **Poxil chon**, "snake medicine," is *Hybanthus verbenaceus* (1–2), perennial, erect or decumbent, branched plants with alternate, elliptic to obovate leaves, 2–5 cm long. The flowers are blue, purple, or white, axillary, about 4–6 mm long, on pedicels 10–12 mm long. The fruit is an ovoid capsule, about 1 cm long, with an acuminate tip. The seeds are round, brown, and smooth, about 2 mm in diameter. It grows in second growth in the temperate and lowland regions.

As an antidote for snakebite, the leaves are brewed and the tea drunk.

23. **Poxil chu'ul**, "breast medicine," is *Spigelia nicotianaeflora* (1–2), a perennial herb with few large opposite broadly ovate leaves and a scorpioid inflorescence of red tubular flowers, 4–8 cm long, with yellow tips. It is locally common in cornfields in the temperate hamlets.

To induce lactation, the root is crushed and boiled with black pepper. The "hot" tea is drunk.

24. **Poxil lukum**, "worm medicine," is *Turnera diffusa* (1–1), a small, densely branched shrub with alternate, dentate, oblong or obovate leaves, 1–2 cm long, pubescent below. The flowers are yellow, almost sessile, with petals 4–8 mm long. The fruit is a subglobose capsule, 1.5–2 mm in diameter. It grows in second growth and on roadsides in temperate lowland areas.

As a remedy for worms, a "cold" tea is taken.

25. **Poxil me'-vinik**, lit. "mother man medicine," i.e., "heartburn medicine," is *Chamaecrista desvauxii* (1–3), a many-branched perennial with large, yellow flowers with obovate petals, 12–20 mm long, at the leaf axils along the stem. The leaves are pinnate into four broadly elliptic to rotund leaflets, 10–21 mm long. The stems, pedicils, petioles, and sepals are glandular pubescent. The legume is pubescent with long, somewhat stiff straw-colored hairs. It is common in second growth and savannas in temperate and lowland areas.

To ease heartburn, men in the lowlands bruise a handful in water. A cup of the "cold" infusion is drunk once or twice.

26. **Poxil satil**, lit. "eye medicine," i.e., "pink eye medicine," is *Diastatea micrantha* (1–2), an erect, delicate herb with a terminal raceme of pale blue flowers, 8–10 mm long, on upward arching pedicels, 1.5–3.5 cm long. The leaves are alternate, ovate to lanceolate, serrate, 1–6 cm long. It occurs in the grassy understory of pine-oak forests in the temperate and highland areas.

To cure pink eye, a tip is cut and three drops of the "cold" sap are placed in the eye once daily for three days.

Extended range: *Drymaria gracilis*.

27. **Poxil sim-nak'al**, lit. "hidden mucous medicine," i.e., "dysentery medicine," is *Crossopetalum parvifolium* (1–1), an erect, branched plant, 2–3 feet tall, with ovate, oblong-ovate or lanceolate leaves, 1–5 cm long. The flowers are minute, red in finely branched axillary panicles. The fruit is subglobose, about 7 mm in diameter, bright red. This plant grows in second growth and tropical deciduous forests in the lowlands.

A "hot" tea is taken as a remedy for dysentery.

28. **Poxil yayijemal**, "wound medicine" (**nichim ninyo** in part, **poxil yayijel, talesob chu'ul tz'i'lel, tux-nuk' tz'i'lel**), refers to the cud weeds *Gnaphalium attenuatum* (2–4), *G. brachypterum* (3–5), *G. roseum* (1–4), and *G. viscosum* (3–3), erect, woolly-leaved herbs with terminal head-like clusters of small composite flowers. The leaves are sessile or clasping linear or narrowly lanceolate and abundant on the stems. They are very common in the understory of pine-oak forests and in second growth of the temperate and highland hamlets.

To speed the healing of cuts, the "hot" woolly down at the ends of the tips is applied to the cut for two or three days. Then the cut is bathed with hot water and new down applied. Alternatively, one to four leaves may be applied to the cut once a day for three days. They may also be brewed and the liquid used for bathing the cut. Or, the cut may be bathed with **k'ox pak' chak** tea and the powder from the burnt leaves applied. The flowers are sold in Tuxtla at Christmas time.

Extended range: *Conyza chilensis* and *Gnaphalium purpureum*

29. **Puj***, "hollow" (**-tik**), refers to cattails and bullrushes.

Extended range: *Cyperus niger, Eleocharis dombeyana, Equisetum hymale* var. *affine, Fuirena simplex,* and *Juncus effusus* var. *solutus.* (These are without reference to specific.)
Specifics: 2.

　a. **Antzil puj**, "female hollow" (**bik'it puj**), refers to the cattails *Typha domingensis* (2–4) and *T. latifolia* (1–1), plants that occur in standing water at all elevations. They have robust simple, erect stems, linear or strap-shaped leaves with parallel veins, 5–25 mm wide, and terminal long, cylindrical, brown spikes of densely crowded unisexual flowers.

Some women who wish to make their hair grow longer or whose hair is falling out pound the rhizomes of this plant on a rock and mix it with the water for washing their hair. They wash their hair with this "cold" water once daily for five days.

　b. **Vinik puj**, "male hollow" (**puj yoyal balamil, tutal vo'**), refers to *Scirpus californicus* (4–6) and *S. validus* (1–2), tall rushes of standing water at high elevations. The stems are round, about 12 mm in diameter. The inflorescence is terminal and has a branched arrangement of brown spikelets about 6–8 mm long.

30. **Sakil nichim**, "white flower," is *Fleischmanniopsis leucocephalum* (2–2), a slender shrub, sparsely branched with opposite, lanceolate, leaves 6–10 cm long with coarsely serrate margins, 3-nerved at the base. The white composite flowers are borne in a large ovoid panicle. This plant grows in the second growth of the temperate and lowland areas.

The flowers are sold in Tuxtla for the fourth Friday of Lent decorations.

31. **Sat pukuj tz'i'lel**, "devil face plant" or "devil eye plant," is *Spigelia humboldtiana* (1–1). This is an erect or decumbent perennial usually glabrous with opposite sessile or short-petiolate, oblong to ovate leaves, 2.5–8 cm long. The flowers are tubular, white, 15–18 mm long, in a terminal, few-flowered spike. The capsule is bilobate, 4–6 mm wide, glabrous. This plant occurs often as a weed in cornfields and in second growth in the temperate and lowland regions.

32. **Sat vet**, "fox face" or "fox eye" (**poxil poslom**), is *Chimaphila umbellata* (2–2), a mottled-leaved herb in the understory of moist pine-oak forests in the highlands. These small suffrutescent plants have whorls of 3 to 7 oblanceolate leaves, 3.5–8 cm long, serrate along the margins. The flowers are terminal at the end of a long peduncle about 10 cm long. The petals are white and pink, about 7 mm long. The capsule is globose, 6–10 mm in diameter.

33. **Tan ka'**, "gray horse" (**ve'el ka'**), refers to the tick clovers *Desmodium amplifolium* (3–6), *D. aparines* (1–5), *D. chiapense* (3–8), *D. maxonii* (2–5), *D. nicaraguense* (4–9), *D. orbiculare* (2–6), *D. skinneri* (2–3), and *D. strobilaceum* (1–3). These are shrubs or herbs with small purple pea flowers and alternate trifoliate leaves. The leaflets are generally ovate with acute apices. The pods are constricted between the seeds and flattened into one plane. The pods, stems, and foliage often are covered with retrorse hairs causing them to stick to rough surfaces. These plants occur in drier habitats throughout the township. The shrubbier species are sometimes classed as "tree."

The trunk of *D. skinneri* is used for firewood. The "medium" bark is applied to cuts. All varieties are eaten by sheep and horses.

Extended range: *Nissolia fruticosa.*

34. Tenten pox, "matted medicine," is *Osbertia stoloniferus* (1–2), an herbaceous perennial with yellow daisy-like flowers about 3 cm across. The flowers are single on a long peduncle, which arises from a basal cluster of narrowly obovate, pubescent leaves, which range from 3 to 8 cm long and 1.5 to 2 cm wide. It grows in the grassy understory of pine-oak forests in the highlands.

The plant is burnt and rubbed on athlete's foot (**chin ta koktik**).

35. Tut (akan aj, juxob ek'en) refers to the horsetails *Equisetum hymale* var. *affine* (3–4) and *E. myriochaetum* (1–2). These occur in moist places and along streams in temperate and highland areas. These are rush-like plants, with hollow, erect, jointed stems with longitudinal ridges. They may be either unbranched as in *E. hymale* or have many jointed branches whorled at the nodes. The fertile stems are terminated by a cylindric cone-like structure containing the spores.

To relieve constipation or bloody dysentery, a small bunch is brewed. One cup of the "cold" tea is taken. This plant is sold in Tuxtla as a remedy for venereal disease. The "cold" tea is drunk two to three times. A handful of "cold" plants may be crushed in cold water and the water used to bathe the head of a person whose hair is falling out.

The plant is used to sandpaper **metate** platforms, hoe and ax handles, and digging sticks. Children use the stems for whistles.

36. Tut nab, "lake **tut**" (**inejo te', punyal tz'i'lel**), is *Sesbania emerus* (3–3), a tall (to 3 m) herb with yellow pea flowers, 14–16 mm long, and elongate, pinnately divided leaves with many oblong leaflets, about 13 mm long, crowded on the rachis. The legumes are linear, to 26 cm long. It occurs in large masses in standing water like outside ditches, low ground, etc., in the lowlands. It is classed variously as "tree" and "plant."

37. Tux-nuk'* (**-tik**) (**tux-nok', tux-nok'***) is cotton *Gossypium hirsutum* (1–4), a plant cultivated by *ladinos* in lowland areas and occasionally escaped along roadsides. It is a coarse shrub with leaves about 5–15 cm long, cordate, and with three ovoid or triangular lobes. The flowers are large, white or yellow fading to pink, with petals 3–5 cm long and a central column of fused stamens. Each flower is subtended by two ovate bracts, which are deeply cut into 9 to 13 lacerations. The capsule is ovate-elliptic with an acuminate tip, 4–5.5 cm long. The seeds are covered with short fuzz and long white cotton fibers. *Ladinos* plant cotton in their yards in the rainy season. They pull off the bolls and flail them. The cotton is spun into thread.

Extended range: *Anoda cristata* and *Croton argenteus.*
Specifics: 2.

a. **K'an-chik tux-nuk',** "yellow **chik** cotton," refers to brown cotton that appears together with the white cotton and was formerly cultivated by the people of Cancuc.

b. **Sakil tux-nuk',** "white cotton," was the substance with which clouds were made.

Cotton thread is now bought commercially. Cotton is used by the stewards to wipe off the saints when they are bathed, and by the holy elders when Christ is bathed. Cotton is also used to swab the arm with alcohol before giving an injection.

Zinacantecs grew cotton about thirty-five years ago. It was planted at a full moon on St. Peter's Day (29 June). The seeds were first mixed in mud to germinate and then planted with a digging stick, 3–4 seeds to a hole, 30 cm apart. When 15 cm tall, the field was weeded. The cotton was picked in December and January.

38. Tzon-te'*, "tree beard" (**-tik**), refers to mosses, lichens, and moss-like higher plants.
Specifics: 5.

a. **Pop tzon-te',** "mat tree beard," refers to leafy lichens.

b. **Tzon-te'al balamil,** "terrestrial tree beard" (**puchleb ninyo, snichim ninyo**), refers to mosses and lichens that occur on the forest floor in dense evergreen cloud forests of the highland areas. *Thuidium delicatulum* (1–3), an especially dense moss, is used at Christmas. It has elongate stems with delicate, feathery branches.

Two bagfuls of *T. delicatulum* are provided by the Stewards of Our Lady of the Rosary on the eighth *Posada* to serve as the bed for the Christ Children. More is provided by the 12 godfathers on the ninth *Posada*. It is used widely to decorate hamlet creches.

c. **Tzon-te'al krus,** "cross tree beard" (**tzon te'**), is spanish moss *Tillandsia usneoides* (1–4), a long, pendent, small, green-flowered epiphyte with narrow gray-pubescent, tangled stems and branches often occurring in great masses on trees on the crests of ridges in temperate and highland areas.

As a remedy for whooping cough, a "hot" tea is taken. The publicans of the previous year gather enough spanish moss to be sewn on their hats for their performance as **tzon-te'** during the Fiesta of St. Sebastian. The publicans' assistants gather two bagsful at midyear's to adorn the Chapel of Our Lord of Esquipulas. Men designated by the magistrate gather spanish moss to decorate the courthouse on Independence Day and to decorate the three arches that are erected for a visit by the governor or the bishop. It is used to decorate the chapel in Sak Lum on the fifth Lenten Friday and is widely used to decorate hamlet creches.

For further medicinal use cf. **nok'ol sik'ol.**

d. **Tzon-te'al te',** "arboreal tree beard," refers to mosses, leafy liverworts, and lichens that cover stems and branches of trees in evergreen cloud forest and wet pine-oak forests of temperate and highland areas.

e. **Tzon-te'al ton,** "rock-growing tree beard," refers to mosses and lichens that cover rocks and north-facing cliffs in temperate and highland areas.

39. Tzun-jol tz'i'lel, "messy-haired plant," is *Nama ja-*

maicense (1–2), an erect, delicate herb with lavender and yellow flowers. The leaves are alternate, broadly obovate-spatulate, 1–8 cm long. The blades are decurrent on the petioles and the petioles, narrowly decurrent on the stems. The flowers are solitary or in groups, sessile in the leaf axils. The capsule is elongate, about 1 cm long, pubescent. It is common in disturbed ground in the temperate hamlets.

The leaves are bound to pack sores.

40. **Ventex chij**, "deer chaplet" or "sheep chaplet," is *Lophospermum turneri* (1–2), a pendent herb with alternate, triangular-cordate succulent leaves, 2–5 cm long, and tubular, purple flowers, 3.5–4.5 cm long. The capsule is globose, 1.5 cm long. It occurs on rock outcrops and faces of limestone cliffs in the temperate hamlets.

41. **Voy mula**, "mule hoof," refers to *Valeriana densiflora* (5–9), *V. sorbifolia* (3–3), and *V. urticaefolia* (1–5), rank-smelling, delicately branched herbs with terminal, small, white flowers. The leaves are mostly basal, petiolate, broadly ovate or rotund with dentate margins or pinnate with dentate leaflets. The inflorescence is dichotomously branched, much exceeding the leaves. They are common in the grassy understory of pine-oak forests and in second growth in temperate and highland areas.

Women who do not wish to bear children or who desire an abortion have a variety of prescriptions to choose from. Three tubers with about 5 cm of stalk attached are brewed. One cup of the "hot" tea is drunk before breakfast and supper for three days. This cure is said to shrivel up the uterus for 12 years. Or the tuber may be ground and mixed with cold water to provide a "cold" infusion that is taken once. Or, one cup of a "hot" tea, provided by brewing 12 stalks, is taken before meals for three days. Or, the tuber is ground and mixed with cold water, brown sugar, and cinnamon to provide a "hot" infusion. During the dry season all signs of the plant disappear; accordingly, during this time, women who have taken the cure are said to grow very thin.

Extended range: *Ageratina muelleri*, *Diastatea micrantha*, and *Eryngium longirameum*.

42. **Xanxan** (**-tik**, **-iltik**) refers to the club mosses and reurrection mosses.

Specifics: 3.

a. **Xanxanil balamil**, "terrestrial **xanxan**" (**muk'ta xanxan**), refers to *Lycopodium clavatum* (1–4) and *L. thyoides* (5–7), creeping dichotomously branched plants with scale-like leaves or dense whorls of linear leaves, 4–8 mm long, and terminal, club-shaped, fruiting bodies. They are common in dense understory of wet pine-oak and evergreen cloud forest of temperate and highland areas.

The entire plants of *L. thyoides* are provided by the Stewards of Our Lady of the Rosary on the eighth *Posada* to decorate the litter of the Virgin Mary and the Christ Children's bed. They are tied to the Christ Children's bed just before they are born. They are sold in San Cristóbal and Tuxtla by Chamulans and by the people of San Felipe during the Christmas season. A plant may be tied around a baby's leg so that it will learn to walk faster (the verb **xanav** means "to walk").

b. **Xanxanil te'**, "arboreal **xanxan**" (**balajtik xanxanil te'** and **ne tz'i' tz'i'lel** in part), refers to *Lycopodium taxifolium* (1–5) and *L. tuerkheimii* (1–5), pendent epiphytes in evergreen cloud forest of highland areas. They are dichotomously branched with scale-like leaves or dense whorls of linear leaves and terminal, club-shaped fruiting bodies. Stems of *L. taxifolium* are up to 3 cm thick with whorls of linear leaves to 2 cm long. Stems of *L. tuerkheimii* are more delicate, up to 1 mm wide, with scale-like leaves.

The plant is used occasionally for thatch and as a fixer for daub.

c. **Xanxanil ton**, "rock-growing **xanxan**" (**muk'ta xanxan, poxil jik'ik'ul obal**), is *Selaginella pallescens* (4–6), a tufted plant that is common on exposed, rocky slopes in temperate and highland areas. The leafy stems are branched and appear flattened due to the small leaves arising in one plane. They are ovate and about 1.5–3 mm long.

As a remedy for whooping cough, it is brewed together with several genera of crustose lichens. **Yikatz toj** and the flowers of **k'ox tz'oban** may be added.

43. **Xenxerva** is ginger *Zingiber officinale* (1–1). It is available in the markets. It is a perennial herb arising from an aromatic rhizome. The stems are a meter high or more with numerous, parallel-veined, sheathing, lanceolate or linear-lanceolate leaves. The flowers are yellowish green, tubular, about 2 cm long, and are borne in a long pedunculate, ellipsoidal dense spike, about 5 cm long. The flowers are subtended by ovate bracts, about 2.5 cm long.

Ginger may be chewed as a remedy for laryngitis, "opening the throat." It is used to flavor corn gruel. It is "hot."

44. **Xinal pox**, "stinky medicine" (**k'anal nich**), is *Melampodium montanum* (4–6), a common, sprawling herb with numerous, pale-yellow daisy flowers about 8–17 mm broad. The leaves are opposite, sessile, oblong-ovate or elliptic, 1–3.5 cm long. The flowers are terminal or slender naked peduncles, exceeding the leaves. It occurs on grassy slopes in the understory of pine-oak forest and in disturbed ground such as cornfields in temperate and highland areas.

As a remedy for "wind" and diarrhea or bloody dysentery, a small bunch is brewed. A cup of the "hot" tea is drunk before breakfast. **Krus jobel** (*Cyperus hermaphroditus*) may be added to the tea.

45. **Xinal tz'i'lel**, "stinky plant," is *Porophyllum ruderale* ssp. *macrocephalum* (1–1), a lowland plant common along roadsides and in second growth. It is an erect, strong-scented annual, sparsely branched with alternate, broadly ovate leaves,

1–3 cm long. The flowering heads are purple and yellow, about 25–28 mm long, on peduncles that are conspicuously thickened above.

As a remedy for stomach "wind," a small bunch is brewed for a "hot" tea.

46. **Yail tz'i'lel**, "hot plant" (**pochajtik anal tz'i'lel, yat nab**), refers to the docks *Rumex crispus* (2–3), and *R. obtusifolius* (3–4), roadside and disturbed field weeds in the highland areas, especially along side streets in towns. They are erect, coarse, perennials with stout stems and mostly basal leaves, oblong or oblong lanceolate, 15–40 cm long, rounded at the base. The flowers are white, very small, and arranged in clusters on the branches of the raceme or panicle. The fruit is an achene enclosed in three wing-like, dry, lacerate or entire, inflated perianth segments.

The "hot" leaf may be bound to a bone break. It may also be crushed and applied to the neck for **poslom**. Formerly, the leaves were gathered occasionally and sold to butchers in San Cristóbal to wrap meat.

47. **Yajan chuch**, "squirrel's ear of corn" (**-tik**), refers to the chlorophyll-less root parasites.

Specifics: 2.

    a. **Batz'i yajan chuch**, "genuine squirrel's ear of corn" (**ajan tz'i'lel, yajan joj**), is *Conopholis americana* (2–4), a pale yellow plant about the size and shape of an ear of corn. It arises from a perennial swollen base and is erect and unbranched. The stem is covered with imbricate sessile scales, which continue upward into the spikate inflorescence. The flowers are tubular about 22 mm long. It occurs in the understory of wet pine-oak and evergreen cloud forests in the highland areas.

    b. **Tzajal yajan chuch**, "red squirrel's ear of corn," is *Helosis mexicana* (2–5), a red, parasitic, mushroom-shaped plant up to 20 cm tall that occurs in the humus of the understory of dense tropical deciduous and seasonal evergreen forests of lowland areas.

48. **Yak'ubal us**, "gnat's night" (**ak'ubal us, ch'a-te' ka'** and **mesjob tz'i'lel** in part, **nak'ubal us, nochleb buluk' sat**), refers to small, densely branched composite shrubs that have a large profusion of white or pink, strongly scented flowers, which are abundantly visited by flies, especially members of the family Tachinidae. Zinacantecs recognize that there are white, **sak**, and pink, **tzoj**, varieties. Included are *Ageratina bustamenta* (1–2), *A. petiolaris* (1–2), *A. pringlei* (2–3), *Fleischmannia pycnocephalum* (1–2), *Peteravenia phoenicolepis* (1–2), *Stevia caracasana* (1–2), *S. connata* (1–2), *S. ovata* (4–7), and *S. serrata* (1–2). These occur in second growth and in the open understory of pine-oak forests of the highland and temperate regions.

The "hot" leaves of *P. phoenicolepis* are boiled and applied to the toes when the flesh around the toenails rots in the rainy season. The flowers of the same plant and of *S. ovata* are used for altar decoration on All Souls' Day. They are sold in the market in Tuxtla.

49. **Yat nab**, "lake penis" (**akan tz'i'lel, koko'on nich nab, yail tz'i'lel, yitaj pale**), refers to *Polygonum portoricense* (1–2) and *P. punctatum* (4–5), tall herbs with erect, dense racemes of white or pink flowers up to 10 cm long and 3-angled fruits. The leaves are alternate, sheathing or petiolate, linear-lanceolate, to 25 cm long. They occur in large colonies in standing water throughout the township.

They are believed to be lethal when consumed by sheep.

50. **Yat tz'i' tz'i'lel**, "dog's penis plant," is *Lactuca graminifolia* (1–1). It is an erect, perennial, with simple, stout stems, naked or with a few basal leaves. These are linear-lanceolate and pinnatifid, up to 20 cm long. The flowers are pink or white in heads, terminal on an openly branched inflorescence. It occurs in the grassy understory of pine-oak forests in the temperate areas.

Literature Cited

1. PUBLISHED WORKS

Alcorn, Janis B.
  1984. *Huastec Mayan Ethnobotany.* Austin: University of Texas.

Aulie, H. Wilbur, and Evelyn W. de Aulie, César Menéses Diaz, Cristóbal López Vázquez
  1978. Diccionario Ch'ol-Español, Español-Ch'ol. *Serie de Vocabularios y Diccionarios Indígenas Mariano Silva y Aceves* (Mexico City), 21.

Becerra, Marcos E.
  1935. Vocabulario de la lengua chol: Que se habla en el districto de Palenque del estado de Chiapas, de la Republica Mexicana. *Anales del Museo Nacional de Arqueología, Historia y Etnografía* (Mexico City), 2:249–278.

Berlin, Brent, Dennis E. Breedlove, Robert M. Laughlin, and Peter H. Raven, editors
  1973. Cultural Significance and Lexical Retention in Tzeltal-Tzotzil Ethnobotany. In *Meaning in Mayan Languages: Ethnolinguistic Studies,* pages 236–275. The Hague: Mouton Press.

Berlin, Brent, Dennis E. Breedlove, and Peter H. Raven
  1974. *Principles of Tzeltal Plant Classification: An Introduction to the Botanical Ethnography of a Mayan-Speaking People of Highland Chiapas.* New York: Seminar Press, Inc.

Breedlove, Dennis E.
  1981. *Flora of Chiapas, Part I.* San Francisco, California: California Academy of Sciences.

Breedlove, Dennis E., and Nicholas A. Hopkins
  1970. Study of Chuj (Mayan) Plants with Notes on Their Uses, I. *The Wasmann Journal of Biology,* 28(2).
  1971. A Study of Chuj (Mayan) Plants, with Notes on Their Uses, II. *The Wasmann Journal of Biology,* 29(1).

Breedlove, Dennis E., and Robert M. Laughlin
  1984. La rama dorada: Mágia y botánica en Zinacantán. *Investigaciones Recientes en el Area Maya,* 1:349–355. [XVII Mesa Redonda, Sociedad Mexicana de Antropología.] San Cristóbal de las Casas: Editorial Fray Bartolomé de Las Casas, A.C.

Bulmer, Ralph, and Michael Tyler
  1968. Karam Classification of Frogs. *Journal of the Polynesian Society,* 77:333–385.

Bunnin, Nicholas F.
  1966. La industria de las flores en Zinacantan. *In* Evon Z. Vogt, editor, *Los Zinacantecos: Un Pueblo Tzotzil de los Altos de Chiapas,* 7:208–232. Mexico City: Instituto Nacional Indigenista, Colección de Antropología Social.

Cancian, Frank
  1965. *Economics and Prestige in a Maya Community: The Religious Cargo System in Zinacantan.* Stanford: Stanford University Press.
  1972. *Change and Uncertainty in a Peasant Economy: The Maya Corn Farmers of Zinacantan.* Stanford: Stanford University Press.
  1986. Las listas de espera en el sistema de cargos de Zinacantán: Cambios sociales, políticos y económicos (1952–1980). *America Indígena,* XLVI(3):477–494.
  1987. Proletarianization in Zinacantán, 1960 to 1986. *In* Morgan D. Machlaclan, editor, *Household Economics and Their Transformations,* pages 131–142. Lanham, Maryland: University Press of America.

Chamberlain, Robert S.
  1948. The Governorship of the Adelantado Francisco de Montejo in Chiapas 1539–1544. *Contributions to American Anthropology and History,* 9:163–207.

Coe, Michael D.
  1980. *In the Land of the Olmec.* Austin: University of Texas Press.

Colby, Benjamin N.
  1966. Ethnographic Semantics: A Preliminary Survey. *Current Anthropology,* 7(1):3–32.

Collier, George A.
  1975. *Fields of the Tzotzil: The Ecological Bases of Tradition in Highland Chiapas.* Austin: University of Texas Press.

Collier, George A., and Daniel C. Mountjoy
  1988. Adaptandose a lacrisis de los ochenta: cambios socio-económicos en Apas, Zinacantán. *Serie Documentos de Trabajo sobre Cambio en el Campo Chiapaneco,* 035-II/88. San Cristóbal de las Casas: Instituto de Asesora Antropolgica para la Región Maya, A.C.

Comparato, Frank E., translator
  1983. *History of the Conquest of the Province of the Iztec by Juan de Villagutierre Soto-Mayor.* Culver City: Labyrinthos.

De Vos, Jan
  1985. La batalla del Sumidero: Antología de documentos relativos a la rebelión de los Chiapanecos, 1524–1534. *Serie Historia Regional,* 5. Mexico City: Editorial Katun, S.A.

Edel, Matthew D.
  1966. El ejido en Zinacantan. *In* Evon Z. Vogt, editor, *Los Zinacatecos: Un Pueblo Tzotzil de los Altos de Chiapas,* 7:163–182. Mexico City: Instituto Nacional Indigenista, Colección de Antropología Social.

Edmonson, Munro S.
  1965. Quiche-English Dictionary. *Middle American Research Institute,* 30. New Orleans: Tulane University.

Fábrega, Horacio, Jr., and Daniel B. Silver
  1973. *Illness and Shamanistic Curing in Zinacantan: An Ethnomedical Analysis.* Stanford: Stanford University Press.

Foster, Mary L., and George M. Foster
  1948. *Sierra Popoluca Speech.* Washington, D.C.: Smithsonian Institution, Institute of Social Anthropology.

Frazer, Sir James George
  1890. *The Golden Bough: A Study in Comparative Religion.* London and New York: MacMillan and Co.

Gage, Thomas
  1655. *A New Survey of the West India's: or, the English American in Travail by Sea and Land.* London: E. Cotes.

García, E.
  1965. Distribución de la precipitación en la Republica Mexicana. *Publicación del Instituto de Geografía de México,* 1:173–191. Mexico City: Universidad Nacional Autónoma de México.
  1973. *Modificationes al sistema de clasificacion climaticá de Koeppen.* Mexico City: Universidad Nacional Autónoma de México.

Harrison, Roy, Margaret Harrison, and Castulo García H.
  1981. *Diccionario Zoque de Copainalá.* Mexico City: Instituto Linguístico de Verano.

Helbig, Karl M.
  1964. *La cuenca superior del Rio Grijalva.* Tuxtla Gutiérrez, Chiapas: Instituto de Ciencias y Artes de Chiapas.

Herbruger, Alfredo, Jr., and Eduardo Díaz Barrios
  1956. *Método para aprender a hablar, leer, y escribir la lengua cakchiquel.* Guatemala City: Tipografía Nacional.

Instituto Nacional de Estadística, Geografía e Informática
1983. *X censo general de población y vivienda, 1980, estado de Chiapas,* 7(1). Mexico City.

Laughlin, Robert M.
1962. El símbolo de la flor en la religión de Zinacantan. *Estudios de Cultura Maya* (Mexico City), 2:123–139.
1975. The Great Tzotzil Dictionary of San Lorenzo Zinacantán. *Smithsonian Contributions to Anthropology,* 19.
1976. Of Wonders Wild and New: Dreams from Zinacantán. *Smithsonian Contributions to Anthropology,* 22.
1977. Of Cabbages and Kings: Tales from Zinacantán. *Smithsonian Contributions to Anthropology,* 23.
1980. Of Shoes and Ships and Sealing Wax: Sundries from Zinacantán. *Smithsonian Contributions to Anthropology,* 25.
1983. Agricultural Prayers of Zinacantan, Chiapas. *Mesoamérica* (La Antigua Guatemala), 4(5):128–167.

Laughlin, Robert M., with John B. Haviland
1988. The Great Tzotzil Dictionary of Santo Domingo Zinacantán: With Grammatical Analysis and Historical Commentary. *Smithsonian Contributions to Anthropology,* 31.

Lenkersdorf, Carlos
1979. *b'omak'umal tojol ab'al–kastiya: Diccionario tojolabal–español.* Volume 1. Mexico City: Editorial Nuestro Tiempo.

Marín, Alfredo Barrera, Alfredo Barrera Vásquez, and Rosa Maria López Franco
1976. Nomenclatura etnobotánica maya: Una interpretación taxonómica, Instituto Nacional de Antropología e Historia, Centro Regional del Sureste. *Colección Científica* (Etnología), 36. Mexico City.

Miranda, Faustino
1952–1953. *La vegetación de Chiapas.* Volumes 1, 2. Tuxtla Gutiérrez, Chiapas: Sección Autográfica, Departamento de Prensa y Turismo.

National Academy of Sciences
1977. *Leucaena: Promising Forage and Tree Crop for the Tropics.* Washington, D.C.

Perchonock, Norma, and Oswald Werner
1969. Navajo Systems of Classification: Some Implications for Ethnoscience. *Ethnology,* 8(3):229–242.

Remesal, Antonio de
1932. *Historia general de las Indias occidentales, y particular de la gobernación de Chiapas y Guatemala.* 2 volumes. Guatemala City: Tipografía Nacional.

Sáenz de Santa María, Carmelo
1940. *Diccionario Cakchiquel–Español.* Guatemala City: Tipografía Nacional.

Sapir, Edward
1929. The Status of Linguistics As a Science. *Language,* 5:207–214.

Schumann, Otto G.
1973. La Lengua Chol, de Tila (Chiapas). *Centro de Estudios Mayas, Cuaderno* (Mexico City), 8.

Slocum, Marianna, and Florencia L. Gerdel
1965. Vocabulario Tzeltal de Bachajón: Castellano–Tzeltal, Tzeltal–Castellano. *Serie de Vocabularios Indígenas Mariano Silva y Aceves* (Mexico City), 13.

Stauder, Jack R.
1966. Algunos aspectos de la agricultura zinacanteca en tierra caliente. *In* Evon Z. Vogt, editor, *Los Zinacantecos: Un Pueblo Tzotzil de los Altos de Chiapas,* 7:145–162. Mexico City: Instituto Nacional Indigenista, Colección de Antropología Social.

Ulrich, Mateo, and Rosemary de Ulrich
1976. *Dicionario Bilingue: Maya Mopán y Español, Español y Maya Mopán.* Guatemala City: Instituto Linguistico de Verano.

Vogt, Evon Z.
1969. *Zinacantan: A Maya Community in the Highlands of Chiapas.* Cambridge: The Belknap Press of Harvard University Press.
1970. *The Zinacantanecs of Mexico: A Modern Maya Way of Life.* New York: Holt, Rhinehart & Winston.
1976. *Tortillas for the Gods: A Symbolic Analysis of Zinacanteco Rituals.* Cambridge: Harvard University Press.

Warfield, James P.
1966. La arquitectura en Zinacantan. *In* Evon Z. Vogt, editor, *Los Zinacantecos: Un Pueblo Tzotzil de Los Altos de Chiapas,* 7:183–207. Mexico City: Instituto Nacional Indigenista, Colección de Antropología Social.

Wasserstrom, Robert
1983. *Class and Society in Central Chiapas.* Berkeley: University of California Press.

Weathers, Kenneth
1946. La agricultura de los Tzotzil de Nabenchauc, Chiapas, México. *America Indígena,* VI(4):315–319.

Whitaker, Anabelle, and Viola Warkentin
1965. Chol Texts on the Supernatural. *Summer Institute of Linguistics, Publications in Linguistics and Related Fields* (Norman), 13.

Ximénez, Francisco
1929–1931. *Historia de la provincia de San Vicente de Chiapa y Guatemala de la orden de predicadores.* 3 volumes. Guatemala City: Tipografía Nacional.

2. Unpublished Works (Including Correspondence)

(* = publication is in possession of Terrence Kaufman, Department of Anthropology, University of Pittsburgh)

Biblioteca del Centro de Investigaciones Ecológicas del Sureste
1982. Campaña Nacional de Eradicación de Paludismo. San Cristóbal L.C.

Berlin, Brent
*1967. Notebook, July.

Bradburn, Anne S., and Victoria R. Bricker
*1986. Flora of Hocabá.

Canger, Una
*1969. Field notes (Lacandón, Teco).

Correa, Patricio
1848a. Parish report, 12 June. Archivo Histórico Diocesano de San Cristóbal.
1848b. Parish report, 11 November. Archivo Histórico Diocesano de San Cristóbal.

de León y Goicoechea, José
1797. Parish report, 14 February. Archivo Histórico Diocesano de San Cristóbal.

de Morales, Nicolas
1793. Letter to Francisco Gabriel de Olivares y Benito, 13 December. Archivo Histórico Diocesano de San Cristóbal.

Escarra, Manuel Ignacio
1819. Parish report, 21 June. Archivo Histórico Diocesano de San Cristóbal.

Hopkins, Nicholas A.
*1980–1982. Tumbalá Chol Word List.

Hurtado, Juan
1788. Edict, 7 January. Tulane University: Latin American Library.

Kaufman, Terrence
*1967–1984. Mayan Vocabulary Surveys. [1967–1968 Mochó, Teco; 1969 Yucatec; 1969–1979 Mam; 1970–1971 Aguácatec, Chorti, Chuj, Ixil, Jacaltec, K'ekchi, Mopán, Pocomam, Sacapultec, Sipacapeño, Tzutujil, and Uspantec; 1982–1984 Huastec.]

Keller, Kathryn C.
*1968. Mayan Vocabulary Survey for Chontal of Tapotzingo.

Laughlin, Robert M.
1965. Letter to B.N. Colby, 10 May.

Lopez, Mariano Jacinto
  1855.   Letter to Feliciano José Laras, 5 July. Archivo Histórico Diocesano de San Cristóbal.
McVicker, Donald E.
  1972.   A Preliminary Archaeological Survey of the Municipio of Zinacantan, Chiapas, Mexico. 33 pages. Harvard University: Harvard Chiapas Project. [Summer field report.]
Monrroy y Calçadilla, José
  1748.   Parish report, 18 August. Archivo Histórico Diocesano de San Cristóbal.

Proyecto Linguístico Francisco Marroquín
  *1971–1978. Mayan Vocabulary Survey. [1971–1978 Cakchiquel, Quiché; 1973–1978 Kanjobal, Pocomchí.]
Samartin, Salvador
  1819.   Edict, 30 June. Archivo Histórico Diocesano de San Cristóbal.
Walker, James
  *1969.   Mayan Vocabulary Survey for Chontal of Tapotzingo.

Appendix 1

Mayan Plant Name Cognates

"Vines"

(Numbers in stub are references for reading horizontal alignments between this and following pages; in the body of the table, superscript numbers refer to notes in the "Notes" section, and subscript numbers apply to references found in the "Sources" section (if there is no subscript number, the term is found in all sources), both at the end of this appendix.)

	Wasteko	Yukateko	Lakantun	Mopan	Ch'orti'	Chontal	Ch'ol	Tzotzil	Col. Tzotzil	Tzeltal
1								botil		xbojt'il chenek'[1]
2	chanak'w[1,3]						kanchenyek'	chenek'[1]	chenek'	chenek'
3	tzanak'w[2]						k'anchenek'[5]			
4								ch'ako'		ch'ajko[1]
5		k'ùum[1,2]	k'uum	k'uum	ch'um	ch'um	ch'ujm	ch'um	ch'um	ch'um[1]
6							ch'um[5]			
7				ch'uum		ch'ijch'um	ch'ijch'um	ch'um-te'		ch'oma te'[1]
8							ch'ich'um[5]			ch'uma te'[2]
9								ch'umte' ch'o		ch'oma te' ch'o[1]
10		iib[1,2]	iib					ibes		
11								ich ak'		ichi ak'[1]
12								jay		jahy[1]
13								kururin		kuranina chin ak'[1]
14								k'an-ak'		k'an ak'[1]
15							mayajl	mail	mail	mayil
16							mokon	makom	makum	makum[1]
17								pataxet		
18								pik'ok'		sk'ok'[1]
19								polotz'		polotz'[1]
20								p'uk		p'ujk[1]
21		sikil				sakir		sakil[2]		
22	tu'	chúuj[2]	chuuj	chuj				tzu	tzu	tzu
23			ch'u'							
24		tz'ool[1]						tz'ol		tz'ol[1]
25	t'uthub		tz'uus			tz'utz'um	tz'usubil	tz'usub	tz'usub	tz'usub[1]
26							tz'usub[5]			
27	wako	j waako[2]						vako' ak'		
28								x'ak'il chenek'[3]	x'ak'il chenek'	tel 'ak' chenek'
29								xlumil chenek'		xlumil chenek'
30								xut		xut chenek'[1]
31	weet'							xvet'		xwek'[1]

287

"VINES"—*Continued.*

(Numbers in stub are references for reading horizontal alignments between this and preceding/following pages.)

	Tojolabal	Chuj	Q'anjob'al	Popti' (Jakalteko)	Mocho	Teko	Mam	Awakateko	Ixil	Uspanteko	K'iche'
1	botil										
2	chenek'					kyenaq'	cheenq			kiinaq'	kinaq'
3											
4											
5	k'um	k'um₁	k'um	k'um	k'uum	k'uum	k'um	k'um	k'um	k'um	k'uum
6											
7								tx'umaa'		ch'ima	ch'imaj₁
8											ch'imaa'₂
9											
10											
11											
12											
13	kururina				kuraríina						
14											
15	mayil										
16											
17					pataxe'k	pataxhet					
18	pik'ok'										
19											
20											
21	sakil	sakil₁	sachil			skiil		xchiil		sakiil	sakiil
22	tzuj	tzu₁	tzu	tzuj	tzuj	tzuu	tzuu	tzuu'	tzuj	tzu	tzuh₁
23		tzuj₂									tzu₂
24	tz'ol										
25	tz'usub	tz'usup₁									
26											
27					wáako						
28	tel 'ak' chenek'										
29	lu'um chenek'										
30											
31											

"VINES"—*Continued.*

(Numbers in stub are references for reading horizontal alignments between this and preceding pages.)

	Sipakapenyo	Sakapulteko	Tz'utujil	Kaqchikel	Poqomam	Poqomchi'	Q'eqchi'
1							
2	knaq'	kinaq'	kynaq'$_1$	kinaq'	kinaq'	kinaq'	keenq'
3			kinaq'$_2$				
4							
5	k'um	k'uum	k'uum$_1$	k'un	k'uum	k'uum	k'uum$_1$
6			k'um$_2$				k'um$_2$
7	ch'may	ch'imaay	ch'maay	ch'ima'$_1$	ch'um'aah	ch'umaa	ch'imah
8			ch'imaay$_2$				
9				ch'imach'oy$_1$			
10							
11							
12							
13						kureriina	
14							
15							
16							
17							
18							
19							
20							
21	skiil	sikiil	sakil	sakil			sakil
22	tzuy		tzu'y$_1$	tzuy	sbh	sbh	sbuh$_1$
23			tzujy$_2$			sb	sbh$_2$
24							
25						t'usuub	
26							
27							
28							
29							
30							
31							

"TREES"

(Numbers in stub are references for reading horizontal alignments between this and following pages.)

	Wasteko	Yukateko	Lakantun	Mopan	Ch'orti'	Chontal	Ch'ol	Tzotzil	Col. Tzotzil	Tzeltal
1								aj[1]	aj	aj
2	oj							aj te'		ajate'[1]
3										
4										
5										
6								ajoj		ajoj[1]
7	akich[1,3]							akit		
8	akitz[2]									
9							atz'am te'[4]	atz'am te'[2]		
10							atz'am tye[5]			
11								be xinich te'[1]		xanich te'[1]
12								boch		bojch[1]
13	baat							bot		bat[1]
14	choo' te[1,3]							chachi'		
15	tzoo' te'[2]									
16								chalon[3,4]		
17	chajib[1,3]							chanib		chanib[1]
18	tzajib[2]									
19	chi'im[1,3]	kìij[1]	kiij	kij	sbk chij	chij	chij	chi[5]	chi	chi
20	tzi'im[2]									
21		chi'[2,3]		chi'	chi'		chi'	chi'		chi'[1]
22							chijtye'	chijil te'		chijil te'[1]
23							chijitye'			
24								chikin-ib		chikinib jij te'[1]
25										chikinib[2]
26								chilkat		
27							chinin[1]	chinin		
28								chix te'	chix te'	
29								ch'a-te'		ch'aj te'[1]
30		ch'i'b[1]	ch'ib	ch'ib			bäk ch'ib[4]	ch'ib[6]		ch'ib[1]
31							ch'ich' ni'[4]	ch'ich' ni'[7]		ch'ich' ni'[1]
32							chijt	ch'it		ch'ijt[1]
33								ch'ix		ch'ix te'[1]
34		k' úuche'[1]	k'úuj che'	k'uche'		ajch'ujte'	ch'ujte'	ch'u te'[8,9]	ch'u te'	ch'ujte'[2]
35							ch'ipäk	ch'upak' te'		ch'opak te'[1]
36								ik'al vinik		winik te'[1]
37	unup			inäp	inup			inop[10]		
38										
39										
40								isbon		siban[1]
41								itzompi		itzam[1]
42	it'ath	ja's[1]	ja'as	ja'as	jaas	ja'as	way ja'as	ja'as[11]		ja'as[1]
43		já'as[2]					wolja'as			waleja'as[2]
44	kakaw te'[2]						kakate'	kakav te'		
45							käkätye'[5]			
46	káakaw[1]	káakaw	kakaw	käkäw	kakaw	käkäw	käkäw	kokov[12]		kakaw
47										
48								k'ail		
49								k'an-te'		k'an te'[1]
50		k'áanis te'[2]						k'anas te'		
51		kaniste[3]								
52					k'ewex		k'ewex	k'evex[13]		k'ewex
53										
54								k'isis[14]	k'isis	k'isis taj
55										
56								k'olk'ox		
57		x k'olo'má'ax[2]						k'olo-max[15]		k'olonax[1]
58	k'olo'ma'ax[3]									

"Trees"—*Continued.*

(Numbers in stub are references for reading horizontal alignments between this and following pages.)

	Wasteko	Yukateko	Lakantun	Mopan	Ch'orti'	Chontal	Ch'ol	Tzotzil	Col. Tzotzil	Tzeltal
59							k'olok'	k'orok' te'		
60								k'oxox te'		k'oxox te'[1]
61								k'uk' toj		k'uk' taj
62										
63								lo'bol		lo'bal[2]
64							makulis	makulixkuat		
65								matz'an-tzotz		matz'am sotz'[1]
66								mes te'[16]		mes te'[1]
67								moy te'		may te'[1]
68			muumuum xukur				momon[1]	mumun		mumun te'[1]
69							momoy[2]			
70							momun[5]			
71							mumún[6]			

"TREES"—*Continued.*

(Numbers in stub are references for reading horizontal alignments between this and following pages.)

	Tojolabal	Chuj	Q'anjob'al	Popti' (Jakalteko)	Mocho	Teko	Mam	Awakateko	Ixil	Uspanteko
1	aj	aj	aj	aj	aaj			aaj₁	aj	aaj
2	ajate'	ajte'₁							a'atze'	áajche'
3			ajawte'₁		ajatee'	jaatzee'		ajatza'n₁	a'tze'	
4			xajawte'₂					ajaatza'n₂	aatze'	
5										
6										
7										
8										
9										
10										
11										sinik-chée'
12										
13			bat		bat	batz				
14										
15										
16					chalu'n					chulúm
17										
18										
19	chij	chiy₁	chi'	sajhchi	kiij	sakyiil	saqchii	chii'₁		kii
20		chij₂						saqchii'₂	saq chij	
21								chii'		
22										
23										
24	chikinib									
25										
26	chiika									
27										
28										
29									k'ib	
30	ch'ib	k'ib₁								
31										
32	ch'it									
33										
34		k'ute'₁	k'ute'			k'uutee'	k'uute			
35	ch'upakchej	ch'upak te'₂								
36										
37	inip	inup	inup	inup		anup		unup	inup	inip
38										
39										
40										
41										
42	ja'as			jas			jaatze			
43										
44										
45										
46	kakaw	kakaw	kakaw	kakaw	kakaw	kaakaaw	kyuw	kikyuj₂	kakaw	kokow
47										
48		k'ayil₂			k'ajil					
49	k'ante'									
50										
51										
52	k'ewex	k'ewex	k'ewex			ky'iiwiix	ch'wix	tz'ujux₁	cy'ewex	k'owax
53								tx'uux₂		k'ewex₂
54	k'i'is	k'isis	k'isis	tz'isis	k'isis	ky'iisiis	tzsis	tz'isis	cy'isis tze'	k'isis
55										
56	k'olk'oxte'									
57										
58										

"TREES"—*Continued.*

(Numbers in stub are references for reading horizontal alignments between this and following pages.)

	Tojolabal	Chuj	Q'anjob'al	Popti' (Jakalteko)	Mocho	Teko	Mam	Awakateko	Ixil	Uspanteko
59										
60	k'oxoxte'									
61		k'u' taj$_1$	q'uq' taj	k'u' taj						
62		k'up' taj								
63	lo'bal									
64										
65										
66		mes$_2$								
67										
68	momon	momon		moomon						
69										
70										
71										

294

"TREES"—*Continued.*

(Numbers in stub are references for reading horizontal alignments between this and following pages.)

	K'iche'	Sipakapenyo	Sakapulteko	Tz'utujil	Kaqchikel	Poqomam	Poqomchi'	Q'eqchi'
1	aaj$_1$	aaj	aaj	aaj$_2$	aj	aaj	aaj	aaj$_1$
2								aj$_2$
3	ajache'$_1$	ajchee'	ajachee'	aj che'$_1$	ajache'$_1$		ahache	
4								
5								
6								
7	baqit$_2$							
8								
9								
10								
11								
12								
13								
14								
15								
16	chalum				chalum			
17								
18					saqkiy	sajkiih	sajkii	chi'
19	kih$_1$	kiiy	saqkiiy	sajkiiy				
20	sajki'$_2$							
21								
22								
23								
24								
25								
26								
27								
28								
29								
30	k'iib$_1$						k'iib	k'iib
31								
32								
33								
34	tyox chee'$_1$		tiyoox chee'	tyoox chee'	tyox che'			
35								
36								
37	inuup		anuup	anuup$_1$	anup$_1$	nuup	nuup	inup
38				nuup$_2$	onup$_1$			
39					unüp$_2$			
40								
41								
42								
43								
44								
45								
46	kakaw$_1$	kakaaw	kakaawa	kokow$_2$	kako'uj$_1$	kikow	kikow	kakaw
47	kaka'w$_2$				kako$_1$			
48								
49								
50								
51								
52	k'awex$_1$			k'wax$_1$	k'evex[13]		k'ebex	
53	k'ewex$_2$			k'ewex$_2$				
54	ki'isiis$_2$		k'isiis	k'siis$_1$	k'isis		k'isiis	
55				k'isiis$_2$				
56								
57								
58								

"TREES"—*Continued.*

(Numbers in stub are references for reading horizontal alignments between this and following pages.)

	K'iche'	Sipakapenyo	Sakapulteko	Tz'utujil	Kaqchikel	Poqomam	Poqomchi	Q'eqchi'
59								
60								
61								
62								
63								
64								
65								
66								
67								
68								
69								
70								
71								

"TREES"—Continued.

(Numbers in stub are references for reading horizontal alignments between this and following pages.)

	Wasteko	Yukateko	Lakantun	Mopan	Ch'orti'	Chontal	Ch'ol	Tzotzil	Col. Tzotzil	Tzeltal
72								mutut		mutut[1]
73				muy	muy	muy	muy[1]	muy[17]		
74								nantzi'		nantzin[1]
75	maap	map[3]					mäp[1]	nap	nap	nap[1]
76							mup[5]			map[2]
77								no'chi'		no'chi'[1]
78								nok		najk[1]
79								nukul pat	nukul pat	nujkupat[1]
80								ok'il te'	ok'il te'	
81	oj	òon[1]	oon	on	un	um		on[18]	on	on
82		òom[2]								
83	uj					un				
84	oj-te'							on te'[19]		on te'[1]
85		otoch[1]	atooch	otoch			otot	otot[20]		
86								paj-'ul[21]		paj'ul'ul
87										
88								pik'in te'		pikin te'
89		piich[2]						pit		
90							po'om	po'on	po'on	po'om[2]
91	hom-te'	pòom[2]	pom	pom		pom	pom	pom		pom
92										
93				p'ataj		pata	pätaj	potov te'		pata te'[1]
94										pata[2]
95								sap-yok		sakyok jij te'[1]
96								saya-vun	saya-Hun	
97		sitit[3]						sitit		sitit
98								soj		soj
99		xpàay che'[2]						soro te'[22]		
100							stzuy	sbil itaj		stzuy
101	thuk							suk[23]		
102		su'n[1]					sun	sun		sun[1]
103		sb'm[1]								jsun[2]
104		súum[2]								
105				úle	te'	te'-ule		te'el uli'		ula[2]
106										
107								tilil		tilil ja'[1]
108		tajte'[1]	tajte'	täkte'	taj te'		taj	toj	toj	taj
109							tyaj[5]			
110	tok'oy							tok'oy	tok'oy	tok'oy[1]
111								ton bek'	ton bek'	
112								tuil te'[1]		tuil te'[1]
113								tulan	tulan	
114								tzajal te'		tzajal te'[1]
115								tzelepat		tzelepat[1]
116	tima'			chimaj	tzimaj		tzima	tzima'		tzima[1]
117										
118										
119										
120										
121								tzima' ch'ix		ch'ix tzima[1]
122						tz'utz' um	tzitz[1]	tzitz		tzitz
123								tzotz-ni' te'		tzotz ni' te'[1]
124								tz'erel		tz'elel[1]
125	t'inche'[1]	tz'iim[1,2]	tz'iin		tz'ijn-te'	tz'in	tz'ijm[1]	tz'in te'		tz'in te'
126	t'intze'[2]						tz'ijn[2]			
127	t'inte'[3]									
128								tz'oban te'		stz'oban[1]
129								tz'utuj te'		tz'utoj te'[1]
130			x ta' uch				ta-uch[6]	uch		
131								vax te'		vax ak'[1]
132						jo'ox	jo'ox	vo'ox		jo'ox
133		xa'n[1]	xa'n	xa'an	xan		xan	xan		xan
134		xa'ax[2]								
135		xaxim[3]						xaxib[24]		xaxib[1]
136	jutukuu'							x'ukun		ujkum[1]
137								yisim bolom		yisim balam

"TREES"—*Continued.*

(Numbers in stub are references for reading horizontal alignments between this and following pages.)

	Tojolabal	Chuj	Q'anjob'al	Popti' (Jakalteko)	Mocho	Teko	Mam	Awakateko	Ixil	Uspanteko
72										
73										
74	nantze									
75	nap		map	map	map	map		mop		mop
76										
77										
78										
79										
80										
81	on	oṅ	on	oṅ		ooj	ooj	ooj	oj	óoj
82										
83										
84			onte'							
85		atut							otzotz	
86	paj'ulul	paj ullte'$_1$								
87		pajulul te'$_2$								
88										
89		pit$_1$		pit	piit	piit				
90	po'om	po'on	pon	pon		po'm	poon	poom		póom
91	pomte'	pom$_1$	pomte'$_1$			poom				
92			pom$_2$							
93	pata	pata		pata'	pataj					
94	pataj									
95										
96										
97	sitit									
98										
99		pay te'	pay te'							
100		tzuy								
101	suk									
102	su'umte'	su'un		sun			su'n	su'n	su'n	suun
103										
104								uul tzee'		tze'il uule
105	ule	hula'$_1$	steal ule$_1$	te' úla						
106			ule$_2$							
107										
108	taj	taj	taj	taj	taj	tzaj	tzaj	tzaj	tzah	chaj
109										
110	tok'oy	tak'uy$_1$				to'q'ooy				
111										
112										
113										
114										
115										
116	tzima	tzima$_1$	tzima	tzima		tzimaa'	tzamaa'		tzima$_{1,2}$	tziimaa
117		tzimaj$_2$							cy'ima$_{1,2}$	
118									cy'imay$_3$	
119									tzimay$_3$	
120									tzimey$_3$	
121										
122	tzitz	tzitz oṅ		tzitz						
123										
124	tzelel									
125	tz'inte'		tz'in	tz'inte'	tz'inte'		tz'untee'	tz'iin		tz'iin
126										
127										
128										
129										
130										
131										
132	jo'ox	ho'ox$_1$	ox	jox	jo'x	o'ox	o'x	o'x		
133	xa'an	xan	xan$_2$				xa'j	xa'j		
134										
135		xa'ax$_2$				xa'ax				
136	ujkun	ukun	ukun							
137										

"TREES"—*Continued.*

(Numbers in stub are references for reading horizontal alignments between this and following pages.)

	K'iche'	Sipakapenyo	Sakapulteko	Tz'utujil	Kaqchikel	Poqomam	Poqomchi'	Q'eqchi'
72								
73					muij		muuy	muy
74								
75	mop$_1$		map	nop				maap
76	map$_2$							
77								
78								
79								
80								
81	ooj	ooj	ooj	ooj	oj	uaj	gooj	ooh$_1$
82								oh$_2$
83								
84								
85	ochooch			oochooch				
86								
87								
88								
89	piit$_1$							
90	poom$_2$	poom		poom$_1$	pom	puam		
91								poom$_1$
92								pon$_2$
93								patahl$_1$
94								patah$_2$
95								
96								
97								
98								
99								
100								
101								
102	su'n		so'n	su'n$_1$	su'n		suun	suun$_1$
103				su'm$_2$				sun$_2$
104	uul$_1$						uula	
105						uul	che'l uul	
106								
107								
108	chaj	chaj	chaj	chaj	chäj	chaj	chaj	chaj
109								
110								
111								
112								
113								
114								
115								
116	tzimah$_1$	tzmaay	tzimaay	tzmaay$_1$	tzimay			
117	tzima$_2$			tzimaay$_2$				
118								
119								
120								
121								
122					tzitz$_1$			
123								
124								ch'elel
125	tz'iin		tz'iin	tz'iin	tz'in$_2$	tz'iin	tz'iin	tz'iin$_1$
126								tz'in$_2$
127								
128								
129								
130								
131								
132								
133					xaan			xaan$_1$
134								xan$_2$
135								
136								
137								

"Plants"

(Numbers in stub are references for reading horizontal alignments between this and following pages.)

#	Wasteko	Yukateko	Lakantun	Mopan	Ch'orti'	Chontal	Ch'ol	Tzotzil	Col. Tzotzil	Tzeltal
1								chak'ak'		xchak'ak'[1]
2		chàay[2]						chaya itaj		
3								chichol		chichol[2]
4								ch'aben		ch'aben[1]
5										
6								ch'aben chij		ch'aben chij[1]
7								ch'il vet		ch'ilwet[1]
8								ch'oliv		ch'oliw[1]
9							xch'uch'[5]	ch'uch'		ch'uch jaben[1]
10								ch'upak	ch'upak'	polotz' ch'upak'[1]
11										
12								ch'upak' joj		ch'upak' joj[1]
13								ech'		ech'[1]
14										
15	ich[1,3]	iik[1,2]	iik	ik	ich	ich	ich	ich	ich	ich
16	itz[2]									
17	ith	ìis[2]	iis	is				is-ak'[1]	is-ak'	is ak' chi'in[1]
18										
19								itaj[2]	itaj	itaj
20	eem	ixim[1]		ixi'im	ixim	ixim	ixim	ixim	ixim	ixim
21								koko'on		kajk'an[1]
22								koyoy		yoy[1]
23								k'axib jobel		ch'axib ak
24	chooklay'[1,3]	la		laj				la[3]		la[1]
25	tzooklay'[2]	làal[2]								
26	tiplay'									
27								matas		majtas[1]
28								met		met
29	maay							moy		may
30								ob		j'ob[1]
31								pa' itaj		pa'itaj[1]
32			pa'ch'				pajch'	paxak'	paxak'	pajchak'[1]
33										pahch'[2]
34				pechak			petek'[1]	petok		pejtak[1]
35							pechek'[5]			pehtak[2]
36								pi		pij chitam[1]
37								pich'	pich'	pich'pich'[1]
38								poxil sal tz'i'		poxil sal[1]
39		puj[1]						puj		xpuj[1]
40		sàajum[2]						saju'		
41								sakil ch'ix[4]		sakil ch'ix wax[1]
42								sat mes		tzatzames[1]
43								tuix	tuix	tux ak[1]
44								tut		tujt[1]
45		tùux[1]	tux					tuxnuk'[5]	tuxnok'	tux[2]
46										
47										
48		tz'iim[1,2]					stsijb	tzib		tzib
49								tzis chauk		tzis chaok[1]
50								tzitz		tzitz ak
51								tzon-te'		tzon te'
52								tzukum jobel		tzujkum ak[1]
53								tz'emeni'		tz'eman[1]
54								tz'ul itaj		stz'ul[1]
55								unen mu		moen[1]
56										muhyem[2]
57								uskun te'		uskum[1]
58								vale'	vale'	wale'[1]
59										wahle'[2]
60								vo'tus		tusus[1]
61							xänxän	xanxan		xanxan wamal[1]
62								ximo'		xi jaben[1]
63								yich joj		yich joj[1]
64								yikatz toj		yijkatz te'[1]

"PLANTS"—*Continued.*

(Numbers in stub are references for reading horizontal alignments between this and following pages.)

	Tojolabal	Chuj	Q'anjob'al	Popti' (Jakalteko)	Mocho	Teko	Mam	Awakateko	Ixil	Uspanteko
1										
2										
3										
4		ch'abin$_1$	tx'abin	tx'abin	ch'aabi'n		tx'aban			
5							tx'abin			
6										
7										
8										
9										
10	chu'pak	ch'ipal			ch'upaq	tx'upaq	ch'upech			
11										
12										
13	ek'	ek'$_2$	ech'	ek'	ek'	x-me'eky'		eek'	ek'	éek'
14									ecy'	
15	ich	ich	ich	ich	iik	iiky	ich	iich	icy	iik
16										
17	isak'	is$_1$	is	is	iis	iis	iis	iis	is	kyeq-e iis
18										
19	itaj	itaj	itaj	itaj		itzaaj		itzaj		íchaj
20	ixim	ixim	ixim	ixim	ixi'm	ixi'm	axi'n	ixi'n	ixi'm	íxim
21	kakapo oj									
22										
23										
24	laj	la$_1$	la$_1$	txola	laj	laaj	laa	laa'	lay	láa
25		la te'	la'$_2$							
26										
27										
28										
29	may				ma'y	ma'y		maay	may	
30										
31										
32	pajak'	patak'$_2$				pajak'				
33										
34	pejtak'	pechak	petzaq'$_1$	petxajh	peechaq	peechaq				
35			pechaq'$_2$							
36	pij									
37										
38										
39										
40										
41			saqk'ix							
42										
43	tuyal	tuyal$_2$								
44										
45	tenok'			tenok'	teenooq'	nooq'	nooq'	nooq'		
46	tenuk'			tuxib						
47										
48		tzib$_1$	tzib	tzib	sijib		txiib	txiib		
49										
50										
51										
52										
53										
54					tz'uulaa'					
55		mu$_1$	mu		muuj					iimúut'
56		muj$_2$								
57										
58		wale'		wale'						
59										
60	jutus	tusus			tuus	xchu'uus				
61										
62										
63										
64										

"PLANTS"—*Continued.*

(Numbers in stub are references for reading horizontal alignments between this and following pages.)

	K'iche'	Sipakapenyo	Sakapulteko	Tz'utujil	Kaqchikel	Poqomam	Poqomchi'	Q'eqchi'
1								
2								
3								
4								
5								
6								
7								
8								
9								
10			ch'ipaq	ch'apaq$_2$	ch'upäq	ch'upaq	ch'upaq	
11							ch'ipaq	
12								
13	eek'			u-saaq eek'$_2$			ek'	
14								
15	iik	iik	iik	iik	ik	iik	iik	iik$_1$
16								ik$_2$
17	iis$_2$			iis	is$_2$	iis	iis	iis$_1$
18								is$_2$
19	ichaaj	ichaaj	ichaaj	ichaaj$_2$	ichaj		ichaaj	ichaj
20	ixiim	ixiim	ixiim	ixiim	ixin	ixiim	ixiim	ixim
21								
22								
23								
24	lah$_1$		lay	yal	ley$_1$	lah ch'uah	lah	laah$_1$
25	la$_2$				läy$_2$			lah$_2$
26								
27								
28								
29				majy	may	mahy		may
30								
31								
32								
33								
34		peetaq				pehtaq		
35								
36								
37								
38								
39							puuj	
40								
41								
42								
43								
44								
45	tuux						nooq'	tuhx
46								nooq'$_1$
47								noq'$_2$
48	chijb			chihb				sisb$_1$
49								
50								
51								
52								
53								
54								
55	imu't$_2$							
56								
57								
58								
59								
60							tuhs	
61								
62								
63								
64								

Tally of Mayan Plant Name Cognates

"VINES"		"TREES"		"PLANTS"		Total of "VINES," "TREES," and "PLANTS"	
Tzotzil	26	Tzotzil	97	Tzotzil	51	Tzotzil	174
Tzeltal	22	Tzeltal	72	Tzeltal	49	Tzeltal	143
Tojolabal	12	Tojolabal	36	Tojolobal	16	Tojolabal	54
Kaqchikel	6	Chuj	33	Chuj	15	Chuj	53
Poqomchi'	6	Ch'ol	32	Mocho	14	Ch'ol	45
Ch'ol	6	Q'anjob'al	23	Teko	12	Q'anjob'al	37
Wasteko	6	Yukateko	22	Popti'	11	Yukateko	37
Yukateko	6	K'iche'	21	Q'anjob'al	11	K'iche'	35
Awakateko	6	Popti'	19	Poqomchi'	10	Teko	34
Chuj	5	Teko	17	Awakateko	9	Mocho	34
Mocho	5	Uspanteko	17	K'iche'	9	Popti'	32
Lakantun	5	Wasteko	17	Tz'utujil	9	Awakateko	32
Teko	5	Awakateko	17	Yukateko	9	Poqomchi'	31
Uspanteko	5	Kaqchikel	17	Q'eqchi'	8	Kaqchikel	30
K'iche'	5	Mopan	16	Mam	8	Tz'utujil	30
Sipakapenyo	5	Tz'utujil	16	Uspanteko	7	Uspanteko	29
Tz'utujil	5	Mam	15	Kaqchikel	7	Q'eqchi'	28
Q'eqchi'	5	Mocho	15	Poqomam	7	Wasteko	28
Sakapulteko	4	Poqomchi'	15	Ch'ol	7	Mam	26
Poqomam	4	Q'eqchi'	15	Ixil	6	Lakantun	22
Chontal	3	Ch'orti'	13	Sakapulteko	5	Mopan	22
Q'anjob'al	3	Lakantun	13	Wasteko	5	Sakapulteko	22
Mopan	3	Sakapulteko	13	Ch'orti'	4	Poqomam	21
Mam	3	Ixil	13	Lakantun	4	Ixil	21
Ch'orti'	2	Chontal	12	Sipakapenyo	4	Ch'orti'	19
Popti'	2	Poqomam	10	Mopan	3	Chontal	17
Ixil	2	Sipakapenyo	8	Chontal	2	Sipakapenyo	17
TOTAL	167	TOTAL	614	TOTAL	292	TOTAL	1073

Notes

In most cases it has not been possible to determine whether the Mayan botanical term includes both the fruit and the tree, plant, or vine that bears it. Similarly, it is seldom clear whether the term for rubber refers only to the sap or also to the rubber tree.

"Vines"

[1]**chenek'** Except for **kanchenyek'**, the yellow bean, Ch'ol terms for bean share the Yukatek cognate **bu'ul**.

[2]**sakil** With the exception of the K'iche' dialect of Miguel Chicáj, **sakiil** refers not to a distinct squash, but rather to edible squash seeds, particularly those of **ch'um**.

[3]**x'ak'il chenek'** The distinction between bush and pole bean is generally made in Mayan languages.

"Trees"

[1]**aj** This term cannot be identified by species in most other Mayan language sources. Often it refers to skyrockets or the cane used for skyrockets.

[2]**atz'am te'** There is no identification for this tree in Ch'ol.

[3]**chalon** The reference of this term and of **tz'erel**, both closely related species of *Inga*, is seldom possible to distinguish in the sources for other Mayan languages.

[4]**chalon** The Kaqchikel term is reported by Herbruger and Díaz Barrios, 1956.

[5]**chi** Cognates of this term in many Mayan languages refer to maguey or, as in Kaqchikel, to the fiber itself.

[6]**ch'ib** There is no identification for this in Ch'ol.

[7]**ch'ich' ni'** There is no identification for this in Ch'ol.

[8]**ch'u te'** This means "god tree." Even though the initial Mayan root has been replaced by a Spanish loan word in K'iche', Sakapulteko, Tz'utujil, and Kaqchikel, the meaning persists unchanged.

[9]**ch'u te'** The Mam term reported from Ostuncalco refers not to cedar, but to *sabino*.

[10]**inop** The ceiba in the Ch'olan and Yukateko languages is referred to by **yax che'** and its cognates.

[11]**ja'as** This term originally referred to mamey, but when bananas were introduced, the term shifted in Yukateko and Ch'olan languages. In Chuj it refers to sapotes generally.

[12]**kokov** The Wasteko term refers to peanuts.

[13]**k'evex** The Kaqchikel term is reported by Sáenz de Santa María.

[14]**k'isis** The K'iche' term is reported by Edmondson (1965) to refer to cedar and juniper (*Juniperus flaccida*).

[15]**k'olo-max** This term is reported by Bradburn and Bricker for *Caesaria nitida*.

[16]**mes te'** Cognates for this term have only been included when it was clear that "broom tree" referred to the same or a related species.

[17]**muy** The Kaqchikel term is reported by Herbruger and Diaz Barrios, 1956.

[18]**on** In Wasteko, **oj** refers to an aromatic avocado, whereas **uj** refers to the common avocado.

[19]**on te'** The Wasteko term refers to the closely related *Nectandra* sp.

[20]**otot** Although this term in Tzotzil refers to bamboo, in Ch'ol, K'iche', and Yukateko, it means house.

[21]**paj-ul** The Chuj term refers to *Lantana*.

[22]**soro te'** This Tzotzil term loaned from Spanish has been included because of the Chuj and Q'anjob'al terms **pay**, **te'**, and the Yukateko **páay che'**.

[23]**suk** The Wasteko term refers to *Leucaena* sp. of similar appearance to *Lysiloma*.

[24]**xaxib** The Chuj term refers to *Calliandra* spp.

"Plants"

[1]**is-ak'** In most Mayan languages, **is** refers to sweet potatoes, although in Popti', **is** is reserved for potatoes and **isaq'** for sweet potatoes. In Q'anjob'al, **isaq'** refers to vines generally.

[2]**itaj** In Tzotzil, as in the other Mayan languages, this term and its cognates refer to edible greens.

[3]**la** This was used in colonial Yukateko (Motul).

[4]**sakil ch'ix** In Q'anjob'al the term refers to *Cirsium pinetorum*.

[5]**tuxnuk'** In most Mayan languages, **tux** refers to cotton seed. In colonial Tzotzil, **nok'** meant cloth. In Poqomchi', **nooq'** refers to thread.

Spelling

In all these languages I have omitted the initial glottal stop, and so, for example, **ich** should be read **'ich**.

'	over a vowel in Yukateko and Uspanteko indicates a high tone on non-final syllable and a falling tone on final syllable.
`	over a vowel in Yukateko indicates a low tone.
ä	is a short, lax vowel in Kaqchikel, whereas in Ch'ol and Mopan, it indicates a schwa.
ü	is a lax, lower high back rounded vowel in Kaqchikel.
cy	is a palatalized ch in Ixil.
jh	is a voiceless, postvelar spirant in Popti'.
ky	is a palatalized k in Ixil.
ñ	is a velar nasal in Popti'.
q	is a postvelar stop.
ṭ	is a retroflex t in Sierra Otóntepec Wasteko.
tx	is a retroflex ch in Q'anjob'al and Popti'.

Sources

Wasteko

   (1) Tantoyuca: Kaufman, 1982–1984

304

(2) Tancanhuítz: Kaufman, 1982–1984
(3) Sierra Otóntepec: Kaufman, 1982–1984
(4) San Luis Potosí: Alcorn, 1984
Yukateko
(1) Ticul: Kaufman, 1969
(2) Hocabá: Bradburn and Bricker, 1986
(3) Marín, Barrera Vásquez, and López Franco, 1976
Lakantun
Canger, 1969
Mopan
San Luis: Kaufman, 1970–1971
Ch'orti'
Jocotán: Kaufman, 1970–1971
Chontal
Keller 1968; Walker, 1969
Ch'ol
(1) Aulie and Aulie, 1978
(2) Schumann, 1973
(3) Whittaker and Warkentin, 1965
(4) Hopkins, 1980–1982
(5) Berlin, 1967
(6) Becerra, 1935
Tzotzil–Zinacantán
Breedlove and Laughlin
Colonial Tzotzil–Zinacantán
Anonymous and Laughlin
Tzeltal
(1) Tenejapa: Berlin, Breedlove, and Raven, 1974
(2) Bachajón: Slocum and Gerdel, 1965
Tojolabal
Lenkersdorf, 1979
Chuj
(1) San Sebastian Coatán: Kaufman, 1970–1971
(2) San Mateo Ixtatán: Breedlove and Hopkins, 1970–1971
Q'anjob'al
(1) Santa Eulalia: Proyecto Linguístico Francisco Marroquín, 1973–1978
(2) Soloma: Proyecto Linguístico Francisco Marroquín, 1973–1978
Popti'–Jacaltenango

Kaufman, 1970–1971
Mocho–Motocintla
Kaufman, 1967–1968
Teko–Mazapa
Cangar, 1969
Mam–Ixtahuacán
Kaufman, 1969–1979
Awakateko
(1) Aguacatán: Kaufman, 1970–1971
(2) Chalchitán: Kaufman, 1970–1971
Ixil–Chajul, Cotzal, Nebaj
Kaufman, 1970–1971
Uspanteko–Uspantán
Kaufman, 1970–1971
K'iche'
(1) Nahualá, Santa Caterina Ixtahuacán–Proyecto Linguístico Francisco Marroquín, 1971–1978
(2) San Miguel Chicáj–Proyecto Linguístico Francisco Marroquín, 1971–1978
Sipakapenyo–Sipacapa
Kaufman, 1970–1971
Sakapulteko–Sacapula
Kaufman, 1970–1971
Tz'utujil:
(1) Santiago Atitlán: Kaufman, 1970–1971
(2) San Pedro la Laguna: Kaufman, 1970–1971
Kaqchikel
(1) Tecpán: Proyecto Linguístico Francisco Marroquín, 1971–1978
(2) Comalapa: Proyecto Linguístico Francisco Marroquín, 1971–1978
Poqomam–San Juis Jilotepeque
Kaufman, 1970–1971
Poqomchi'–San Cristóbal
Proyecto Linguístico Francisco Marroquín, 1973–1978
Q'eqchi'
(1) Cahabón: Kaufman, 1970–1971
(2) Lanquín: Kaufman, 1970–1971
Botanical collections were made for Tzotzil, Tenejapa Tzeltal, Tojolabal, Hocabá Yukateko, San Mateo Ixtatán Chuj, and Wasteko.

Appendix 2

Glossary of Botanical Terms

acaulescent	stemless or apparently so.
accrescent	enlarging with age; inflated; usually pertaining to the calyx.
achene	a small, dry, hard, unopening, 1-seeded fruit.
acuminate	gradually tapering to a sharp point, the sides more or less pinched in before reaching the tip.
acute	sharp pointed, less tapering than acuminate.
aggregate	collected into dense clusters but not united.
aggregate fruit	a fleshy fruit formed from the clustering together of pistils that were distinct in the flower; example: raspberry.
alternate	having one leaf or branch at a given level on the stem; having one part of a flower between or alternating with other parts.
amplexicaul	clasping the stem.
annual	completing the life cycle in one growing season.
anther	the part of the stamen containing the pollen.
apetalous	without petals.
apex	tip, the extreme end, the growing point of a root or stem.
apical	situated at the tip.
apiculate	having a small sharp point.
appendage	a secondary part attached to a main structure.
appressed	lying flat or close against something; often refers to hairs.
areole	a small, clearly marked space; a term frequently used to denote small spine-bearing areas on the stem of a cactus.
aril	an appendage growing at or about the hilum, or point of attachment, of a seed.
arillate	with an aril.
attenuate	gradually narrowed.
awn	a terminal bristle-like appendage.
axil	upper angle formed by a leaf or branch with the stem.
axillary	in an axil.
axis	the central stem or supporting structure along which parts or organs are arranged.
basal	relating to or situated at the base.
berry	a pulpy fruit with immersed seeds and no true stone.
bilabiate	two-lipped.
bilocular	two-celled.
bract	a modified or reduced leaf situated near a flower or inflorescence (adj. bracteate).
bulb	a leaf bud with fleshy scales or leaf bases, frequently underground.

bulbil	small bulbs arising around the main bulb.
bur	a seed or fruit bearing spines or prickles.
burl	an overgrown knot or an excrescence on a tree often formed at the juncture of the trunk with the root.
bush	a low thick shrub without a distinct trunk.
caespitose	growing in dense clumps or tufts.
calyx	the outer series of the floral envelopes, usually green.
campanulate	bell-shaped or cup-shaped with a flaring rim.
capitate	head-shaped, aggregated into very dense clusters.
capsule	a dry fruit opening by definite pores or slits and made up of more than one pistil.
carpel	a simple pistil or element of a compound pistil.
catkin	a spike or spike-like, usually pendulous inflorescence of unisexual flowers.
caudex	the woody base of an otherwise herbaceous perennial (pl. caudices).
clavate	club-shaped, thickened towards the apex.
cleft	cut about to the middle.
connate	the union of like structures.
cordate	of a conventional heart shape, usually with a notch at base and pointed tip.
corm	a bulb-like, fleshy, underground stem.
coriaceous	texture of leather.
corolla	the inner series of the floral envelope; collective name for petals.
corymb	a flat-topped flower cluster in which the outermost flowers bloom first.
cotyledon	the seed leaves or first leaves of the embryo, often functions as the first leaf of a seedling.
crenate	toothed with teeth rounded at apex.
crenulate	crenate with small teeth.
crown	an inner appendage to a petal or the throat of a corolla.
culm	a hollow or pithy stem found in grasses and sedges.
cyme	a convex or flat-topped flower cluster with central flowers opening first.
decompound	more than once divided or compound.
decumbent	reaching out with the tip ascending.
decurrent	running down the stem, below the insertion; usually said of leaves.
dense	said of inflorescences where the flowers are crowded.
dentate	toothed with teeth directed outward, not forward.
digitate	fingered; shaped like an open hand; compound with parts radiating out from a common point like fingers on a hand.
disk flowers (disk floret)	the regular tubular flowers on the heads of Asteraceae.
distichous	in two vertical rows.
distinct	separate; like parts not at all united.
divaricate	widely divergent.
drupe	a fleshy, unopening, one-seeded fruit (drupaceous).
ellipsoid	an elliptic solid.
elliptic	shaped like an ellipse; in the form of a flattened circle more than twice as long as broad.
elongate	drawn out in length.
entire	with an even margin.

ephemeral	lasting for one day or less.
epiphyte	a plant that grows on other plants, but not parasitically.
epiphytic	relating to epiphytes.
equitant	folded over as if astride.
everted	turned outward.
fascicle	a close cluster (adj. fasciculate).
fertile	capable of producing fruit and seeds.
filament	any thread-like body.
filamentous	composed of threads.
filiform	very fine and narrow; thread-like.
fistulous	hollow and cylindrical throughout, like onion leaves.
flabellate	fan or wedge-shaped.
foliate	having leaves.
follicle	a dry fruit with one pistil and splitting down one side only.
fourmerous	having four like parts.
fruit	the ripened pistil with all its accessory parts.
fusiform	spindle-shaped; thickest near the middle and tapering toward each end.
glabrous	without hairs.
globose	spherical, rounded, shaped like a globe.
glomerule	a dense crowded cluster, usually of flowers.
glumes	a pair of bracts at the base of a grass spikelet.
hastate	shaped like an arrowhead but with the basal lobes pointing outward (compare sagittate).
heartwood	the innermost and oldest wood next to the pith.
herb	a plant with no persistent woody stem above the ground.
herbaceous	with the texture, color, and properties of an herb.
hilum	the scar or point of attachment of a seed.
hispid	with stiff and rigid bristles or bristle-like hairs.
imbricate	overlapping, as shingles on a roof.
incised	cut sharply and usually irregularly, commonly describes leaf margins.
incurved	bending inwards towards the axis or attachment.
indehiscent	remaining persistently closed; not opening by definite lines or pores.
indigenous	native to the area.
inflorescences	the flowering part of a plant, almost always used for a flower cluster; the arrangement of the flowers on the axis.
insectivorous	consuming insects; used of those plants which capture insects and absorb nutriment from them.
internode	the part of the stem between two nodes or joints.
involucre	a whorl of distinct or united leaves or bracts subtending a flower cluster.
laciniate	narrowly incised or slashed; leaf margins cut in narrow and usually pointed lobes.
lanceolate	lance-shaped; much longer than broad; broadest toward the base and tapering to the tip.
lance-ovate	a shape between lanceolate and ovate.
leaflets	a segment of a compound leaf.
legume	the fruit in the pea family which is a simple pod opening in two pieces.
linear	long and narrow, of uniform width.

308

lobe	a division or segment of an organ, usually rounded.
lobed	bearing lobes.
lyrate	describes leaves parted with the terminal segment large and rounded and the lower lobes small.
meristem	a region of growth or actively dividing cell tissue.
monecious	unisexual flowers with the male and female elements in the same individual.
monocot	a plant having only one cotyledon or seed leaf.
mucilaginous	slimy or mucilage-like.
multifid	divided into many segments.
node	the place on a stem where leaves or branches originate.
nut	a hard, one-seeded, indehiscent fruit.
nutlet	a small nut.
oblanceolate	inversely lanceolate, attached at the tapered end.
oblong-oval	oval, but much lengthened, with the sides parallel.
obovate	inversely ovate, attached at the narrow end.
obpyramidal	inversely pyramidal, with the point of attachment at the small end.
opposite	having two leaves or branches at a node; having one part placed before another in a flower.
orbicular	a two-dimensional figure circular in outline.
oval	broadly elliptic.
ovate	shaped like the longitudinal section of an egg with the broader end downwards.
ovoid	an egg-shaped solid.
palmate	the lobes or divisions attached or running down toward one place at the base (compare pinnate).
panicle	a loose, branched flower cluster (adj. paniculate).
pappilate	bearing minute conical projections.
pedicel	the stalk of a flower in a flower cluster (adj. pedicellate).
peduncle	the stalk of a single flower or flower cluster.
pedunculate	borne upon a peduncle.
perennial	a plant lasting for three years or more; a stem not dying back over the winter.
perianth	the floral envelopes, the calyx or corolla or both.
petal	a division of the corolla.
petiolate	with a petiole.
petiole	the stalk to a leaf blade or to a compound leaf.
peltate	shield-shaped, attached to a stalk by the lower surface and not by the margin.
phyllary	one bract of an involucre.
pinnate	with the leaflets arranged on each side of a common axis.
pinnatifid	pinnately divided into lobes, but not cut to the midrib.
pistil	the female or seed-bearing structure of a flower, when complete consisting of ovary, style, and stigma.
pit	a small depression.
pith	the spongy center of a stem, surrounding or joining to the inner part of the vascular bundles.
plicate	folded in plaits, usually lengthwise on the order of a folding fan.
prop roots	aerial roots arising at the base of a plant and providing extra support for the plant.
pubescent	clothed with hair, the hair usually fine and soft.
raceme	a simple flower cluster in which pedicellate flowers are borne on a common and usually elongate axis.

rachis	the axis of an inflorescence or a compound leaf.
rank	a vertical row.
receptacle	the part of the flower that bears the organs of the flower such as the petals, stamens, and sepals; the expanded portion of the flower stalk that bears the collected flowers of a head as in Asteraceae.
recurved	curved outward, downward or backward.
reflexed	abruptly bent or turned backward or downward.
reniform	shaped like a kidney bean.
reticulate	netted; with a network.
rhizomatous	having the characters of a rhizome.
rhizome	any prostrate more or less elongated stem growing partly or completely beneath the surface of the ground.
root	the descending axis of the plant without nodes and absorbing moisture from the ground.
rootstock	a rhizome.
rosette	a circular cluster of leaves.
rosulate	in the form of a rosette.
rotate	wheel-shaped, flat and circular in outline.
rugose	with wrinkled or creased surface.
runner	a very slender stolon-like stem rooting at the apex.
sagittate	shaped like an arrowhead, with the basal lobes directed backward; refers to leaves.
salverform	a corolla with a slender tube abruptly expanding into a flat limb.
samara	an indehiscent winged fruit.
saxicolous	growing on rock.
scabrous	rough to the touch.
scape	a leafless flower stalk arising from the ground.
scapose	bearing a scape or resembling one.
scorpioid	coiled at the apex like the tail of a scorpion.
scurf	small, bran-like scales on the stem and leaves (adj. scurfy).
secund	arranged on one side only; unilateral.
serrate	with sharp teeth directed forward.
serrulate	diminutive of serrate.
sessile	without a stalk.
sheath	a tubular structure, as the lower part of a grass leaf.
shrub	a woody perennial plant smaller than a tree and usually with several basal stems.
silique	a narrow, many-seeded capsule characterstic of the mustard family in which the valves split from the bottom and leave the placenta and false partition on which the seeds grow.
sinuate	strongly wavy-margined.
sori	the aggregation of sporangia or spore-bearing organs on the underside of a fern frond.
spadix	a spike with a thick and fleshy axis, usually densely flowered with imperfect flowers.
spathe	a broad sheathing bract enclosing a spadix.
spatulate	broad and rounded at the apex and tapering at the base; flattened, spoon-shaped.
spine	a sharp-pointed, rigid, deep-seated outgrowth from the stem.
spinescent	bearing a spine or ending in a spine-like sharp point.

spinulose	beset with small spines.
stamen	the male organ of a flower, consisting of filament, anther, and pollen.
stipitate	provided with a stipe or with a slender stalk-like base.
stolon	a horizontal stem, creeping a rooting at the nodes, giving rise to a new plant at its tips.
subcordate	somewhat or almost cordate or heart-shaped.
subglobose	somewhat or almost globe-shaped.
subsessile	having a very short petiole, pedicel, peduncle, or stalk; almost sessile.
suffrutescent	somewhat shrubby.
tap root	a root with a stout tapering body.
tendril	a slender structure derived from the stems or leaves by means of which a plant may make itself secure.
tepal	a term used to denote perianth parts when petals and sepals can not be differentiated.
terete	round in cross section, cylindrical.
thorn	a stiff, hard, sharp-pointed emergence more deeply seated than a prickle.
tomentose	clothed with dense, matted woolly hairs.
tomentum	the covering of closely interwoven and tangled hairs in a tomentose surface.
trifoliate	a compound leaf with three leaflets.
trimerous	having three like parts.
tripinnate	pinnate three times.
truncate	squared off at the tip or base as if cut off with a straight blade; usually describes leaves.
tuber	a short thickened underground stem.
tubercule	a small, rounded structure.
tuberculate	bearing small processes or tubercules.
tuberous	having or resembling a tuber.
umbel	an inflorescence in which the branches arise from the same point like the ribs of an umbrella.
umbellate	in or like an umbel.
unifoliate	having only one leaf or leaflet.
uricating	stinging.
valvate	opening by valves; splitting open along a suture line; having edges which do not overlap.
vernation	the arrangement of leaves in a bud.
verticillate	with three or more leaves or other structures arranged in a circle about a stem or other common axis.
villous	bearing long weak hairs.
viscid	having a sticky surface.
whorl	the arrangement of similiar parts, such as leaves, in a circle around an axis (adj. whorled).
wing	a thin and usually dry extension bordering an organ.

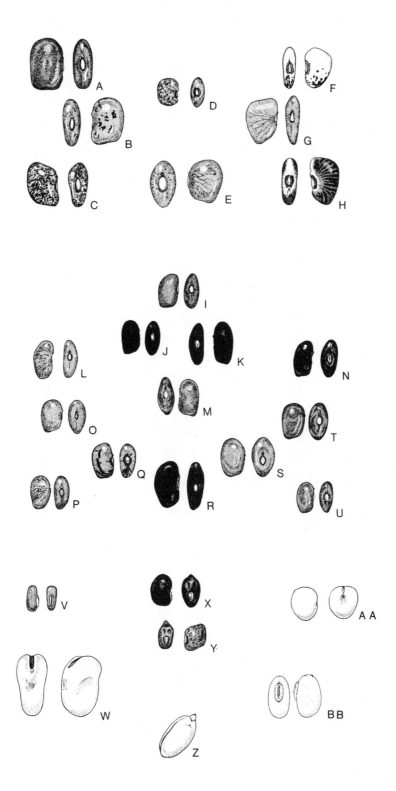

PLATE 1.—Chenek': A, tzajal botil (*Phaseolus coccineus*); B, sakil tz'ibal botil (*Phaseolus coccineus*); C, tzajal tz'ibal botil (*Phaseolus coccineus*); D, xut (*Phaseolus coccineus*); E, k'anal ibes (*Phaseolus coccineus* ssp. *darwinianus*); F, sakil xvet' (*Phaseolus lunatus*); G, tzajal xvet' (*Phaseolus lunatus*); H, tz'ibal xvet' (*Phaseolus lunatus*); I, tzajal xlumil (*Phaseolus vulgaris*); J, batz'i ik'al xlumil (*Phaseolus vulgaris*); K, muk'ta ik'al xlumil (*Phaseolus vulgaris*); L, sak-vayan xlumil (*Phaseolus vulgaris*); M, tzajal xk'un xlumil (*Phaseolus vulgaris*); N, ik'al x'ak'il (*Phaseolus vulgaris*); O, chana x'ak'il (*Phaseolus vulgaris*); P, k'anal x'ak'il (*Phaseolus vulgaris*); Q, tz'ibal x'ak'il (*Phaseolus vulgaris*); R, muk'ta ik' (*Phaseolus vulgaris*); S, tzo' t'ul (*Phaseolus vulgaris*); T, tzajal xlumil (*Phaseolus vulgaris*); U, tzajal xlumil (*Phaseolus vulgaris*); V, tzajal aros chenek' (*Vigna umbellata*); W, sakil javas (*Vicia faba*); X, ik'al kántela chenek' (*Vigna unguiculata*); Y, k'anal kántela chenek' (*Vigna unguiculata*); Z, sakil karvensa (*Pisum sativum*); AA, manya chenek' (*Arachis hypogaea*); BB, javas kajve (*Mucuna puriens* var. *utilis*).

PLATE 2.—Ch'um-te': A, polotz' (*Cyclanthera langaei*); B, ch'um-te' (*Cucumis anguria*); C, xantiya ak' (*Melothria pendula*); D, xavon ak' (*Cayaponia attenuata*); E, ch'ix ch'um-te' ch'o, xenebal pox (*Sicyos microphyllus*).

PLATE 3.—Makom: A, batz'i makom (*Rubus adenotrichus*); B, tzajal makom (*Rubus humistratus*); C, tuxum makom (*Rubus coriifolius*); D, ch'ail makom (*Rubus fagifolius*); E, makom tz'i'lel (*Duchesnea indica*); F, makom ch'ix (*Buettneria aculeata*); G, xoto-chak (*Rubus eriocarpus*).

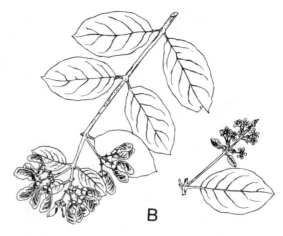

PLATE 4.—Pek' me'el: A, ne saben (*Heteropteris beecheyana*); B, chenek' ak', pek' me'el, yok'tz'i'ak' (*Canavalia hirsutissima*).

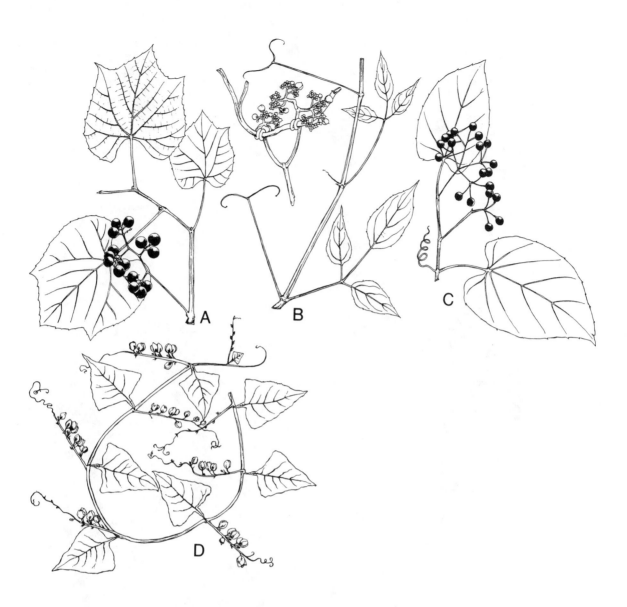

PLATE 5.—Tz'usub: A, batz'i tz'usub (*Vitis bourgeana*); B, ve'el inatab (*Ampelocissus acapulcensis*); C, sakil tz'usub, ve'el inatab (*Cissus cacuminis*); D, sakil tz'usub (*Antigonon flavescens*).

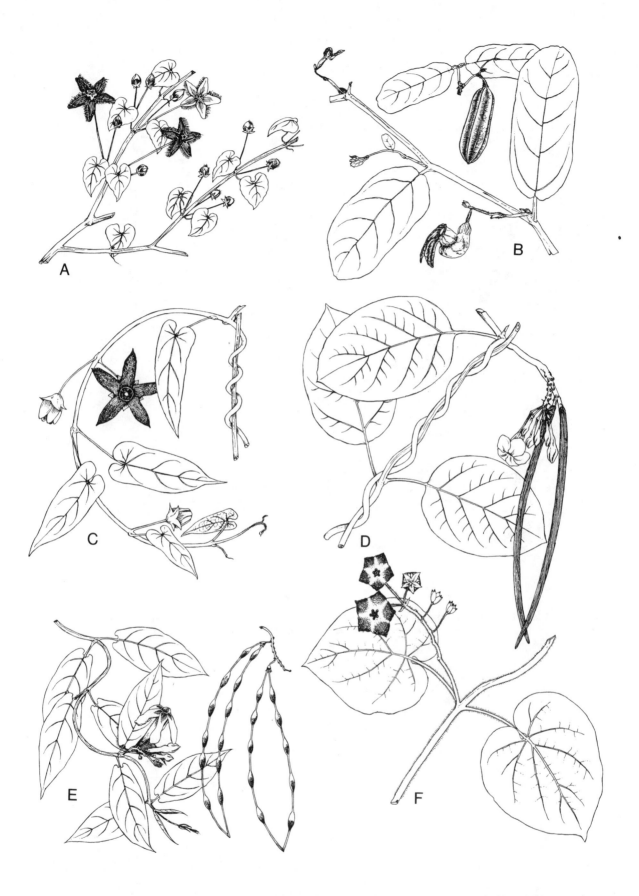

PLATE 6.—Tz'usub: A, (x) k'ox puyu', (x) kranata ak' (*Gonolobus barbatus*); B, vako ak' (*Aristolochia sericea*); C, lo'bol ak' (*Gonolobus uniflorus*); D, ch'uxuv ak' (*Mandevilla tubiflora*); E, ch'uxuv ak' (*Mandevilla subsagittata*); F, pojov ak' (*Matelea* sp.). ((x) = extended range.)

PLATE 7.—Aja-te'es: A, aja-te'es (*Gaultheria odorata*); B, k'ox aja-te'es (*Vaccinium confertum*); C, tzis uch (*Litsea glaucescens*).

PLATE 8.—Bak teʻ: A, ventex mol (*Picramnia tetramera*); B, bak teʻ (*Dodonea viscosa*); C, ajval teʻ (*Stillingia acutifolia*); D, majob ik'al (*Jacquinea macrocarpa*).

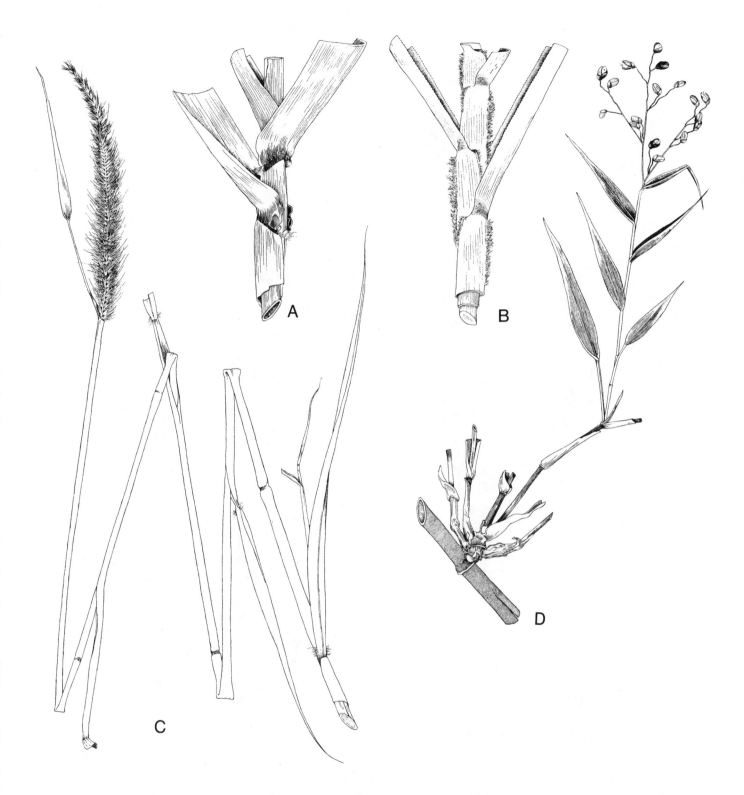

PLATE 9.—Bix: A, antzil aj (*Phragmites australis*); B, vinik aj (*Gynerium sagittatum*); C, meno (*Pennisetum purpureum*); D, ik'ob chij (*Lasiacis divaricata*).

PLATE 10.—Bix: A, muk'ta ne kotom (*Chusquea foliosa*); B, yaxal otot (*Bambusa vulgaris*); C, antzil bix (*Olmeca reflexa*); D, ton bix (*Otatea fimbriata*); E, chanib (*Rhipidocladum pittieri*); F, k'ox ne kotom (*Chusquea liebmannii*).

PLATE 11.—Bot: A, bot (*Heliocarpus donnell-smithii*); B, be xinich te' (*Cordia alliodora*); C, sakil sal-te' (*Jatropha curcas*); D, tzajal sal-te' (*Bursera simaruba*).

PLATE 12.—Bot: A, mail te' (*Pseudobombax ellipticum*); B, putzkuy (*Cochlospermum vitifolium*); C, ch'ilim te' (*Hymenaea courbaril*); D, jasínto te' (*Morus celtidifolia*) (isolate).

PLATE 13.—Bot: A, akit (*Guazuma ulmifolia*); B, (x) akit (*Neopringlea viscosa*); C, bik'it choch (*Stemmadenia obovata*); D, tux-nuk' te' (*Luehea candida*). ((x) = extended range.)

PLATE 14.—Chalon: A, tz'erel (*Inga punctata*); B, chalon (*Inga vera* ssp. *spuria*).

PLATE 15.—Chijil teʼ: A, chʼix akʼ (*Celtis iguanaea*); B, batzʼi chijil teʼ (*Sambucus mexicana*); C, batzʼi chix teʼ (*Prunus serotina*).

PLATE 16.—Chijil te': A, batz'i paxamum (*Malpighia mexicana*); B, muk'ta paxamum (*Symplocos vernicosa*); C, yaxal ch'it (*Xylosma intermedium*); D, sakil ch'it (*Eugenia laughlinii*); E, tzajal ch'it (*Schoepfia vacciniiflora*); F, yisim bolom (*Xylosma flexuosum*).

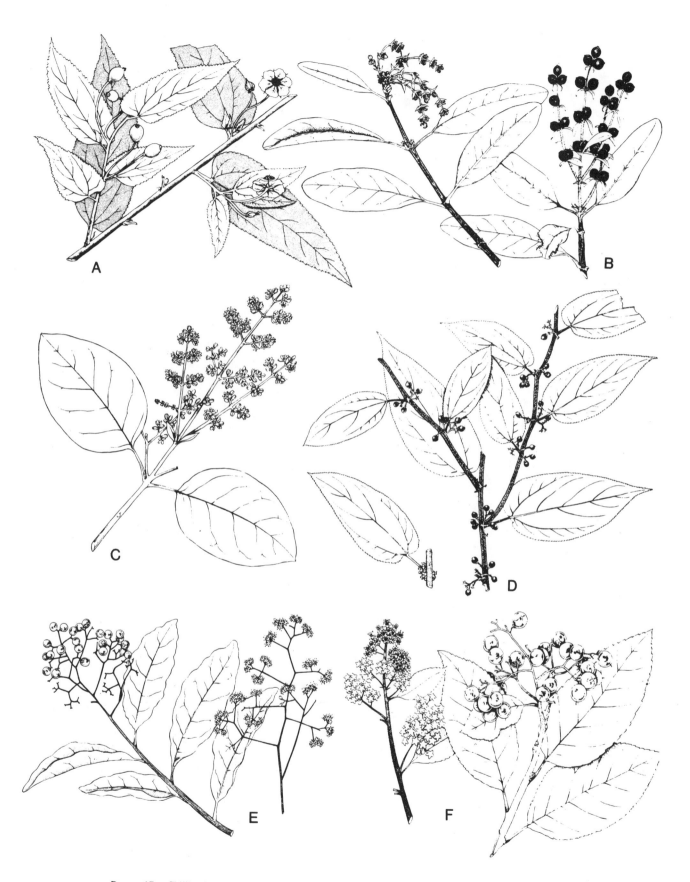

PLATE 17.—Chijil teʻ: A, makulixkuat (*Muntingia calabura*); B, ik'al vinik (*Garrya laurifolia*); C, treno (*Ligustrum lucidum*); D, vax teʻ (*Trema micrantha*); E, nampívo (*Ehretia tinifolia*); F, ik'al teʻ (*Ehretia latifolia*).

PLATE 18.—Chilkat: A, arsyal te' (*Baccharis trinervis*); B, bik'it ch'a-te' (*Ageratina ligustrinum*); C, ch'ail pox (*Calea urticifolia*); D, batz'i chilkat (*Senecio salignus*); E, poxil ik' (*Stevia polycephala*).

PLATE 19.—Jabnal: A, jabnal (*Oreopanax peltatus*); B, k'am-xoch' (*Chiranthodendron pentadactylon*); C, k'orok' te' (*Cecropia peltata*).

PLATE 20.—Jabnal: A, mumun (*Piper auritum*); B, mumun te' (*Piper jaquemontianum*).

PLATE 21.—K'an-te': A, k'an-te' (*Diphysa floribunda*); B, yax-te' (*Eysenhardtia adenostylis*); C, milob ch'o te' (*Gliricidia sepium*); D, yax-'ib te' (*Senna tonduzii*); E, brasil (*Haematoxylon brasiletto*).

PLATE 22.—K'an-te': A, sakil kánela te' (*Hauya elegans*); B, tzajal kánela te' (*Calycophyllum candidissimum*).

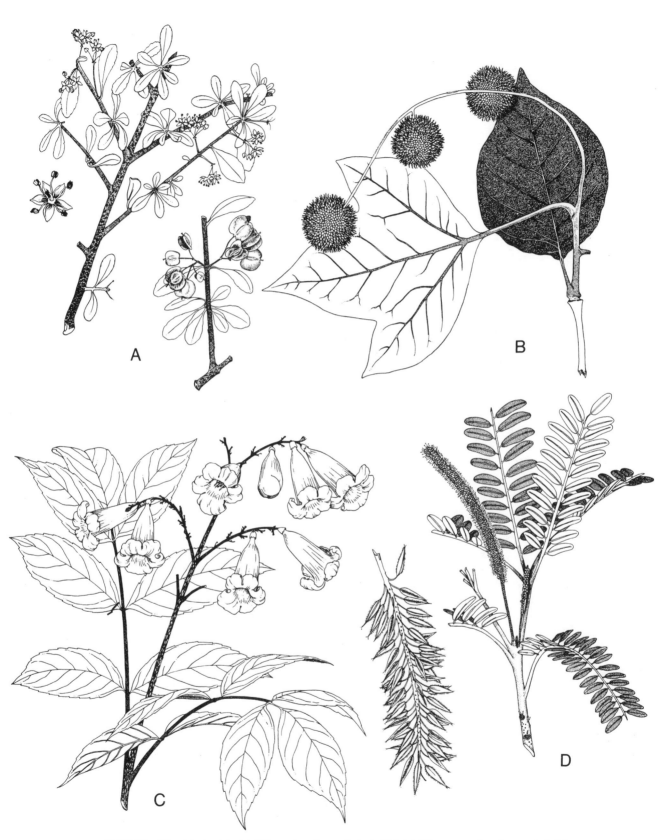

PLATE 23.—K'an-te': A, pinto te' (*Wimmeria pubescens*); B, jach'ub te' (*Platanus mexicana*); C, putzul chij (*Tecoma stans*); D, kamaron te' (*Alvaradoa amorphoides*).

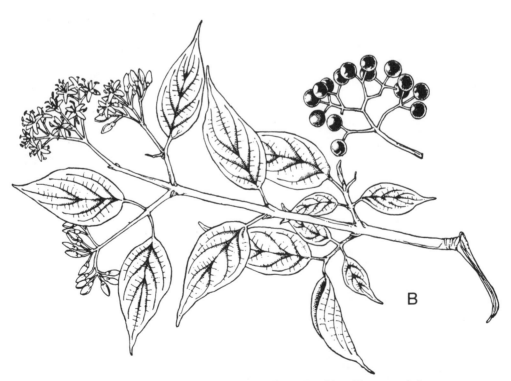

PLATE 24.—K'at'ix: A, k'at'ix (*Crataegus pubescens*); B, isbon (*Cornus excelsa*).

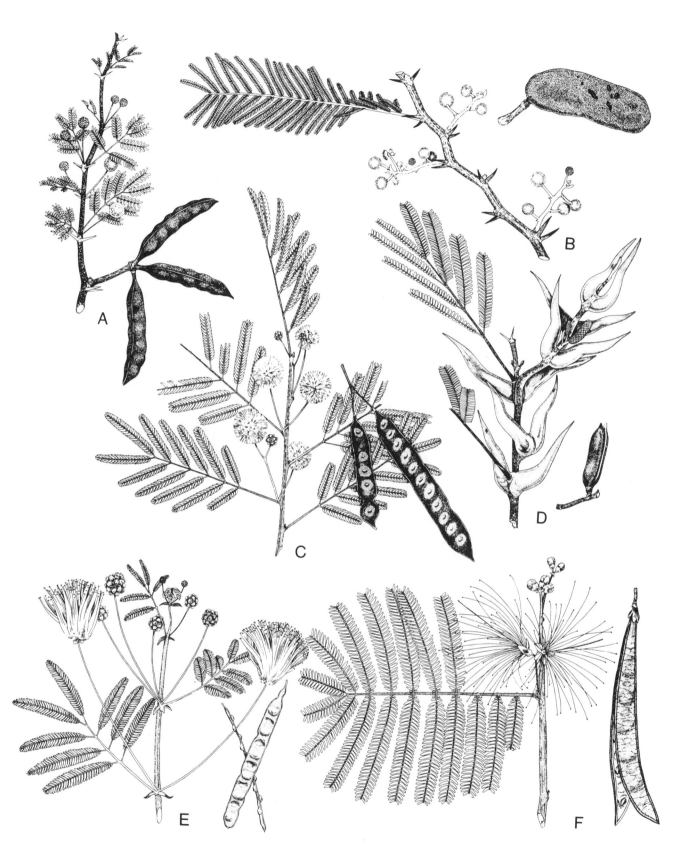

PLATE 25.—Olnob: A, sakil ch'ix (*Acacia farnesiana*); B, kevrajacha (*Acacia pennatula*); C, batz'i xaxib (*Acacia angustissima*); D, chojchoj (*Acacia cornigera*); E, muk'ta xaxib (*Calliandra portoricense*); F, ch'ich' ni' (*Calliandra grandiflora*).

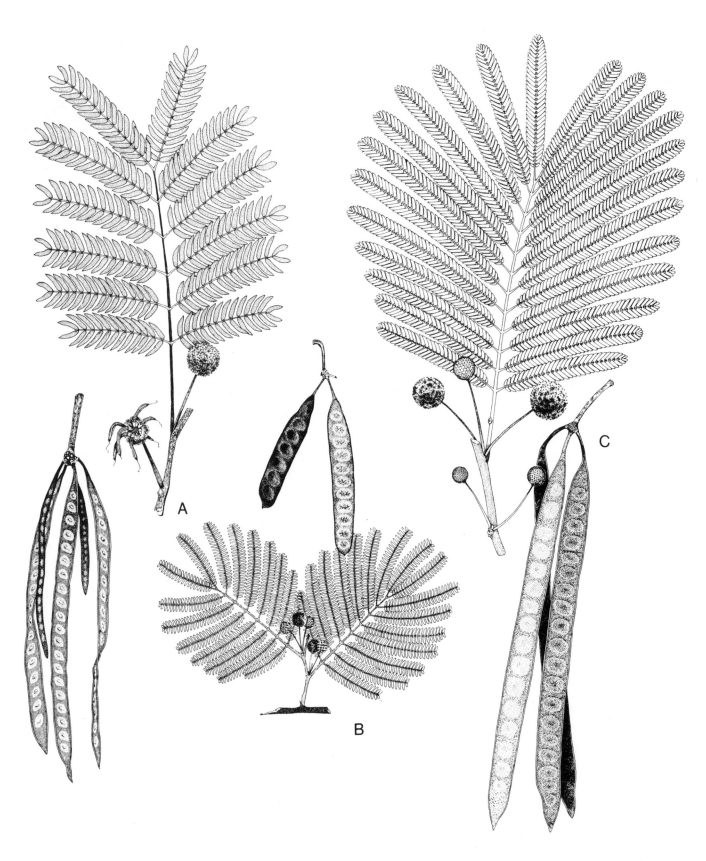

PLATE 26.—Olnob: A, batz'i olnob (*Leucaena leucocephala*); B, tzajal olnob (*Leucaena diversifolia*); C, paka' olnob (*Leucaena collinsii*).

PLATE 27.—Olnob: A, pit (*Enterolobium cyclocarpum*); B, molíno te' (*Poeppigia procera*); C, vamuch te' (*Pithecellobium dulce*); D, voy chij te' (*Bauhinia divaricata*).

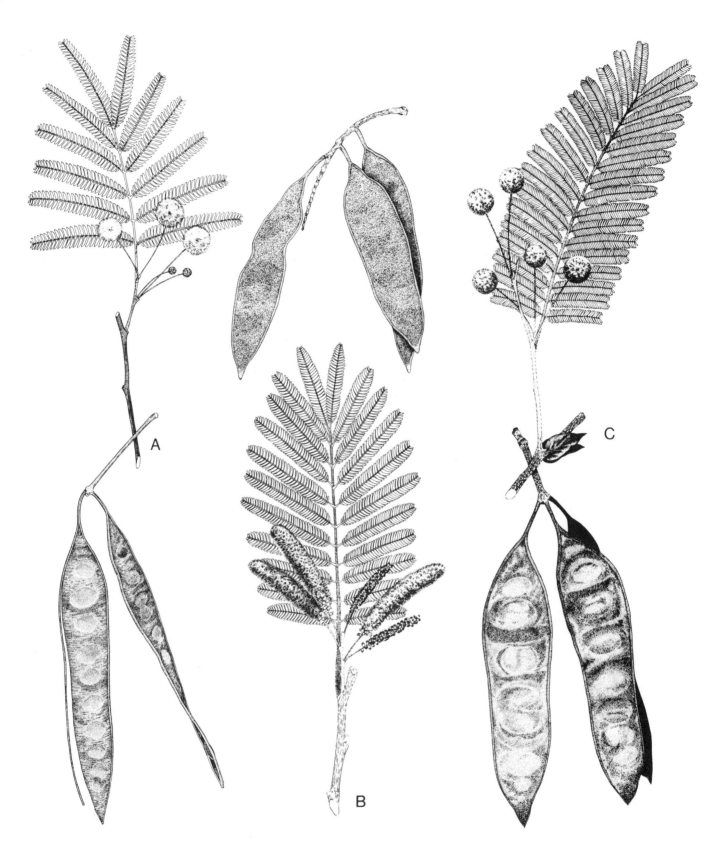

PLATE 28.—Olnob: A, ik'al suk (*Lysiloma divaricatum*); B, ik'al suk (*Lysiloma acapulcensis*); C, sakil suk (*Lysiloma auritum*).

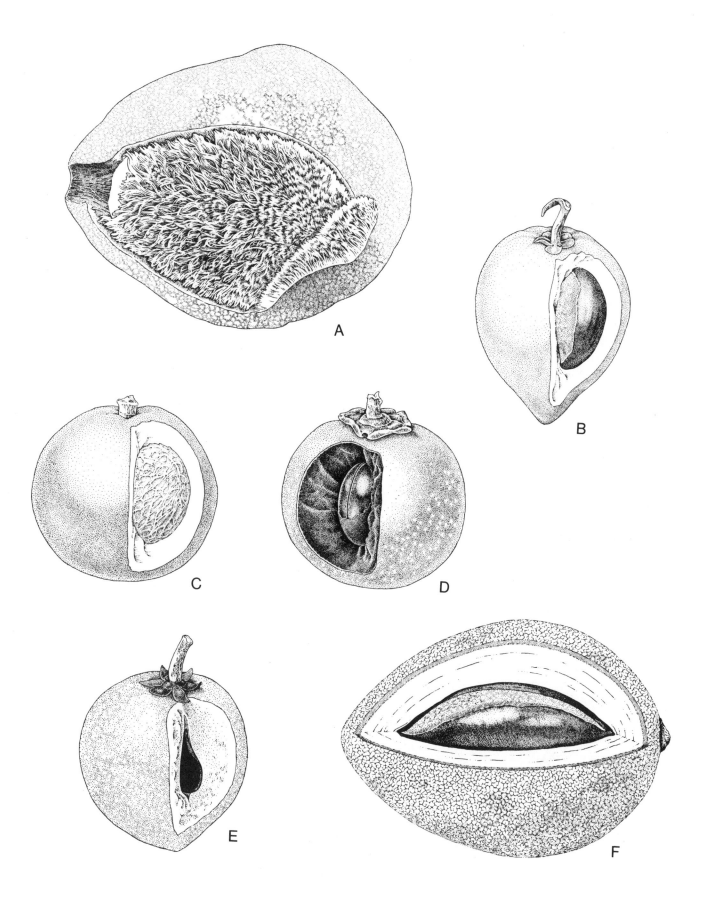

PLATE 29.—On: A, itzompi (*Licania platypus*); B, no'chi' (*Pouteria campechiana*); C, ch'ulul aj-te' (*Casimiroa edulis*); D, uch (*Diospyros digyna*); E, muy (*Manilikara achras*); F, ja'as (*Pouteria mammosa*).

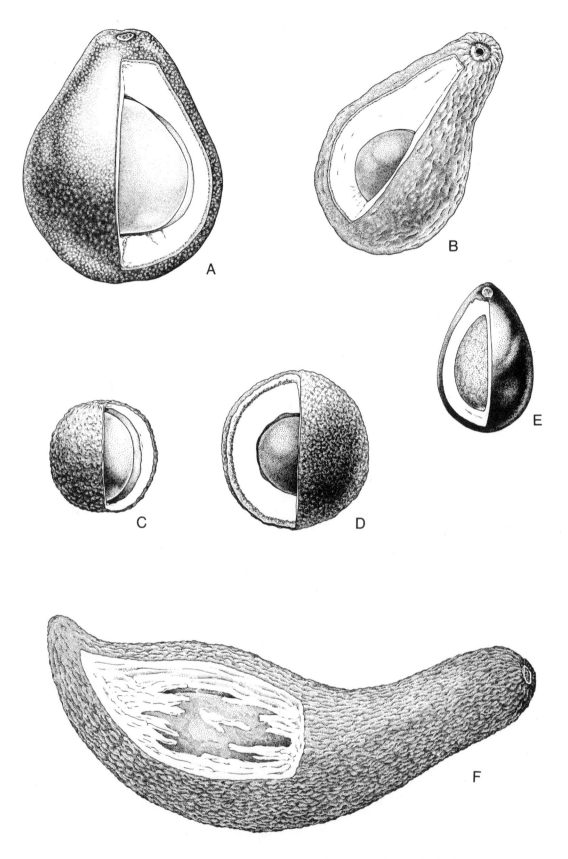

PLATE 30.—On: A, yax-'on (*Persea americana*); B, yax-'on (*Persea americana*); C, ch'ail on (*Persea americana*); D, batz'i on (*Persea americana*); E, tzitz (*Persea americana* var. *drymifolia*); F, chinin (*Persea schiedeana*).

PLATE 31.—Pitz'otz': A, pitz'otz' (*Monnina xalapensis*); B, sat pukuj (*Solanum aligerum*); C, ve'el kulajte' (*Cordia spinescens*).

PLATE 32.—Po'on: A, mojan (*Ceiba aesculifolia*); B, inop (*Ceiba pentandra*); C, bik'it ch'u te' (*Cedrela oaxacensis*); D, batz'i jovos (*Spondias mombin*); E, po'on ch'ix (*Ximenia americana*).

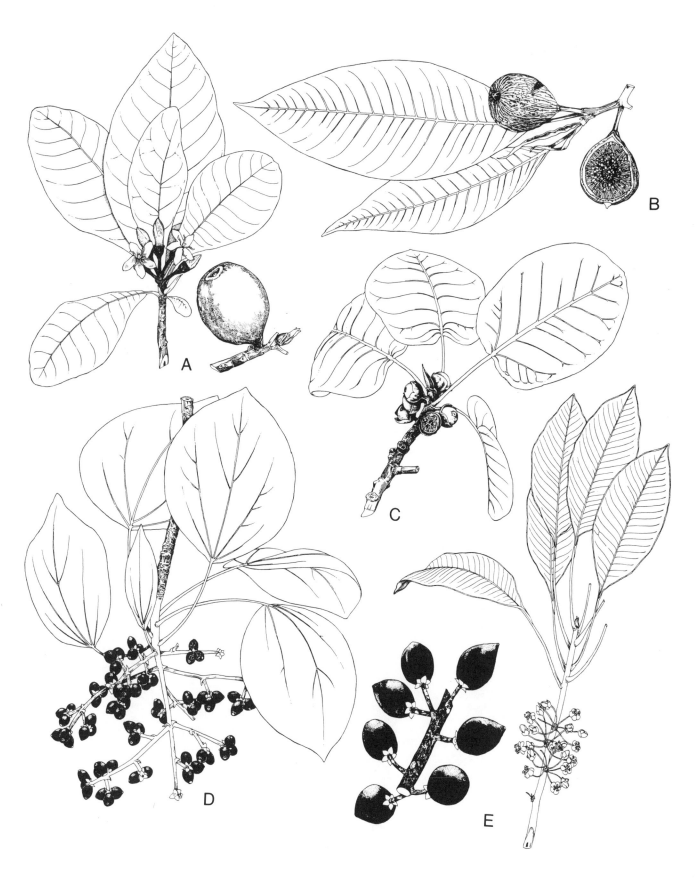

PLATE 33.—Po'on: A, maluk (*Genipa caruto*); B, amat (*Ficus glabrata*); C, mutut (*Ficus cookii*); D, kajanab te' (*Oreopanax capitatus*); E, yaxal jovos (*Mastichodendron capiri* var. *tempisque*).

PLATE 34.—Sun: A, k'ail (*Smallanthus maculatus*); B, sun (*Tithonia tubaeformis*); C, ton k'ail (*Montanoa hexagona*); D, tzojoj (*Lagascea helianthifolia*).

PLATE 35.—Tilil: A, batz'i k'oxox te' (*Ternstroemia oocarpa*); B, k'ol-k'ox (*Phyllanthus grandifolius*); C, yaxal mol (*Licania arborea*).

PLATE 36.—Tilil: A, tzajal k'os (*Parathesis chiapensis*); B, karnéro te' (*Coccoloba barbadensis*); C, bak amuch te' (*Clethra mexicana*); D, k'ojom (*Rapanea juergensenii*).

PLATE 37.—Tulan: A, batz'i chikin-ib (*Quercus crispipilis*); B, jayal pat chikin-ib (*Quercus laurina*); C, sakil chikin-ib (*Quercus elliptica*); D, tz'otz'op (*Quercus acutifolia*).

PLATE 38.—Tulan: A, muk'ta kachu toro te' (*Bucida macrostachya*); B, yaxal kachu toro te' (*Godmania aesculifolia*).

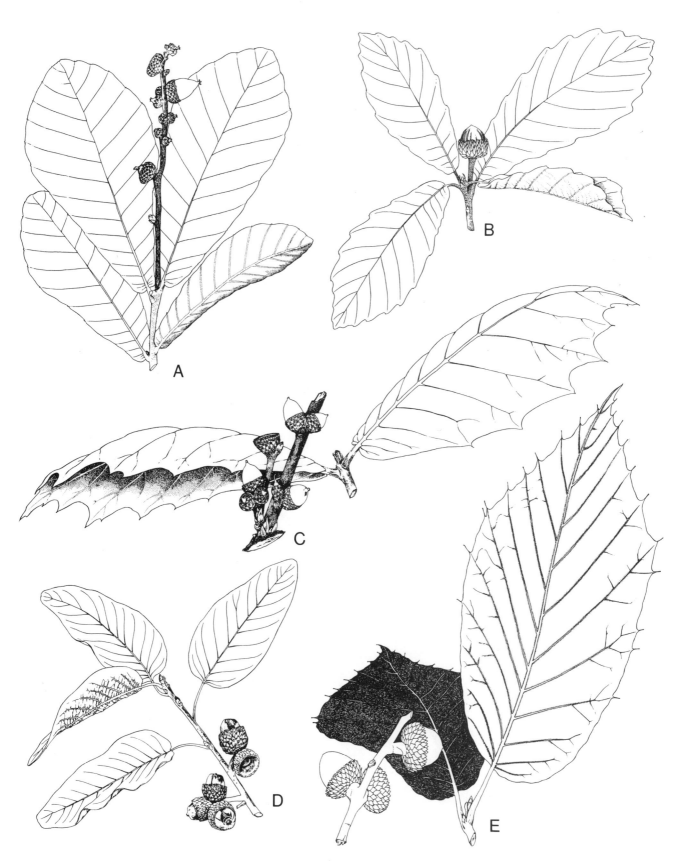

PLATE 39.—Tulan: A, sakil tulan (*Quercus peduncularis*); B, k'an-tulan (*Quercus segoviensis*); C, batz'i te' (*Quercus crassifolia*); D, k'evex tulan (*Quercus polymorpha*); E, sap yok (*Quercus candicans*).

PLATE 40.—Tulan: A, tz'utuj te' (*Ostrya virginiana* var. *guatemalensis*); B, sakil nok (*Alnus acuminata* ssp. *arguta*); C, k'ox paj-'ul (*Rhus terebinthifolia*); D, muk'ta paj-'ul (*Rhus schiedeana*).

PLATE 41.—Tzelo-pat: A, sakil sitit (*Vernonia deppeana*); B, tzajal sitit (*Pluchea odorata*); C, batz'i suil itaj (*Sinclairia glabrum* var. *hypoleucum*); D, k'ox suil itaj (*Sinclairia andrieuxii*).

PLATE 42.—Tzelo-pat: A, batz'i tzelo-pat (*Buddleia skutchii*); B, chan-tzelav tzelo-pat (*Buddleia crotonoides*).

PLATE 43.—Tzotz-ni' te': A, ajo' te' (*Saurauia scabrida*); B, kastanya (*Sterculia apetala*).

PLATE 44.—Tzotz-ni' te': A, tzotz-ni' te' (*Viburnum jucundum*); B, sak-nich te' (*Lippia chiapensis*); C, k'ux-pevul (*Solanum chrysotrichum*).

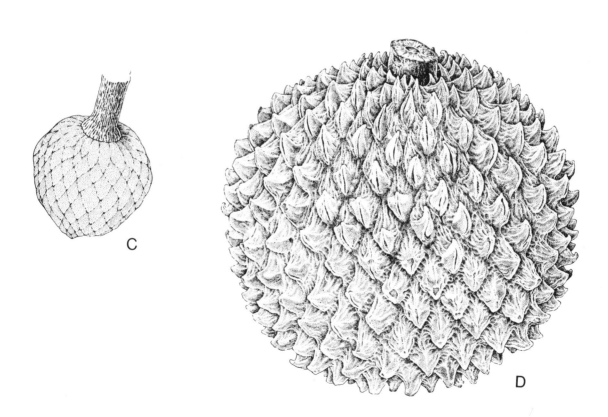

PLATE 45.—Te' (isolates): A, papaúsa k'evex (*Annona diversifolia*); B, batz'i k'evex (*Annona cherimola*); C, k'anal k'evex (*Annona reticulata*); D, chin-jol k'evex (*Annona purpurea*).

PLATE 46.—Ch'aben: A, batz'i ch'aben (*Crotalaria mucronata*); B, chenek' chij (*Lupinus elegans*); C, ch'aben ka' (*Crotalaria acapulcensis*); D, tzukum tz'i'lel (*Dalea lutea* var. *gigantea*); E, poxil mako' (*Haplophyton cinereum*); F, mesob jol bakal (*Marina scopa*).

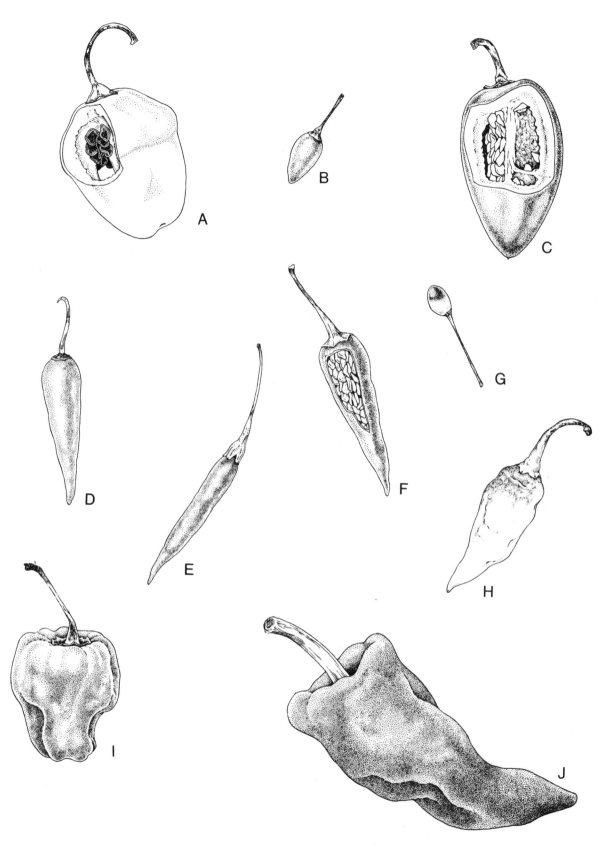

PLATE 47.—Ich: A, k'anal ich (*Capsicum pubescens*); B, jlok'ol-chak ich (*Capsicum annuum*); C, morte ich (*Capsicum annuum*); D, yich kurik (*Capsicum annuum*); E, bak ich (*Capsicum annuum*); F, natikil ich (*Capsicum annuum*); G, tzo' mut ich (*Capsicum annuum* var. *aviculare*); H, sakil ich (*Capsicum annuum*); I, pujkan ich (*Capsicum pubescens*); J, chileancho (*Capsicum annuum*).

PLATE 48.—Ich: A, unen mu (*Solanum americanum*); B, ye aja chon (*Solanum angustifolium*); C, yich joj (*Lycianthes ciliolata*); D, chuchuʻ (*Solanum mammosum*); E, tzoʻ mut ich (*Capsicum annuum* var. *aviculare*).

PLATE 49.—K'ojom: A, poxil chuvaj (*Polygala costaricensis*); B, poxil pat ka' (*Psychotria erythrocarpa*); C, muk'ta akuxa tz'i'lel (*Geranium goldmanii*); D, k'ox akuxa tz'i'lel (*Erodium cicutarium*); E, sakil akuxa tz'i'lel (*Geranium seemanii*); F, yok' tz'i' (*Plantago australis* ssp. *hirtella*); G, chintuli' jobel (*Plantago linearis*); H, poxil yerva (*Elytraria imbricata*); I, poxil sep' (*Pinaropappus spathulatus* var. *chiapensis*); J, k'ojom (*Ranunculus petiolaris*).

PLATE 50.—Moy: A, sakil kámpana nichim (*Bouvardia longiflora*); B, tzajal kámpana nichim (*Hibiscus rosa-sinensis*); C, moy (*Nicotiana tabacum*); D, bik'tal kámpana nichim (*Escobedia guatemalensis*); E, batz'i kámpana nichim (*Datura candida*).

PLATE 51.—Moy: A, yaxal kámpana tz'i'lel (*Achimenes grandiflora*); B, tzajal kámpana tz'i'lel (*Lonicera pilosa*); C, k'anal kámpana tz'i'lel (*Ludwigia octovalvis*); D, poxil aja-chon (*Martynia annua*).

PLATE 52.—Pak' chak: A, muk'ta pak' chak (*Kearnemalvastrum lacteum*); B, k'anal sat mes (*Sida rhombifolia*);
C, sakil sat mes (*Waltheria americana*); D, sakil sat mes (*Melochia tomentosa*); E, sakil pem k'ulub (*Borreria laevis*); F, batz'i pem k'ulub (*Verbena carolina*).

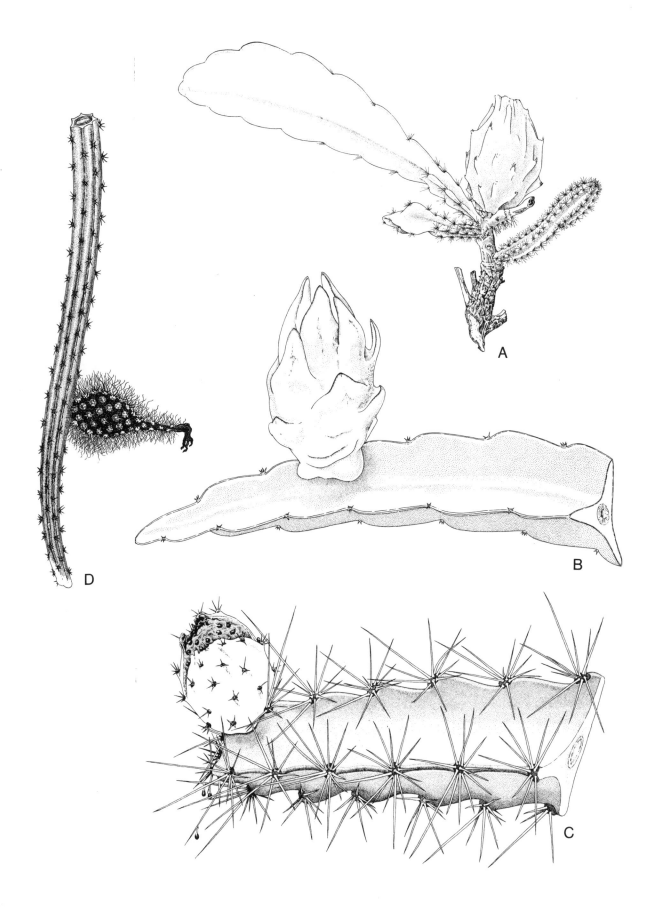

PLATE 53.—Petok: A, batz'i chikin ton (*Epiphyllum crenatum* var. *kimnachii*); B, muk'ta chikin ton (*Hylocereus undatus*); C, ch'ixal amuch (*Acanthocereus horridus*); D, ne bolom (*Selenicereus grandiflorus*).

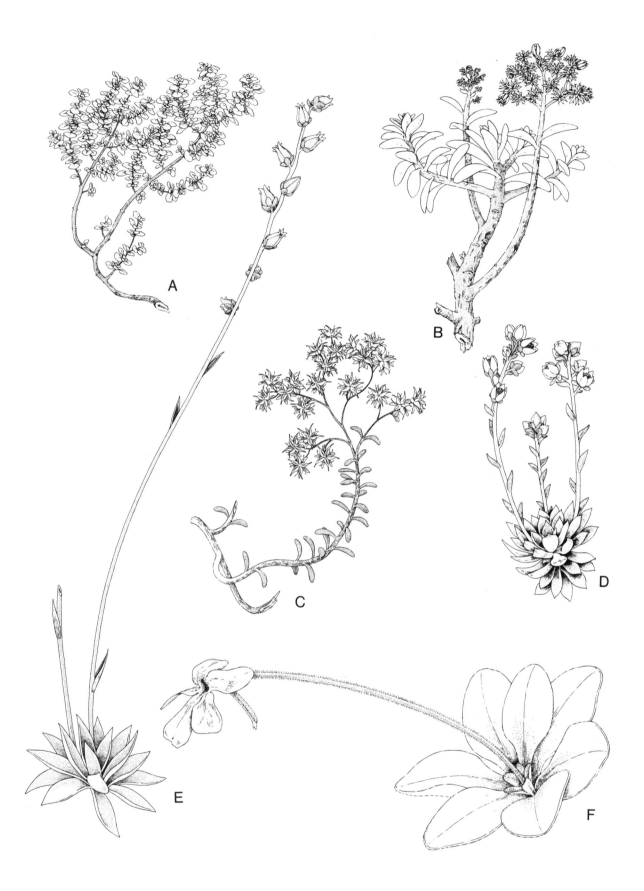

PLATE 54.—Pimil anal: A, tontikil pimil anal (*Pilea microphylla*); B, batz'i pimil anal (*Sedum praealtum*); C, k'ox pimil anal (*Sedum guatemalensis*); D, poxil yat chij (*Echeveria bella*); E, poxil chin (*Echeveria mucronata*); F, poxil eal (*Pinguicula moranensis*).

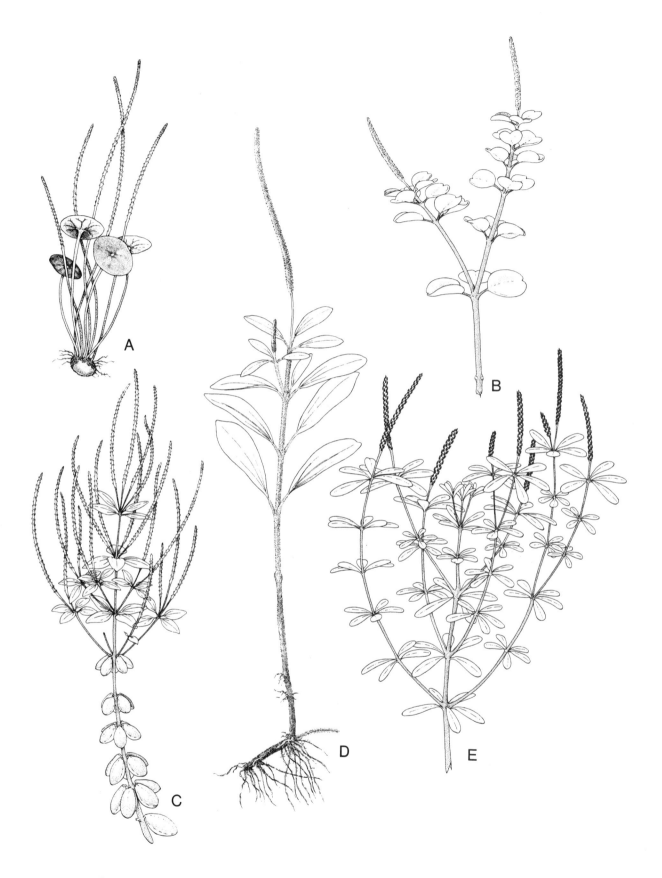

PLATE 55.—Pimil anal: A, sentavo tz'i'lel (*Peperomia campylotropa*); B, setajtik vixobtakil (*Peperomia deppeana*); C, vixobtakil chon (*Peperomia heterodoxa*); D, muk'ta vixobtakil (*Peperomia humilis*); E, batz'i vixobtakil (*Peperomia galeoides*).

PLATE 56.—Pitzak': A, alpajo (*Medicago sativa*); B, tzajal pitzak' (*Melilotus indica*); C, batz'i pitzak' (*Trifolium amabile*); D, muk'ta pitzak' (*Trifolium repens*); E, muk'ta vala-pojov (*Begonia fischeri*); F, tzajal pitzak' (*Medicago polymorpha*); G, mail tz'i'lel (*Houstonia serpyllacea*); H, k'ox vala-pojov (*Oxalis corniculata*); I, batz'i vala-pojov (*Oxalis galeottii*); J, poxil me'-vinik (*Oxalis frutescens* ssp. *angustifolia*); K, chak'ak' (*Spilanthes americana*); L, chikin ch'o (*Dichondra argentea*); M, poxil chuvaj (*Anagallis arvensis*); N, tzotz-ni' tz'i'lel (*Hieracium stuposum*).

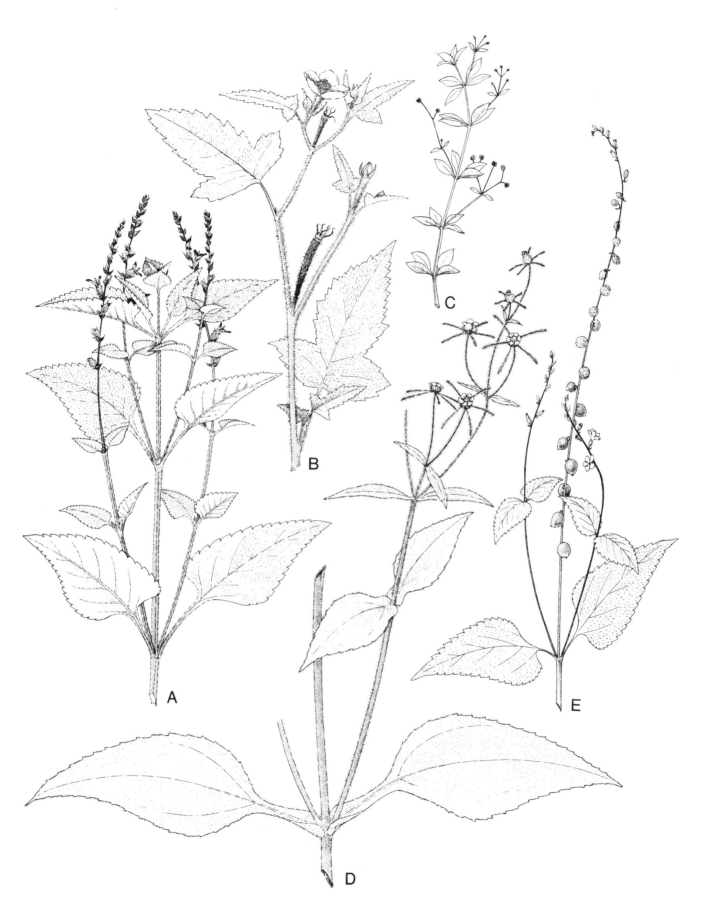

PLATE 57.—Pom tz'unun: A, k'ox nap'ap' tz'i'lel (*Salvia misella*); B, k'anal nap'ap' tz'i'lel (*Mentzelia aspera*); C, bik'it nap'ap' tz'i'lel (*Galium uncinulatum*); D, batz'i nap'ap' tz'i'lel (*Siegesbeckia jorulensis*); E, yaxal nap'ap' tz'i'lel (*Priva lappulacea*).

PLATE 58.—Pom tz'unun: A, yax-'ulan pom tz'unun (*Salvia urica*); B, puj-'akan pom tz'unun (*Priva aspera*); C, k'anal pom tz'unun (*Cuphea cyanea*); D, yaxal pom tz'unun (*Salvia polystachya*); E, tzajal pom tz'unun (*Salvia excelsa*); F, sakil pom tz'unun (*Hyptis urticoides*); G, muk'ta pom tz'unun (*Hemichaena rugosa*).

PLATE 59.—Pom tz'unun: A, poxil k'ok' (*Loeselia mexicana*); B, tentzun (*Ruellia inundata*); C, yich'ak ch'o (*Hamelia patens*); D, ba ikatzil (*Fuchsia splendens*); E, primon (*Lobelia laxiflora*); F, poxil majbenal (*Cuphea pinetorum*).

PLATE 60.—Pom tz'unun: A, yalem bek'et (*Castilleja integrifolia*); B, j'ak'-'uch (*Castilleja arvensis*); C, tzajal kampana (*Lamourouxia viscosa*); D, latzbil tonal pox (*Salvia lasiantha*); E, sten uch (*Stachys coccinea*); F, nochleb buluk' sat (*Salvia tilliifolia*).

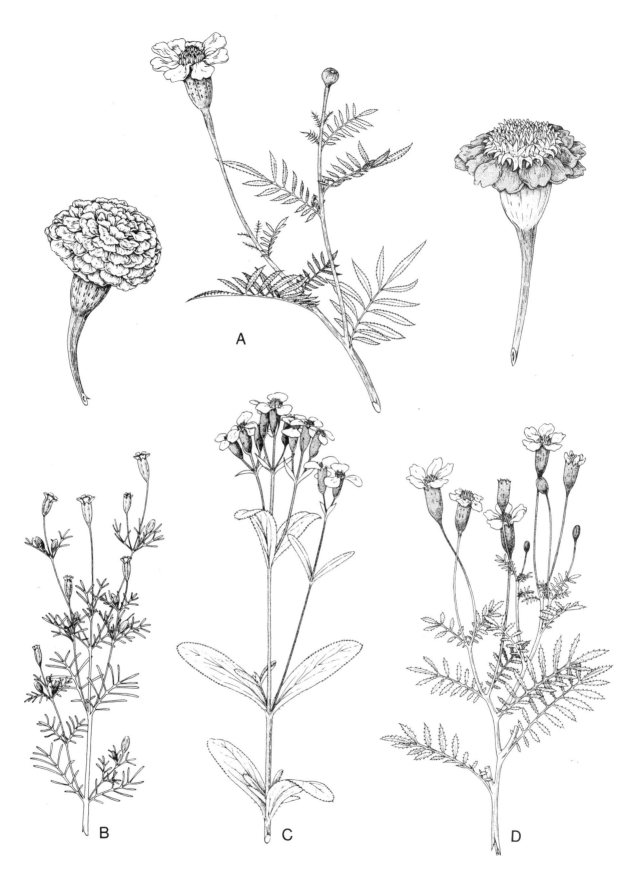

PLATE 61.—Vo'tus: A, vo'tus (*Tagetes erecta*); B, tzitz tz'i'lel (*Tagetes filifolia*); C, tzitz (*Tagetes lucida*); D, k'ox vo'tus (*Tagetes tenuifolia*).

PLATE 62.—Vo'tus: A, vo'tus tz'i'lel (*Schkuhria anthemoidea*); B, tzutzub (*Linum mexicanum*); C, tzitz pox (*Hypericum uliginosum*); D, nochleb vonon (*Cuphea aequipetala*).

PLATE 63.—Yama chauk: A, inojo (*Foeniculum vulgare*); B, krem pox (*Micropleura renifolia*); C, keb chij (*Eryngium ghiesbreghtii*); D, enkaje (*Ammi majus*); E, perejil (*Petroselinum crispum*); F, keb chij (*Eryngium carlinae*); G, kulantu (*Coriandrum sativum*).

PLATE 64.—Yama chauk: A, kulantu ch'o (*Donnellsmithia juncea*); B, kulantu ch'o (*Apium leptophyllum*); C, kulantu ch'o (*Berula erecta*); D, kulantu ch'o (*Daucus montanus*); E, kulantu ch'o (*Parthenium hysterophorus*).

PLATE 65.—Yama chauk: A, tuturu (*Thalictrum guatemalense*); B, tzis chauk (*Tagetes nelsonii*); C, jok'leb tzo'op tz'unun (*Digiticalia chiapensis*); D, sakil nichim te' (*Jasminum mesneyi*); E, chichik'uy (*Piqueria trinervia*).

PLATE 66.—Yama chauk: A, tut (*Equisetum myriochaetum*); B, yama chauk (*Arracacia bracteata*); C, yama chauk (*Prionosciadium nelsonii*); D, voy mula (*Valeriana sorbifolia*); E, yama chauk (*Aralia humilis*); F, yama chauk (*Arracacia nelsonii*); G, kámusa te' (*Bocconia arborea*).

Index 1

Plant Index (Latin)

(Boldface = page(s) of principal entry)

Index 2

Plant Index (Tzotzil)

(Boldface = page(s) of principal entry)

327

Index 3

Plant Index (English)

(Boldface = page number(s) of principal entry)

336